GEORGE E. LARGE, C.E., University of Washington, is Professor Emeritus and former Chairman of the Department of Civil Engineering at The Ohio State University. He is a Past President of the Central Ohio Section of the American Society of Civil Engineers and a member of the American Concrete Institute Committee 318 on Building Code Requirements for Reinforced Concrete. Professor Large has maintained an extensive consulting practice as a registered civil and structural engineer.

T. Y. CHEN, Ph.D., University of Illinois, is Associate Professor of Civil Engineering at The Ohio State University. He previously taught at the University of Illinois and Dartmouth College. He has also served as designing engineer with architectural firms.

REINFORCED CONCRETE DESIGN

GEORGE E. LARGE

T. Y. CHEN

THE OHIO STATE UNIVERSITY

Third Edition

THE RONALD PRESS COMPANY • NEW YORK

PREFACE

This textbook has been planned for students who are acquiring their basic understanding of reinforced concrete design. The present is a transition period in which the *ultimate strength design* method (USD) is gradually replacing *working stress design* (WSD). To prevent possible confusion, the two methods are taken up separately in the two Parts of this Third Edition. The complete computation for prestressed beams, involving both methods, is covered in the last chapter. At the end of Chapter 8 a brief supplementary WSD treatment of footings follows the USD discussion.

Chapters 2 through 5 include the rock-bottom fundamentals: beam bending, shear effects, and columns. The student needs to concentrate on these topics in order to attain, finally, a clear understanding of the field. With this book, he starts at an elementary level and is led from his fundamental mechanics to the development of new algebraic expressions. The beginning of the course can be a period of discipline using only the USD bending methods of Chapter 2.

The problems method of instruction presented arose from long experience in teaching undergraduate students of civil engineering and architecture. The authors believe it to be the best method for developing the student's understanding of basic principles. Each new topic is introduced by an instructional example, and solved, part by part, using techniques already familiar. Next, the student practices on similar problems. Finally, he retraces his work with algebraic symbols and evolves a formula, or possibly a chart. In this problems method, the student develops a sense and habit of orderliness in computations that will serve him in good stead in his professional practice.

In addition to the brief practice problems, this book includes longer problems for laboratory or home computation work. Emphasis is placed on designing, as distinguished from analysis. The full-page design calculation sheets, begun in Example 2–4, lead the student engineer to the requisite sense of organization and completeness.

All students of design need practice in interpreting a code and following it. Many illuminating discussions arise from such experience. In the design problems of this book, the 1963 American Concrete Institute Building Code has been followed with but few exceptions.

The advent of the requirement that all reinforced concrete columns must be designed for some bending has finally resulted in quite a series of new Code formulas, which tend to be unintelligible unless the student has the fundamental background developed in Chapters 4 and 5. Accordingly, throughout these chapters emphasis is placed on the fundamental concepts of column behavior rather than upon the ACI formulas. In particular, the reduction of column strengths from the ideal short-column status to the slender-column status is explained in detail. A number of illustrative examples are presented in order to make sure that nothing remains in doubt in the student's mind, particularly for columns that fail in tension.

Furthermore, Chapter 5 presents an expanded version of an extremely flexible European procedure (Mörsch's procedure) for designing unsymmetrical reinforcement near two opposite faces of a rectangular column section. For the practicing designer who uses the American Concrete Institute column charts, it is hoped that Articles 5–24 and 5–25 will be found helpful and illuminating.

The authors wish to express their appreciation to Dean Harold A. Bolz and Dr. Hamilton Gray of The Ohio State University, who provided the space and facilities for making the finished manuscript possible. We also are especially indebted to Abba G. Lichtenstein, consulting engineer, Ridgefield, New Jersey, a civil engineering graduate of Ohio State, whose actively enthusiastic encouragement made the project possible. To Mrs. Large goes appreciation of her patience and cooperation during this preoccupation.

GEORGE E. LARGE
T. Y. CHEN

Columbus, Ohio
    January, 1969

CONTENTS

PART I

Ultimate Strength Designing

System" T-Beam Forms. Economy of USD Beams. Failure Stages
of Under-reinforced Beams. Required Code Minimum Reinforcement
for Beams. Control of Deflections. Calculation of Immediate Deflection. Calculation of Long-Time Deflection. Summary of Ultimate
Strength Designing for Flexure.

FLEXURAL AND ANCHORAGE BOND STRESS. Introduction. Flexural
Bond Stress, u. Anchorage Bond Stress. Summary of Flexural and
Anchorage Bond Stress. SHEAR, DIAGONAL TENSION, AND WEB REIN-
FORCEMENT. Introduction. Commentary on the Items of Stirrup-
Designing Procedure of Example 3–3 and the Corresponding Solution.
Refined V_{uc} Calculation. Designing Bent Bar Web Reinforcement.
Locating Bar Bend-down Points. Summary of Shear, Diagonal Ten-
sion, and Web Reinforcement.

Introduction. Types of Columns. Spiral Versus Tied Columns.
Ultimate Strength of Centrically Loaded Short Columns. Certain ACI
Column Design Details. The Plastic Centroid. Eccentrically Loaded
Short Columns—Preliminary Discussion. Rectangular Sections with
Reinforcement near Two Faces—Numerical Examples. Summary and
Discussion of Short-Column Examples 4–2 Through 4–7. Interaction
Curves for Columns. Rectangular Sections with Reinforcement near
Four Faces. Circular Columns. Effect of Bars Approximated by Thin
Tubular Steel. ACI Code Short-Column Strength Formulas. Biaxial
Bending of Columns.

SLENDERNESS EFFECTS ON COLUMN STRENGTH. Introduction. Buck-
ling of Centrically Loaded Columns. Beam-Columns—Introduction.
Behavior of Beam-Columns Without Sidesway. Behavior of Beam-
Columns With Sidesway. Buckling and Bending of Columns—A Sum-
mary and Additional Remarks. ACI Provisions for Slender Columns—
Compression Failure. ACI Provisions for Slender Columns—Tension
Failure. ULTIMATE STRENGTH INVESTIGATION OF SLENDER COLUMNS.
Introduction. Investigation Using an Interaction Curve. Investiga-
tion Without Interaction Data. Slender-Column Investigation: Given
e, To Find $P_{u,sl}$. Slender-Column Investigation: Given $P_{u,sl}$, To Find
e or $M_{u,sl}$. ULTIMATE STRENGTH DESIGNING OF COLUMNS. Introduc-

tion. Centrically or Nearly Centrically Loaded Columns. Design of a Rectangular Tied Column for ACI Minimum Eccentricity. Design of a Circular Spiral Column for ACI Minimum Eccentricity. Rectangular Columns Subjected to Heavy Bending—Approximate Procedure for Designing Reinforcement near Two Bending Faces. Rectangular Columns Subjected to Heavy Bending—Approximate Procedure for Designing Reinforcement near Two Bending Faces, with Variations. Mörsch Procedure for Designing Reinforcement near Two Bending Faces of Rectangular Columns—Introduction. Mörsch Procedure— Case I: Tension over Part of the Cross Section. Mörsch Procedure— Case II: Compression over Entire Cross Section. Mörsch Procedure—Further Remarks. Use of Column Design Aids. Numerical Examples of Column Designing by Charts.

Method of Flat Slab Design. Limitations of the Empirical Method. Bending Moments. Effective Width of Strips. Flat Slab Design Example by the Empirical Method. *Empirical Method of Flat Slab Column Design.* Limitations on Column Size. Column Design Moments—Empirical Method. Flat Slab Column Design Examples— Empirical Method. Flat Slab Design by the Elastic Method. Summary of Flat Slab Designing.

ULTIMATE STRENGTH METHOD. Introduction. The Action of Earth Under Load. Footing Calculations. The Design of Reinforced Concrete Footings. The Design of Eccentric Footings. Comments upon Eccentric Footing Designing. The Design of Two-Way Reinforced Concrete Footings. Combined Footings. Combined Footing Designing. Shear in Combined Footings. The Contraflexure Localities. Ground Slope and Pedestals. Pile and Mat Footings. Summary of Footing Design. WORKING STRESS METHOD. Nonuniform Soil Bearing (W-S). Design of Plain Concrete Footings.

PART II

Working Stress Designing

Introduction. Reinforced Concrete Beams. Student Problem Work. Investigation Versus Design. Practical Design Considerations. The Design Sketch. T-Beams. T-Beam Design. "Pan System" T-Beam Forms. Beam Investigation by the Mc/I Method. Doubly Reinforced Beam Investigation by the Code $2n$ Approximation to Creep Effect. Deflection of Working-Stress-Designed Beams. Summary of Working Stress Designing for Flexure.

FLEXURAL BOND STRESS VERSUS ANCHORAGE BOND STRESS. Introduction. Calculation of the Flexural Bond Stress Related to Beam Shear by the Unit Slice Method. Anchorage Bond Stress. SHEAR, DIAGONAL TENSION, AND WEB REINFORCEMENT. Horizontal Shear Unit Stress. Diagonal Tension Reinforcement. Stirrups. Commentary on the Items of Stirrup Designing Procedure of Example 10–5 and the Corresponding Solution. Continuation on Web Reinforcement. Summary of Bond, Anchorage, Shear, and Diagonal Tension.

11 RETAINING WALLS   432

Introduction. Forces upon Retaining Walls. The Coulomb Theory of Earth Pressure. The Stability Requirements. The Strength Requirements. Choice of Earth Pressure Methods. *Retaining Wall Designing.* The Proportioning of a Cantilever Retaining Wall (Large's Method). The Checks upon Stability. The Reinforcement. Bar Arrangement. Splicing of Bars for Tension. Design of Base Shear Key. Shrinkage and Temperature Reinforcement. Drainage Features. Counterfort Retaining Walls. Summary of Retaining-Wall Design.

12 TIME-DEPENDENT STRAINS: CREEP OF CONCRETE   461

Terms and Definitions. Creep Diagrams and Elasticity. Effect of Impulsive Loads Versus Dead Load. The Nature of Creep. The Formula for Creep Under Sustained Stress. Long-Time Creep Predictions from the Results of Tests. *Creep in Axially Loaded Members. Creep in Columns. Creep in Flexural Members.* Bending Stresses and Deflections of Singly Reinforced Beams with Lapse of Time. Creep of Doubly Reinforced Beams. Prediction of Long-Time Slab or Beam Deflections from 24-Hour Experimental Data. Summary of Creep of Concrete.

13 EFFECT OF SHRINKAGE AND TEMPERATURE CHANGE   481

Introduction. AXIAL SHRINKAGE. Effect of Change in Moisture Content. Calculation of Shrinkage Stresses. ECCENTRIC SHRINKAGE (WARPAGE). Effect of Concrete Shrinkage upon the Stress in the Tensile Reinforcement of Beams and Slabs. TEMPERATURE CHANGE. Resemblance of Temperature Change to Shrinkage. The Code Requirements for Shrinkage and Temperature Reinforcement, Section 807. Contraction and Expansion Joints. Summary of Shrinkage and Temperature Change.

14 PRESTRESSED CONCRETE BEAMS   498

Introduction. Concept of a Prestressed Beam. The Basic Mechanics of Prestressing. Discussion of the Prestressed Slab Design. Final Comment on the Prestressed Slab Design. Types of Prestressed Beams. The Loading Stages of Prestressed Beams. THE LOSSES OF STEEL PRETENSION. Introduction. *The Early Losses—At Transfer.* The Loss Due to the Relaxation of the Steel. The Loss Due to the Elasticity of the Concrete. *The Later Losses.* The Loss Due to Shrinkage of the Concrete. The Loss Due to Creep of the Con-

crete.   Total Losses.   The Nature of the Losses of Steel Pretensioning.
WSD PRETENSIONED GIRDER DESIGNING.   Proportioning the Girder.
W-S Investigation of Pretensioned Girder Stresses.   Maximum and
Minimum Flexural Steel Contents.   Comments upon the Flexural
Investigation.   Prediction of the Ultimate Resisting Moment, M_u, of
Prestressed Flexural Members.   Resistance to Initial Cracking.
Alternate Sections for Prestressed I-Girders.   The Web Reinforcement
of the Pretensioned Girder.   A Summary of Stirrup Designing.   The
Prediction of the Immediate and Long-Time Deflections of the Pre-
tensioned I-Girder.   Anchorage of Pretensioned Reinforcement.   POST-
TENSIONED BEAMS.   Posttensioning Versus Pretensioning.   Mechanical
End Anchorages.   Summary of Prestressing Principles.

APPENDIX

REINFORCED
CONCRETE
DESIGN

INTRODUCTION

A. The Making of Concrete

1–1. CONCRETE

Concrete is artificial stone made from *portland cement* and inert filler materials called *aggregates* which are mixed with water to a plastic consistency and placed in forms to harden and gain strength.

Greater firesafety is possible with concrete than with almost any other building material. It is relatively economical, easy to place, and highly weather resistant when properly made.

Those responsible for concrete construction work should realize that they are manufacturers as well as constructors. Such is not the case with steel structures, the material for which is all made in a permanent plant under strict and continuous control. Some concrete is still made at the job site, sometimes under adverse weather conditions, and complete control of the process is usually not possible. Furthermore, the class of labor ordinarily available leaves much to be desired, though everyone *thinks* he knows how to make concrete. Continuous supervision is imperative if the reliable material contemplated in the chapters of this text is to be created.

1–2. PORTLAND CEMENT

The cementing material now known as *normal standard portland cement* was first made in England about 140 years ago [1].[1] Since it will set and gain strength under water, an invaluable property in connection with

---

[1] Numbers in brackets refer to the list of references at the end of each chapter.

the construction of river and harbor works, it is classed as a *hydraulic*[2] cement.

In 1926 The American Society for Testing and Materials (ASTM) adopted the following definition:

> Portland cement is the product obtained by finely pulverizing clinker produced by calcining to incipient fusion an intimate and properly proportioned mixture of argillaceous and calcareous materials, with no additions subsequent to calcination excepting water and calcined or uncalcined gypsum.[3]

1–3. HIGH EARLY STRENGTH PORTLAND CEMENTS

In response to the demand for shorter construction periods, premium brands of portland cement, compounded to develop a greater percentage of the final strength during the first several days, began to appear in the late 1920's. They are called *high early strength portland cements* to distinguish them from (standard) portland cement. Figure 1–1 shows the extent to which high early strength portlands outdo standard portlands at early ages. The final strength of concrete made from high early strength portland cement should be assumed to be about the same as that made from standard portlands. It may be used whenever its extra cost is offset by the value of the earlier use of the structure. The use of additional standard portland cement in a mix gives high early (and later) strengths, but the practice has the disadvantage of causing greater shrinkage of the mass in curing, with the attendant dislocations and danger of cracking.

[2] For a detailed discussion of other cementing materials both old and new, see any standard text on materials of construction or plain concrete.

[3] The more recent definition is less descriptive.

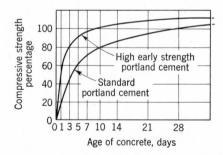

Fig. 1–1. Test strength of concrete at early ages relative to the design standard 28-day strength. (Courtesy of the Ohio State Highway Testing and Research Laboratory)

1–4. CONCRETE AGGREGATES

Aggregates are the so-called *inert* materials, both fine and coarse, which are used with the cement paste to increase greatly the bulk of a mix. Their presence also prevents excessive shrinkage of the mass.

Care in the selection of aggregates is of the utmost importance. The stone must be hard, tough, strong, sound, clean, graded, and free of organic impurities. A poor aggregate is likely to deteriorate, or expand under severe weather conditions, causing disintegration of the concrete. Some aggregates can react adversely with the cement, also causing disintegration. Siliceous sands and gravels and igneous rock sources are generally excellent, while soft materials such as shale should never be tolerated for structural concrete. The ASTM standard tests should always be performed upon strange or doubtful aggregates.

Cement is the most expensive ingredient of a concrete mix, so aggregates are used to extend a sack of cement to as many cubic feet of concrete as possible; but there is a practical limit to the aggregate content of a mix. The amount of water required to make a mix plastic is roughly proportional to the amount of aggregate to be moistened. The cement-water paste may be thought of as a liquid glue whose true function is to coat the aggregate particles. If the aggregate content is doubled, approximately twice as much water will be needed. This means that the glue will be correspondingly diluted, thus halving the concrete strength.

1–5. AGGREGATE SIZE AND GRADING

Since a cubic foot of 2-in. gravel has only one-fourth as much surface area to be moistened as a cubic foot of 1-in. gravel, one should use as large a coarse aggregate as possible. A maximum size up to one-fifth of the least dimension of the member may be used. The aggregate should contain appreciable amounts of a variety of particle sizes smaller than the maximum size so that all void spaces will thereby be filled with smaller sizes, including those of the smallest particles of sand. These smaller particles contribute smoothness, or *workability*, to the mix. However, an *excess* of sand increases void space, and demands additional moistening water. A practical balance must be struck between the use of proportionately more gravel to make more concrete from a given amount of cement, and proportionately more sand to improve workability.

1–6. ABRAMS' STRENGTH LAW

In 1918, Professor Duff A. Abrams, of the Lewis Institute, announced important findings [2] from the results of a comprehensive series of com-

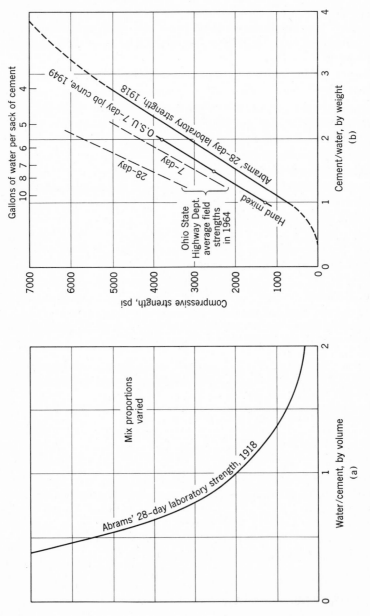

Fig. 1-2. Effect of cement and water content upon the compressive strength of standard portland cement concrete. (After Abrams)

pression tests on cylindrical concrete specimens. He had found that *the compressive strength of workable mixes varied inversely with the water/cement ratio, regardless of the proportions of the mixes,* as shown in Fig. 1–2a. The ramifications of this discovery were quite far-reaching, and it continues to be the most important one ever made in concrete technology.

In Fig. 1–2b the reversed curve shows Abrams' findings replotted on a cement/water basis. This latter arrangement has some advantages, especially since the curve is a straight line between the 1000- and 5000-psi strengths, which is the practical range of most concretes. The new strength ratio is shown on a weight basis in conformity with the present trend in stating concrete proportions.

Abrams' strength law may be restated as follows:

With given materials and conditions of test, the compressive strength of concrete varies directly with the cement/water ratio, provided the mix is of a workable consistency.

1–7. MIX DESIGN FROM A SEVEN-DAY JOB CURVE

EXAMPLE 1–1

Given the mix data and the 7-day job curve of Fig. 1–2b.

Required to deduce the proportions of the mix for 4000-lb. standard portland cement concrete at the 28-day age to which reinforced concrete specifications are referred.

Solution. Referring to Fig. 1–1, we must have 0.7(4000) = a 2800-lb. strength at 7 days. From Fig. 1–2b this strength will be attained by using a c/w ratio of about 1.6.

Interpolating between the quantities (not shown) of aggregates used in the most workable of the 1.5 and 2.0 c/w mixes:

$$\begin{array}{ccc} c & s & c.a. \end{array}$$
Use 1:1.9:2.8 by weight, 7 gal. of water per sack of cement (94-lb.)

Make a final adjustment of aggregate content on the job. *If the aggregates get wet during the course of the work decrease the water added at the mixer until the slump is restored.*

1–8. CONCRETE-MAKING FUNDAMENTALS

To close this brief treatment [3] on concrete making, the factors affecting strength are, in the order of their importance:

1. The cement/water ratio of the concrete,
2. The extent to which the chemical reactions of the cement have progressed,

as influenced by:
(a) keeping the mass warm
(b) keeping the surfaces wet
(c) allowing plenty of curing time
3. The age of the cement since ground, and the particular brand involved,
4. The particular aggregates used.

To make concrete which is dense, impermeable, and highly resistant to severe weather, as well as strong:

1. Use a high cement/water ratio,
2. Employ a well-graded aggregate combination,
3. Mix thoroughly, for uniform distribution of the ingredients,
4. Place carefully to avoid honeycombed areas, but do not overtrowel exposed surfaces,
5. Wet-cure for an extended period.

1–9. THE ABSOLUTE VOLUMES METHOD OF ESTIMATING QUANTITIES OF MATERIAL FOR CONCRETE

It is highly important to be able to compute quickly the amounts of concrete materials to "order out" to a job of known size, or yardage. Such facility is second in importance only to a clear understanding of Abrams' findings.

Let us first consider how much concrete will result from mixing known quantities of the ingredients, as indicated by the proportions of the mix. **The absolute (or solid) volumes method assumes that there will be no voids whatever in the concrete as placed, and that the sum of the "solid" volumes of the cement, sand, coarse aggregate, and water will be the amount of concrete made.** For these purposes it is necessary to remember that the absolute, or solid, unit weights of cement and good aggregate stone are about 195 and 165 lb. per cu. ft., respectively, that a sack of cement weighs 94 lb., and that 7½ gal. of water make a cubic foot. If a mix is stated *by volume*, it is necessary also to know the bulk weights of the aggregates per cubic foot, which vary from about 90 to 110 lb. for good natural stone aggregates.

EXAMPLE 1–2

A mix was designed 1:1.9:2.8 by weight, 7 gal. of water per sack of cement, as in Art. 1–7.

Required. (a) To predict the yield[4] of the mix by the Method of Absolute Volumes, and (b) to prepare an order for enough materials to make 30 cu. yd. of this concrete.

[4] *Yield* is the number of cubic feet of concrete made from one sack of cement.

Solution. (a) Yield:

Material	Proportions	Quantity	Calculations	Absolute Volume
Cement	1.0	94 lb.	$94/195$	0.48 cu. ft.
Aggregate	1.9 2.8			
Total	4.7	442 lb.	$442/165$	2.68
Water		7 gal. (58 lb.)	7/7.5	0.93
			Yield =	4.09 cu. ft. per sack

(b) Quantities for 30 cu. yd. of concrete:

$$\text{Required number of 1-sack batches} = \frac{30(27)}{4.09} = 198$$

Order:

198 sacks of cement

$$\frac{198(1.9)(94)}{2000} = 17.7 \text{ tons of sand}$$

$$\frac{198(2.8)(94)}{2000} = 26.0 \text{ tons of coarse aggregate}$$

$$198(7) = 1390 \text{ gal. of water}$$

1–10. WEIGHT OF CONCRETE

Concrete structures must first be capable of carrying their own dead weight, which is relatively large and can never be neglected in designing.

An examination of the table in the preceding Example 1–2 will reveal that 594 lb. of material were used to make 4.09 cu. ft. of concrete. This is 145 lb. per cu. ft., which is the figure recommended by Sec. 1102(a) of the American Concrete Institute "Code"[5] for the weight of unreinforced natural stone concrete. The use of reinforcing steel adds about 5 lb., so 150 lb. per cu. ft. is used as the dead load in designing reinforced (stone) concrete members.

The weight of concretes made from lighter aggregates, and of standard concrete block in place, should be taken as given in the following tables

[5] See p. 20 for a full explanation of references to this Code and to specifications of other organizations.

for the different types of mix:

Lightweight Aggregate Concretes	Lb. per cu. ft. Unreinforced
Slag concrete	130–140
Haydite (burned clay) concrete	95–100
Vermiculite (expanded mica) filler concrete	35–40

8 in. × 16 in. Concrete Blocks	Lb. per sq. ft. of Wall, Including Mortar
Stone aggregate	
12-in. wall	78
8-in.	54
Haydite aggregate	
8-in. partition or wall	35
4-in.	24

B. Strength Properties of Concrete

1–11. RELATIVE STRENGTHS

In discussing the several strength properties of concrete, it has been customary to relate them to the **ultimate compressive strength** of 6-by-12-in. test cylinders, f'_c, as a standard. The percentages shown in Table 1–1 for 3000-lb. concrete are similar to those of stone concretes of other strengths.

Tensile strength is such a small percentage of the compressive strength that it is ignored entirely in ordinary reinforced concrete beam calculations. Instead, tensile resistance is provided by longitudinal steel bars well embedded in the tension side, in other words, by *reinforced* concrete construction. Plain concrete axial tension members are never permitted, though a safe *bending* tensile strength of $1.6 \sqrt{f'_c}$ is relied upon in the design of unreinforced footings. Examine the table of Sec. 1002 of the American Concrete Institute (ACI) Code.

The most common reliance upon concrete tensile strength is to provide a portion, usually $1.1 \sqrt{f'_c}$, of the tensile resistance needed to resist the combination of horizontal and vertical shear in the tension side of beams, which results in **diagonal tension** at about 45° to the horizontal. This matter is taken up in detail in Chapters 3 and 10 in connection with the design of *stirrups*.

Table 1–1. 3000-lb. Stone Concrete Relative Ultimate Strengths and Factors of Safety

Type of Strength and Stress Distribution	Ultimate Strength		ACI WSD Code Design Allowable psi	Corresponding Ultimate Factor of Safety	Comment
	As Percentage of Compressive	In psi			
Compressive:		(f'_c)			
Spiral column, uniform axial	100	**3000***	750	4.0	* From tests. The hazards differ.
Beam, extreme fiber bending	100	3000†	1350	2.2	† As usually taken.
Tensile:					
Beam end diagonal (shear-related)	6.7	200‡	60	3.3	‡ The *initial* diag. cracking is considered the ultimate cracking.
Axial, Thaulow's§ cylinder splitting test results	10.0‖	300 (min.)	—	—	§ *Proc. ACI*, 1957, Vol. 53, p. 699, Figs. 1 and 3.
Bending, tensile at bottom fibers of pedestals and unreinforced footings	13.3	400 (min.)**	88††	4.5	** Equals the modulus of rupture. See Fig. 2–23. †† ACI Sec. 2307(b).
Bond:					
To 1-in. A305 deformed (bottom) bars	—	—	262 but varies with bar diameter, etc.		Ref. ACI Code, Sec. 1301.
Shear:					
Pure, on keys, etc. (no normal stresses)	20 (min.)	600 (min.)	240‡‡	2.5 (min.)	‡‡ AREA 1954 ruling.

‖ Refer also to the 3000-lb. concrete test results by J. A. Hanson, *Proc. ACI*, 1961, Vol. 58, p. 1.
NOTE: WSD means "working stress design," discussed in Art. 2–6.

Shear strength, as revealed by the *punching shear* resistance to pushing a cylindrical slug out of a steel plate, is never observed in concrete, since the underside of a concrete slab subjected to a downward concentrated load always suffers an enlarged conical breakout, due to the diagonal tensile weakness. Consequently the pure shear strength of concrete can seldom be utilized except across keys at construction joints.

Bond strength is the resistance developed by concrete to the pulling out of a steel bar embedded therein. The whole philosophy of reinforced concrete beam design is based upon the assumption that a bond [4] exists between the steel and concrete which prevents relative movement between them as load is applied. The amount of bond strength that can be developed depends largely upon the *area of contact* between the two materials. Tests show that it exists first as a limited adhesion between the two materials, and later as a frictional resistance to sliding after the adhesion is destroyed by a very small slippage, and very importantly as shear and bearing resistance against any projecting irregularities on the surface of the bar.   Due to this superior bond value, bars manufactured with a very rough outside surface, called *deformed bars*, have entirely replaced plain bars.   For an illustration of several types of deformed bars see Plate 1–1.

The bending strength of plain concrete footings is limited by their very low tensile strength in relation to the compressive.   However, the

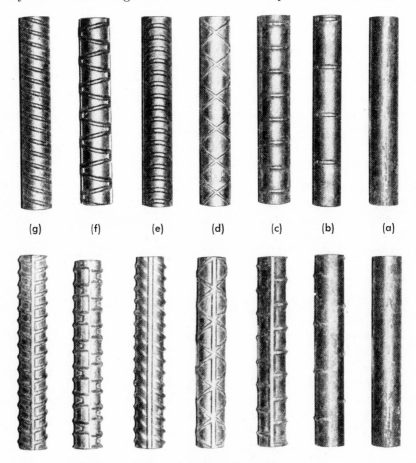

(g)   (f)   (e)   (d)   (c)   (b)   (a)

(g) "Hi-Bond" bar of Inland Steel Company.
(f) "Bethlehem" bar of Bethlehem Steel Company.
(e) "Crescent" bar of Sheffield Steel Corporation.
(d) "Diamond" bar of Jones & Laughlin Steel Corporation.
(c) "Multi-Rib" bar of Laclede Steel Company.
(b) "Carnegie" bar of Carnegie-Illinois Steel Corporation.
(a) The plain (round) bar.

Plate 1–1. Typical reinforcing bar shapes.

(unreinforced) tensile bending strength of an extreme fiber at failure, or tensile **modulus of rupture,** as computed from the fundamental formula $f_t = Mc/I$, using the applied bending moment at failure, has an average value of roughly 15 per cent of the compressive strength of ordinary concretes, which is about 1.5 times the *axial tensile strength* of the concrete. This is because the actual *tensile* bending stress distribution at failure is not linear, due to several causes to be discussed later.

1–12. MODULUS OF ELASTICITY

The ratio of unit axial stress to unit axial deformation, the slope of the stress-strain line, is called the *modulus of elasticity.* It has a fixed tensile value, E_s, of 29,000,000 psi for all steel bars regardless of such factors as ultimate strength, heat treatment, size, or method of rolling.

For concrete in compression, E_c depends largely upon the ultimate strength, f'_c, and the type of aggregate used.

1–13. DETERMINATION OF E_c BY TEST

When compressed, concrete immediately deforms elastically, but with lapse of time an additional *inelastic* deformation, called *creep* (Chapter 12), develops, so the long-time *total* deformation is non-linear.

The early investigators secured stress-strain test data *slowly,* which resulted in a curved line from the outset, as in (a) of Fig. 1–3. Its slope

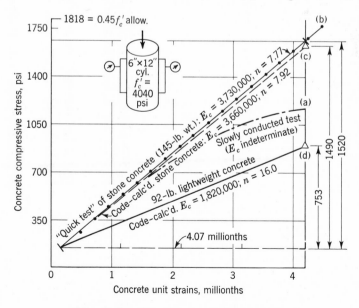

Fig. 1–3. E_c: test versus calculated.

varied so much that it proved unsuitable for securing dependable values of E_c, the *elastic* modulus.

In 1935 Professor J. R. Shank, of The Ohio State University, began to get *straight line* stress-strain test data, as at curve b in Fig. 1–3, by (1) preloading the test cylinder a few times to relieve initial strains, and (2) practically eliminating the creep strain by taking all the required strain data during less than *one minute* of continuous uniformly increasing load application. The slope of the resulting *straight line* b in Fig. 1–3 became the experimental value of E_c.

1–14. DETERMINATION OF E_c BY CALCULATION

The straight line curve c of Fig. 1–3 has been computed for the 4040-psi test cylinder, using the new Code formula $E_c = 33w^{3\!4} \sqrt{f'_c}$ of Sec. 1102(a) developed by Dr. Adrian Pauw. Since curve c lies close to the "quick test" curve b, *this ACI formula yields reliable elastic values of E_c* which may be used to predict the *immediate* (or "instantaneous") deflection of a reinforced concrete beam, as well as to compute stresses.

1–15. LIGHTWEIGHT AGGREGATE CONCRETE

Concretes of the usual strengths are now being made using the previously mentioned more compressible man-made aggregates, at a considerable saving in dead load. As shown by curve d of Fig. 1–3, such a 92-lb. concrete will have an E_c value only about half as great as a 145-lb. natural stone concrete, but twice as great a corresponding contribution to immediate beam *deflection*.

Although the corresponding modular ratio, $n = E_s/E_c$, of ACI Table 1002(a) is thereby doubled, it causes such a small change in beam *strength* calculations that the Code specifies the use of the smaller (stone concrete) n-values for *all strength* calculations, which cuts in half the number of beam strength charts, or tables, that would otherwise be required.

C. The Reinforcing of Concrete

1–16. BEAM REINFORCEMENT

As previously stated, concrete is strong in compression but relatively weak in tension. For slender steel bars exactly the reverse is true. Thus when the two materials are used together each makes up for the deficiency of the other.

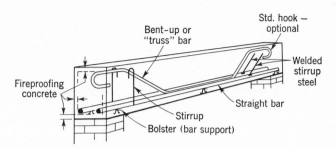

Fig. 1–4. Types of beam-reinforcing steel.

Figure 1–4 shows the four common types of beam reinforcement. Both the straight and bent-up **principal reinforcing** bars are relied upon to resist the heavy bending tension in the bottom over the central portion of the span. Toward the ends of the span, where the bending moment is small, fewer bottom bars are necessary, so some may be "bent up" so that their inclined portion may be utilized to resist the diagonal tension resulting from beam shear. In continuous beam construction their horizontal upper portions are continued across the supports to resist the tension in the top in that locality. Refer to the illustrations of Chapter 6.

There are seldom enough bent bars available for resisting all the diagonal tension, so additional small U-shaped bars, called **stirrups,** are usually necessary. Since they become stressed in tension they must pass underneath the bottom steel. In recent years *welded stirrups* have appeared. They may be placed at any desired angle, as shown.

In first-class construction the horizontal reinforcement is supported on devices called **bolsters,** or **chairs,** which hold it in place during construction operations. They come in a variety of standard heights to suit most situations.

Since steel is not fireproof, the bars carrying computed stress must usually be kept from one to two inches within the outside surface of each member. This outer shell, shown in the figure, is called **fireproofing concrete,** though some of it is also relied upon for strength.

1–17. COLUMN REINFORCEMENT

Examples of column reinforcement will be found in the illustrations of Chapter 4. In them the **vertical reinforcement** is the principal reinforcement. It shares the compressive load with the concrete. The whole is confined by **lateral reinforcement** which surrounds the column horizontally and consists of individual **ties** or a continuous **spiral,** all as shown in Fig. 4–1.

1–18. SHRINKAGE AND TEMPERATURE REINFORCEMENT

Slabs and walls must not only be reinforced by *principal reinforcement* against the design loads to which they are subjected, but also in the lateral direction perpendicular thereto to resist the effects of shrinkage and temperature change.

In drying, following the wet-curing period, concrete shrinks a maximum of about 0.0005 of its length. To whatever extent the adjacent construction interferes with this movement the concrete tends to become stressed in tension; so a small percentage of steel must be used to resist it. The action is largely reversible upon complete re-wetting.

Similarly, concrete must be allowed to contract with a lowering of temperature about 0.000006 of its length per degree Fahrenheit.[6] Thus a fall in temperature of 83 degrees causes as much shortening as drying shrinkage. A *rise* in temperature above that prevalent during curing is attended by a corresponding expansion, for which provision must be made.

The amount of *"shrinkage and temperature" reinforcement* usually provided is approximately $\frac{1}{5}$ of 1 per cent, as required by specifications. There are indications that more should be used, and that the percentage to be provided in each case should be computed from fundamental mechanics. The effect of longitudinal shrinkage upon the relatively large percentage of principal reinforcement in a member is to cause compressive stresses therein which are usually disregarded.

1–19. GRADES OF REINFORCING STEEL

Concrete-reinforcing steel is widely available in ten bar sizes ranging from $\frac{1}{4}$-in. round to about $1\frac{13}{32}$-in. round, and as wire for column spirals, wire mesh for shrinkage and temperature reinforcement of slabs and walls, and welded bar mats for floors and roofs. Metallurgically it comes in three grades, namely, *intermediate, hard*, and *high strength*. The minimum yield points, ultimate strengths, and relative unit deformations thereof, are shown in Fig. 1–5.

For practical purposes **the yield point is the limit of useful strength of reinforcing bars,** since higher stresses cause permanent deformation, or **set.** This means that the bar does not return to its original length when the load is removed, leaving an open crack in the concrete. Note that in Sec. 1003 the American Concrete Institute allowable stresses contemplate a factor of safety of from 2.0 to 2.5 against yielding for reinforcement of not over 60,000-psi yield point.

---

[6] For steel the coefficient is 0.0000065, or almost the same.

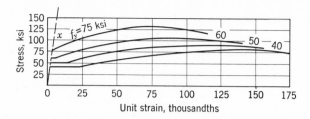

Fig. 1–5. Stress-strain curves of concrete-reinforcing steels.

The wire mesh is cold-drawn from a hard-grade steel and has a higher yield point than that shown in Table 1–2.

1–20. EFFECT OF STEEL DUCTILITY UPON PERFORMANCE OF REINFORCED CONCRETE MEMBERS

A steel that would fracture at point x in Fig. 1–5 would have no ductility. Reinforced concrete beams made therefrom would fail without any warning and actually fall apart if the tensile strength of the steel were reached. All the steels used to manufacture concrete-reinforcing bars are *ductile,* having a considerable range of inelastic deformation between the yield point and the actual breaking point. Consequently the failure of reinforced concrete beams in a testing machine is seldom sudden. When the yield point stress in the tensile steel in the bottom of a beam is reached, small cracks which have developed in the adjacent concrete begin to "open up," giving ample warning of overload.[7] With a very ductile steel these cracks will continue to open until the beam

[7] If the loads applied are dead weights, as many are in service (as distinguished from testing machine loading), the bars stretch rapidly, concrete crushes, and ultimate failure ensues much more quickly.

Table 1–2. ASTM Required Minimum Strengths for Concrete-Reinforcing Bar Steels

Type	Yield Point, ksi	Ultimate Tensile Strength, ksi
Billet steel, high strength	75	100
Billet steel, 60 ksi ⎫ Rail* steel, hard grade ⎭	60	90
Billet or axle, hard grade ⎫ Rail* steel, regular ⎭	50	80
Billet or axle, intermediate grade	40	70

* Re-rolled from used rails.

sags ridiculously, but the steel will not actually break nor will the beam come apart.   The amount of ductility needed in any particular member is a matter of judgment, with a majority favoring the intermediate grade of steel.

Reinforcing steel should also preferably be ductile enough so that *hooks* of relatively small radius, shown in Fig. 1–4, can be cold-formed on the job without breakage.   However, the importance of this preference is fast disappearing because the modern deformed bars seldom require hooks.

1–21. REINFORCING BAR SHAPES, SIZES, AND DESIGNATIONS

Plate 1–1 shows, from right to left, the development of some typical concrete-reinforcing bar shapes.   In the lower photograph each bar has been rotated through 90° to reveal the longitudinal rib, when present. Bars (e), (f), and (g) are representative of recent developments.

Reinforcing bars originally were plain round rods, such as at (a), which had relatively poor resistance to slippage through the concrete. For a number of years slow progress was made through types (b), (c), and then to (d).   Well-organized research therein was pursued through the 1930's and into the 1940's.   Recent tests [4] have shown that bars such as (e), (f), and (g), having *closely spaced transverse projections*, called **deformations,** which conform to ASTM Specification A305 for deformed-bar cross sections, are so superior in bond value that hooking their ends adds very little strength.   Such bars are referred to as the A305 *deformed bars* or *high-bond bars.*   Bars which do not meet the ASTM requirements are no longer rolled for concrete reinforcement.

The *nominal diameter* of a deformed bar equals the diameter of a plain round bar of the same weight per foot.   Due to the volume of metal in the transverse deformations, the effective, or root, area of a bar is now about 91 per cent of the nominal one used in design calculations. Therefore a computed stress of 20,000 psi in the reinforcement actually means about 21,900 psi.

Bar Sizes and Designations.   The selection of steel for concrete reinforcement must ordinarily be limited to the first ten (widely stocked) round standard bars, whose areas are shown in the upper part of Table 1–3.   Although only the first seven of them represent rounds of exactly $\frac{1}{8}$-in.-increment diameters, all the bars are now known by their *numbers,* namely, the nearest number of whole eighths of an inch included in the nominal diameter of the bar.   On today's drawings, 3–#4 @ 6″ means three $\frac{1}{2}$-in. rounds at 6 in. as formerly stated.

Note, in Table 1–3, that the perimeter per unit of cross-sectional area,

Table 1–3. Standard Concrete-Reinforcing Bar Sizes

ASTM Mfg. Spec.	Standard Bar Designations	Standard (Nominal) Bar Areas, sq. in.	Nominal Dimensions, in.		Perimeter per sq. in. of Area
			Diameter	Perimeter	
A305	#2*	0.05	0.25	0.79	16.0
	#3	0.11	0.375	1.18	10.7
	#4	0.20	0.50	1.57	8.0
	#5	0.31	0.625	1.96	6.4
	#6	0.44	0.75	2.36	5.4
	#7	0.60	0.875	2.75	4.6
	#8	0.79	1.00	3.14	4.0
	#9	1.00†	1.13	3.54	3.54
	#10	1.27†	1.27	3.99	3.14
	#11	1.56†	1.41	4.43	2.84
A408	#14S	2.25	1.693	5.32	2.36
	#18S	4.00	2.257	7.09	1.77

* Bar #2 comes in plain rounds only.

† These areas are those of the former 1-in., $1\frac{1}{8}$-in., and $1\frac{1}{4}$-in. square bars re-formed into the round shape.

the measure of bar bond efficiency, varies widely, being greatest for the smallest-sized bar.

In selecting bars, use the largest suitable size, since the bars less than $\frac{3}{4}$ in. in diameter not only cost more per pound but also require much more setting labor (per pound).

1–22. STANDARD SPECIFICATIONS FOR DESIGNING REINFORCED CONCRETE STRUCTURES

Although this text deals principally with the mechanics of reinforced concrete, its application to the common problems of design has been influenced greatly by the practical experience of countless structural engineers and by the results of tests conducted at the universities and elsewhere. One learns from them that some variables are relatively unimportant, while others must receive close attention. As a result, certain everyday rules and methods have been developed, standardized, and published for the benefit of all, and are called *standard specifications*. When making any practical design, engineers always make reference to one such "book of rules" even though it may not be followed in its entirety.

The best American practice is represented by the 1963 American Concrete Institute "Building Code Requirements for Reinforced Concrete." (Copies of this 144-page booklet are available at all Portland Cement Association district offices.) The Code was revised in 1941, 1947, 1951, 1956, and again in 1963. It has been followed in most of the illustrative examples of this text. Reference to the Code is made by section number (sometimes preceded by "ACI" or "Code"): "Sec. 1102(c)" would be typical. References other than to the ACI Code will give the organization's name.

1–23. THE ACI MANUAL OF STANDARD PRACTICE

The American Concrete Institute, in cooperation with the Concrete Reinforcing Steel Institute, publishes a 9-by-11-in. looseleaf manual "for *detailing* reinforced concrete structures." This book consists principally of foldout drawings of typical reinforced concrete structural elements, together with detailed information on bar bending, hooks, column ties, bolsters, and other accessories. Since there is seldom time for making complete drawings in courses in reinforced concrete, the "Manual" fills a long-felt need by bridging the gap between theory and practice. It should be in the library of everyone entering the field.

REFERENCES

1. TROXELL, G. E., and DAVIS, H. E. *Composition and Properties of Concrete.* New York: McGraw-Hill Book Co., Inc., 1956.
2. ABRAMS, D. A. "Design of Concrete Mixtures," *Bulletin No. 1*, Structural Materials Research Laboratory, Lewis Institute, Chicago.
3. PORTLAND CEMENT ASSOCIATION. 16-mm. sound color films obtainable on loan: "The Drama of Portland Cement," 30 min.; "How to Make Quality Concrete," 33 min.; "From Mountains to Microns," 14 min.; "Principles of Quality Concrete," 36 min.
4. CLARK, ARTHUR P. "Bond of Concrete Reinforcing Bars," *Proc. ACI*, 1950, Vol. 46, p. 161.

Part I

Ultimate Strength Designing

BENDING OF BEAMS

2–1. BEAM FUNDAMENTALS

In structural engineering one deals repeatedly with three types of members, namely, tension members, compression members, and bending members called *beams*. This classification, of course, is not to be taken rigidly since, for instance, a member may be subject to direct compression as well as bending, and so on. This chapter is devoted to beam behavior, and it is of utmost importance that the student secure a firm grasp of the basic concepts contained here.

Consider a beam such as that shown in Fig. 2–1. On a section perpendicular to its longitudinal axis, the loads produce *normal stresses* and transverse *shearing stresses*. The resultant of the normal stresses is, in the absence of axial loads on the beam, a couple, called the **bending moment** (B.M.). The resultant of the shearing stresses is a transverse force, called the *beam shear* (V). The bending moment and the beam shear on the section are the equilibrants of all the forces (loads and reactions) which act on the part of the beam to one side of the section in question. Bending moments and beam shears usually vary along the span of a beam, and in order to check its safety, it is necessary to find the "critical sections" where they have their greatest values.[1]

Beams composed of the same material throughout, such as steel or timber beams, are said to be *homogeneous*. If additionally the material is linearly elastic, the theory of *straight line variation of stress* from maximum compression at the top fiber to maximum tension at the bottom fiber applies to them directly. The level where the bending stress is zero is called the **neutral axis** (N.A.). In homogeneous elastic beams it is at the **centroid** of the cross section, which may be found by taking *moments of areas* about some convenient horizontal line. The familiar $s = Mc/I$

[1] Students for whom this discussion is not an adequate review will wish to restudy the section on beams in their strength of materials text.

formula for bending stress is the algebraic expression of the above relationships.

However, reinforced concrete beams are not homogeneous, since they consist of two materials, steel and concrete. For *designing* them the $s = Mc/I$ formula is not directly applicable. A different method of approach, called the **internal couple method,** must be used, and thoroughly mastered.

2–2. HOMOGENEOUS BEAM STRESS ANALYSIS BY THE INTERNAL COUPLE METHOD

Since the $s = Mc/I$ formula is unsuitable for designing reinforced concrete beams, let us try to get along without it in the simpler case of finding the maximum stress in a homogeneous beam.

EXAMPLE 2–1

Given an 8-by-20-in. timber beam carrying a uniformly distributed load[2] of 0.7 kip per lin. ft. (klf) over its 20-ft. span, and a concentrated load of 7.0 kips at 4 ft. from the left end. Refer to parts (a) and (e) of Fig. 2–1.

[2] A kip equals 1000 pounds, a convenient structural unit.

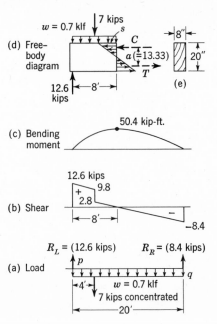

Fig. 2–1. Beam diagrams and the internal couple.

It is required to find the maximum bending stress, in pounds per square inch, by the internal couple method.

Solution. As in all beam problems, first find each *reaction* by making a summation of the moments of loads and reactions about the other *reaction point*. Clockwise moments are taken as positive:

$$\Sigma M \text{ about } q \equiv 0$$
$$20R_L - 0.7(20)[10] - 7.0[16] = 0$$
$$R_L = 12.6 \text{ kips}$$

Similarly, by moments about p, $R_R = 8.4$ kips.
Check by ΣV:

$$+12.6 + 8.4 - 7.0 - 0.7(20) = 0$$

The shear diagram (Fig. 2–1b) is next constructed (1) to locate the spanwise point of maximum bending moment and (2) to evaluate the maximum bending moment by computing the area of the shear diagram (either end):

$$M_{max} = \frac{8.4}{2}(12) = 50.4 \text{ kip-ft.}$$

To find the maximum bending stress, remove at (d) one end of the beam as a *free body in equilibrium* under its loads, reaction, and the resultant internal forces, C and T. Noting that each of the latter must act at the centroid of the stress distribution triangle, the arm, a, of the *internal couple* $Cjd = Tjd$ is found to be 13.33 in.

At the cut section, the **moment of the internal couple** (*resisting* moment) must equal the **external bending moment** of the reaction and loads:

$$Cjd = M$$
$$13.33C = 50.4(12)(1000)$$
$$C = 45{,}350 \text{ lb.}$$

Let s (Fig. 2–1d) be the maximum stress. By definition, **C is the summation** of all compressive forces; namely, the **volume of the "wedge" of compressive stress:**

$$\frac{s}{2}(10)(8) = C = 45{,}350$$
$$s = \underline{1134 \text{ psi}} \qquad\qquad \text{Ans.}$$

This beam is safe if the timber allowable stress is greater than 1134 psi. Check the above work by the $s = Mc/I$ formula.

TIMBER BEAM PROBLEM

2–1. A timber beam, of the built-up section shown in Fig. 2–2, has a simple span of 14 ft. It carries a uniform dead plus live load of 0.8 klf, and a concentrated load of 4 kips at 4 ft. from the right end.
    (a) Find the maximum bending stress, using the internal couple method. Recognize the variation in beam width.
    (b) Check (a) by the $s = Mc/I$ formula.
    (c) Evaluate C, the total compressive force.

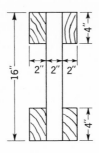

Fig. 2–2

2–3. REINFORCED CONCRETE BEAMS

When steel is embedded in concrete in a manner which assists it in carrying imposed loads, the combination is known as *reinforced concrete.* Since, as shown in Table 1–1, the axial tensile strength of concrete is only about 10 per cent of the compressive, it is obvious that beam strength can be increased tremendously by the use of steel in the tension side. In fact, it is customary to disregard the relatively small tensile strength of the concrete in computing the bending strength of reinforced concrete beams, and to rely entirely upon the tensile steel.

Figure 3–10 illustrates typical beam cracking at failure in test. In the central portion of the span, where the bending moment was greatest, the tension cracks are approximately normal to the bending reinforcement. *Reinforced concrete designing consists largely in predicting the position and direction of **potential cracks** in concrete, and in preventing the development thereof by locating sufficient steel across their predicted directions.*

A. Singly Reinforced Concrete Beams

2–4. FAILURE OF REINFORCED CONCRETE BEAMS

Failure of reinforced concrete beams in flexure occurs when either (1) the concrete of the compression side fractures near f'_c, the test cylinder ultimate compressive strength, or (2) the steel gradually reaches f_y, its tensile yield point strength. In the latter case the beam does not collapse, but tensile cracks develop, and later open so widely, due to the yielding, that deflection becomes excessive. Its practical usefulness having been badly impaired thereby, the beam is said to have *failed.*

So-called *"balanced beams,"* as commonly designed in the past by the straight line (elastic) theory of bending stress, nearly always failed by yielding of the tensile steel. This indicated a greater reserve of compressive strength in the concrete of such beams than is suggested by the ratio 2:2.22 between the Code design safety factors; each factor is itself derived as the ratio between failing and working stresses, $40{,}000/20{,}000 = 2$ for steel and $f'_c/0.45f'_c = 2.22$ for concrete. The actual factor for the concrete of such beams has been nearer $3\frac{1}{3}$, since, due to the *creep* property (taken up in Chapter 12), the true safe-working load extreme compressive fiber stress is seldom over two-thirds of the value computable by the straight line (elastic) method. Nevertheless, it is generally agreed that the factor of safety for concrete should always be somewhat higher than that for steel because it is a brittle type of material which often gives little or no warning of approaching failure.

2–5. WHITNEY'S EARLY WORK

In the late 1930's Charles S. Whitney[3] analyzed failure test data from over 300 beam tests [1] conducted throughout the world, and therefrom introduced to American engineers the convenient "compressive stress block" method of predicting the ultimate strength of reinforced concrete beams. (Refer to Fig. 2–4.) He also particularly studied those tests in which the investigators could not be sure whether the steel or the concrete failed first, and found that the average concrete stress block depth, a, for such *singly reinforced "balanced" beams* at failure was about $0.54d$.

Also, by plotting (as in Fig. 2–3) the test failure bending moments,

[3] Of Amman and Whitney, Consulting Engineers, New York.

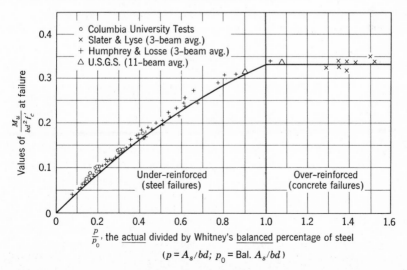

Fig. 2–3. Whitney's *calculated* beam ultimate strengths graph compared with the test results. (See *Trans. ASCE*, 1940, Vol. 105, p. 1763.)

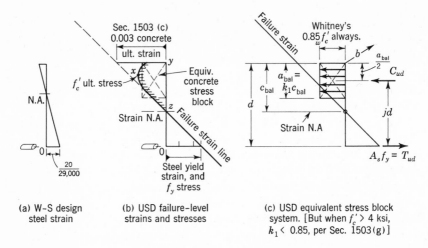

(a) W–S design steel strain

(b) USD failure–level strains and stresses

(c) USD equivalent stress block system. [But when $f_c' > 4$ ksi, $k_1 < 0.85$, per Sec. 1503(g)]

Fig. 2–4. Balanced ultimate strength beam stress and strain relationships versus working stress relationships.

M_u, divided by bd^2, and further by f'_c, all the rectangular-section test beams of various sizes and concrete strengths were put upon the same strength basis. Along the horizontal axis, the p/p_0 relation created a distinct separation between under-reinforced and over-reinforced cases. Whitney's *balanced* steel content p_0 turned out to be 4.3 per cent for a combination of 3750-lb. concrete and 40,000-psi-yield-point steel.

2–6. INTRODUCTION TO THE ULTIMATE STRENGTH DESIGN OF REINFORCED CONCRETE BEAMS

Following much research, the Code now recognizes two widely different methods for dealing with the bending of members, namely, *ultimate strength design* and *working stress design*, the newer and the older method, respectively. (These are frequently abbreviated to USD and WSD, respectively. Occasionally, the phrasing is varied in this book by dropping the word "design," giving the abbreviations U-S and W-S instead.)[4] They differ primarily in the higher and lower stress levels, respectively, at which the designing is done. As shown in Fig. 2–4b, USD is performed at the yield-point stress of the steel, while WSD

---

[4] To avoid confusion, the two methods are taken up in widely separated chapters: **Part I**—Chapters 2 through 8 present, by USD, beam bending and shear, short and slender columns, continuous floor systems, and footings. **Part II**—Chapters 9 through 11 present, by WSD, beam bending and shear, also retaining wall designing; Chapters 12 through 14 present the creep and shrinkage properties of concrete, and the designing of prestressed beams by WSD, supplemented by the investigating thereof by an U-S procedure.

usually takes place at the 20-ksi stress shown imposed on the strain graph (a), the stress that has been widely used in the past to design all kinds of beams at the *service load* level.

On the tension side at (b), the f_y steel *stress* has been plotted to coincide with the failure *strain* line, but above the strain neutral axis many of the concrete stresses (shaded) fall progressively short of it!

As one takes up the subject of the inelasticity of beams, *it is quite important to recognize that the traditional straight line variation of flexural stress,* so much used in elastic calculations, *does not exist in concrete's inelastic range.* It *is* true that there is a straight line variation of *strain* throughout both ranges, as has been demonstrated many times by taking *strain* gage readings during testing. But the *stress* variation in the inelastic range is some kind of curve which is not easily determined experimentally [2], since there are very few research devices which may be said to measure *stress* that is not proportional to strain.

To avoid having to deal repeatedly with the curved *concrete stress distribution* [3] within the compressive *strain triangle of* Fig. 2–4b, Whitney evolved the convenient *compressive-stress rectangle* in (c), both[5] dimensions of which are 0.85 of those of the shaded *stress figure xyz,* and so define an equivalent compressive *"stress block"* proportional[6] to $(0.85)^2$. Of course, one should not consider that the actual compressive stresses are so distributed; only that the method is a great convenience for computing the internal resisting moment $C_{ud}(jd)$.

2–7. LOAD FACTORS AND THE ϕ FACTOR

In designing[7] reinforced concrete beams by the USD method, a value of ultimate (bending) moment must first be established by greatly increasing the given *service* dead and live loads by factors of safety called **load factors,** and by a ϕ **factor.** The use of the former guards against *overloading;* the latter insures against possible *understrength* of the member due to such defects as under-dimensions, weak material, or poorly located steel.[8]

Both types of factors must always be used in computing the *design ultimate moment, M_{ud}.*

[5] But not so for concrete strengths greater than 4000 psi. Refer to Sec. 1503(g).
[6] See previous note.
[7] As distinguished from *investigating* an existing beam.
[8] As stated by Lin [4], "The primary purpose of ultimate strength design is to attain a more uniform degree of safety of the parts when a structure is loaded close to its failure strength." The resulting design should contain relatively less material in localities where the live/dead load ratio is small, but more where that ratio is large, thereby attaining the desired failure strength with a smaller amount of material.

Table 2–1. ACI Factors for Ultimate Strength Flexural Designing *

(A) Against overloading: Have load factors.	Since the stated service loadings may be exceeded: Used to find the *load-factored* moment:

$$1.5M_D + 1.8M_L = M_{uf}$$

Herein, subscript f indicates a load-*factored* value.

(B) Against understrength: Have ϕ factor = 0.9.†	Since a member may be weak due to deficient dimensions, misplaced steel, weak material, etc.: Used to *increase* the load-factored moment to the *design moment* value:‡

$$M_{uf}/0.9 = 1.11M_{uf} = M_{ud}$$

Subscript d indicates a *d*esigning value.

---

* For computing the design ultimate bending moments from the service load moments. Alternately, for *investigating* beams, see Art. 2–14.

† For ϕ-values for diagonal tension, bond, anchorage, and column action, see ACI Sec. 1504.

‡ Note that the total ultimate moment used for *flexural* designing reflects the effects of both the load factors and the ϕ factor, and can be stated as:

$$M_{ud} = 1\tfrac{2}{3}M_D + 2M_L$$

in which M_D and M_L are simply the service load moments.

The following computation illustrates the use of the factors in calculating M_{ud} for the beam of Example 2–2 (below).

An 11.1-ft. simple span beam is to carry dead and live uniformly distributed service loads of 11.1 and 33.2 kips respectively. Find the design ultimate moment, M_{ud}. (Refer to Table 2–1.)

Solution. By $WL/8$:

$$M_D = 15.4 \text{ kip-ft.}, \quad M_L = 46.0 \text{ kip-ft.}$$

By load factors:

$$M_{uf} = 1.5M_D + 1.8M_L = 23.1 + 82.9 = 106 \text{ kip-ft.}$$

From ϕ factor:[9]

$$M_{ud} = M_{uf}/\phi = 106/0.9 = 1.11(106) = 118 \text{ kip-ft.}$$

for designing.

See also Examples 2–3 and 2–4.

[9] It is unfortunate that the relationship $\phi = 0.9$ became thus established, since it must be used inversely with the moments, while the load factors apply directly.

2–8. STEPS FOR U-S DESIGNING A STRAIN-BALANCED BEAM

Refer to Example 2–2:

1. Calculate from the service loads the load-factored ultimate moment M_{uf}. (Refer to Art. 2–7.)
2. From M_{uf}, calculate the design ultimate moment, $M_{ud} = (M_{uf}$ divided by the ϕ factor of 0.9). (See Art. 2–7.)
3. From the balanced strain relationships of Secs. 1602(e) and 1103(a), express in terms of d the balanced beam strain neutral axis depth, c_{bal}. (Refer to Fig. 2–4c.)
4. Express therefrom the *balanced* concrete "stress block" depth a_{bal}, using c_{bal} and Sec. 1503(g). (See Fig. 2–5.)
5. From block geometry, $C_u jd = M_{uf}/\phi = M_{ud}$, find required d and A_s, balanced.
6. Calculate $p_{bal} = p_b = A_{s,bal}/bd$, the *theoretical* maximum steel ratio, but not to be relied upon to prevent failure via concrete. To do this, refer to Fig. 2–5. Alternately, it is possible to compute p_b from the strength constants of the two materials by equating $T_u = C_u$, from which

$$p_b = \left(\frac{0.85k_1f'_c}{f_y}\right)\left[\frac{0.003}{0.003 + (f_y/E_s)}\right] \qquad (2\text{–}1)$$

which is one form of Formula 16–2 of Sec. 1601(b).

STUDENTS: Utilize the above formula to verify the 2.75 per cent value in Example 2–2 below. Such large *balanced* beam p-values are not permitted in practice. See Example 2–3 below. The ACI maximum permitted value is $(\tfrac{3}{4})p_{bal}$.

2–9. COMMENTS ON U-S DESIGNING

Articles 2–6 through 2–8, plus Table 2–1 and the Code references, lead to the following convenient rules:

1. The strain neutral axis, c, as a fraction of d, varies only with f_y.
2. The factor, k_1, used with c to calculate the equivalent block depth, a, is

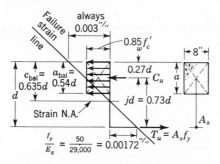

Fig. 2–5. Balanced designing.

always 0.85, except for concretes stronger than 4000 psi, for which see Sec. 1503(g).

3. The flexural understrength factor, $\phi = 0.9$, should be applied at the *bending moment* level of the calculations.
4. Never call the stress block depth, a, a neutral axis distance.
5. The *strain* neutral axis distance, c, is the relevant one.

EXAMPLE 2–2

Balanced Ultimate Strength Beam Designing

Given, from Art. 2–7, a load-*f*actored *u*ltimate moment, $M_{uf} = 106$ kip-ft. Design for $M_{uf}/\phi = 118$ kip-ft., the *d*esign *u*ltimate moment, M_{ud}. Refer to Arts. 2–8 and 2–9 and Table 2–1. This theoretically balanced case is for $f'_c = 3000$ and $f_y = 50,000$ psi, and utilizes the failing strains of *both* the materials. See Sec. 1602(e). See also Sec. 1600. From ACI Table 1002(a), $E_s = 29,000,000$ psi.

Required. Taking a width b of 8 in., to compute the required d and A_s.

Solution. From Secs. 1602(e) and 1103(a):

$$c_{\text{bal}} = \frac{0.003}{0.003 + (50/29,000)} (d) = 0.635d$$

From Sec. 1503(g), k_1, for 3000-lb. concrete, is 0.85.

Balanced "stress block" *depth* $a_b = k_1 c_b = 0.85(0.635d) = 0.54d$ (a_b is the *balanced*-beam value). From $C_u jd = M_{uf}/\phi = M_{ud}$:

$$0.85_w(3)\underbrace{[0.54d(8)]}(0.73d) = 118(12)$$
$$C_u$$

Therefore, $d^2 = 176.0$, and   reqd. $d = 13.26$ in.

Corresp. $T_u = C_u = 146.0$ kips $= 50(A_s)$,   reqd. $A_s = 2.92$ sq. in.   Ans.

Corresp. Sec. 1600 $p_b = A_s/bd = 2.92/(8)(13.26)$
$$= \quad 2.75\%, \text{ the } balanced \text{ percentage}$$

See corresponding result in table of Problem 2–3.

Comment. The block depth a (in terms of d), for any steel percentage less than the balanced one, may be gotten by a proportion upon the p-values. But not so for the "arm of the couple," jd, which gets lengthened.

In Example 2–3 below, the lesser Code maximum steel content used insures that any possible failure due to overloading or understrength will remain a slow ductile one via the yielding of the reinforcement.

EXAMPLE 2–3

U-S Designing To Insure a Ductile Failure

ACI Maximum p ($= \frac{3}{4}p_b$)

Required to alternately redesign the beam section of Example 2–2 to prevent a sudden compressive type of failure via the concrete. Maintain b at 8 in. Required: $d = ?$ $A_s = ?$ Choose bars and make final design sketch (Arts. 2–12

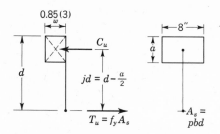

Fig. 2–6. Code's $(\tfrac{3}{4})p_b$ designing.

and 2–13).   Specifications: 3000 and 50,000 psi. $M_{ud} = 118$ kip-ft., as before.
   Solution.   From Fig. 2–6 and Sec. 1601(b):

$$p_{\max} = (\tfrac{3}{4})2.75\% = 2.06\%$$
$$\text{Ex. 2–2}$$
$$T_u = f_y A_s$$
$$= (50)(0.0206)(8)(d)$$
$$= 8.24d \text{ kips}$$
$$a_{\max}(<a_{\text{bal}}) = (T_u = C_u = 8.24d)/(0.85_w)(3)(8)$$
$$= 0.404d = (\tfrac{3}{4})(0.54d)$$
$$jd = d - 0.202d = 0.798d$$
$$M_{ud} = T_u jd = 8.24d(0.798d) = 118(12)$$

Therefore,
$$d^2 = 215, \text{ and} \qquad \text{reqd. } d = 14.65 \text{ in.}$$
$$\underline{\text{Reqd. } A_s = pbd = 0.0206(8)(14.65) = \underline{2.42 \text{ sq. in.}}} \quad \textbf{Ans.}$$

Three #8 bars from Table 1–2 are not quite enough if actual d is only 14.65 in.
Corresp. reqd. total depth $= 14.65 + 0.50 + 0.50 + 1.50$ in. $=$ 17.15 in.
                                  bar rad.   stirr.   fpg.
   Comments.   Always finally select the total depth of beams to the safer whole
inch, and recalculate the steel.   See Continuation Example 2–4 and Art. 2–10.

In designing practice, never use a *p*- or *a*-value greater than $\tfrac{3}{4}$ of the theoretically balanced one.

This beam is *under-reinforced*, judged by the "Whitney-balanced" ideal one
of Example 2–2.   The decreased *p*- and *a*-values reveal it.   The smaller steel
percentage demanded that it be deeper.   But C_u and a are smaller, so failure
would be by the (desirably) slow yielding of the steel (without fracture thereof).

The specified concrete stress, f'_c, prefixed by Whitney's 0.85, is used for the
compressive stress in all USD beam bending situations.

EXAMPLE 2–4

U-S Designing for a Chosen Greater Beam Depth

Given the beam of Example 2–3 with $M_{ud} = 118$ kip-ft., but with its total
depth h arbitrarily increased to 18 in., which is greater than that required by the
Code.   Use $f'_c = 3000$ psi and $f_y = 50,000$ psi, $b = 8$ in., and $d = 18 - 2 - \tfrac{1}{2}$
$= 15.50$ in., from a trial bar dimension.

Required to compute the new required A_s, choose bars, and make "final design
sketch" per Art. 2–13.

Solution.   See Fig. 2–7, which incidentally also shows a recommended arrangement of design calculations.

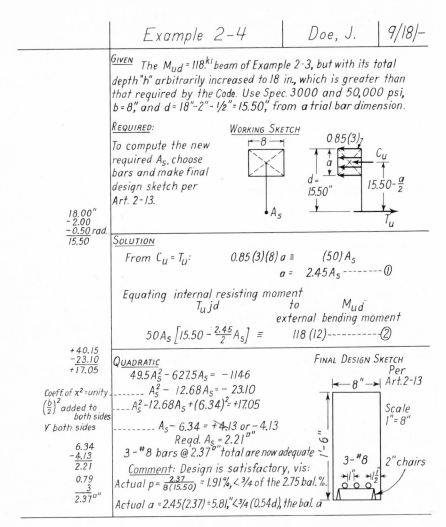

Fig. 2–7.   Recommended arrangement of calculation sheets.

2–10. PRACTICAL DESIGN CONSIDERATIONS

Unless otherwise noted, the designer's choice of steel must be limited to the ten smaller concrete-reinforcing bar stock sizes shown in Table 1–3. Sections 804 and 808 of the Code[10] govern the spacing and covering of

[10] The American Concrete Institute "Building Code Requirements for Reinforced Concrete" referred to in this text is available at Portland Cement Association district offices.

The calculations of design sheets are based on the 1963 ACI Code, and additionally, as regards earth pressures on retaining walls (Chapter 11), on the 1953 American Railway Engineering Association (AREA) Specification.

bars. The minimum clear vertical space between beam bars is 1 in. *Horizontally*, the minimum clear distance is the nominal diameter of the bar, but it must never be less than 1 in., nor less than one and one-third times the maximum size of the coarse aggregate. The outer surface of all beam steel must be covered with a minimum of $1\frac{1}{2}$ in. of concrete all around to serve as fireproofing.

It is customary to round off the beam width, b, and the total depth, h, to a whole number of inches. The standard heights of the reinforcing bar supports, called *chairs*, are also an influence.[11] See Fig. 2–7.

2–11. STUDENT PROBLEM WORK

This textbook is based upon the idea that one learns principally from personal attempts made after having watched another's performance. The **Examples** are followed by groups of **Problems,** the solution of which will develop the thorough understanding of the subject which comes with practice.

The importance of being systematic about such calculations is very great. Poorly arranged, slovenly, and unclear figures lead to arithmetical errors which obscure the learning process. A well-organized sheet, similar to Fig. 2–7, is familiar to students of *engineering problems* courses and should be emulated by all. In engineering offices, lasting first impressions often are formed from the manner in which the novice *arranges* his first calculations. See also Art. 2–13, "The Final Design Sketch."

2–12. DESIGN VERSUS INVESTIGATION

All reinforced concrete beam problems are of two types, *design* or *investigation*. It is very important that the student early learn to distinguish between them, since the methods of attack are quite different in the two cases.

I. **Design problems.** Designing is deciding upon the dimensions of a section. In these problems the ultimate bending moment and the failure stresses for both steel and concrete are given.

Required: To find all or some of the dimensions of the beam cross section, including that of the steel reinforcement.

There are several cases of these problems, of which Examples 2–2, 2–3, and 2–4 have already been covered.

II. **Investigation problems.** Such problems call for a strength investigation, or review, of an existing or proposed beam, all the dimensions of the concrete and steel being given, together with their strengths.

[11] Refer also to the ACI "Manual of Standard Practice for Detailing R/C Structures" for illustrations and standard heights of bolsters and chairs.

Required: With the failure unit stresses given, to find the ultimate resisting moment, or load, that the beam can carry (taken up later).

R/C BEAM DESIGNING PROBLEMS

Always take the weight of reinforced dense natural stone concrete at 150 lb. per cu. ft.

★

2–2. As in Example 2–3, design the depth, d, and the required steel, A_s, for the same 118 kip-ft. M_{ud}. Maintain $b = 8$ in., but "the specification" now is for $f'_c = 5000$ and $f_y = 40,000$; $E_s = 29,000,000$ psi.

Ans.   Reqd. $d = 11.30$ in., $A_s = 3.95$ sq. in.

2–3. Calculation for Basic USD Data. For reference in solving problems involving various combinations of f'_c and f_y (see table, facing).

Do first the two sets indicated by ( ).

Refer to Secs. 1103(a), 1503(g), 1601(b), and 1602(e).

2–4. Given an $M_{ud} = 156$ kip-ft. and a specification consisting of $f'_c = 4500$ ($k_1 = 0.825$), and $f_y = 50,000$ psi.[12]

(a) Sketch the beam *strain* geometry, and evolve from fundamental ideas the algebraic expressions for balanced c, a, and p; also Code a_{max} and p_{max}.

(b) From these calculate the required d and A_s for a Code beam 9 in. wide.

Ans.   Reqd. $d =$ in., $A_s =$ sq. in.

2–5. Design the smallest possible beam[13] with a d of 16 in. for an ultimate moment, M_{ud}, of 250 kip-ft.   Report the theoretical b and A_s.

Partial answer: Reqd. $b = 13.5$ in.

2–6. Redesign the beam[14] of Problem 2–5 for 1.8% of steel.   The d still is 16 in.

Make scale design sketches of the beams designed in Problems 2–5 and 2–6, and comment.

2–7. Calculate the theoretically required b, d, and A_s for an ultimate strength beam[15] with b equal to $d/2$ and 3.3% of steel.   The ultimate bending moment is 300 kip-ft.   What will happen if it is further overloaded?

2–8 (Individual). It is desired to completely design a reinforced concrete slab for the loading platform shown in Fig. 2–8.   Assume a 1-ft. strip of slab for study, estimate the dead load at 150 lb. per cu. ft., and adjust as found necessary.   Observe the minimum slab thickness requirement of Sec. 909(b).

Do not initially assume a value of d.   Let it work out algebraically.

Design total slab thickness to *nearest* half-inch and use only standard reinforcing bars, all one size, spaced from 3 to 6 in. center to center, by half-inches.   Provide

[12] Because the f_y used in the beam section of Example 2–3 also is greater than 40,000 psi, Sec. 1507(a) requires the later calculation of the deflection of the corresponding beam, according to directions in Sec. 909.   In this connection also refer to WSD Chapter 9, and to the deflection principles of your strength of materials textbook and courses.   Furthermore, the steel content is greater than the $0.18f'_c/f_y$ maximum.

[13] Unless otherwise noted, take $f_y = 40,000$ and $f_c = 3000$.   No design to have more steel than the Code maximum percentage.

[14] See note to Problem 2–5.

[15] See Footnote 13.

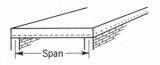

Fig. 2–8

Data and Partial Answers for Problem 2–3

f'_c (psi)	f_y (psi)	c_{bal} from Strain N.A.	a_{bal} ($= k_1 c_{bal}$)	From $C_u = T_u$ $\dfrac{0.85 k_1 f'_c}{f_y}\left(\dfrac{87{,}000}{87{,}000+f_y}\right) =$	Bal. p p_b	ACI Code Maxima		
						p_{max} ($= 0.75 p_b$)	Chart Ordinate M_u/bd^2 (psi)	Stress Block a_{max} ($= 0.75 a_{bal}$)
5000 ($k_1 = 0.8$)	60,000 50,000 40,000	( )	( )	( )	( )	3.24%	1312	0.381d
3000 ($k_1 = 0.85$)	60,000 50,000 40,000	( )	( )	( )	( )	( )	( )	( )
3000 ($k_1 = 0.85$)	60,000 50,000 40,000	0.635d	0.54d	$0.433(^{87}\!/_{137})$	$= 2.75\%$	2.06%	821	0.405d
2500 ($k_1 = 0.85$)	60,000 50,000 40,000							

exactly one inch of cover for the bars.   As always, make a final design sketch (Art. 2–13).

Use the thinnest slab consistent with the above instructions and the USD method.

Cases	Specification	Live Load, psf	Span, ft.
Series A:	50,000–4000	300	10
29 assignable com-	*40,000–3000	*250	*14
binations	60,000–5000		12
			13
			11
Series B:	40,000–4000	300	10
30 combinations	50,000–5000	250	11
	60,000–3000		12
			13
			14

* Sample answer.   Make slab 7 in. thick and use #5 bars spaced at 4 in. c.c.

2–13. THE FINAL DESIGN SKETCH

The designer's decisions are summarized in final design sketches of the member, such as on Fig. 2–7.   They are made principally to save the time of supervisors and draftsmen who must read "the answer" at a glance.   They should always be made to scale (same scale vertically as horizontally), with the scale stated.   The outside dimensions of the concrete are clearly shown.   The number of bars, their location, spacing, and bar size number, and the concrete coverage thereof must be included. The dimensions most useful to the construction man are presented, e.g., the total beam depth, and the chair height, not d.   No decimal measurements are to appear.   Finally, make sure that the calculations submitted are up to date with the dimensions on the final design sketch.

A *complete* design sketch shows all the dimensions necessary for planning the forms and setting the steel, without straining the eyes or exercising mental arithmetic.   Incomplete ones are not tolerated.   Design sketches are usually required of students at the completion of all design problems.

2–14. SINGLY REINFORCED BEAM INVESTIGATIONS FOR THE CODE'S ULTIMATE RESISTING MOMENT, M_u

An existing beam section may be either under- or over-reinforced. Since the method of attack upon such investigations is entirely different in the two cases, the existing percentage of steel must be calculated early, and compared with the Code's maximum percentage for under-reinforced beams.   The concrete stress block unit stress is again to be taken at the Whitney failure value of $0.85f'_c$, but in the over-reinforced case the remaining work is primarily a matter of *strains* instead of stress.

To **investigate**[16] a reinforced concrete beam section to find its ultimate internal resisting moment, M_u, first compute its actual steel ratio p and compare it with the maximum p of Sec. 1601(b).

If the actual p is the lesser, the beam is considered an *under-reinforced* one, the M_u of which is determined in the manner of Example 2–5 below.

Alternatively, if the actual p-value is greater than that from Sec. 1601(b), C_u may be quadratically evaluated from a flexure *strain* diagram wherein the unknown steel strain, ϵ_s, is stated in terms of the 0.003 concrete compressive failure strain.   The decreased value of *over-reinforced* beam steel stress follows.   A sudden concrete compressive failure results (Example 2–6).

EXAMPLE 2–5

Code U-S Investigation of an Under-reinforced Beam

Given the 8-in. wide beam of design Example 2–3, as $(\frac{3}{4})p_{bal}$ designed from a load-factored M_{uf} of 106 kip-ft. from Art. 2–7; the corresponding *designing* M_{ud} being 118 kip-ft.   The specification is 50,000 and 3000 psi.   (*Found:* Reqd. $d = 14.65$ in., reqd. $A_s = 2.42$ sq. in.)

Required.   To independently investigate the section for its ultimate resisting moment.

Solution.   Actual $p = A_s/bd = 2.42/(8)(14.65) = 2.06\%$.   From Sec. 1601(b):

$$\text{Code max. } p = \left(\frac{3}{4}\right)\left(\frac{0.85k_1f'_c}{f_y}\right)\left(\frac{87,000}{87,000 + f_y}\right)$$

$$= \left(\frac{3}{4}\right)\frac{(0.85)(0.85 \times 3)}{50}\left(\frac{87}{137}\right) = \qquad \underline{2.065\%}$$

Comparing, *the beam is under-reinforced*.   From Fig. 2–9 and $C_u \equiv T_u : 0.85(3)(8)$ (a) $\equiv A_s f_y = 2.42(5) = 121$ kips.

Also, $a = 5.92$ in., $a/2 = 2.96$ in., $jd = 11.69$ in., $T_u jd = \qquad \underline{118 \text{ kip-ft.}}$

Code's ultimate internal **resisting moment**, $M_u = \phi T_u jd = \qquad \underline{106 \text{ kip-ft.}}$

Remarks.   Since the beam was conservatively proportioned in Example 2–3 for a *maximum* ultimate *designing* moment, M_{ud}, of $M_{uf}/\phi = 106/0.9 = 118$ kip-ft., it is also correspondingly conservative to consider the ultimate *internal resisting moment* of this beam to be only $0.9(118) = 106$ kip-ft.

Such a beam would fail primarily due to slow yielding of the reinforcement,

---

[16] When examining the sufficiency of an existing or proposed R/C flexural member, the term **investigation** is best used for identifying the work, since the word *analysis* has such general usage in structural engineering that the reader will be in doubt as to what is meant.

Also, the term *review* incorrectly suggests simply a step-by-step retracing of the original designing operation.   Instead, an **investigation** should be conducted as independently of the original designing calculation as possible.

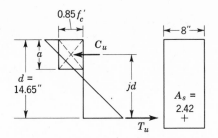

Fig. 2–9.   Stress investigation for M_u.

accompanied by tensile cracking of the bottom concrete in the central part of the span.

If preferred, the *in*vestigational M_u may well be designated M_{ui}.

EXAMPLE 2–6

Code U-S Investigation of an Over-reinforced Beam

Given the 8-by-14.65-in. ($b \times d$) beam of Example 2–5, except that it is now **over-reinforced** with 3.63 sq. in. of steel.   Specification: 50,000 and 3000.

Required.   To investigate for its ultimate resisting moment, M_u, and the corresponding steel stress f_s.

Solution.   Over-reinforced beams, failing via the concrete, are best studied from the *strain* diagram, as in Fig. 2–10, with concrete failure strain at 0.003, and steel strain, ϵ_s, unknown at f_s/E_s.   Now

$$\epsilon_s = (0.003)\,\frac{(14.65 - c)}{c}$$

Also

$$f_s = E_s\epsilon_s = 29,000(\epsilon_s) = \frac{87(14.65 - c)}{c}\text{ ksi}$$

Then

$$T_u = A_s f_s = 3.63\left[\frac{87(14.65 - c)}{c}\right] = \frac{4626.6 - 315.8c}{c} = C_u = 17.34c$$

$$c^2 + 18.21c = 266.7,\text{ by quadratic solution } c = 9.585 \text{ in.}$$
$$a = 0.85c = 8.15 \text{ in.,} \quad a/2 = 4.07 \text{ in.,} \quad jd = 10.58 \text{ in.}$$
$$C_u = 17.34c = 166.2 \text{ kips}$$

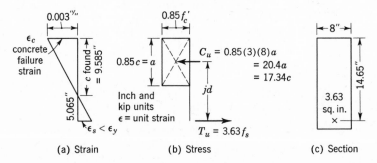

Fig. 2–10.   *Strain* investigation for M_u and f_s.

Undiminished $M = C_u jd = \dfrac{166.2}{12} (10.58) = 146.6$ kip-ft.

Investigational $M_u = \phi M = 0.9(146.6) = $ 132.0 kip-ft.   Ans.

Verifications $\begin{cases} \text{From } T_u = C_u: \ f_s = \dfrac{166.2}{3.63} = 45.8 \text{ ksi}, <50 \text{ ksi, as expected.} \\[4mm] \text{Via } strains: \ \epsilon_s = \dfrac{45.8}{29{,}000} = 0.00158, \end{cases}$

$$\epsilon_c = 0.00158 \left(\frac{9.585}{5.065} \right)$$
$$= 0.003, \text{ as originally.}$$

Remarks. Expect disastrous sudden concrete compressive fracture failure. This section is unacceptable. Its $p = 3.1\%$, which is $>$ Code's 2.065% maximum.

This method is fully applicable even when the steel excess is greater.

B. Doubly Reinforced Beams

2–15. U-S CALCULATION OF DOUBLY REINFORCED BEAM STRENGTHS

Double reinforcement is necessary when a beam must be shallower than can be safely reinforced with the Code *maximum p single* reinforcement content.

Whether designing or investigating, doubly reinforced beams are calculated by considering that they consist of two internal couples, namely, the familiar concrete-steel *web couple* and a supplementary steel *"flange"* couple, as at (b) and (c) in Fig. 2–11.

Consider the total tensile steel area, A_s, to consist of two parts. One is A'_s, which matches an identical (compressive) steel area in the top to form the (flange) steel couple element, (c) in Fig. 2–11. The rest of the bottom steel area is $A_s - A'_s$, which corresponds to the bottom reinforcement of the singly reinforced rectangular beam section element (b) in

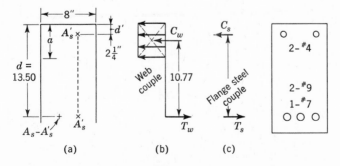

Fig. 2–11. Designing double reinforcement.

the figure, since it works with the compression concrete area to form the web couple.

To *design* such a beam, first provide the ACI stated maximum single reinforcement for the web couple. Then take care of the remaining bending moment with a steel couple. See Example 2–7.

To *investigate* such a beam for ultimate resisting moment, follow the "Method" stated in Example 2–8.

EXAMPLE 2–7

U-S Design of Beam Double Reinforcement

Given $f'_c = 3000, f_y = 50,000, M_{ud} = 118$ kip-ft., and $b = 8$ in., as in Example 2–3 and Table 2–1.

It is required to redesign the beam to have a d of only 13.50 in., employing double reinforcement centered $2\frac{1}{4}$ in. from the top. Compute the required top and bottom steel areas.

Method.
1. Provide the Code maximum p single reinforcement, $A_s - A'_s$, and calculate the corresponding M_{ud_w} so carried.
2. Allocate the remaining bending moment, M_{ud_s} to a supplementary "steel couple," $T_s(d - d')$, and select all bars.

Solution. (1) From basic Examples 2–2 and 2–3, and table of Problem 2–3: $c_{bal} = 0.635d$, $a_{bal} = 0.54d$. Also Code $p_{max} = 2.06\%$, corresp. $a_{max} = 0.404d$. Hence,

$$a_{max} = 0.404(13.50) = 5.45 \text{ in.}, \ a/2 = 2.72 \text{ in.}, \ jd = 10.78 \text{ in.}$$

Reqd. $A_s - A'_s = pbd = 0.026(8)(13.50) = 2.217$ sq. in. of single reinforcement
$$M_{ud} = 118.0 \text{ kip-ft.}$$
At (b): $M_{ud_w} = A_s f_y jd = 2.217(50)(10.78/12) = \underline{100.0}$

(2) At (c): Remaining M_{ud_s} to be taken care of by the steel couple
$$T_s(d - d') = 18.0 \text{ kip-ft.}$$

Reqd. A'_s for steel couple $= \dfrac{M_{ud_s}}{f_y(d - d')}$
$$= 18(12)/50(11.25) = \underline{\text{Total top steel} = 0.382 \text{ sq. in.}}$$
$$(A_s - A'_s) + A'_s = 2.217 + 0.382 = \underline{\text{Total bottom steel} = 2.60 \text{ sq. in.}}$$

Comment. Reference to Table 2–2 and Example 2–3 will show that beams appreciably shallower than called for by the Code's maximum p ultimate strength method are uneconomical of steel. They also may deflect too much. Refer to Secs. 1507 and 909.

EXAMPLE 2–8

Code U-S Investigation of Doubly Reinforced Beam

Given the doubly reinforced beam section of Fig. 2–12, and specification: $f'_c = 3000$ psi and $f_y = 40,000$ psi.

Required to find the ultimate resisting moment, M_u.

Table 2-2. Summary of Rectangular Beam Designing*

Example	Case	b (in.)	d (in.)	Reqd. A_s (sq. in.)	Bar Choice	Remarks
2-3	The Code's "p_{max} beam"—an ideal.	8	14.65	2.42	2-#10	The Code's shallowest singly reinforced beam.
2-4	The Code's beam above arbitrarily made *deeper*.	8	15.50	2.21	1-#9 and 1-#10	By quadratic solution. Saves some steel.
2-7	The Code's beam made *shallower* by using double reinforcement.	8	13.50	Top 0.38 Bot. 2.60 Total 2.98	2-#4, ⎰2-#9, ⎱ and 1-#7	Saves concrete at an excessive cost in steel.

* Design ultimate bending moment, M_{ud} = 118 kip-ft.; specification: f'_c = 3000 and f_y = 50,000. All concrete dimensions shown are in inches.

Calculation of basic data.

$$k_1 = 0.85 \text{ for } f'_c \text{ of 3 ksi, and } E_s = 29{,}000 \text{ ksi}$$

$$c_{bal} = \frac{0.003}{0.003 + (40/29{,}000)}(d) = 0.685d$$

$$a_{bal} = k_1 c_{bal} = 0.85(0.685d) = 0.582d$$

$$a_{max} = (\tfrac{3}{4})a_{bal} = (\tfrac{3}{4})(0.582d) = 0.436d$$

From balanced $C_u = T_u$:

$$p_{bal} = \frac{0.85k_1(3)}{40}\left[\frac{29{,}000(3)}{29{,}000(3) + f_y}\right] = 3.72\%$$

$$p_{max} = (\tfrac{3}{4})p_{bal} = (\tfrac{3}{4})(3.72\%) = 2.79\%$$

PART I

Method. (1) Separate the beam section into two couples: a "web couple" at (b) and (b') of Fig. 2-12, and a "steel couple" at (c) and (c').

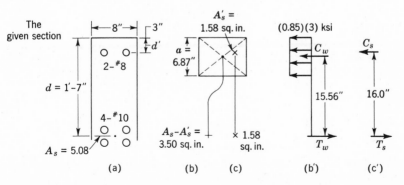

Fig. 2-12. Ultimate strength investigation of doubly reinforced beam.

(2) The desired M_u is the sum of the two corresponding ultimate resisting moments, taking all steel at f_y stress.

Solution.   *Web couple:* At (b), $A_s - A'_s = 4(1.27) - 1.58 = 3.50$ sq. in. By $C_w = T_w$:

$$a = \frac{(A_s - A'_s)f_y}{(0.85f'_c)(b)} = \frac{3.50(40)}{0.85(3)(8)} = 6.87 \text{ in.}   \text{Use.}$$

$$< a_{max} = 0.436(19) = 8.29 \text{ in.}$$

Also, $p - p' = (A_s - A'_s)/bd = 3.50/(8)(19) = 2.30\%$. This is less than the Code maximum single reinforcement percentage of 2.79%, so tensile failure is guaranteed. Then,

$$M_{u_w} = \phi(A_s - A'_s)f_y(d - 0.5a)$$
$$= 0.9(3.50)(40)(19 - 3.44)(\frac{1}{12}) =   \quad\quad 163 \text{ kip-ft.}$$

Steel couple: See (c) and (c') of Fig. 2–12.

$$M_{u_s} = \phi A'_s f_y(d - d')$$
$$= 0.9(1.58)(40)(19 - 3)(\frac{1}{12}) =   \quad\quad 76 \text{ kip-ft.}$$
$$\text{Total } M_u = M_{u_w} + M_{u_s} = 163 + 76 =   \quad\quad 239 \text{ kip-ft.}   \text{Ans.}$$

PART II

Method. (3) Determine if the above work is consistent with the *failure strains.* The method used above is simple, but a different choice of greater top steel at (a) could have resulted in its not being stressed up to the f_y value previously relied upon to produce the upper force C_s of the steel couple at (c'). In such a case, a complete re-investigation utilizing consistent strains would be necessary.

The strain-related calculations for the **maximum permissible top steel area** begins in Fig. 2–13a, with the strain corresponding to f_y compressive stress impressed at the level of the top steel. *This is a good beginning for all cases of doubly reinforced beam investigation.* The lower portion of Fig. 2–13a will be taken up in Art. 2–20.

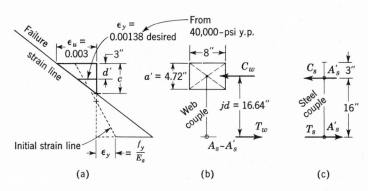

Fig. 2–13.   Strain determination of top steel action.

Solution. *Dimensions.* Taking the top steel strain as equal to ϵ_y (Fig. 2–13a), we get

$$\frac{c}{d'} = \frac{c}{3} = \frac{\epsilon_u}{\epsilon_u - \epsilon_y} = \frac{0.003}{0.003 - 0.00138} = 1.85, \text{ so } c = 5.55 \text{ in.}$$

$$a' = 0.85(5.55) = 4.72 \text{ in.}, \ a'/2 = 2.36 \text{ in.}, \text{ and } jd = 16.64 \text{ in.}$$

Steel areas:

$$A_s - A'_s = C_w/f_y = 4.72(8)(0.85)(3)/40 = \begin{array}{l} 5.08 \text{ sq. in.} = \text{total bot. st. } A_s \\ \underline{2.41} \text{ sq. in.} = \text{reqd. min. for web} \\ 2.67 \text{ sq. in.} \quad \text{element at (b)} \end{array}$$

Therefore, **the permissible maximum for top steel, A'_s at (c) is 2.67 sq. in.**
Note that, under *Dimensions*, the strain-related block depth a' of 4.72 in. is considerably less than the former depth a. Also note how it was used to calculate the minimum required bottom $(A_s - A'_s)$ of 2.41 sq. in.
The Code-allowed maximum $(A_s - A'_s)$ is

$$0.0279(8)(19) = 4.24 \text{ sq. in.}$$

Minimum top steel.   Equals $A_s - (A_s - A'_s) = \overset{4-\#10}{5.08} - 4.24 =$
$$0.84 \text{ sq. in., minimum.}$$

Since the actual A'_s of 1.58 sq. in. is within the range of the two values above (2.67 and 0.84 sq. in.), the top steel stress *is* 40,000 psi.
Therefore the *distribution* of all the steel is satisfactory, and the early-computed ultimate resisting moment of 239 kip-ft. has proven correct.
Comment.   Due to the tendency for top bars to buckle under compression, they should be located farther from the outside surfaces of the concrete than tensile bars. Stirrup-type *ties* are an excellent safeguard. Refer to Code Sec. 806(c) specifying such reinforcement.

DOUBLY REINFORCED BEAM PROBLEMS

Unless otherwise noted, take $f_y = 40,000$ and $f'_c = 3000$ psi. No design to have more single reinforcement than the Code maximum percentage.

2–9. Given a *design ultimate moment*, M_{ud}, of 861 kip-ft. Design double reinforcement for a beam with $b = 15$ in. and $d = 26.09$ in. Center the top steel 3 in. downward. Submit all the justifying calculations.
                    Ans.   Put 2–#8 in the top and 8–#11 in the bottom.
2–10. A beam has a b of 12 in. and a d of 19 in., and has 4–#7 bars centered 3 in. from the top. There are 6–#10 bars in the bottom.
Calculate the ultimate resisting moment, M_u, and comment thereon.
Demonstrate whether or not the top bars reach f_y stress.
2–11 (Individual). Design U–S double reinforcement for the case assigned. The specification is $f_y = 40,000, f'_c = 3000$. The maximum single reinforcement is to be 0.72 of the Code's $(\frac{3}{4})p_{bal}$ content, which is 2% closely. (Show verification of this.) Also see Fig. 2–21.
Provide 2-in. cover for the bottom steel, at sides and bottom. Conveniently center the top steel 3 in. down.
Observe a minimum clear horizontal spacing of one bar diameter, but not less than one and one-third times the 1-in. aggregate maximum size, nor one inch. Use two layers in the bottom, all one size, spaced at one inch clear, vertically. Use one layer in the top, all one size but not necessarily the same as the bottom bar size, and consisting of not less than two bars.

Independently investigate your design, working from your final design sketch. Demonstrate that it meets the *failure strain criteria* of Example 2–8, making several clear *statements* thereon.

Verify the singly reinforced steel percentage.   The ultimate resisting moment of an economical design should not differ from the load-factored one used by more than 2%. Show such a calculation.

Name	Case	Width b, in.	Total Depth h, in.	Load-factored Ultimate Bending Moment, M_{uf}, kip-ft.
	a	11	25	340
	b	12	27	430
	c	12	23	320
	d	11	26	370
	e	9	22	225
	f	12	28	579
	g	14	27	560
	h	15	23	410
	i	11	29	510
	j	14	32	735
	k	14	39	1150
	l	15	25	495
	m	12	32	670
	n	11	24	340
	o	14	28	590
	p	16	31	840

C. T-Beams

2–16. INTRODUCTION

Wide beams with concrete missing from the tension side are called *T-beams*. The undercut portion of Fig. 2–14 shows at (b) how a great deal of concrete may be saved thereby. Furthermore, the resulting T-beams can then carry more superimposed load, equal to the weight of the concrete removed. Thus, the removal of *this* material from the section makes it stronger!

Technically, a T-beam is one consisting of a horizontal compression flange, or **slab,** and a vertical web, or **stem,** so proportioned that the neutral axis falls below the slab, as at Fig. 2–14a. If the recess extends upward some lesser distance, as shown dotted in (b) and (c), the neutral axis may fall within the slab, in which case rectangular beam calculations apply, in spite of appearances to the contrary.

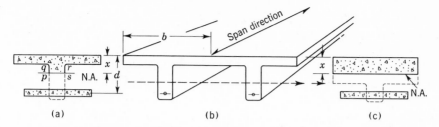

Fig. 2–14. T-beams and otherwise (WSD).

Tests have shown that there is a limit to the width of slab that may be relied upon to *act with the stem* as a beam. Section 906(b) wisely limits b to (1) one-fourth of the T-beam span, (2) the center-to-center distance between stems, or (3) the stem thickness plus 16 times the slab thickness, whichever is the smallest.

To insure integral action, stem and slab must be placed monolithically.

EXAMPLE 2–9

Code U-S Investigation of a T-Beam

Given the T-beam section of Fig. 2–15 and specification: $f'_c = 3000$ psi and $f_y = 40,000$ psi. For corresponding other "basic data" refer to the heading of Example 2–8, and to Code Sec. 1601 and 1603.

Required to find the ultimate resisting moment, M_u.

Solution. Trial as a rectangular beam 24 in. wide, with $c < 4$-in. flange thickness:

$$p_{rect} = 4(1.56)/(24)(17) = 1.53\%$$

From $C_u = T_u$, $c = \dfrac{pf_y d}{0.85 k_1 f'_c} = \dfrac{0.0153(40)(17)}{0.85(0.85)(3)} = 4.79$ in.

$$> 4.00 \text{ in. flange, } \therefore \text{ not a rect. beam.}$$

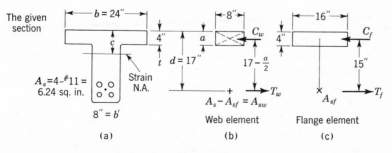

Fig. 2–15. T-beam investigation.

Recalculation as a 2-couple T-beam:

Flange element steel, from $T_f = C_f$, $A_{sf} = 0.85f'_c(b - b')t/f_y$

$$= \frac{0.85(3)(16)(4)}{40} = 4.08 \text{ sq. in.}$$

6.24 sq. in.

Remainder for web = $\overline{2.16}$ sq. in.

Web element: $A_{s_w} = 2.16$, depth $a = \dfrac{A_{s_w}f_y}{0.85f'_c b'} = \dfrac{2.16(40)}{0.85(3)(8)}$

$$= 4.24 \text{ in., } > 4.0 \text{ in., O.K.}$$

Corresponding $p = \dfrac{2.16}{8(17)} = 1.59\%$, $<$ Code max. of $\underline{2.79\%, \text{ O.K.}}$

Comment. Although the flange element has a balanced steel content, as permitted by Sec. 1603(b), the web element, reinforced for only 1.59/2.79 of the ACI max. p, will insure a steel yielding failure for the section as a whole.

Failure moment.

$$M_{u_w} = \phi f_y A_{s_w}(d - 0.5a) = 0.9(40)(2.16)(17 - 2.12)(\tfrac{1}{12}) = \quad 96.5$$
$$M_{u_f} = \phi f_y A_{s_f}(d - 0.5t) = 0.9(40)(4.08)(17 - 2)(\tfrac{1}{12}) = 183.5$$
$$M_u = \underline{280.0} \text{ kip-ft.} \quad \underline{\text{Ans.}}$$

The required stem thickness, b', is dictated by the beam shear, and is taken up in Chapter 3.

A continuing floor slab with stems only a very few feet apart, as in Fig. 2–14, is called *concrete joist* construction.

T-beam problems are also of two types, *investigation* and *design*, depending respectively upon whether the dimensions of the beam cross section are known or to be found, as in rectangular beams. Two cases of T-beams will be taken up, one investigation and one design. The student should note the parallelism of the T-beam cases with those of rectangular beams.

2–17. U-S T-BEAM DESIGNING

T-beam design theory involves one more variable than in rectangular beams, namely the slab thickness, t. In Example 2–10, both the vertical dimensions were given, with A_s and the required slab (or flange) width to be found. With this much freedom the work is straightforward, except that usually the dead load is initially unknown. It must then be estimated, introduced into the design ultimate bending moment, and the designing work later thoroughly retraced (preferably in color), using the actual dead load of the section evolved.

The procedure of Example 2–10 is convenient when the forms can be carpenter-built to any dimensions.

Example 2–11 involves designing a beam (concrete joist) to suit standardized dimensions, e.g., the pan depths of Fig. 2–20.   In it an important additional "Rough trial" for d is necessary, taking choices of bars until a suitable depth emerges.

In pan T-beams, when the depths of the strain neutral axis and compressive stress block are greater than the thickness of the flange, a separate additional flange couple must be dealt with, as happened in Example 2–9.

Isolated T-Beams

EXAMPLE 2–10

Code U-S Designing of T-Beam Steel and Flange Width

Given a design ultimate moment, $M_{uf}/\phi = M_{ud}$, of 333 kip-ft. and a specification of $f'_c = 3000$, $f_y = 40,000$ psi.   The given dimensions are a 5-in. flange thickness, t, a depth, d, of 14 in., and a web thickness of 11 in., as in Fig. 2–16a.

Refer to Secs. 1601 and 1603; also to the calculation of the "basic data" in the introductory portion of Example 2–8.

Required to design the necessary reinforcement.

Basic data (rectangular section).

$$c_{\max} = (\tfrac{3}{4})c_{bal} = 7.20 \text{ in.}$$

Ultimate strain N.A. distance, $c_{bal} = 0.685d$, $a_{bal} = 0.582d$, Code $a_{\max} = 0.436d$

Corresp. $p_{\max} = 2.79\%$

Method of solution.   Reinforce the web (b) to the Code maximum percentage, design the flange (c) for the rest; refer to Code Sec. 906, and to the figure.

Web element.   Since $c_{\max}$, the strain N.A. distance, is 7.20 in., and $a_{\max} = 6.10$ in., we have a true T-beam.   At (a),

Web $A_s = p_{\max}b'd = 0.0279(11)(14) = 4.29$ sq. in.

Corresp. T_w at (b) $= A_sf_y = 4.29(40) = 171.5$ kips

Corresp. $M_{u_w} = f_yA_{s_{web}}\left[d - \dfrac{a}{2}\right] = (40)(4.29)\left[\dfrac{14 - 3.05}{12}\right] = $ __156.7 kip-ft.__

Flange element takes care of remaining B.M. of $333 - 156.7 = $ __176.3 kip-ft.__

Reqd. $T_f = C_f = 176.3(12)/(14 - 2.5) = 184$ kips

Reqd. $A_{s_f} = {}^{184}\!/_{40} = 4.60$ sq. in.   Reqd. total steel area $= 8.89$ sq. in.

Reqd. total flange overhang $= C_f/0.85f'_ct = 184/0.85(3)(5) = 14.4$ in.

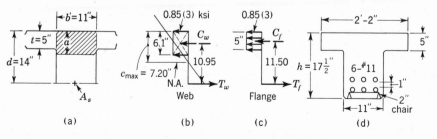

Fig. 2–16.   U-S T-beam designing.

Final design.   As shown in Fig. 2–16d, *make overall flange width 2 ft. 2 in.*[17] *and*
Use 6–#11 bars, of total area 9.36 sq. in.

Pan T-Beams

EXAMPLE 2–11

Code U-S Designing for Joist Depth and Steel

Given a service loading of 220 psf on a 20-ft. simple span.   Specification:
$f'_c = 3000$, $f_y = 40,000$ psi.   The slab thickness is 2 in. and the two steel bars
rest on 1-in. chairs; all other dimensions are available in Fig. 2–17.

Required to design for the pan depth and the steel, following Fig. 2–17 and
Fig. 2–20.

Solution.   Ultimate bending moments are:

$$M_{u_{fL}} = w_L L^2/8 = 0.22(2.17)(20)^2/8 = 23.8 \text{ kip-ft.,} \qquad \begin{array}{l} \text{L/F} \\ \times\ 1.8 = 42.9 \text{ kip-ft.} \end{array}$$

$M_{u_{fD}}$: Estimating D.L. at 30% of L.L.,

$$\qquad\qquad\qquad\qquad \text{find 7.15 kip-ft.,} \qquad\qquad \times\ 1.5 = \overline{10.7 \text{ kip-ft.}}$$

$$\text{Trial } M_{uf} = \overline{53.6} \text{ kip-ft.}$$

$$\text{Trial design } M_{ud} = \overline{59.5} \text{ kip-ft.}$$

Rough trial for pan depth, taking 2–#9 bars from the table of Chapter 1:

$$\text{Trial } d = \frac{M_{ud}}{f_y A_s j} = \frac{59.5(12)}{(40)(2.0)7/8} = 10.2 \text{ in.,} \qquad \text{try a 10-in. pan.}[18]$$

T-beam or rectangular?   Trying "block depth," $a = 2$-in. slab thickness.
Then T_u would be $f_y A_s = (40)(2) = 80$ kips.   Corresponding C_u would be
$(0.85f'_c)bt = (0.85)(3 \text{ ksi})(26)(2) = 132.8$ kips.   Therefore, $a < 2.0$ in., *so have
a rectangular beam 26 in. wide.*

$$d = \quad 10.43$$

$$\text{True } a = \frac{T_u}{0.85f'_c b} = \frac{80}{0.85(3)(26)} = 1.205 \text{ in., } a/2 = 0.60 \text{ in.} \qquad \frac{-0.60}{}$$

$$jd = \overline{\quad 9.83} \text{ in.}$$

[17] For the greater *maximum* flange width permitted to be relied upon, see Code
Sec. 906.

[18] Since slab thickness is commensurate with bar radius plus bar cover, d approximates pan depth.

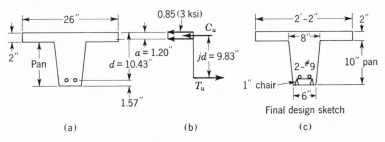

Fig. 2–17.   U-S pan T-beam designing.

Ultimate resisting moment $= M_u = T_u jd = (80)(9.83/12) = 65.6$ kip-ft.
    of trial section > 59.5 above

Corresponding $p = A_s/bd = \dfrac{2.00}{26(10.43)} = 0.74\%,$

$< $ Code p_{max} of 2.79%, O.K.
$> $ ACI Sec. 911(a) p_{min} of 0.5%, O.K.

Correction of design M_{ud} *to embrace the actual dead load:* From above,

$$M_{uf_L} = 23.8(1.8) = 42.9 \text{ kip-ft.}$$
$$w_D = \frac{26(2) + 7(10)}{144} (0.15) = 0.127 \text{ klf, } M_{uf_D} = \frac{0.127(20)^2}{8} (1.5) = 9.5$$

Corrected total $M_{uf} = \overline{52.4}$ kip-ft.
Design $M_{ud} = 58.3$ kip-ft.
    < 59.5 used.

Final comments.   Since the joist has been proportioned for a bending moment
only 2% greater than the "corrected design M_{ud}," no further correcting is needed
on this score.

Plate 2–1.   Use of precast double-T floor slabs.   (Courtesy of Portland Cement Association)

Overall, the joist is about 12% overstrong.

Use 2 + 10 joist with 2–#9 bars.

See final design sketch at (c).

But if a 12-in. pan, which is 20% deeper, be considered with 2–#8 bars which are 21% weaker, a very efficient design might work out,[19] marred only by 2 inches more loss of headroom.

2–18. "PAN SYSTEM" T-BEAM FORMS

Figure 2–20 illustrates how T-beam construction is facilitated by employing removable metal forms, called "pans," which are used repeatedly on a rental basis. The most common pan width is 20 in. and that of the soffit plank 5 in., making the b of the slab 25 in. The standardized depths of pans available are 6, 8, 10, 12, and 14 in. The pans of some systems are devised for early removal and reuse, while the soffit and shoring remain until the concrete has attained full strength. A conservative minimum slab thickness is $2\frac{1}{2}$ in.

In pan T-beam *designing*, the dimensions of the slab are usually predetermined, leaving only the pan depth and steel area to be found.

One procedure is to try two or three pans, computing the necessary steel, and then to decide which is the most suitable and economical. The deeper pans require less steel but more concrete, have greater dead weight, and sometimes interfere with headroom.

T-BEAM PROBLEMS

Take the Code and $f'_c = 3000$, $f_y = 40,000$ psi, unless otherwise noted.

2–12. Calculate the ultimate resisting moment for the Fig. 2–18 beam. Specifications: $f'_c = 4000$, $f_y = 50,000$ psi. <u>Ans. $M_u = 204$ kip-ft.</u>

2–13. (a) Set up the algebraic expressions for finding the concrete dimensions and the required steel for a singly reinforced T-beam of the accompanying proportions (Fig. 2–19) and the maximum steel content.

(b) If the total ultimate resisting moment, M_u, is 275 kip-ft., evaluate the concrete and steel dimensions. Consult Sec. 1603(c). <u>Ans. $d = 17.23$ in., $A_s = 6.52$ sq. in.</u>

2–14. Seeking a better solution for Example 2–11, it has been proposed to change the pan to a 12-in. one, and use 2–#8 bars. Investigate this section for ultimate resisting moment, and report upon safety and economy.

[19] Due to an additional increase in the arm of the internal couple resulting from a decrease in stress block depth a.

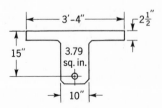

Fig. 2–18

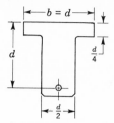

Fig. 2–19

2-15 (Individual). Design of a Pan-Construction T-Beam Floor (Concrete Joist). Refer to Fig. 2–20 for dimensions of available forms. Take a slab thickness, t, of $2\frac{1}{2}$ in. Provide exactly 1-in. cover vertically and laterally. There are no stirrups. Allow a minimum clear distance of one diameter between bars, but never less than 1 in. Refer to Art. 2–10. Use two bars of only one size in a design. The (simple) span is 20 ft. center to center of supports. Take the weight of reinforced concrete at 150 lb. per cu. ft.

Required (for the case assigned):
(a) Follow the order of procedure of Example 2–11.
(b) Early include the effect of an estimated dead load of the joist. This work is to be retraced later (preferably in color) after the section has been designed, to reflect the effect of the actual dead load.
(c) To get a trial pan depth, be sure to utilize the simple "Rough trial" expression.
(d) Establish the total depth of the joist to the deeper half-inch.
(e) Include the calculation which demonstrates whether the joist is actually a T-beam or a rectangular one.
(f) Finally, prepare a "final design sketch" per Art. 2–13.

| Student's Name | Indiv. Case | Specification | | Safe Working Live Load, lb./sq. ft. of floor |
		Steel f_y	Concrete f'_c	
	a	40,000	3000	580
	b	40,000	3000	250
	c	40,000	3000	40
	d	50,000	4000	650
	e	50,000	4000	300
	f	50,000	4000	40
	g	40,000	4000	625
	h	40,000	4000	275
	i	40,000	4000	40
	j	50,000	3500	650
	k	50,000	3500	300
	l	50,000	3500	40
	m	40,000	3500	600
	n	40,000	3500	225
	o	40,000	3500	40

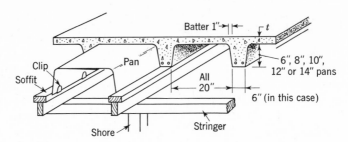

Fig. 2–20.   Pan system forms for a concrete joist floor.

2–19. ECONOMY OF USD BEAMS

In Fig. 2–21 the ultimate strengths of beams designed by the USD and WSD methods with the same percentages of steel are compared.   The WSD failure strengths were predicted from their design-allowable stresses, using the factors of safety.   Note that both methods lead to closely the same ultimate strength up to about $1\frac{1}{4}$ per cent steel.   Beyond this point, one sees that the WSD method is ultraconservatively incorrect for predicting ultimate strengths; and widely so for steel percentages greater than about 2 per cent.

The portion of each curve that is to the right of the p_{bal} point represents cases of ultimate failures via the concrete.   The ultimate strength method recognizes that considerably more compressive resistance exists in the "stress block" of the upper portion of a beam than would exist if the concrete compressive stress distribution actually were triangular.

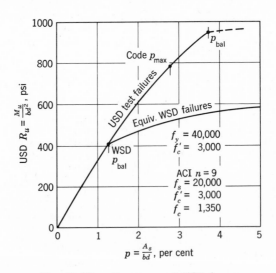

Fig. 2–21.   Economy of USD beams.

2–20. FAILURE STAGES OF UNDER-REINFORCED BEAMS

When a beam is under-reinforced, *initial* failure will be due to yielding of the steel, as illustrated in Fig. 2–22a, while the top fiber concrete stress[20] is at less than the failure value f'_c.

At (b), due to a small increase in load, the tensile concrete cracks have *opened*, due to the inelastic strain so produced in the yielded steel. This large additional strain (pictured) had *pushed the neutral axis much farther up*, as shown. The depth of concrete in compression, c, is now considerably less, but the *average* f_c is correspondingly greater, so C_u is almost unchanged. However, *its centroid has moved upward*, and the correspondingly longer new arm, jd, reflects the increased final bending moment.

Tests [2] have verified that the ultimate concrete stress, f'_c, occurs a few inches below the top of beams. Also, recall that separately applying the multiplying factor of 0.85 to both f'_c and the depth to the (strain) neutral axis c gets C_{ud}, the volume of the stress block, as formerly. Refer to the upper portion of Fig. 2–4c.

Remembering that the Fig. 2–22 beam was under-reinforced, one sees that, *finally, whether a beam is over-reinforced or under-reinforced, the concrete stress block unit stress is always to be taken at the 0.85f'$_c$ value*. Sufficient block depth, a, is then taken so that the failure strength of the compressed concrete, C_u, will match the steel's yield point strength, T_u.

When starting an U-S investigation of an I, T, or odd-shaped beam section, whether singly or doubly reinforced, always begin by "spinning

[20] In the interest of simplification and clarity, the understrength factor, ϕ, has been omitted from this discussion.

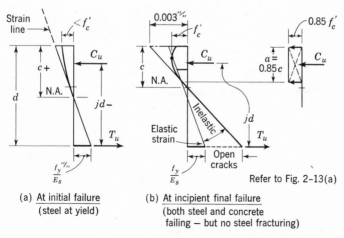

Fig. 2–22. Failure stages of an under-reinforced beam.

off" flange couples of steel and concrete until nothing remains except a singly reinforced rectangular (web) element, such as was taken up at the beginning of this chapter. Thereupon the following questions will arise:

1. Does the given beam function as a T-beam, or a rectangular one?
2. Will the initial failure be via tension or compression?
3. Will final failure be accompanied by excessive deflection or obvious fracturing?
4. Will final failure occur gradually or suddenly?

2-21. REQUIRED CODE MINIMUM REINFORCEMENT FOR BEAMS

In addition to the familiar maximum percentage of flexure steel set to prevent compressive failure, a *minimum* percentage exists to insure against even more disastrous *sudden tensile* steel failure.

Beams that are relatively too deep in relation to their span and loading, such as *wall beams* and *grade beams*, may require so little flexure steel as usually computed that they would be weaker as transformed[21] reinforced sections than if they were unreinforced! Under small overload such a beam will **suddenly crack from bottom to top,** and the accompanying shock sometimes actually *fractures* the reinforcement, causing a **fall-down** failure—the worst kind.

The possibility of such a failure can be eliminated by requiring for all beams a *minimum steel content section* strong enough to exceed the ultimate *plain concrete* bending strength thereof. The problem is to provide a reinforced section, the (diminished) ultimate moment capacity of which is assuredly greater than the corresponding (unreinforced) *maximum* modulus of rupture (failure) test moment capacity, namely, $M_{ur} = f'_{cb}(bh^2/6)$, a bending *tensile* concrete failure.

The ultimate resisting moment capacity of an under-reinforced section is, from *tensile steel* failure, $M_u = \phi pbd(f_y)[d - a/2]$, wherein a, for the very small steel percentages involved, may be taken at or around $0.06d$.

Before equating these ultimate moments to find the required minimum steel percentage, it is necessary to deduce a value of f'_{cb}, the ultimate bending strength of plain concrete, known as the **modulus of rupture.**[22] In this case, a *maximum* value thereof **must be used** in order that the steel to be provided to "take over" the concrete's tensile action shall be adequate.

In Fig. 2-23, observe the "scatter" of Kesler's rupture test data.

The Code, in Sec. 2609(c), introduced the lower curve, $f'_{cb} = 7.5 \sqrt{f'_c}$, to predict the *initial* cracking, not failure, of prestressed (reinforced) beams.

[21] Refer to the WSD transformed sections of Chapter 9.
[22] Refer to Table 1-1 of Chapter 1.

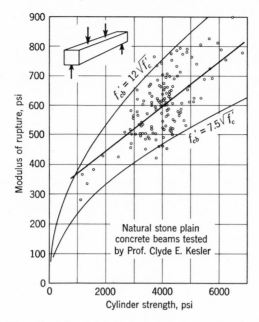

Fig. 2–23. Modulus of rupture versus compressive strength.

But herein we are primarily interested in *maximum* possible values, as represented by the uppermost curve, $f'_{cb} = 12 \sqrt{f'_c}$; and in order to have some margin, 1.25 thereof will be used for calculating minimum flexural reinforcement. Also, 4000-lb. concrete will be chosen as the usual "top strength" concrete, the tensile strength of which is great, and calls for even more take-over steel.

Furthermore, a lightly reinforced beam with a $d = 60$ in. would have a total depth, h, of about 63 in., so $h = 1.05d$ has been conveniently used here:

$$\text{Min. } M_u \equiv M_{ur}$$

$$\phi(pbd)f_y[d - 0.03d] \equiv (1.25)(759) \left[\frac{b(1.05d)^2}{6} \right]$$

from which, as derived by Howard Simpson, the required $p_{\min} = 200/f_y$ [ACI Sec. 911(a)].

For 40,000-psi-yield-point steel this calls for a minimum of 0.5 per cent, but see Sec. 911(a) for the recourse in case the calculations lead to less.

Summary. *Thus both the **maximum** and the **minimum** permissible steel percentages exist for the same general purpose,* namely, to prevent the sudden type of ultimate failure of beams which is characteristic of concrete fracturing, whether *compressive* or *tensile*, respectively.

EXAMPLE 2–12

Beam Steel Designing Controlled by Code "Min. p"

Given an ultimate design $M_{ud} = 410$ kip-ft.; a specification: $f'_c = 4000$, $f_y = 40,000$ psi; the section of Fig. 2–24a; Kesler's Chart; and Code Sec. 911(a).
Required to evolve a safe "min. p" steel content.
Solution.

$$Z = \frac{bh^2}{6} = \frac{10(62)^2}{6} = 6410 \text{ in.}^3$$

$$M_{ur} = f'_{cb}Z = \frac{\overset{\text{margin}}{(1.25)(759)(6410)}}{12,000}$$

The middle term (759) of the numerator above comes from the modulus-of-rupture test data. The possible plain concrete tensile ultimate resisting moment (to be outdone by steel) = 507 kip-ft.

Since the design M_{ud} moment of 410 kip-ft. $< M_{ur}$, overload could result in sudden plain concrete tensile failure.

Calculation of required A_s:

$$C_u jd = M_{ud}$$
$$(0.85)(4)(10)(a)[60 - a/2] = 12(410) \text{ kip-in.}$$

From quadratic, $a = 2.46$ in. only, $C_u = 0.85(4)(10)(2.46) = 83.6$ kips $= T_u$.
To resist 410 kip-ft., the required min. $A_s = 83.6/40 = 2.09$ sq. in., corresp. $p = 2.09/10(60) = 0.35\%$, $<0.5\%$ Code reqd.

Per Code Sec. 911(a), *recalculation* of required A_s for $(\frac{4}{3})M_{ud}$:

$$0.85(4)(10)(a)[60 - a/2] \equiv 6560 \text{ kip-in.}$$

corresp. $a = 3.31$ in., and C'_u is then $34(3.31) = 112.6$ kips $= T'_u$.

Corresp. new $A_s = 112.6/40 = 2.82$ sq. in. reqd. for $(\frac{4}{3})M_{ud}$.
Corresp. new $p = 2.82/10(60) = 0.47\%$, not enough.
With $d = 4$ ft. $11\frac{15}{16}$ in.:   Provide 3–#9 bars.

Corresp. actual $p = \dfrac{3.0}{10(59.94)} = 0.501\%$ O.K.

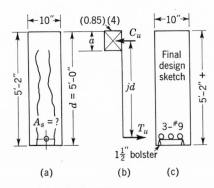

Fig. 2–24.   Minimum-p beam.

2–22. CONTROL OF DEFLECTIONS

In addition to having adequate strength, R/C flexural members must also have sufficient stiffness to prevent excessive deflections which tend to adversely affect the serviceability and/or appearance thereof.

Beams designed by the older *working stress* method of Chapter 9 have normally proven adequately stiff, but the newer shallower beams, which result principally from (1) the use of highly stressed steels and (2) designing by the ultimate strength method, often require the precautionary checking of deflections at the working (service) load level demanded by Secs. 1507 and 909.

The amount of deflection depends partly upon how deeply the tensile concrete has been hair-cracked by the loading. But in localities where the flexural tensile stresses induced in the concrete are less than the modulus of rupture, $7.5 \sqrt{f'_c}$, of Fig. 2–23, there is no flexural cracking, so the concrete moment of inertia thereat, I_c, is actually appreciably greater, and the contribution to deflection is less. Elsewhere, in regions of larger bending moment, the effective concrete section (for calculating deflection only) will be similar to the transformed one of Fig. 2–25b, or of Example 9–1 of WSD Chapter 9.

EXAMPLE 2–13

Prediction of the Deflections of a Doubly Reinforced Beam

Given the 15-ft. simple span beam section of Example 2–7 and Fig. 2–11, as doubly reinforced U-S designed for an M_{ud} of 118 kip-ft. There is a service-level uniformly distributed live loading of 1.39 kips per ft., and a superimposed dead loading (from partitions) of 0.58 kips per ft., plus the beam's own weight of 0.133 kips per ft., making the load-factored bending moment, M_{uf}, of 106 kip-ft. The beam's total depth, $h = t$, is 15½ in. Refer to Table 2–2.

The specification $f'_c/f_y/n$ is 3000/50,000/9, wherein n is E_s/E_c from Code Sec. 1002. Also, refer closely to Secs. 1507 and 909.

2–23. CALCULATION OF IMMEDIATE DEFLECTION (Example 2–13)

A. Predict the immediate midspan deflection at the Sec. 1507 service (working) load level, namely, (1) under *full* dead load plus (2) that *portion* of the live load considered equivalent to being permanently sustained, taken at 60 per cent in this example.

Necessity. Code Sec. 1507 requires [6] the calculation of such a deflection (a) if the net tensile steel content, $p - p' > 0.18 f'_c/f_y$; which in our Fig. 2–25a equals $(2.60 - 0.40)/(8)(13.50) = 2.04$ per cent versus $0.18(3000/50,000) = 1.08$ per cent; or (b) if $f_y > 40,000$ psi; both of which demand the deflection calculation in this case. Refer now to Sec. 909(c).

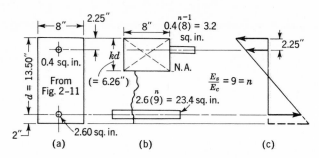

Fig. 2–25. Transformed section for predicting the immediate (elastic) deflection.

Code Sec. 909(c) rule. An easy rule[23] exists for finding whether the uncracked gross concrete section of Fig. 2–25a, or that of the cracked transformed section of Fig. 2–25b, is to be used in calculating the I_c for determining the deflection [6].

In this case, $pf_y = 2.60(50,000)/(8)(13.50) = 1200$ psi, which is > 500, so the transformed section is to be used. (Refer to W-S Example 9–7.)

To find[24] the neutral axis:

$$8(kd)(kd/2) + 3.2(kd - 2.25) \equiv 2.34(13.50 - kd)$$

Found: $kd = 6.26$ in., $I_c = 1940$ in.^{4}, $E_c = 29,000,000/9 = 3222$ ksi.

Immediate deflection A. Refer to the preceding introductory statement of Example 2–13. The loading needed is:

$$
\begin{aligned}
&\quad\quad\quad\quad\text{superimp.}\\
w_D \quad &= \quad 0.58 \quad + 0.133 = 0.713 \text{ kips/ft.}\\
0.6w_L &= 0.6(1.39) \quad\quad\quad = \underline{0.834}\\
&\quad\quad\quad\quad\quad\quad\quad\quad\quad 1.55 \text{ kips/ft. total}
\end{aligned}
$$

$$\text{Immediate } \delta = \frac{5wL^4}{384E_cI_c} = \frac{5(1.55)(15)^4(12)^4}{12(384)(3222)(1940)} = 0.338 \text{ in.}$$

2–24. CALCULATION OF LONG-TIME DEFLECTION (Example 2–13)

This additional deflection occurs under continued (sustained) load, and is due principally to creep and shrinkage of concrete (Chapters 12 and 13).

---

[23] The basis for the rule is that if the gross (plain) concrete tensile bending stress is greater than the ultimate, namely, the $7.5\sqrt{f'_c}$ *modulus of rupture* of Fig. 2–23, the concrete area will be decreased by hair-cracking, so the cracked transformed section of Fig. 2–25b should be used to calculate E_cI_c, the deflection modulus of rigidity [6].

In the case at hand, total $w = 2.1$ kips per ft., and $M = 59$ kip-ft., so $f'_{cb} = M/S = 59(12,000)(6)/(8)(15.5)^2 = 2200$ psi; $\gg$ the $7.5\sqrt{f'_c}$ of 410 psi, so the beam is deeply cracked, as shown in Fig. 2–25b.

[24] The expressions of WSD Example 9–11 are similar.

Table 2–3. Factors for Additional Long-Time Deflection*

Time Since Loaded, t	F		
	$A'_s = 0$	$A'_s = (\frac{1}{2})A_s$	$A'_s = A_s$
1 mo.	0.60	0.42	0.27
3 mo.	0.94	0.75	0.53
6 mo.	1.17	0.94	0.68
1 year	1.42	1.07	0.77
$2\frac{1}{2}$ years	1.72	1.16	0.82
5 years	1.95	1.21	0.86

* Deduced from Fig. 12–5.

Both develop rapidly, but soon slow down; meantime, the concrete transfers some of its stress to whatever compressive reinforcement is present, which decreases deflection.   Table 2–3 has been prepared from Fig. 12–5, a graph of long-time creep-plus-shrinkage trends [7].

B. Predict the immediate plus the 5-year long-time additional dead load plus 60 per cent live load deflection.   Refer to Table 2–3.

Solution (of B).   The long-time (time-dependent) additional deflection depends upon A'_s/A_s, which is $0.40/2.60 = 0.154$.

Referring to the assigned 5-year period in Table 2–3, or preferably to the 60-month ordinate of Fig. 12–5, one sees that the desired F-value is at about $\frac{1}{3}$ the way from 1.95 to 1.21; so,

$$F = 1.95 - (0.154/0.5)(1.95 - 1.21) = 1.72$$

Therefore, the 5-year dead plus 60 per cent live load long-time *total* deflection of Case B equals:

$$0.338(1.0 + 1.72) = 0.92 \text{ in.}$$

DEFLECTION PRACTICE PROBLEMS

2–16. Referring to Code Sec. 909(e)(2), determine whether the subject beam can be expected to meet the span/360 limitation[25] for floors.

Ans.   Deflection = 0.18 in., versus 0.50 in. limit, so O.K.

2–17. Referring to Code Sec. 909(f), demonstrate whether the beam will meet this limit.

2–25. SUMMARY OF ULTIMATE STRENGTH DESIGNING FOR FLEXURE

Ultimate strength designing for flexure differs from the earlier working stress method in that the computing is done at the *failing strain levels* of the two materials.   From Fig. 2–4b, these are at the established 0.003

[25] In testing, the immediate live load deflection required herein is the most easily secured.

ultimate strain for concretes, and at the yield point strain of the steel. The proven straight-line variation of strain defines the neutral axis shown.

On the tension side, the steel's stress and strain have been drawn coincident.

On the compression side of Fig. 2–4b the upper levels of the (shaded) concrete *stress* distribution fall so far short of the corresponding *strain* line that an *equivalent* rectangular figure, called the *concrete stress block*, is widely used for computing the internal compressive force, C_u, and the corresponding internal resisting moment, $C_u jd$, since many tests have demonstrated the accuracy of the method. Refer to Fig. 2–4c. Recall that the WSD elastic modular ratio, n, is not used in USD calculations.

To ensure against disastrous sudden failures of beams via the concrete, the ACI limits the maximum tensile steel content, p_{max}, of a singly reinforced rectangular section beam to three-fourths of that required for the theoretically ideal (p_{bal}) balanced strain design (Examples 2–3 and 2–2, respectively).

The method for predicting the ultimate resisting moment of such an under-reinforced beam contemplates that at final failure both the steel and concrete stresses will be at their failing values. This is mostly because the *continuing* inelastic elongation of the reinforcement pushes the strain neutral axis upward, decreasing the depth of the compression stress block, and the area of concrete in compression, until the concrete fails secondarily (Art. 2–20).

Beams and slabs are designed for flexure using the *design ultimate* bending moment. It is computed by increasing each service-level load by a particular factor of safety which is called a *load factor;* and further by using an *understrength factor*, $\phi = 0.9$. This enables the engineer to make more economical and better balanced designs of members and structures.

In designing, the load-factored bending moment, M_{uf}, is *increased* by dividing by ϕ; and the required dimensions of the section are conservatively evolved from this design value of bending moment, M_{ud}.

In *investigating* an existing section, the dimensions thereof and the failing strengths of the materials are used to calculate a *decreased* investigational value of internal resisting moment, M_u, by finally conservatively multiplying by ϕ.

M_{ud} and M_u will differ by ϕ, since a section originally *designed* for M_{ud} can later get "rated down" if it is conservatively *investigated*, using ϕ to get to the value of internal resisting moment, M_u.

Rectangular section beams that are too shallow for the bending moment to be carried must be doubly reinforced. First calculate how much of the design ultimate bending moment can be carried if it is singly reinforced with the ACI maximum steel percentage. Then take care of the remaining bending moment with a supplementary *steel couple*, at f_y stress, both at bottom and top.

T-beams may be similarly designed by first computing how much of the design ultimate bending moment can be carried by a singly reinforced rectangular element whose width is the thickness of the web. Then the remaining bending moment is taken care of by proportioning a concrete *flange element*, and designing its corresponding steel.

In Fig. 2–21 it is evident that a given USD beam, reinforced with $2\frac{1}{2}$ per cent of steel, has almost 50 per cent greater indicated ultimate strength than the corresponding WSD-designed one with the same amount of steel! This is because USD mobilizes, via the stress block, a great deal more compressive resistance than when the concrete compressive stress volume is considered triangular.

Both the ACI maximum and minimum permissible steel percentages exist for the same general purpose, namely, to prevent the sudden type of ultimate failure of beams which is characteristic of concrete fracturing, whether compressive or tensile, respectively.

CONTINUATION PROBLEM

2–18. Calculate the predicted ultimate resisting moment of the Flexicore type of floor slab section of Fig. 2–26. Carefully develop your own method from the philosophy behind Examples 2–5, 2–8, and 2–9. The properties of circular segments are available in Chart C–5 of Appendix C. Take 3750-lb. concrete and 50,000-psi-yield-point steel.

Additionally, state whether the failure will occur suddenly or gradually, via steel or concrete, in compression or tension.

QUESTIONS

1. Define: *working stress design, ultimate strength design, stress block*, and *Whitney's method*.

2. Distinguish between: stress and strain, under-reinforcement versus over-reinforcement, load factor and factor of safety, elastic and inelastic range, ACI maximum reinforcement and Whitney's balanced reinforcement.

3. (a) Tell how to design the following *sections* by the ultimate strength method:

Balanced, rectangular   Doubly reinforced, rectangular
By Code max. p, rectangular   T-beam
By Code min. p, rectangular

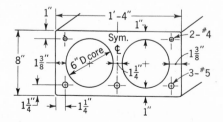

Fig. 2–26. Flexicore type of precast floor-slab section.

(b) Tell how to investigate the above sections.

4. Trace, step by step, by sketches, the stresss and strain action of an under-reinforced, singly reinforced rectangular beam from low load to complete destruction, explaining all stages of its performance.

5. Tell clearly at what stage, and in what sense, the understrength factor, ϕ, is applied (a) in designing, (b) in investigating.   Just what deficiencies are allowed for by its use?

6. Why sometimes calculate by strains instead of stresses?   Point out two strain cases: one of designing and one of investigating.

7. Comment upon and explain this statement: Whether a beam is over-reinforced or under-reinforced by the ultimate strength criterion, it will fail through crushing of the concrete if enough load is applied.

REFERENCES

1. WHITNEY, CHARLES S.   "Plastic Theory of Reinforced Concrete Design," *Trans ASCE*, 1942, Vol. 107, p. 251.

2. VANDEGRIFT, L. E., and HERR, L. A.   "Studies of Compressive Stress Distribution in Singly Reinforced Concrete [Beams] near the Point of Failure," *Bulletin No. 144*, Ohio State University Engineering Experiment Station, July 1951.

3. MATTOCK, A. H., KRIS, L. B., and HOGNESTAD, EIVIND.   "Rectangular Concrete Stress Distribution in Ultimate Strength Design," *Proc. ACI*, 1960–1961, Vol. 57, p. 875.

4. LIN, T. Y.   "Load Factors in Ultimate Design of Reinforced Concrete," *Proc. ACI*, 1952, Vol. 48, p. 881.

5. KRIZ, L. B., and LEE, S. L.   "Ultimate Strength of Over-Reinforced Beams," *Proc. ASCE*, 1960, Vol. 86, No. EM 3, p. 95.

6. AMERICAN CONCRETE INSTITUTE.   "Commentary on Building Code Requirements for Reinforced Concrete (ACI 318-63)," *ACI Publication SP-10*, 1965, pp. 19–22, clarifying some troublesome new clauses of the Code.

7. BRANSON, DAN E.   "Deflections of Reinforced Concrete Flexural Members," *ACI Journal*, June 1966, p. 637.

BOND, SHEAR, AND DIAGONAL TENSION IN BEAMS

A. Flexural and Anchorage Bond Stress

3–1. INTRODUCTION

Although the concrete of the tension side of a beam is considered of no value in bending, the strength of its bond to steel bars is a large adhering force without which there could be no reinforced concrete, since its technology assumes no relative movement, or slippage, between steel and concrete. Although usually thought of as a glue between these elements, *bond* is partly made up of shearing resistance, plus largely a bearing resistance of the concrete against the numerous transverse lugs (called *deformations*) of the modern bars.[1]

Fundamentally, *flexural bond stress per inch*, Σou, is the rate, ΔT, in pounds per inch of clear span, at which beam flexural stress gets into the reinforcement. It is proportional to the beam shear, V.

EXAMPLE 3–1

Flexural Bond Stress

Given the 12-ft. beam of Fig. 3–1 and the single concentrated load shown, together with the dimensional characteristics of the section.

Required to *investigate* its safety in flexural bond stress, and to develop a formula for it.

Solution. Refer to Fig. 3–1.

Right side of unit slice: C_{47} by ΣM about point p. Referring to Table 2–1(B) and Example 2–5:

$$0.9(0.85 \times 3)(14)(a_{47})[24 - 0.5(a_{47})] = 4700 \text{ kip-in.}$$

---

[1] If the concrete cover for the bars is too thin, splitting of the concrete tends to occur longitudinally of the bars as a secondary result of the bearing against the lugs.

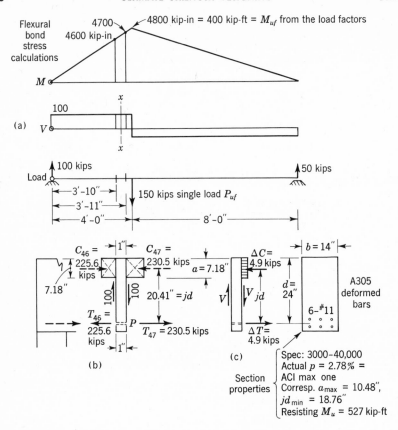

Fig. 3–1. USD flexural bond forces on the one-inch slice.

or,

$$-16.05a_{47}^2 + 771a_{47} = 4700$$

2) 7.18
−3.59
24.00
———
20.41

Hence, $a_{47} =$ 7.18 in.

Corresponding $jd =$ 20.41 in.

Corresponding $C_{47} = 0.9(0.85 \times 3)(14)(7.18) =$ 230.5 kips

Left side of unit slice (conveniently using the same jd value on both sides of the unit slice):

Necessary decrease from $C_{47} = \Delta M/jd = 100$ kip-in./20.41
= 4.90 kips

$$\therefore C_{46} = 225.6 \text{ kips}$$

Check by ΣM_p:

100 kips (1 in.) $+ (230.5 - 225.6)[20.41] \equiv 0$, $100 - 100 = 0$.   Check.

Flexural bond stress at section x-x due to the 150-kip concentrated ultimate load only: Dividing the difference of the T's by the area of contact between the steel and the concrete, and by the understrength factor of Sec. 1504(b):

$$u_u = \frac{(230.5 - 225.6)1000}{6(1.41)(1 \text{ in.})\underset{\phi}{(0.85)}} = 217 \text{ psi}$$

From USD Code Sec. 1801(c)(1), the permissible maximum bond stress is

$$\frac{9.5}{D} \sqrt{f'_c} = \frac{9.5(54.8)}{1.41} = 370 \text{ psi}, \qquad >217 \text{ psi}, \; \therefore \; \text{O.K.}$$

Generalization.   See the unit slice of Fig. 3–1b:

$$M_{n+1} - M_n = V, \text{ the beam (vertical) shear} \qquad \text{(from mechanics)}$$

Also,

$$(T_{n+1} - T_n)jd = V$$
$$T_{\text{difference}} = \Delta T = V/jd \tag{3-1}$$

Basically, flexural bond stress, $u = V_{uf}/\Sigma ojd$, wherein Σo is the total bar perimeter at the beam section studied.   For *ACI USD calculations* thereof, Sec. 1801 requires the use of

$$u_u = V_u/\phi\Sigma ojd \tag{3-2}$$

where ϕ is the bond understrength factor, per Sec. 1504(b).

N.B.: In Eq. 3–2, the ACI symbol V_u is the same as the symbol V_{uf} used in this book.

3–2. FLEXURAL BOND STRESS, u

Basically, from Fig. 3–1c, $\Sigma ou = V/jd$ is the rate, ΔT, of 4.9 kips per inch of span, at which beam flexural stress gets into the reinforcement of the left portion of the beam.   From zero at the left end, its accumulation over 3 ft. 10 in. gives the 225.6 kips of tension at the left side of the slice.

Flexural bond stress, u, proportional to ΔT, is computed over the *clear* span of a beam or slab, at chosen sections of high beam shear, and wherever some of the bars may be terminating.

In this simplified numerical case (Example 3–1), the ϕ-increased flexural bond stress, u_u, proved uniform over the whole 4-ft. distance, at 217 psi USD stress, versus the USD permissible stress of 370 psi, or 59 per cent of the permissible.

Flexurally, the 3 ft. 11 in. section was USD-loaded to $^{400}\!/_{527} = 76$ per cent of its expected failure moment, so if it should finally be loaded to its failing *flexural* strength, the corresponding flexural *bond* stress would be at about $^{59}\!/_{76} = $ only 78 per cent of its failing value.   Based thereon, the beam failure would be the desirable slow yielding type, rather than a sudden one characteristic of bar slippage.

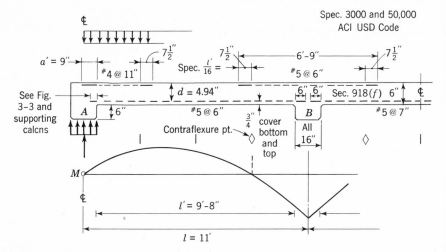

Fig. 3–2. Anchorages of slab top and bottom reinforcement of Example 3–2.

3–3. ANCHORAGE BOND STRESS [1]

This stress, proportional to the whole value of T, is sometimes designated u_a. *Anchorage* itself is typically an addition to the length of a tensile bar to prevent its slippage under load. The importance of this subject can hardly be overestimated. The occasional failure of a reinforced concrete member, or structure, has seldom been traced to a yielding of flexure steel or diagonal tension (web) reinforcement or to a compressive failure of the concrete, but is usually due to *bar slippage*, caused by insufficient embedment of the ends thereof into a concrete locality free of tensile stress.

If the anchorage distances at each end of every bar were shown on the drawings in some distinguishing manner, *and dimensioned*, their omission would not occur through oversight. Refer to Fig. 3–2.

EXAMPLE 3–2

Given the left end portion of the continuous slab and beam floor design shown in Fig. 3–2. The USD specification is 3000 and 50,000. Refer to Sec. 1801(b) and (c).

It is required to design the anchorage portions of both top and bottom bar groups.

Solution. (a) *Anchorage of intermediate top steel at B.* This steel cannot properly reinforce the 5 ft. 6 in. distance between the contraflexure points shown *unless the bar ends are extended* (anchored) into the adjoining (compressed) concrete, so as to develop some resistance to bar slippage. At such points it is unnecessary to provide enough additional length to match the full tensile value of the bars because the bending moment there is *supposed* to be zero. Therefore,

Code Sec. 918(e) requires a *partial anchorage* of $\frac{1}{16}$ of the 9 ft. 8 in. clear span, which is closely the $7\frac{1}{2}$ in. shown boldly. See also Sec. 918(b).

(b) *Anchorage of end top steel at A.* At such ends of floor systems, *full anchorage* is required, which must be strength-computed. To do this, calculate the USD tensile capacity of one #4 bar in pounds or kips, and equate to it the corresponding bond resistance developable over the unknown *anchorage* distance, a', measured from the inside face of the end support:

$$0.85u_u\Sigma o a' = 0.9f_y A_s \quad [f_y \text{ from } M_{uf}/0.9 \text{ of Code Sec. 1801(b)}] \quad (3\text{--}3)$$

so the required anchorage is

$$a' = \frac{0.9f_y A_s}{0.85u_u\Sigma o} \quad (3\text{--}4)$$

Regarding u_u, refer to Code Sec. 1801(c)(1). Assuming A305 (deformed) bars, the permissible design ultimate anchorage bond stress is $9.5\sqrt{f'_c}/D$, but not to exceed a maximum value of 800 psi. These bars are not classified as top bars since there is not at least a 12-in. depth of plastic concrete to settle from underneath them as consolidation and shrinkage take place, which would decrease their effective perimeter, Σo, to about 70 per cent of the formula value above.

Evaluating the required full anchorage by Eq. 3–4:

$$\text{Reqd. } a' = \frac{0.9A_s f_y}{0.85u_u\Sigma o} = \frac{0.9(0.20)(50,000)}{0.85(800)(1.57)} = 8.4 \text{ in.}$$

Extend end top bars 9 in. past the inside face of beam A.

(c) *Anchorage of bottom steel at end A.* For this work [2] the left end of the floor system has been redrawn as Fig. 3–3, and the USD gravity loading shown, since they are needed to establish the forces at section q-q, the inside face of beam A.

Investigational.

Slab   6.00
#5 rad. − .31
Cover   − .75
_____
$d = 4.94$

M_{uf} = clockwise moment upon section q-q
    = (3.16 kips)(8) − 0.44(4) = 23.5 kip-in.

Continuation of Example 3–2:

Spec. 3000 and 50,000
ACI USD Code in this case

Pertinent forces
concerning bottom
steel at A

Refer to last of
Sec. 904(c):
$wl' = 0.66(9.67')$
    = 6.4 kips

See left and right
division there of

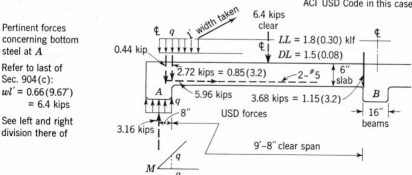

Fig. 3–3. Calculating anchorage for bottom steel at end A.

At q-q, $T_{uf} = M_{uf}/jd = 23.5/$ (0.80) $(4.94) = 5.96$ kips per ft. of slab
$$\text{Est. USD } j$$
width.

And $f_s = T_{uf}/A_s = 5.96/2(0.31) = 9.6$ ksi $=$ only 19% of 50-ksi capacity.

Designing. End anchorage required of #5 bottom bar, as adapted from Eq.
3–4:

$$\text{Reqd. } a' = \frac{T_{uf}}{0.85u_u\Sigma o} = \frac{5960}{0.85(800)(2)(\tfrac{5}{8})\pi}$$

$$= 2.23 \text{ in. if both bars left in bottom.}[2]$$

Code Sec. 918(f) requires that "at least $\frac{1}{4}$ of the positive moment reinforcement in continuous spans be extended into the support at least 6 in."

If half the bars were discontinued, the required 4.5-in. anchorage ($= 2 \times 2.23$) would be safely less than the 6-in. arbitrary minimum; but see the stringent requirements of Sec. 918(c) which discourage such cut-offs in zones of tensile concrete.

Conservative decision: Extend *all* bottom bars 6 in. past the inside face of the end beams A (and A').

The well-established 15 per cent Code inequality of clear span end shears was used to compute the small net bending moment of 23.5 kip-in. at section q-q. The corresponding small flexural tensile stress in the steel of 5.96 kips per 12-in. width became the basis for computing the 2.23-in. required anchorage distance, but note that this steel stress was only 9.6 ksi instead of the much larger limiting value.

The Code's 6-in. partial anchorage distance clause applicable here in lieu of bond calculations will ordinarily be found to be well on the safe side, as our 2.23-in. routine calculation demonstrates.

3–4. SUMMARY OF FLEXURAL AND ANCHORAGE BOND STRESS

In a reinforced concrete beam, the difference of the bending moments at two adjacent parallel sections causes a corresponding difference in the flexure steel tensions, ΔT_u, which results in a tendency for bar slippage through the concrete due to *flexural bond stress.* This bond stress, u_u, varies directly with the beam shear, but inversely with jd (the arm of the internal couple), and with the perimeter, Σo, of all the bars crossing the section. Shallow beams subject to heavy shear and having only a few large bars tend to have prohibitively high bond stress.

This *flexural* bond stress, $u_u = V_u/\Sigma ojd$, is proportional to the *rate,* ΔT_u, at which flexural bond accumulates over the *clear* spans of beams.

The ends of a reinforcing bar must also be correspondingly **anchored** (by bar extension when needed) within a region of zero or compressive concrete stress by enough anchorage length, a', on both sides thereof to develop the computed stress therein, at a value not to exceed the Code

---

[2] Actually another case of partial anchorage, since the flexure steel in this end locality is only $\frac{1}{5}$ stressed.

Sec. 1801 permissible bond stress for bars of such diameter, surface condition and elevation within the member.

Such anchorage bond stress, $u_{ua'}$, is proportional to the *whole* value of T_u at the point in question, and is permitted to be considered uniformly distributed over the whole length of the anchorage, whether the bar is straight, or curved to a radius no less than that of the "standard hooks" of Code Sec. 801.   When this *anchorage* bond stress proves to be less than 0.8 of the permissible, the adjacent flexural bond stress need not be computed.

Partial anchorage.   Except at supports, every bar shall be extended beyond the point of zero flexural stress a distance of 12 bar diameters, but not less than distance d [Code Sec. 918(b)].

Ending bars in tensile zone prohibited.   No flexural bar shall be ended in a zone of tensile concrete stress unless at least one of the alternate stringent requirements of Code Sec. 918(c) is met.

Top bars handicap.   Due to the tendency for plastic concrete to settle from underneath horizontal bars that are more than 12 in. above the bottom of a "pour,"[3] only 70 per cent of their perimeters can be used when calculating bond stress.   Refer to Code Sec. 1801(c)(1).

Special limiting bond values.   For #14 and #18 bars, compression (deformed) bars, and plain bars, consult Code Sec. 1801(c)(2), (3), and (4).

QUESTIONS

1. At a given section of a reinforced concrete beam, how does true horizontal shear vary vertically (a) below the neutral axis, (b) above the neutral axis?

2. Is flexural bond stress a form of shear?   Explain thoroughly concrete's distribution of bond upon a modern deformed bar.

3. Distinguish algebraically between unit flexural bond stress and unit anchorage stress, with respect to T_u.

4. Evolve a formula for required anchorage length, a', in terms of bar diameter and failing unit stresses (a) for bottom bars, (b) for top bars.

5. It has been stated that flexural bond stress is always calculated at points along the clear span, while anchorage stress is calculated outside it.   If true, mention two or three exceptions.

BOND AND ANCHORAGE PROBLEMS

For both problems deduce your section constants from those given at the beginning of Example 3–1, recognizing that less flexure reinforcement is being used.   Specification: 3000 and 40,000.

3–1. (a) Calculate the maximum flexural bond stress at each end of this beam (Fig. 3–4).

(b) Calculate the corresponding ACI permissible flexural bond stress, and comment upon the (a) results.

3–2. For the same beam, loading and specification as in Problem 3–1:

(a) Calculate the anchorage bond stress at each anchored end of each bar, and compare with the permissible.

(b) Comment upon the propriety of this bar arrangement.

[3] The proper term is *placement*.

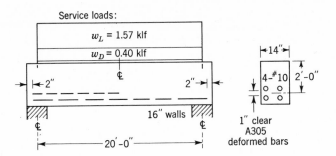

Fig. 3–4.   Bond stress problems.

B. Shear, Diagonal Tension, and Web Reinforcement

3–5. INTRODUCTION

Although the shear strength of concrete is fairly large in relation to the compressive (see Table 1–1), large values thereof tend to result in hazardous *tensile* concrete stress, the failure value of which is relatively small.   Moreover, this tension normally acts in a diagonal direction. It is the principal tensile stress of classical mechanics and Mohr Circle trigonometry.   In reinforced concrete calculations it should be thought of as *diagonal (principal) tension*.

In designing, if the computed value of diagonal tension stress is excessive, *web reinforcement* (e.g., stirrups) is provided to take care of the excess thereof.

Referring to the unit slices of Fig. 3–1b and Eq. 3–1, wherein a unit slice was utilized to compute the unit flexural bond stress upon the surface of the reinforcement, one might also have computed unit horizontal (or vertical) shear stress, v, by dividing the $T_{\text{diff}} = V/jd$ by the beam width b, obtaining 350 psi, and *calling it* unit diagonal tension, as was done in the past.   This procedure was justified by sketching a unit *cube* (Fig. 3–5)

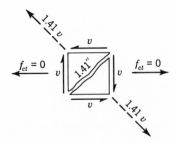

Fig. 3–5.   Equilibrium of total forces on the one-inch cube.

within the lower portion of the *unit slice*, and examining it as a free body under the four unit shears only, since the surrounding concrete had been presumed already cracked flexurally. From statics, or Mohr's Circle, the resulting 45° *maximum* unit tensile stress intensity, t_d, was shown to be the same as the corresponding unit vertical (or horizontal) shear stress value, namely, $t_d = V/bjd = v$, the former practice.

However, recent research [3] has indicated that the diagonal tension stress intensity, t_d, has not yet been closely enough determined to justify the precision suggested by retaining j in the above formula. Consequently, Code Sec. 1701(a) states: The *nominal* ultimate shear stress, *as a measure of diagonal tension*, t_{ud}, shall be computed by:

$$v_u = \frac{V_u}{bd} \qquad \text{[ACI Formula 17–1]}$$

In diagonal tension stress calculations, the nominal unit vertical and horizontal shears and the diagonal tension are considered equal in magnitude.[4]

Materials finally fail via normal stress or shear, whichever is the weaker. Concrete's unconfined shear failure unit strength is approximately one-fourth of its compressive, but the tensile is less than one-half of this shear strength. If the unit cube's four shear forces, v, of Fig. 3–5 are progressively increased, they combine into two opposing resultant diagonal tensile forces which soon reach their low tensile failure strength, accompanied by the 45° diagonal fracturing shown perpendicular thereto. Refer to Table 1–1.

SHEAR, BOND, AND DIAGONAL TENSION PRACTICE PROBLEMS

For these three problems, take the specification: $f'_c = 2500$, $f_y = 50,000$, $v_u = 90$ and 300, $u_u = 250$ and 125 psi for deformed and plain bars, respectively.

3–3. A singly reinforced beam carries a uniformly distributed dead and live *load-factored* loading totaling 4.0 kip per lin. ft. over a simple span of 16 ft., center to center of 12-in. walls, and two concentrated loads of 24 kips each, symmetrically located 3 ft. each side of the center line of span. The beam is 16 in. by 25 in. ($b \times d$), and has three $1\frac{1}{4}$-in. plain round bars. There are no stirrups.

(a) Investigate the beam for both flexural bond and diagonal tension unit stresses at the following sections:

> 2 ft. 6 in. from center of span
> 5 ft. from center of span
> At the inside face of wall

Work from fundamental principles, taking unit slices, as in Example 3–1.
Make for each section a free-body sketch of the slice taken, showing *all*

---

[4] It is unfortunate that the important term *diagonal tension* is mentioned only twice in Code Chapter 17. The *direction* of this tension (also obtained easily from Mohr's Circle) is often highly important for locating reinforcement, or in analyzing a failure, and is *never in the same direction* as that of the shear.

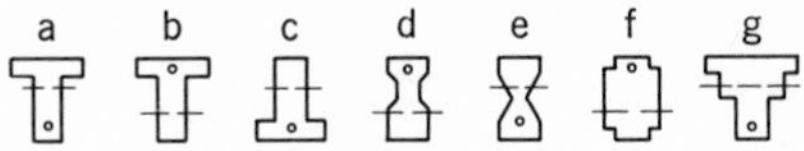

a   b   c   d   e   f   g

Fig. 3–6

forces exactly as applied, with their *values* as computed.   The summations $\Sigma H = 0, \Sigma V = 0,$ and $\Sigma M = 0$ must be satisfied on each sketch.

(b) Check by the formulas.

(c) Make a large half-span graph on $8\frac{1}{2}$-by-11-in. graph paper from the findings, plotting V, v, and u against span distance.   Plot also the permitted values of v and u and *report* upon the safety of the beam in these respects.

(a+) Alternately work individually at three sections, s in., $s + 28$ in., and $s + 56$ in. from the center of span, as assigned by the instructor.

3–4. In the sections pictured in Fig. 3–6, the steel indicates the tension side, and the neutral axes are at the levels shown.

(a) Show clearly for each case what width to use in calculations for maximum diagonal tension unit stress.

(b) Formulate a rule defining the width to take in computing unit diagonal tension for any section.

(c) Show clearly, for each case pictured, the width to take in calculating p, the steel ratio, for use with the bending stress chart of Appendix A, where applicable.

3–5. (a) Calculate the maximum flexural bond stress in Fig. 3–7 and show the comparison with the permissible.

(b) Calculate the required length of anchorage, a', recognizing that such top bars are governed by a decreased permissible bond stress, per Sec. 1801(c)(1).

(c) Sketch typical diagonal tension cracks.

(d) Dimension the spanwise locality theoretically needing diagonal tension reinforcement.

(e) Calculate the theoretically required number of #3 stirrups needed.   Refer to Example 3–3 below.

(f) Calculate the vertical stirrup spacing at section Y-Y.

(g) Find the maximum unit diagonal tension.

(h) Calculate the theoretical point along the span where one flexure bar may be discontinued.

EXAMPLE 3–3

The Design of Stirrup[5] Reinforcement

Given the beam, loading, and specification of Fig. 3–8a.

[5] Unless otherwise noted, vertical stirrups are always meant herein.

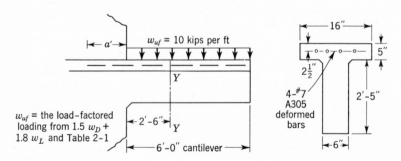

Fig. 3–7.   Cantilever bond and anchorage.

Item (f) of Example 3-3 Procedure

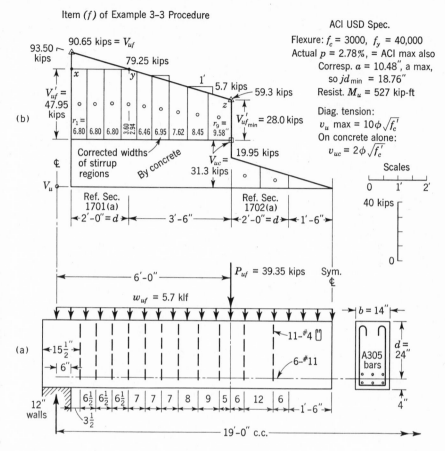

Fig. 3–8.　Design of stirrup reinforcement.[6]

Required procedure[7]

(a) Check the given concrete dimensions and steel for adequacy in bending, flexural bond, and anchorage [Code Secs. 1504 and 1801(a), (b), and (c)].

Ans.　Safe in all 3 respects.

(b) Demonstrate that the maximum diagonal tension is not too high, but that stirrups are needed [Secs. 1705(b) and 1701(c)].

(c) Clearly draw to scale, and dimension, the beam shear area requiring stirrups [Sec. 1701(c)].

(d) Determine the suitable maximum stirrup size and, incidentally, the minimum [Secs. 1703(a), 1706(a) and (b)].

(e) Calculate the theoretically required number of stirrups needed ($= \Sigma s V'_{uf}/ sV'_{uf}$). Round off to the safe number, N.

---

[6] For information on stirrups, refer to Code pages 46, 73, and 74.

[7] Part (a) should be done as preparatory home work.

(f) Compute the widths of the N stirrup *regions*, and therefrom the spacings of the stirrups.

(g) Calculate the empirically required additional stirrups, and space them.

Solution. Refer to Fig. 3–8. (Also, refer to Art. 3–6 below for a detailed commentary.)

Procedure item → 　(b) *Diagonal tension values.* From ACI Secs. 1705(b) and 1504(b):

$$10\phi \sqrt{f'_c} = 8.5 \sqrt{3000} = \qquad\qquad 465 \text{ psi limit}$$
$$\text{Max. } v_{uf} = V_{uf}/bd = 90{,}600/14(24) = 270 \text{ psi}, \quad <465, \quad \text{O.K.}$$

Sec. 1701(c) limit on unreinforced web is:

$$v_{uc} = 2\phi \sqrt{f'_c} = 2(0.85)(54.8) = \qquad\qquad 93 \text{ psi}$$
$$\text{Corresp. } V_{uc} = v_{uc}bd = 93(14)(24)/100 = 31.3 \text{ kips}$$

Since $270 > 93$, use stirrups.

Provide stirrups over 5 ft. 6 in., from inside face of support to the concentrated load.

(c) V'_{uf} = portion of beam shear to be resisted by stirrups. See upper portion of Fig. 3–8b, and Sec. 1701(a).

(d) *Suitable maximum stirrup size.* Dictated by min. V'_{uf} from Sec. 1703(a) A_v formula, and Sec. 1706(a) max. s of $d/2$ from Fig. 3–9.

$$\text{Max. } A_v = sV'_{uf,\,min.}/\phi f_y d = 12(28)/0.85(40)(24) = 0.41 \text{ sq. in.}$$

Maximum spacing is $d/2$ since max. v_u used is only $79{,}250/14(24) = 236$ psi, versus $6\phi \sqrt{f'_c} = 6(0.85)(54.8) = 279$-psi limit of Sec. 1706(a).

Try #4 stirrups at 0.40 sq. in., but do not allow the last spacing to exceed 12 in.

(d') *Minimum* $A_v = 0.0015(s_{max}b) = 0.0015(12)(14) = 0.25$ sq. in., from Sec. 1706(b). But since finally no *strength-computed* spacing exceeded 9 in., the #4 stirrups at 0.40 sq. in. proved O.K.

(e) *How many stirrups theoretically required?* A matter of V'_{uf} shear areas and Sec. 1703(a). Since sV'_{uf} for one stirrup $= \phi A_v f_y d$, the theoretical number of required stirrups is:

$$N = \frac{\Sigma s V'_{uf}}{sV'_{uf} \text{ of one stirrup}} = \frac{24(47.95) + 42(47.95 + 28.0)(0.5)}{(0.85)(0.4)(40)(24) \text{ kip-in.}}$$

$$= \frac{1150 + 1595}{326} = 8.4$$

This means 9 stirrups between x and z.

(f) *Determination of stirrup regions and spacings.* See Table 3–1.

(g) *Additional stirrups* are empirically required beyond the V_{uc} point, for a distance d [Code Sec. 1702(a)], *to guard against variations in the distribution of the loads.* Two additional #4 stirrups at $d/2$ spacing have been provided. Section 1706(b) controls the minimum size of such stirrups. See item (d') above.

3–6. COMMENTARY ON THE ITEMS OF STIRRUP-DESIGNING PROCEDURE OF EXAMPLE 3–3 AND THE CORRESPONDING SOLUTION

(b) First, examine the beam shear diagram of Fig. 3–8 and the accompanying diagonal tension portions of the Specification. V_{uc} limits the portion of the whole beam shear at a section which may be assigned to be taken care of by relying upon the small (diagonal) tensile strength of the concrete alone; the remainder of the beam shear at any section, designated V'_{uf}, is to be taken care of by the stirrup steel to be designed. Note the horizontal line which separates these two portions of each beam shear ordinate. For its level refer to the 31.3-kip value to be found in the item (b) calculations of the solution.

Throughout all diagonal tension expressions be sure to use the applicable understrength coefficient of 0.85, per Sec. 1504(b). The reason for using a value for diagonal tension and bond that is less than the (0.9) one used in flexural calculations is to insure that the undesirable sudden fracturing type of failure characteristic of an anchorage or diagonal tension type of failure will not occur.

The Code also limits, in Sec. 1705(b), the *total* beam shear (and diagonal tension) at any section. In this case it is well below the 465-psi limit. Theoretically, the locality needing stirrups is only 5 ft. 6 in. long because the end reaction (Fig. 3–8a) gets distributed over the 12-in. thickness of the wall (and more), and effectively prevents the opening of diagonal tension cracks thereover.

(c) Furthermore in the above connection, Sec. 1701(a) permits the beam shear at distance d from the face of the support to be the greatest that web reinforcement (e.g., stirrups) need be designed for. Note the cut-off line x-y on Fig. 3–8b.

(d) To select intelligently the proper size of stirrup, one must visualize the *beam shear area geometry* of Code Formula 17–4 of Sec. 1703(a). It says that each stirrup of area A_v takes care of a *shear diagram area* defined by a vertical measurement V'_{uf} and a horizontal distance s, which is the stirrup spacing. Once the suitable stirrup size has been determined, the corresponding $s(V'_{uf})$ beam *shear areas* should all be equal.[8] Near the support they will be tall and slender, but become shorter and wider as the V_{uc} point is approached, as in Fig. 3–8b.

To insure that every possible 45° diagonal tension crack is prevented from developing, Fig. 3–9 and Sec. 1706(a) require that stirrup spacings, s, must normally not exceed $d/2$ inches. In item (d) this demand was used, in conjunction with the *minimum* V'_{uf}, to calculate the #4 *maximum* stirrup size. Note that "all stirrups are twins" with respect to A_v.

---

[8] Ordinarily the same size of stirrup is used *throughout* a given beam.

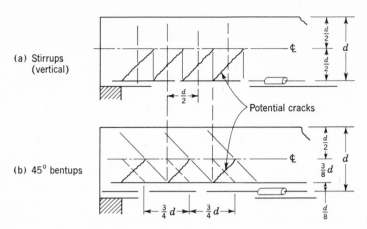

Fig. 3–9. Code USD maximum spacing of web reinforcement where the total diagonal tension is less than $6\phi \sqrt{f'_c}$ (or $3\sqrt{f'_c}$ in WSD).

(d′) The *minimum* size of stirrup for a given beam is governed by the Sec. 1706(b) demand that the stirrup area must not be less than 0.0015 times the corresponding tributary concrete area normal to it. This is related to the demand of Sec. 807(a) for the 0.0020 shrinkage and temperature steel ratio.

(e) The calculation of the theoretically required number, N, of stirrups of a chosen size for a given beam is often an important matter in connection with shear and diagonal tension. Many graduates may seldom need to compute stirrup spacings, but may be confronted repeatedly with predicting the *tonnage* of stirrup steel when making bids or firm estimates on jobs.

For N, simply divide the *whole* sV'_{uf} area by the sV'_{uf} for one stirrup.

(f) To determine the stirrup spacings which appear across the bottom of Fig. 3–8a, first work out the widths, r, of the *stirrup "regions,"* in the middle of each of which a stirrup is to be located. Starting at the face of the support, compute r_1, the width of the *first region*, working in tabular form as in Table 3–1.[9] Since the x-y boundary is horizontal, we have three equal-width regions, r_1, r_2, and r_3, and 0.53 of r_4 to the left of point y.

Continuing from point y, verify the rest of the region widths of the first column, which were gotten using the (conservative) "step approximation," but later corrected in the last column of Table 3–1.

The first of these is irregular. It started out to be the last 0.47 of r_4, namely, 0.47(6.80) = 3.20 in., but subject to later decreasing because of the slope involved.

[9] Utilizing the algebraic expression for N of preceding operation (e).

Table 3–1. Determination of Stirrup Regions for Beam of Example 3–3*

(Principally by the Step Approximation Method)

Regions r, and Their Widths†	Corresponding Decrease in V'_{uf} $= w_{uf}r/12 = 0.475r$	V'_{uf} for Next Region	Corrected Region Widths, r
$r_1 = \dfrac{sV'_{uf}}{V'_{uf}} = \dfrac{326 \text{ kip-in.‡}}{47.95 \text{ kips}} = 6.80$ in.	—	—	—
$r_2 = $ 6.80	—	—	—
$r_3 = $ 6.80	—	—	—
From pt. x = 20.40 in.			
$0.53r_4 = $ 3.60 in.			$\Sigma = 24.00$ in.
pt. y .... 8.20 in.			
$0.47r_4 = $ (yet uncorrected)	$5.7(3.20)/12 = 0.475r = 1.52$ kips	46.43 kips	2.94 in.
$r_5 = 326/46.43 = 7.02$	$\times\ 0.475 = 3.34$	43.09	6.46
$r_6 = 326/43.09 = 7.56$	$\times\ 0.475 = 3.59$	39.50	6.95
$r_7 = 326/39.50 = 8.26$	$\times\ 0.475 = 3.92$	35.58	7.62
$r_8 = 326/35.58 = 9.17$	$\times\ 0.475 = 4.35$	31.33	8.45
	35.21 in., <42 in.		
$r_9 = 326/31.33 = 10.40$			9.58§
	Sum = 45.61 in., >42 in., O.K.		42.00 in.

Shrink-back factor = 42.0/45.61 = 0.92, used to supply the intermediate data of the last column.

* Refer to item (f) of Procedure of Example 3–3.
† Beginning at face of left support.
‡ The 326 kip-in. per stirrup is from item (e).
§ 9.58 in. <12 in., the $d/2$ Specification maximum spacing, so #4 bar choice proved O.K.

79

The region widths r_5 through r_9 were "step-method" approximated, and their widths shrunken back in the last column so that all nine stirrup regions fit the 5 ft. 6 in. distance.

The midpoints of the stirrup regions of Fig. 3–8b were located, projected down to (a) as stirrup locations, and dimensioned to the nearest inch.[10]

Stirrup anchorage. As shown in Fig. 3–8a, stirrups (and bentup bars) are normally extended to within fireproofing distance of the compression face of beams in order to fully anchor them within the compressive stress area. Refer also to Fig. 3–11, which similarly involves bentup bars.

3–7. REFINED V_{uc} CALCULATION

Formula 17–2 of Code Sec. 1701(d) recognizes that the reserve strength in the flexure bars of simple beam end localities enables them to function as *horizontal stirrups!* Consequently, the use of this formula leads to v_{uc} and V_{uc} values greater than previously used herein, *and fewer stirrups.* Unfortunately, the computation involved is considerably longer than that of Table 3–1, so Formula 17–2 should probably be reserved for use only when a large number of identical members is involved.

Interestingly enough, if ϕ is omitted from Formula 17–2, one has v_{cr}, the V_{cr}/bd prediction of diagonal tension cracking[11] of an unstirruped locality!

Diagonal tension cracking often starts at the neutral axis level (where the unit shear stress classically has its maximum value) and may progress both downward and upward therefrom.

STIRRUP-REDESIGNING PROBLEM

3–6. Redesign the stirrups for the beam of Example 10–4 and Fig. 10–7 of WSD Chapter 10, by the USD method, following USD Chapter 17 of the Code and taking $f'_c = 3000$ and $f_y = 40{,}000$ psi, all as in Example 3–3.

Report what differences in results were found.

3–8. DESIGNING BENT BAR WEB REINFORCEMENT

This method of designing to resist diagonal tension consists of making use of the low-stressed portions of flexural bars. It involves bending the bars either upward or downward, usually at 45°, and extending them along the opposite horizontal face, as shown in Fig. 3–11 for a cantilever beam.

---

[10] In this case, in order to better demonstrate the method, some stirrups were located by half-inches.

[11] Mohr's Circle determinations are quite acceptable up to cracking, which is about 18 per cent above the V_c level, above which concrete is not relied upon to resist diagonal tensile stress anyway.

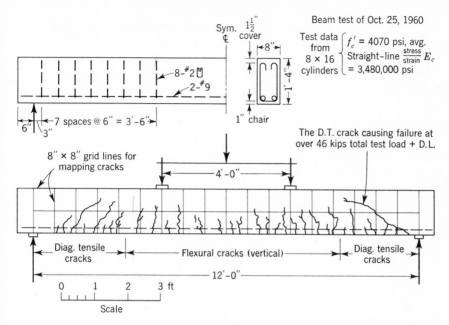

Fig. 3–10. Typical pattern of cracking of a stirruped beam at failure.

Table 3–2 summarizes the corresponding sets of allowable stresses to use with the USD load-factored forces.

Beam width for diagonal tension calculations. Since diagonal tension occurs only on the tension side of a beam, the beam width to use in diagonal tension calculations is "the least width on the tension side" that lies between the neutral axis and the tensile steel. It is designated b'.

Table 3–2

ACI USD Specification: $f'_c = 3000$, $f_y = 40,000$ psi

Flexure $\begin{cases} \text{ACI max. } p = 2.78\%: & a_{max} = 0.436d, \quad j = 0.782d \\ \text{This beam } p = 1.89\%: & a = 0.296d, \quad j = 0.852d, \quad 6.00 \text{ sq. in.} \end{cases}$

A_s

Diagonal tension $\begin{cases} v_u \text{ max.} = 10\phi \sqrt{f'_c} = 466 \text{ psi, the overall limit with web reinforcement.} \\ \text{If } v_u \leq 6\phi \sqrt{f'_c} = 279 \text{ psi} \begin{cases} (\frac{3}{4})d \text{ is max. } 45° \text{ web bar spacing.} \\ (\frac{1}{2})d \text{ is max. vert. web bar spacing.} \end{cases} \\ v_{uc} = 2\phi \sqrt{f'_c} = 93 \text{ psi} \end{cases}$

Bond* $\begin{cases} \text{Flexural: Top bars, } u_u = 6.7 \sqrt{f'_c}/D, \text{ but not over 560 psi.} \\ \text{Anchorage: See Sec. 1801(b). Also Sec. 919 requires 24 diameters min.} \\ \qquad \text{anchorage for web reinforcement.} \end{cases}$

*These are to be used with the load-factored values divided by a ϕ of 0.85.

In true T-beams this means taking the thickness of the web (stem). When the stem is tapered, as in pan T-beam construction, the Code permits the average tensile width to be used.

EXAMPLE 3–4

The Design of 45° Bent Bar Web Reinforcement for a Cantilever Beam

Given the T-shaped 10-ft. cantilever beam of Fig. 3–11 carrying a load-factored loading, w_{uf}, of 7.4 klf.

Referring to flexure Chart A–1 of Appendix A, the ultimate resisting moment, M_u, of the 6–#9 bars at face of the wall has been found to be 375 kip-ft., which

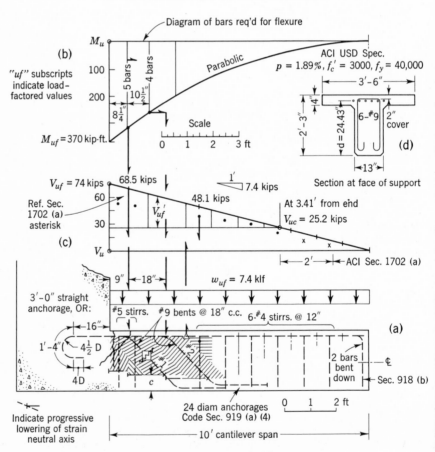

Cantilever Beam with Bent Bar Web Reinforcement

Fig. 3–11. Design of 45° web reinforcement.

is greater than the 370-kip-ft. load-factored moment of the 7.4-klf loading; so the section is adequate in flexure.

Required to design the needed web reinforcement, and to anchor it. Utilize as many of the #9 bars as practicable, and finish out with stirrups.

Recognize the unusual hazards* involved by correspondingly designing somewhat more conservatively than the Code requires.

Solution.   (a) *Diagonal tension.*

$$\text{Max. } v_{uf} = \text{conservatively } \frac{V_{uf}}{b'j^*d} = \frac{74,000}{13(0.852)(24.43)} = \underline{273 \text{ psi}}$$
$$\text{min.}$$

Since $273 < 466$ psi allowable of Sec. 1705(b), $\underline{\text{O.K.}}$

Since $273 < 279$ psi of Sec. 1706(a):

$$\underline{18 \text{ in. is max. spcg. of } 45° \text{ bent bars.}}$$

(b) *Carryable by concrete.*   From Sec. 1701(c), the allowable unit shear on an unreinforced web is

$$\text{Max. } v_{uc} = 2\phi \sqrt{f'_c} = 2(0.85)(54.8) = \underline{93 \text{ psi}}$$
$$\text{Corresp. } V_{uc} = V_{uc}b'j^*d = 93(13)(0.852^*)(24.43)/1000 = \underline{25.2 \text{ kips}}$$

So $(74 - 25.2)$ kips must be carried by the steel.

Hazards (see Fig. 3–11a):

1. A top bar left end slippage would be completely disastrous (anchorage).
2. Left end.   Coincidence of maximum shear and moment, and *their crackings*.
3. Locality of greatest diagonal tension (cross-hatched) is much deeper than a $d/2$ half-depth, and results in a shallow bottom anchorage locality.

Flexure vs. diagonal tension.   Since the V_{uc} value of 25.2 kips is less than the 74-kip load-factored maximum shear at the wall, diagonal tension reinforcement is needed.   Some #9's will be utilized by bending them down at 45°, but their ideal position for reinforcing an sV' shear area often gets overridden by the necessity for bending them elsewhere to meet the demands of the bending moment diagram for flexure steel area (see Table 3–3), or to satisfy some Code clause regarding the spacing of web reinforcement.

Sample 5–#9 bars investigation.   To find the bend-down point.   Referring to Fig. 3–12,

$$C_u = T_u = 0.85f'_cb'a = A_s(f_y)$$
$$= 0.85(3)(13)a = 5(40)$$

From which

$$a = 6.04 \text{ in., } a/2 = 3.02 \text{ in., } jd = 21.41 \text{ in.}$$
$$\text{Investig. } M_u = \phi T_u jd$$
$$= 0.9(200)(21.41/12) = 321.3 \text{ kip-ft.}$$

3–9. LOCATING BAR BEND-DOWN POINTS

Ideally, each bent bar should be centered in its parallelogram-shaped region of diagonal tension, as pictured in Fig. 3–11a.   From Fig. 3–9, the maximum 45° bar spacing, s, or parallelogram width, is $(\frac{3}{4})d$, say 18 in. in this case.   This (arbitrarily) locates the bend point of bar #1 at 9 in.

---

* Throughout this discussion, an asterisk calls attention to items of extra conservatism employed, in view of the special *hazards* (mentioned below), and other uncertainties.

Table 3–3. Calculation of Flexurally Safe Bend-down Points

$b = 13$ in., $d = 24.43$ in., $f_c = (0.85)(3) = 2.55$ ksi, M_{uf} at wall $= 7.4(10)^2/2 = 370$ kip-ft.

Number of #9 Bars in Top	Corresponding T_u (kips)	a from $T_u = C_u$ (in.)	Corresp. Flexural Arm jd (in.)	ACI Ultimate Resisting Moment M_u (kip-ft.)	Ratio of Resisting Moment M_u to 370 kip-ft. M_{uf} at Wall	Moment Diagram Tangent Distance Proportional to $\sqrt{\text{Col. 6}}$ (ft.)	Distance of Flexural Bend-down Point from Face of Wall (ft.)	$c = a/0.85$ = Compres. Concrete Height to Strain N.A. (in.)
Col. (1)	(2)	(3)	(4)	(5)	(6)	(7)	(8)	(9)
Investig. at wall								
6	240	7.24	20.81	375*	—	—	—	—
5	200	6.04	21.41	321.3	0.868	9.32	0.68	7.11
4	160	4.82	22.02	264.3	0.714	8.45	1.55†	5.68
3	120	3.62	22.62	203.7	0.550	7.42	2.58	4.26

* But note in Fig. 3–11b that the bending moment from the applied loading is safely only 370 kip-ft.
† But later actually bent down at 2.2 ft. from the wall to get it in the center of its parallelogram of diagonal tension.

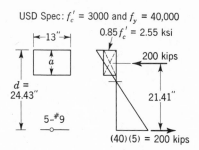

Fig. 3–12

from the wall, as shown, if the sV'_{uf} shear diagram area can thereby be satisfied.

From Code Sec. 1704(c), and conservatively* inserting the jd value of 21.41 in. from Table 3–3:

$$sV'_{uf} = \frac{\phi A_v f_y j^* d}{0.707} = \frac{(0.85)(1.0)(40)(21.41 \text{ in.})}{0.707} = 1030 \text{ kip-in.}$$

This equals the maximum sV'_{uf} area that one 45° bent bar can take care of.

Now the *actual* sV'_{uf} area *tributary* to bar #1 $= 18(68.5 - 25.2) =$ only 780 kip-in. This design is wastefully safe due to the 18-in. Code limitation on spacing, whether the bent bar is small or large, so we must accept it.

So far, there is a large triangular-shaped tensile locality underneath bar #1 which will finally get taken care of in the usual way (by the two #5 stirrups shown).

For a bent-bar design for diagonal tension to be sound, it is necessary to cover *all* the concrete area on the *tensile* side of the neutral (strain) axis with web reinforcement. Note that five such areas have been cross-hatched.

Ideally, acceptable anchorage of tensile bars cannot be achieved in a tensile concrete locality. The lower right-hand anchorage length for bar #1 begins at the typical level c, and at the cross-mark on the bar, and is surrounded by compressed concrete.

Although the V'_{uf} values are smaller in the locality of bent bar #2, still it must not be assigned more than an 18-in. maximum parallelogram region. In order to center it in its parallelogram, it was necessary, at (b), to move its bend point about 3 in. farther from the wall than the moment diagram demanded.

In this beam [5] more bars could have been bent down, but the preceding two illustrate the method.[12]

---

[12] When there are several bent bars to be used to resist diagonal tension it is easier to work with sV'_{uf} ordinates on the moment diagram.

To finish the designing, begin again at the leftmost (triangle) point on the still unreinforced region, which is closely 3 ft. from the wall.   Choose a stirrup of such a size that, at the Code maximum stirrup spacing of $\frac{1}{2}d$ = 12 in., it will suit the V'_{uf} of 22.9 kips thereat, as shown in (c). A #4 stirrup size, found to be good for V'_{uf} of 25.0 kips, was adopted for use here, and throughout the rest of the beam, including the two empirically determined ones outside the V_{uc} point.   Some stirrup steel might have been saved by using #3 stirrups instead.

It is left to the student to investigate the choice of #5 stirrups for the 9- and the 8-in.-width triangular areas just outside the wall; also, to look up the Code anchorage clauses and check the two alternate schemes for the all-important anchorage at the wall [Secs. 1801(c)(1) and 801].

Comment.   It would also be interesting to redesign the diagonal tension reinforcement using stirrups alone throughout the beam.   In many cases, utilization of some of the flexure steel for diagonal tension effects no saving in total steel.   Nevertheless, some well-experienced designers insist upon bending some bars in deep important members to get a "feeling of truss action," and "to knit everything together" in highly stressed localities.

3–10. SUMMARY OF SHEAR, DIAGONAL TENSION, AND WEB REINFORCEMENT

In a reinforced concrete beam, the difference of the bending moments at any two chosen sections causes a corresponding difference in the horizontal flexural forces, which produces *horizontal shear* in the concrete that is presently considered to have a uniform psi value over the whole d depth of the beam.

Spanwise, the unit horizontal (and vertical) shears, v, vary directly with the beam shear, but inversely with the beam width and d depth. Beams of small cross-sectional area that are subject to heavy external shear can have destructively high unit shearing stresses.

The distinct relative *tensile* weakness of concrete invites the particular combination of unit vertical and horizontal shearing stresses which results in a unit *diagonal tension* at 45° to the horizontal, also of an intensity, v, over sections normal thereto.

Reinforced concrete beams are prevented from failing prematurely in diagonal tension [4] by providing *web reinforcement*, which is preferably aligned normal to the direction of the potential diagonal cracking.

In a well-designed simple span beam, *diagonal tensile cracking* near the supports does not develop in test until considerably more than the design service load has been applied, so the concrete is relied upon to resist a portion of the diagonal tension [5].   On the other hand, some *minute flexural tensile cracking* usually occurs in the central region of large bending moment *before* all of the design service load has been applied, so the tensile strength of *that* bottom concrete is prematurely destroyed.

The total unit diagonal tension, v, is controlled in designing by providing sufficient beam depth, and minimum width, b', on the tensile side. Diagonal tension ("web") reinforcement is usually needed near the supports of short beams, but is often unnecessary in longer spans.

To allow for unanticipated variations in the *distribution* of the loading throughout spans, the Code now requires that all flexural members contain an empirically determined amount of web reinforcement *additional to* that demanded by the accepted theory. Typically, it calls for providing two additional stirrups beyond the V_{uc} point. A specified minimum *percentage* for the *web* reinforcement also exists.

REVIEW PROBLEM

3–7. A singly reinforced rectangular section simple span beam with stirrups is to be designed.

The starting data are: ACI USD Code, $f_y = 40,000$, $f'_c = 3000$, maximum $v_u = 10\phi \sqrt{f'_c}$, $v_{uc} = 2\phi \sqrt{f'_c}$, and u values for deformed bars from Sec. 1801. The beam is supported on 12-in. walls, and has a total length of 11 ft. 0 in., making the center-to-center span for loading and bending calculations 10 ft. 0 in. The *service-level* loads are:

> Live = a uniformly distributed 2 kpf over the 10 ft., plus a midspan concentrated load of 112 kips.
> Dead = the weight of the beam at 150 lb. per cu. ft.

Procedure. Preliminary calculations have indicated that a section with $b = 17$ in., $h = 3$ ft. 2 in. and 4-#11 bars resting on a 2-in. bolster will probably be adequate for flexure. Present your verification of it to the instructor before beginning the stirrup designing.

Early make a beam shear diagram, to scale, and calculate V_{uf} at midspan, V_{uc} and V_{uf} at face of wall. Show their values on the diagram.

Be sure to calculate for the largest stirrup usable at the $d/2$ maximum spacing (as formerly) and compute the number needed. Work out their spacings as in Example 3–3. Use only one size of stirrup.

Calculate the anchorage required for the bottom steel. Refer to the text matter near Fig. 3–3, and satisfy Code Sec. 918(f) also.

Finally, on a single 8½-by-11-in. sheet of good graph paper prepare a **final design sketch** to the scale 1 in. = 10 in. Draw a half side view and a cross-sectional view of the beam, together with the shear diagram *all in projection with each other.* Show all steel to scale. Show standard hooks on the stirrups per Code Sec. 801(a)(1).

QUESTIONS

6. What is the connection between the *principal tension* of mechanics and the *diagonal tension* of reinforced concrete? To what extent is the Mohr Circle technique applicable in reinforced concrete?

7. Sketch the expected diagonal tension cracking for a fixed-ended reinforced concrete beam. Make sure the cracks are correct in (a) location and (b) direction.

8. Explain any relation between the use of stiffeners on the webs of steel plate girders and the need for web reinforcement in reinforced concrete beams. Make your answer clear with a sketch of the actions involved.

9. Comparing bent bars and stirrups: Which is the more efficient? Convenient? Expensive?

10. Should stirrups be placed inverted (a) in cantilever beams, or (b) near the (restrained) ends of continuous beams? Why? Is there a solution to the practical difficulty involved?

11. Is there any Code USD flexural or shear regulation which, in effect, sets a minimum cross-sectional area for reinforced beams? Explain.

12. Mention at least two circumstances which call for increased length of anchorage of bars.

13. How are the maximum and minimum possible *sizes* of stirrup bars to be determined for a particular beam? How do you find the maximum *spacing* thereof?

14. Why must only 70 per cent of a bar's perimeter sometimes be relied upon for anchorage? What about the case of a vertical bar?

15. Exactly what portion of (a) a stirrup, or (b) a bent bar can legitimately be considered as anchorage length?

REFERENCES

1. FERGUSON, PHIL M., and THOMPSON, J. NEILS. "Development [anchorage] Length of High Strength Reinforcing Bars in Bond," *Proc. ACI*, 1962, Vol. 59, pp. 887–922.

2. MATHY, ROBERT G., and WATSTEIN, DAVID. "Investigation of Bond in Beam and Pull-out Specimens with High-Yield-Strength Deformed Bars," *Proc. ACI*, 1960, Vol. 57, pp. 1071–1090.

3. "Shear and Diagonal Tension (Part 2, Report of ACI–ASCE Committee 326)," *Proc. ACI*, 1962, Vol. 59, p. 277.

4. GURALNICK, S. A. "Shear Strength of Reinforced Concrete Beams," *Trans. ASCE*, 1960, Vol. 125, p. 603.

5. GURALNICK, S. A. "High-Strength Deformed Steel Bars for Concrete Reinforcement," *Proc. ACI*, 1960, Vol. 57, p. 241.

4

SHORT COLUMNS UNDER AXIAL COMPRESSION AND BENDING

4–1. INTRODUCTION

A **column** is a structural member subjected to direct compression parallel to its longitudinal axis, with or without bending. Additionally, transverse shears may be present, as well as torsional moments, but their effects will be excluded from this discussion. The columns considered here will be mainly those having a cross section with at least one axis of symmetry; this axis and the other centroidal axis perpendicular thereto constitute the principal axes of the cross section. When bending is present, it may be *uniaxial* or *biaxial*, that is, with respect to one or both of these principal axes. Most of the discussion here is concerned with uniaxial bending. The complicated matter of biaxial bending will have to be dealt with briefly, near the end of this chapter.

The general case of combined axial compression and bending reduces to that of pure flexure when axial compression is altogether absent. When the effects of axial compression are small relative to those of bending, there results a "beamlike" kind of column. When bending is completely absent, the column is simply **axially** or **centrically loaded.** Although truly centrically loaded columns are rare, they deserve some attention because they constitute the limiting case at one extreme of the range of columns from the standpoint of the relative magnitudes of the axial load and the bending moment.

Column behavior is further affected by a number of factors, among which are the presence of restraints along the length of a column, its unsupported length relative to its lateral dimensions, the possibility of relative transverse end movements (the so-called *sidesway* in building

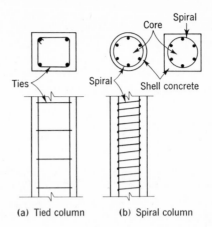

Fig. 4–1. Tied and spiral columns.

columns), instability, and so on.   These important factors will be temporarily disregarded at the beginning of our discussion, which amounts to saying that we will begin with the consideration of what are referred to as **short columns. Slender columns,** for which account must be taken of the effects of their slenderness and possibility of sidesway, will be considered in Chapter 5.

4–2. TYPES OF COLUMNS

Plain concrete columns are barred by the ACI Code unless the height is equal to or less than three times the least lateral dimension; in that case the member is called a *pier* or *pedestal*.   The most common type of concrete column is reinforced with longitudinal bars as **main reinforcement,** which are held in place by some kind of hooping, called **lateral reinforcement.**   The longitudinal bars are usually located near the periphery of a column, where they are most effective in resisting possible bending.   Each of these bars tends to act somewhat like an individual column, and tends to buckle in the direction of least opposition, which is usually outward. The lateral reinforcement, while serving the purpose of holding the longitudinal bars in position during the placing of the concrete, can additionally prevent the longitudinal bars from buckling outward and bursting the concrete cover if it is closely spaced and of adequate strength.

The lateral reinforcement may consist of a number of individual **lateral ties,** as shown in Fig. 4–1a, in which case the column is called a **tied column.**   Alternately, a **spiral column** contains a closely spaced, continuous **spiral** winding as its lateral reinforcement, as in Fig. 4–1b.   Usually, tied columns are rectangular in cross section and spiral columns are round, but either type may be of any desired shape.

Other types of columns are: **composite columns,** which are spiral columns encasing within their cores structural steel or cast iron shapes; **combination columns,** which are structural steel columns encased in concrete reinforced with wire mesh; and **concrete-filled steel pipe columns.** These types will not be taken up in this textbook.

4–3. SPIRAL VERSUS TIED COLUMNS

Numerous tests have shown that a spiral column behaves almost identically like an otherwise identical, tied column up to a load which might be called the *column yield point.*   In other words, before the column yield point is reached, the spiral adds practically nothing to the column strength.   A typical qualitative curve showing the column load versus the longitudinal strain of the columns in such tests is shown in Fig. 4–2, in which the curve marked *1-2* represents the load-strain relation up to the column yield point for both the tied and spiral columns.

After the column yield point is reached, the tied and spiral columns behave quite differently.   As shown by curve *2-3* in Fig. 4–2, the tied column fails suddenly, accompanied by violent breakouts of the concrete and outward buckling of the main reinforcement between the ties. Hence the ultimate load of a tied column is virtually its yield-point load. In the case of the spiral column after reaching the yield point, the concrete shell outside the spiral starts to crack and spall off.   Upon the gradual loss of the shell concrete and increasingly large deformation, during which the column load drops, the spiral comes into action.   It exerts inward supportive (confining) pressure on the concrete core, thus helping the column to continue to carry load until finally the spiral yields and/or bursts, precipitating the final failure of the column.

The load-strain relation for the spiral column beyond the yield point is typified by the dashed curves in Fig. 4–2.   If the spiral is heavy, the ultimate load may be larger than the column yield-point load; if the spiral

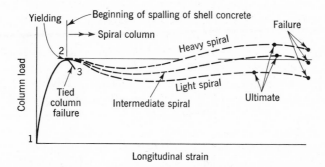

Fig. 4–2. Typical performance of reinforced concrete columns.

is light, the column continues to carry load beyond the yield point but not as much as the load at which the shell starts to spall. An intermediate amount of spiral, just sufficient to make up for the loss in strength due to the spalling of the concrete shell, will result in an ultimate load very close to the yield-point load. A quantitative design for the amount of spiral to achieve this will be given in Art. 4–5.

It is seen that the failure of a tied column is sudden while that of a spiral column is preceded by adequate warning. Hence, even though the ultimate capacity of a spiral column having an amount of spiral just sufficient to make up for the loss of the shell is not much larger than that of an otherwise identical tied column, the spiral column is much *tougher*. For this reason, Sec. 1504 of the ACI Code recommends that the understrength factor, ϕ, to be applied to column strengths computed on the basis of ideal materials and dimensions, be taken as 0.75 for spiral columns and 0.70 for tied columns, provided that the lateral reinforcement be as specified in Secs. 806 and 913(b).

4–4. ULTIMATE STRENGTH OF CENTRICALLY LOADED SHORT COLUMNS

For many years column design was on an elastic basis, which established a fixed ratio of steel stress to concrete stress, via the ratio E_s/E_c, of the moduli of elasticity of the two materials. However, column investigators found much higher steel stresses than indicated by elastic analysis, known now to have been due to concrete creep and shrinkage. As previously mentioned in Art. 1–13, concrete yields or creeps with lapse of time, even at low loads. Drying shrinkage produces a somewhat similar effect. Hence, the concrete of columns thereby gradually relieves itself of part of the load originally accepted, by unloading it upon the steel [1]. Due to this "buck-passing" characteristic, the ratio of steel stress to concrete stress becomes dependent upon the above-mentioned time-dependent deformations, which in turn are influenced by a great variety of factors, such as the age and quality of the concrete, the method of curing, the duration of the loading, and so on. Accordingly, an elastic analysis using a linear stress-strain assumption can hardly be expected to predict the stresses in the concrete and steel even before the column load attains the yield-point value, point *2* in Fig. 4–2.

A comprehensive series of column tests was conducted at Lehigh University and at the University of Illinois (principally during the decade 1930–1940), which is usually referred to as the ACI "Reinforced Concrete Column Investigation" [2, 4]. The results obtained therein are most significant. They show [2] that the steel and concrete stresses are not related in any fixed ratio; hence, the actual stresses even under safe working loads cannot be predicted with any reasonable accuracy. However, the tests did show that the ultimate strength of a column is independent of the history of loading or the sequence of progressive stressing of the concrete and steel as the load builds up. They showed specifically that, whether (upon increase of loading) the steel reaches its yield point first, thereby raising the concrete stress until its ultimate strength is reached, or vice versa, either the ultimate strength of axially loaded tied columns, or the yield-point strength of axially loaded spiral column (corresponding to point 2 in Fig. 4–2) is reached when the column load becomes approximately equal to:

$$P'_0 = 0.85f'_c(A_g - A_{st}) + A_{st}f_y \qquad (4\text{--}1a)$$

where P'_0 = *ideal* ultimate strength of centrically loaded short tied columns[1]

= *ideal* yield-point strength of centrically loaded short spiral columns

= *ideal* ultimate strength of centrically loaded, short tied *or* spiral columns (with adequate spiral just sufficient to compensate for the loss of shell concrete)

f'_c = standard cylinder compressive strength of concrete

A_g = gross concrete area of the column

A_{st} = total area of the longitudinal reinforcement

f_y = yield strength of the longitudinal reinforcement.

Equation 4–1a gives the ultimate strengths of centrically loaded short columns for *ideal* materials and dimensions. To provide for the likelihood of deviation from these ideal conditions, Sec. 1504(b) of the ACI Code recommends an understrength factor ϕ to be applied to the ideal strength P'_0 to yield under USD the *dependable* ultimate strength of a practical, centrically loaded short column, P_0. Thus,

$$P_0 = \phi P'_0 \qquad (4\text{--}1b)$$

where $\phi = 0.75$ for spiral columns and 0.70 for tied columns.

4–5. CERTAIN ACI COLUMN DESIGN DETAILS

Although it is premature to delve into all the aspects of actual column design, it is perhaps appropriate at this time to give some preliminary attention to certain design details and limits as recommended by the 1963 ACI Code. These are given below, and, where necessary to clarify or explain the Code requirements, accompanied by comments and/or

---

[1] This 0.85 coefficient (shown as 0.85_w in Fig. 2–4c) was originated by C. S. Whitney as a factor for size and slenderness to relate the indicated compressive strength of 6-by-12-in. test cylinders, f'_c, to that of more slender full-sized members.

examples.   For a fuller treatment of design considerations, the reader should, of course, refer to the Code.   Also, he will do well to consult Reference 3 for more elaborate commentary on the Code requirements.

Limiting Column Dimensions.   Section 912(a) stipulates the following *minimum column sizes:* Principal columns must be of 10-in. diameter minimum for round sections and of 8-in. side dimension minimum for rectangular sections, with a minimum gross area of 96 sq. in.   Auxiliary columns, at intermediate locations and not continuous from story to story, must be 6 in. minimum in dimension.

Limits for Longitudinal Reinforcement. *Minimum clear spacing of longitudinal bars or adjacent splices.*   Here the Code requires $1\frac{1}{2}$ in., $1\frac{1}{2}$ times the bar diameter, or $1\frac{1}{2}$ times the maximum aggregate size, whichever is the largest [Secs. 804(d) and (e)].   Normally, the clear spacing between the bars is much larger than this minimum unless "bundled" column bars are used, for which Sec. 804(f) applies.

Minimum and maximum amounts of longitudinal bars.   Section 913(a) provides that the total area of longitudinal bars must range from 1 to 8 per cent of the gross cross-sectional area, with a minimum bar size of #5, and a minimum of six bars for spiral columns and four bars for tied columns.

The *lower limit* is needed because some reinforcement is necessary to help the column resist some bending, which always exists whether or not recognized in the computations, and also to reduce the effects of concrete creep and shrinkage.   It was mentioned in Art. 4–4 that, due to concrete creep and shrinkage, the column steel stress is increased, and this increase in steel stress, according to test results [4], becomes larger as the ratio of the longitudinal reinforcement decreases.   Unless a lower limit is specified for the amount of reinforcement, the steel stress may increase to the yield level under sustained service loads.

The *maximum limit* of longitudinal reinforcement content may be considered as a practical maximum in terms of economy and requirements for placing.   Further, the test columns of the ACI "Column Investigation" [2, 4] included reinforcement ratios no greater than 6 per cent.   Originally, maximum ratios of 8 and 3 per cent were recommended for spiral and tied columns, respectively.   These were revised to 8 and 4 per cent, respectively, in the 1936 Code, and subsequently the maximum limit for tied columns with bending was raised to 8 per cent in the 1956 Code.   Since the 1963 Code requires bending to be considered in the design of all columns, the uniform maximum ratio of 8 per cent has been adopted for both types of columns.

Limits for Lateral Reinforcement. *Concrete protection for spirals and ties.*   Section 808(c) stipulates a minimum of $1\frac{1}{2}$ in. or $1\frac{1}{2}$ times the maximum aggregate size, whichever is the larger.

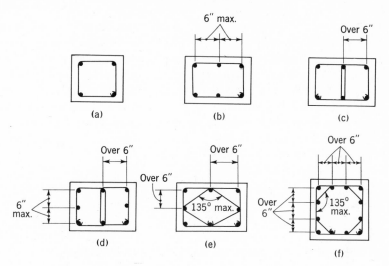

Fig. 4–3.   Typical tie arrangements.

Tie steel content.[2]   Section 806(b) stipulates a minimum tie size of #2, with a maximum tie spacing equal to the smallest of 16 longitudinal bar diameters, 48 tie diameters, and the least column dimension.   The ties should be so arranged that every corner and alternate longitudinal bar is laterally supported by the corner of a tie having a maximum included angle of 135°, and the maximum distance of a laterally unsupported bar from a laterally supported bar is 6 in.   Figure 4–3 shows typical tie arrangements satisfying the Code provision.

This tie arrangement represents a relaxation from the 1956 Code, which required, for every longitudinal bar, lateral support equivalent to that provided by a 90° corner of a tie.   While ties do to some extent confine the concrete core, and add to the ductility of the column, although not as efficiently as the closely spaced, continuous spirals (imperfect end anchorage of individual ties being another detrimental factor), tests revealed no appreciable difference between ultimate strengths of columns with the full tie requirements and no ties at all.   Accordingly, the 1963 Code liberalizes the tie requirements for ordinary columns by increasing the maximum included angle from 90° to 135° and exempting bars which are within 6 in. on each side of adequately supported bars.[3]

[2] The 1963 ACI Code does not yet contain a provision for the amount of tie steel. A common rule for tie size requires its area to be at least 2 per cent of the area of all the longitudinal bars confined by it.   This rule has its origin in the design of lacing in structural steel built-up columns, and its applicability to reinforced concrete columns is debatable.

[3] However, in limit design wherein members must be ductile enough to allow rotation to take place while maintaining the desired resistance, that is, to permit the formation of *plastic hinges,* heavier ties may be needed to furnish this ductility.

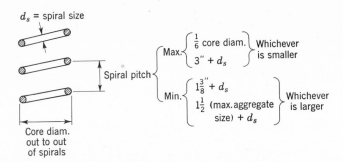

Fig. 4–4. Limits for spiral pitch.

Spiral steel content. As mentioned in Art. 4–3, the spiral in a spiral column comes into play only after the spalling of the shell concrete, and then enables the column to continue carrying load after the column yield point. In order that the ultimate load be about the same as the yield-point load, the proper amount of spiral required may be found by equating the loss in strength due to the spalling of the shell concrete to the contribution to the strength by the spiral. Now, the loss in strength from the shell concrete is

$$0.85f'_c(A_g - A_c) \tag{1}$$

in which A_c is the area of the concrete core from out to out of the spiral. Tests have shown [4] that, pound for pound, the spiral is at least twice as effective in its contribution to the column strength as longitudinal reinforcement. So if

$$p_s = \frac{\text{volume of spiral in a given length of column}}{\text{volume of concrete core in the same length}}$$

then the contribution of the spiral to the column strength may be conservatively estimated at

$$2(p_s A_c)f_{ys} \tag{2}$$

in which f_{ys} is the yield-point strength of the spiral. Equating (1) to (2), one finds

$$p_s = 0.425[(A_g/A_c) - 1](f'_c/f_{ys}) \tag{3}$$

Section 913(b) modifies the coefficient 0.425 to 0.45 so that Formula 9–1 of the Code reads as

$$p_s = 0.45[(A_g/A_c) - 1](f'_c/f_{ys}) \tag{4-2}$$

with the stipulation that f_{ys} must not exceed 60 ksi. Hence the ACI spiral formula provides a slight excess over the shell strength as an added margin of assurance.

As to the spiral size and its pitch, Sec. 806(a) stipulates a minimum spiral diameter of $\frac{1}{4}$ in. for rolled bars or No. 4 AS&W gage for drawn wires, with limits for its pitch as indicated in Fig. 4–4. It should be noted that, for columns of about 12-in. diameter or smaller, it may not be possible to meet both the maximum and minimum limits for the spiral pitch as shown in Fig. 4–4. A revision of these limits is now under consideration by ACI Committee 318.

EXAMPLE 4–1

Given a 20-in. round spiral column with 8–#9 bars as longitudinal reinforcement, as shown in Fig. 4–5a, 4000-lb. concrete, 50,000-psi-yield-point longitudinal reinforcing steel and 60,000-psi-yield-point spiral steel, and 1-in. maximum aggregate size.

Required to find the ideal ultimate capacity of the section as a centrically loaded short column, and to design the spiral. Use the ACI Code, USD.

Solution.

Gross concrete area: $A_g = \pi(10)^2 = 314$ sq. in.

Area of main reinforcement: $A_{st} = 8.00$ sq. in.

Ideal ultimate capacity of centrically loaded short column:

$$\begin{aligned}
P'_0 &= 0.85f'_c(A_g - A_{st}) + f_y A_{st} \\
&= 0.85(4.0)(314 - 8.00) + 50.0(8.00) \\
&= 1440 \text{ kips}
\end{aligned}$$

Dependable ultimate capacity of centrically loaded short column:

$$\begin{aligned}
P_0 &= \phi P'_0 \\
&= 0.75(1440) = \qquad\qquad \underline{1080 \text{ kips}} \quad \text{Ans.}
\end{aligned}$$

With a cover of $1\frac{1}{2}$ in. for the spiral, the concrete core out to out of spirals has a diameter of 17 in. and an area

$$A_c = \pi(8.5)^2 = 227 \text{ sq. in.}$$

Section 913(b) provides that the required volumetric percentage of spiral reinforcement, p_s = volume of spiral/volume of concrete core, is

$$\begin{aligned}
p_s &= 0.45[(A_g/A_c) - 1](f'_c/f_{ys}) \\
&= 0.45[(\tfrac{314}{227}) - 1](\tfrac{4}{60}) = 1.15\%
\end{aligned}$$

This calls for a spiral volume of $(1.15\%)(227) = 2.61$ cu. in. per in. of column height.

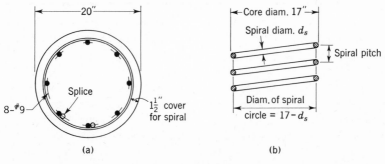

Fig. 4–5. Spiral column investigation and spiral design.

According to Sec. 806(a), the center-to-center spiral pitch should lie within the following limits:

Maximum: $17/6$ = 2.83 in. or 3 in. + d_s, of which 2.83 in. governs.

Minimum: $1\frac{3}{8}$ in. + d_s, or $1\frac{1}{2}$(1 in.) + d_s = $1\frac{1}{2}$ in. + d_s, of which the latter governs.

Spiral rod[4] selection:

First trial taking $\frac{1}{2}$-in. rounds, d_s = 0.5 in., spiral area = 0.20 sq. in. Limiting range of pitch: 2.83 in. maximum and 1.50 + 0.50 = 2.00 in. minimum. Taking a column height equal to the spiral pitch, the volume of one turn of spiral is approximately $\pi(17.0 - 0.5)(0.20)$ cu. in., from Fig. 4–5b. The required spiral volume in this height is (2.61)(required pitch). Equating the two volumes,

$$2.61 \text{ (reqd. pitch)} = \pi(17 - 0.5)(0.20)$$

from which

$$\text{Reqd. pitch} = 3.97 \text{ in.}$$

Since the limiting maximum pitch is 2.83 in., $\frac{1}{2}$-in. spirals are therefore uneconomical.

Second trial taking $\frac{3}{8}$-in. rounds, d_s = 0.38 in., spiral area = 0.11 sq. in. The required pitch is given by

$$2.61 \text{ (reqd. pitch)} = \pi(17 - 0.38)(0.11)$$
$$\text{Reqd. pitch} = 2.20 \text{ in.}$$

The limiting range is 2.83 in. maximum and 1.50 + 0.38 = 1.68 in. minimum. Therefore,   Use $\frac{3}{8}$-in. spiral rod at $2\frac{1}{8}$-in. pitch.   Ans.

The longitudinal reinforcement percentage is 8.00/314 = 2.55%, which is within the 1 to 8% range of Sec. 913(a). The longitudinal steel bars are now on a (17 − 0.75 − 1.13) or 15.12-in. diameter. This makes the center-to-center spacing of bars 5.94 in., which leaves (5.94 − 1.13 − 1.13) = 3.68 in. clear spacing at possible splices. This satisfies the minimum clear spacing requirements of Secs. 804(d) and (e).

4–6. THE PLASTIC CENTROID

In Art. 4-4, the ultimate capacities of a centrically loaded short column are shown to be given by Eqs. 4–1. Such a column is one in which the direct load is to be applied at a point, called the **plastic centroid** of the section, which, according to Sec. 1900(b), is defined as the centroid of resistance of the section computed for the assumption that the concrete is stressed uniformly to $0.85f'_c$, and the steel is stressed uniformly to f_y. Accordingly, the plastic centroid and the *geometric* centroid of a section do not always coincide. Both centroids will lie on an axis of symmetry with regard to both the concrete dimensions and the steel arrangement, but their locations on this axis will be different if the section has only one, and no more than one, axis of symmetry. When there is more than one axis of symmetry, the two centroids are coincident at the intersection of

---

[4] Available in $\frac{1}{4}$-, $\frac{3}{8}$-, $\frac{1}{2}$-, and $\frac{5}{8}$-in. rounds.

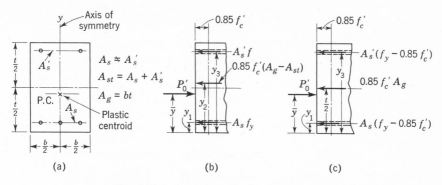

Fig. 4–6. Location of plastic centroid.

the axes; for example, for the spiral column of Example 4–1, Fig. 4–5, the center of the column is its geometric as well as plastic centroid.

Whether or not the plastic centroid coincides with the geometric centroid, its location may always be determined by taking moments of the resistances of the concrete and the steel. For instance, consider the rectangular section of Fig. 4–6a, which has unequal amounts of reinforcement on two opposite faces, A_s and A'_s, but which otherwise is symmetrical about the y-axis. The plastic centroid lies on the y-axis, and its position (marked by $P.C.$) is to be located. The stresses and the resisting forces corresponding to the centrically loaded condition are shown in (b), where P'_0 is the axial load to be applied at $P.C.$, the resisting force from the net concrete area is $0.85f'_c(A_g - A_{st})$, acting at the centroid of the *net* concrete area, and the resisting forces from the reinforcement, A_sf_y and A'_sf_y, acting respectively at the centroids of A_s and A'_s. Equilibrium of forces requires:

$$P'_0 = 0.85f'_c(A_g - A_{st}) + A_sf_y + A'_sf_y \qquad (1)$$

Taking moments of the forces about the bottom face of the section, and noting the lever arms of the forces as indicated in (b), one gets,

$$P'_0\bar{y} = 0.85f'_c(A_g - A_{st})(y_2) + A_sf_y(y_1) + A'_sf_y(y_3) \qquad (2)$$

From Eqs. 1 and 2, one may easily compute $\bar{y}$, which locates $P.C.$ from the bottom face. This requires, however, a prior determination of y_2, which defines the location of the *net* concrete area. More conveniently, the forces in Fig. 4–6b may be replaced by an equivalent system as shown in (c), which consists of the resisting force of the *gross* concrete area, $0.85f'_cA_g$, acting at the centroid of the gross concrete area, namely, at distance $t/2$ from the bottom face, and the resisting forces of the reinforcement stressed to $(f_y - 0.85f'_c)$. Equilibrium of forces gives:

$$P'_0 = 0.85f'_cA_g + (A_s + A'_s)(f_y - 0.85f'_c) \qquad (3)$$

which is seen to be identical to Eq. 1 above.   Now, taking moments about the bottom face:

$$P'_0\bar{y} = 0.85f'_cA_g(t/2) + A_s(f_y - 0.85f'_c)(y_1) + A'_s(f_y - 0.85f'_c)(y_3) \quad (4)$$

which, together with Eq. 1, yields $\bar{y}$.   The statical equivalence of the two force systems used should be obvious.   In writing the moment equation, one may more conveniently sum up the moments of the forces about the centroid of A_s.

EXAMPLE 4–2

Given a rectangular column section with longitudinal reinforcement and specifications as shown in Fig. 4–7a.

Required to find the plastic centroid of the section and its ideal ultimate capacity if the column is short and centrically loaded.

Solution.   The direct load P'_0 is to be applied at the *plastic centroid*, marked *P.C.*, to produce the centrically loaded condition.   The resisting forces, or their more convenient equivalent, are shown in (b), in which the force on the gross concrete area is shown to act at mid-depth of the section, and the reinforcement is stressed to $(f_y - 0.85f'_c)$.   The necessary calculations are recorded in the following table, in which the moments of the forces are taken about the centroid of the reinforcement A_s:

Forces, kips	Distance from A_s, in.	Moment About A_s, kip-in.
$2.00(50 - 3.4) = \quad 93.2$	13.0	1212
$18(18)(3.4) \quad = 1101.6$	6.5	7160
$4.54(50 - 3.4) = \quad 211.6$	0	0
Sum $= 1406.4$		8372

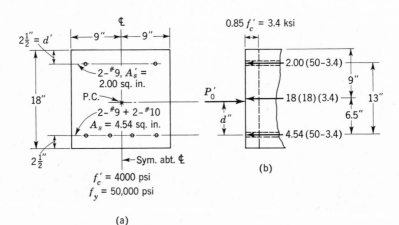

$f'_c = 4000$ psi
$f_y = 50,000$ psi

(a)

(b)

Fig. 4–7. Locating the plastic centroid.

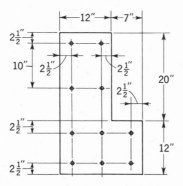

Fig. 4–8.   Problem 4–3.

Hence, the ideal ultimate capacity of the centrically loaded short column is

$$P'_0 = \hspace{3cm} 1406 \text{ kips} \quad \underline{\text{Ans.}}$$

and the plastic centroid of the section is at a distance d'' from the centroid of A_s given by

$$d'' = 8372/1406.4 = \hspace{2cm} 5.95 \text{ in.} \quad \underline{\text{Ans.}}$$

Applying an understrength factor of $\phi = 0.70$ to P'_0 gives 984 kips as the *dependable* ultimate capacity load of the corresponding practical column.

CENTRICALLY LOADED COLUMN PROBLEMS

Unless otherwise noted for the following problems, take 4000-lb. concrete of 1-in. maximum aggregate size and 60,000-psi-yield-point steel for *all* reinforcement, and assume all columns are *short* and *centrically loaded.*   Follow the ACI Code.

4–1. A 20-in. square spiral column has 8–#10 vertical bars arranged on a circle. Allow $1\frac{1}{2}$-in. cover for spirals.   Find the *ideal* ultimate capacity load, P'_0, of the section, design the spiral, and check to see if the amount of longitudinal reinforcement and the clear spacing of bars satisfy the Code.
Ans. $P'_0 = 1934$ kips. $\frac{1}{2}$-in. rounds @ 2 in.

4–2. A 14-by-20-in. rectangular tied column has a line of 3–#6 bars along one of the 14-in. sides and a line of 3–#9 along the opposite side, all centered $2\frac{1}{2}$ in. inward therefrom.   Find the *ideal* ultimate capacity load, P'_0, and locate the plastic centroid of the section.   Recommend a tie arrangement, size, and spacing.
Ans. $P'_0 = 1197$ kips.   P.C. at 6.90 in. from the line of 3–#9 bars.

4–3. An L-shaped tied column is reinforced with 10–#9 bars arranged as shown in Fig. 4–8.   Find the *ideal* ultimate capacity load P'_0 and the plastic centroid.   Recommend the required ties (i.e., tie arrangement, size, and spacing).

4–7. ECCENTRICALLY LOADED SHORT COLUMNS—
PRELIMINARY DISCUSSION

Introduction.   When a direct load is not applied at the plastic centroid (Art. 4–6) of a column section, bending is produced in addition to direct compression, and the column is then said to be **eccentrically loaded.**[5]

---

[5] Unless otherwise noted, hereafter all eccentricities or bending moments will be implicitly understood to refer to the **plastic centroids of sections being considered.**

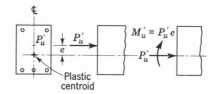

Fig. 4—9. Eccentrically loaded column section.

An eccentric load on a section may always be converted to a direct load of equal magnitude applied at the plastic centroid of the section *plus* a bending moment equal to the load multiplied by the eccentricity. Thus, if the ideal, short-column capacity load of an eccentrically loaded column section, such as that shown in Fig. 4–9, is given by P'_u together with its eccentricity e, it may also be given as P'_u, understood to be acting at the plastic centroid, together with its concurrent capacity moment of M'_u where $M'_u = P'_u e$. Hence, the eccentricity $e = M'_u/P'_u$.

The ϕ-Factor. According to the ACI Code, the *dependable* ultimate capacities of a *practical*, short column, P_u and M_u, are obtained by multiplying respectively both the corresponding ideal capacities, P'_u and M'_u, by the same understrength factor ϕ; thus, $P_u = \phi P'_u$, and $M_u = \phi M'_u$. Hence the eccentricity e, whether computed on the basis of P'_u and M'_u or on the basis of P_u and M_u, remains unchanged; that is, $e = M'_u/P'_u = M_u/P_u$. However, certain complications will be seen to arise, and further attention to this matter will be given in Chapter 5. In the meantime, only *ideal* ultimate capacities are considered.

Minimum Eccentricity. In order to provide some resistance to the bending which is virtually unavoidable in any practical column, Sec. 1901(a) of the ACI Code requires all columns to be designed for a minimum eccentricity of $0.05t$ for spiral columns, and $0.10t$ for tied columns, where t is the overall depth of a rectangular section or the diameter of a round section. Again, for the time being, only the ideal column will be considered, and this requirement will be taken up in Chapter 5.

Assumptions and Guiding Principles—A Recapitulation. The analysis of eccentrically loaded short columns involves no new assumptions or principles besides those already used in the pure flexural analyses of Chapter 2. These are set forth in Sec. 1503 of the ACI Code, and are briefly recapitulated here because of their importance.

Concrete *strains* vary linearly over the depth of a section, and the strains in the concrete and those in the reinforcing bars at the same point are equal. Based on tests, concrete in compression is considered to crush at an ultimate strain in the extreme fibers of 0.003. The tensile strength of the concrete is normally considered negligible. At ultimate strength, concrete stress is not linearly distributed, but its distribution may be approximated by an equivalent rectangular stress block with an intensity of $0.85f'_c$ and a stress block depth a, related to neutral axis distance c from the extreme compressive fiber by $a = k_1c$, in which k_1 is assumed to be 0.85 for f'_c up through 4000 psi, and $[0.85 - 0.05(f'_c - 4000)/1000]$ for f'_c over 4000 psi. Steel stress is assumed to be linearly related to steel strain by the elastic modulus E_s taken at 29,000,000 psi until the yield point f_y, corresponding to the yield strain ϵ_y, is reached; beyond the yield point, steel stress is assumed to remain at f_y.

Beyond these principles, the only tools needed for a short-column analysis are the basic conditions of equilibrium.

Effect of e. Before taking up the numerical examples of the next article, it is instructive to examine qualitatively the effect of the eccentricity e on the action of a column. This may be done by reference to Fig. 4–10, which depicts the entire gamut of column action as a result of varying e from zero to infinity. For simplicity's sake, a rectangular section with reinforcement near two opposite faces, A'_s and A_s, and subjected to P'_u at an eccentricity of e, is considered. The content A'_s is usually referred to as the compressive reinforcement, whereas A_s is referred to as the tensile reinforcement; but the latter will be seen to be a misnomer. A better way to differentiate the two quantities of reinforcement is to define A'_s as that on the same side of the plastic centroid as the load P'_u, and A_s as that on the other side.

As the table of Fig. 4–10 shows, when e is zero, the moment M'_u is zero, and $P'_u = P'_0$ of the centrically loaded case. The concrete is uniformly stressed to $0.85f'_c$ and all the reinforcement is stressed to f_y compressively, the entire cross section being in compression. Concrete strain reaches the maximum value of 0.003. Whether concrete strain reaches this maximum value first or whether steel yields first is of no consequence, since, as stated in Art. 4–4, the ultimate capacity remains materially the same regardless of the history of loading. The mode of failure is necessarily compressive. The neutral axis distance c may be imagined to be infinity.

When there is no axial load, i.e., $P'_u = 0$, we have the case of pure flexure, and M'_u takes on a particular value, say, M'_0. The corresponding value of e may be considered to be infinity. The neutral axis distance c is less than the depth t, and tension exists over part of the section.

When the eccentricity is between these two extreme values, two types of conditions may prevail. For smaller eccentricities, the entire cross section is in compression, and the neutral axis distance c is larger than, or in the limit equal to, the depth t. For larger eccentricities, c is less than t, and tension exists over part of the section.

Figure 4–10 shows that, for smaller eccentricities, $c \geq t$, compression exists over the entire section, and the failure is compressive. Except for

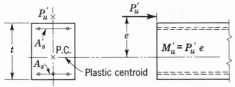

Eccentricity	Loading	Strains	Stresses	Failure mode	
$e = 0$	$P_u' = P_0'$ P.C. $M_u' = 0$	**Centrically loaded** 0.003 — ϵ_s' — ϵ_s — $c = \infty$	$0.85 f_c'$ — f_y — f_y	Compression over entire section	Compression failure
$0 < e < \infty$	P_u' e P.C. $M_u' = P_u' e$	**Small eccentricities** 0.003 — ϵ_s' — ϵ_s — $c \geq t$ — N.A.	$0.85 f_c'$ — a — f_s' — f_s	Compression over entire section	Compression failure
		Large eccentricities 0.003 — ϵ_s' — $c < t$ — N.A. — ϵ_s	$0.85 f_c'$ — f_s' — a — f_s	Tension over part of section	Tension or compression failure depending on ϵ_s: If $\epsilon_s > \epsilon_y$, tension failure; If $\epsilon_s = \epsilon_y$, balanced condition; If $\epsilon_s < \epsilon_y$, compression failure
$e = \infty$	$P_u' = 0$ P.C. $M_u' = M_0'$	**Pure flexure** 0.003 — ϵ_s' — N.A. — $c < t$ — ϵ_s	$0.85 f_c'$ — f_s' — a — f_s	Tension over part of section	

Fig. 4–10. Column action in relation to the eccentricity, e, measured from the plastic centroid.

the limiting case of the centrically loaded condition, the reinforcement A'_s may or may not have yielded according as $\epsilon_s' \geq \epsilon_y$ or $\epsilon_s' < \epsilon_y$.

For larger eccentricities, up to the pure flexure case, $c < t$, and tension exists over part of the section. The mode of failure may be tensile or compressive, depending on whether $\epsilon_s > \epsilon_y$ or $\epsilon_s \leq \epsilon_y$. In any case, the compressive reinforcement A'_s may or may not have yielded.

4–8. RECTANGULAR SECTIONS WITH REINFORCEMENT NEAR TWO FACES—NUMERICAL EXAMPLES

The following numerical examples illustrate how, by first principles alone, a rectangular column may be investigated. The column sections considered have reinforcement placed near the two most highly stressed faces. Rectangular sections with reinforcement near all the four faces will be considered in Art. 4–11. Only *ideal, short-column* ultimate capacities are evaluated; the application of the understrength factor ϕ, and slenderness effects will be dealt with in Chapter 5.

General Data for Examples 4–3 Through 4–7

Given the column section of dimensions and specifications as shown in Fig. 4–11. This is the same section as investigated in Example 4–2, which was found to have its plastic centroid at $d'' = 5.95$ in. from the centroid of the reinforcement A_s, or at 0.55 in. from the mid-depth of the section. The eccentric load P'_u is applied at a distance of y in. from the mid-depth of the section as shown. Accordingly, the eccentricity of the load, when referred to the plastic centroid, is

$$e = y + 0.55 \text{ in.}$$

and when referred to the centroid of the reinforcement A_s, is

$$e' = y + 6.50 \text{ in.} = e + 5.95 \text{ in.}$$

In each example, the *ideal, short-column* ultimate capacities, i.e., P'_u and $M'_u = P'_u e$, are desired.

EXAMPLE 4–3

Given the general data of Fig. 4–11 and the case of pure flexure, corresponding to $P'_u = 0$, $e = \infty$.

Required to find the *ideal, short-column* capacity moment $M'_u = M'_0$ (see notation used in Art. 4–7).

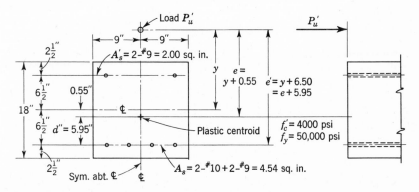

Fig. 4–11. Column section investigated in Examples 4–3 to 4–7.

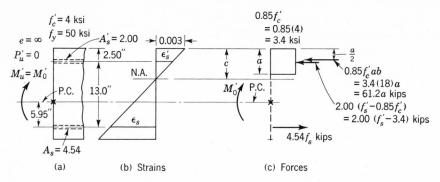

Fig. 4–12. Example 4–3—pure flexure.

Solution. When subjected to pure flexure, the section behaves as a doubly reinforced beam section, the analysis of which was discussed in Chapter 2. Hence, the following calculations are given without much explanation, except with the note that the effect of the area of concrete displaced by the compression reinforcement has been taken into account. As was explained in Art. 4–6, this may be conveniently done by considering an equivalent system of forces which consists of the force on the *gross* area of concrete in compression; the force(s) from the reinforcement *lying within the compressive concrete stress block*, stressed to its actual stress *less* $0.85f'_c$; together with forces from the tensile reinforcement.

With compression over part of the section, the strains and forces are as shown in Fig. 4–12. The steel strains are, from (b),

$$\epsilon'_s = (0.003)\left(\frac{c - 2.50}{c}\right)$$

$$\epsilon_s = (0.003)\left(\frac{15.5 - c}{c}\right)$$

Subject to later verification, assume that failure is controlled by tension and that the compression reinforcement has not yielded. Therefore the steel stresses are:

$$f'_s = E_s\epsilon'_s = 29,000(0.003)\left(\frac{c - 2.50}{c}\right) = (87)\left(\frac{c - 2.50}{c}\right) \text{ ksi}$$

$$f_s = f_y = 50 \text{ ksi}$$

With these substituted in the force expressions shown in Fig. 4–12c, and summing up the forces for equilibrium, we get

$$61.2a + 2.00\left[(87)\left(\frac{c - 2.50}{c}\right) - 3.4\right] = 4.54(50)$$

Now, $a = k_1 c = 0.85c$; with this substitution, the above equation becomes

$$52.0c + (174)\left(\frac{c - 2.50}{c}\right) - 6.8 = 227$$

Multiplying both sides by c, and transposing and simplifying, we get a quadratic equation in c:

$$52.0c^2 - 59.8c - 435 = 0$$

Solving,
$$c = 3.52 \text{ in.}$$
$$a = 0.85(3.52) = 3.00 \text{ in.}$$

Now, check the assumptions by computing the steel strains:

$$\epsilon_y = f_y/E_s = 50/29{,}000 = 0.00172$$

$$\epsilon_s = (0.003)\left(\frac{15.5 - 3.52}{3.52}\right) = 0.0102 \quad > \epsilon_y$$

$$\therefore \text{ Tensile failure, as assumed.}$$

$$\epsilon'_s = (0.003)\left(\frac{3.52 - 2.50}{3.52}\right) = 0.00087 \quad < \epsilon_y$$

$$\therefore A'_s \text{ has not yielded, as assumed.}$$

The value of M'_0 may now be computed. Since the resultant of the resistances is $P'_u = 0$, M'_0 is the sum of the moments of the resistances taken about any point. Taking moments about, say, the centroid of A_s, one obtains:

$$M'_0 = \left\{ 52.0(3.52)\left(15.5 - \frac{3.00}{2}\right) + \left[174\left(\frac{3.52 - 2.50}{3.52}\right) - 6.8 \right](13) \right\} \frac{1}{12} =$$
$$260.8 \text{ kip-ft.} \quad \text{Ans.}$$

EXAMPLE 4–4

Given the general data of Fig. 4–11, and that the load is applied at mid-depth of the section, i.e., $y = 0$.

Required to find the *ideal, short-column* capacity load, P'_u.

Solution. For $y = 0$, the eccentricity of the load is, as shown in Fig. 4–13a,

$$e = 0.55 \text{ in.} \quad \text{with respect to the plastic centroid}$$

or,

$$e' = 6.50 \text{ in.} \quad \text{with respect to the centroid of } A_s$$

As the eccentricity e is small, it is reasonable to assume compression existing over the entire cross section, subject to verification. The strain diagram is then as shown in (b), wherein the neutral axis lies outside the section or at the lower face of the section, that is, $c \geq 18$ in.

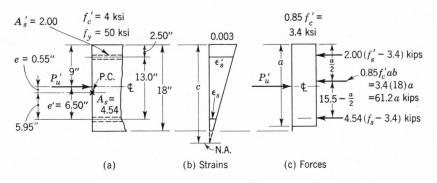

Fig. 4–13. Column of Example 4–4.

The stress block is shown in (c) with a depth of $a = 0.85c$, and the force on the concrete is then $(61.2)(a)$ kips. It should be noted that a must not exceed the depth of the section, or 18 in.

The forces in the reinforcement are then:

$$2.00(f'_s - 3.4) \text{ kips in top bars } A'_s$$
$$4.54(f_s - 3.4) \text{ kips in bottom bars } A_s$$

the effect of the areas displaced by the bars in the concrete having been included.

Whatever the steel stresses f_s and f'_s may be, the conditions of equilibrium are that the sum of the forces be zero and that the sum of their moments about *any* point be zero. Therefore:

$$P'_u = 61.2a + 2.00(f'_s - 3.4) + 4.54(f_s - 3.4)$$

and taking moments more conveniently about the centroid of the reinforcement A_s,

$$P'_u e' = P'_u(6.5) = 61.2a(15.5 - \tfrac{1}{2}a) + 2.00(f'_s - 3.4)(13)$$

Now, subject to later verification, assume that the top bars A'_s have yielded, and that the bottom bars A_s have not, that is:

$$\epsilon'_s \geq \epsilon_y, \text{ and } f'_s = f_y = 50 \text{ ksi}$$

and

$$\epsilon_s < \epsilon_y, \text{ and } f_s = E_s \epsilon_s \text{ where } \epsilon_s = 0.003 \left(\frac{c - 15.5}{c} \right)$$

With $E_s = 29,000$ ksi, $f_s = (87) \left(\dfrac{c - 15.5}{c} \right)$ ksi.

When these are substituted into the equilibrium equations, we get

$$P'_u = 61.2a + 2.00(50 - 3.4) + 4.54 \left[87 \left(\frac{c - 15.5}{c} \right) - 3.4 \right]$$

$$= 61.2a + 93.2 + 4.54 \left[87 \left(\frac{c - 15.5}{c} \right) - 3.4 \right] \tag{1}$$

$$P'_u(6.5) = 61.2a(15.5 - \tfrac{1}{2}a) + 93.2(13)$$
$$= 61.2a(15.5 - \tfrac{1}{2}a) + 1211.6 \tag{2}$$

These two equations involve the unknowns P'_u, a, and c, but since a and c are either related by $a = 0.85c$, or else $a = 18$ in., there are actually only two unknowns. At this stage, it is of course not known whether c is such that $0.85c$ is smaller than or just equal to 18 in. Assuming that $c = a/0.85 = 1.176a$, and substituting Eq. 1 into Eq. 2, we get:

$$\left\{ 61.2a + 93.2 + 4.54 \left[87 \left(\frac{1.176a - 15.5}{1.176a} \right) - 3.4 \right] \right\} (6.5)$$

$$= 61.2a \left(15.5 - \frac{a}{2} \right) + 1211.6$$

which, upon multiplication by $1.176a$ and transposition and collection of like terms, and followed by a division by the coefficient of the term containing a^3, reduces to

$$a^3 - 18a^2 + 60.84a - 1107 = 0 \tag{3}$$

This cubic equation may be solved quite easily by a numerical procedure described in Appendix B, and may be shown to have two imaginary roots and a real root of $a = 18.03$ in.

This value of a exceeds the maximum allowed value of 18.00 in. by only an insignificant amount, and, in a practical case, may be accepted. But, in order to illustrate what is to be done if the excess should be too large, the following revision of the equilibrium equations is given. Equations 1 and 2 are rewritten with the value of a set equal to 18.00 in. to read:

$$P'_u = 61.2(18.00) + 93.2 + 4.54 \left[87 \left(\frac{c - 15.5}{c} \right) - 3.4 \right]$$

$$= 1101.6 + 93.2 + 4.54 \left[87 \left(\frac{c - 15.5}{c} \right) - 3.4 \right]$$

$$= 1574.4 - \frac{6130.25}{c} \tag{4}$$

$$P'_u(6.5) = 1101.6[15.5 - \tfrac{1}{2}(18.0)] + 1211.6$$
$$= 8372 \tag{5}$$

From Eq. 5, P'_u is readily found to be $8372/6.5 = 1288$, and with this value of P'_u, Eq. 4 becomes

$$1288 = 1574.4 - \frac{6130.25}{c}$$

from which

$$c = \frac{6130.25}{1574.4 - 1288} = 21.40 \text{ in.} \quad \text{(with a corresponding } 0.85c = 18.19\text{)}$$

Now, to verify the assumptions that A'_s has yielded and A_s has not, compute the steel strains:

$$\epsilon_y = 0.00172$$

$$\epsilon'_s = (0.003) \left(\frac{21.40 - 2.50}{21.40} \right) = 0.00265 \quad > \epsilon_y$$

$$\epsilon_s = (0.003) \left(\frac{21.40 - 15.5}{21.40} \right) = 0.00083 \quad < \epsilon_y$$

which show the correctness of the assumptions. Hence, the ideal, short-column capacity load is

$$P'_u = \qquad\qquad \underline{1288 \text{ kips}} \quad \underline{\text{Ans.}}$$

which, coupled with the given eccentricity of $e = 0.55$ in., gives a corresponding capacity moment:

$$M'_u = 1288(0.55)(\tfrac{1}{12}) = \qquad \underline{59.0 \text{ kip-ft.}} \quad \underline{\text{Ans.}}$$

EXAMPLE 4–5

Given the general data of Fig. 4–11, and that the load is applied at a distance of $y = 10$ in. "above" the mid-depth of the section.

Required to find the *ideal, short-column* capacity load, P'_u.

Solution. For $y = 10$ in. as shown in Fig. 4–14a, the eccentricity is $e = 10.55$ in. with respect to the plastic centroid, or $e' = 16.50$ in. with respect to the centroid of the bottom bars. With this eccentricity, it is assumed that compression

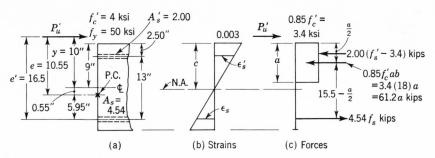

Fig. 4–14. Column of Example 4–5.

exists over only part of the section, and the bars A_s are therefore in tension. The strains and the forces are then as shown in (b) and (c). Summing up the forces, and summing up their moments about the centroid of reinforcement A_s, the equilibrium equations are:

$$P'_u = 61.2a + 2.00(f'_s - 3.4) - 4.54f_s$$
$$P'_u(16.5) = 61.2a(15.5 - a/2) + 2.00(f'_s - 3.4)(13)$$

It is now assumed that the strength of the section is governed by compression, that is, A_s has not yielded at ultimate load; further, the top bars A'_s are assumed to have yielded at ultimate load. These assumptions, subject to verification, result in the following steel stresses:

$$f_s = E_s\epsilon_s = 29{,}000(0.003)\left(\frac{15.5 - c}{c}\right) = (87)\left(\frac{15.5 - c}{c}\right)\text{ksi}$$

and

$$f'_s = f_y = 50\text{ ksi}$$

The equilibrium equations then become:

$$P'_u = 61.2a + 2.00(50 - 3.4) - 4.54(87)\left(\frac{15.5 - c}{c}\right)$$

$$= 61.2a + 93.2 - (395.0)\left(\frac{15.5 - c}{c}\right) \quad (1)$$

$$P'_ue' = P'_u(16.5) = 61.2a(15.5 - \tfrac{1}{2}a) + 93.2(13)$$
$$= 61.2a(15.5 - \tfrac{1}{2}a) + 1211.6 \quad (2)$$

These two equations may be solved in two different ways: either combining the two to form a cubic equation and solving it; or solving the two equations as they are by an iterative process which is described below.

If one chooses to solve Eqs. 1 and 2 as they are, the iterative process consists of the following steps of calculation:

1. Assume a reasonable value of a, and compute therefrom a trial value of c by the relation $c = a/0.85$; or vice versa;

2. With these values of a and c, enter Eq. 1 and compute a trial value of P'_u;

3. Compute the right side of Eq. 2, and divide the result by the trial value of P'_u. This gives a trial value of e' to be compared with its true value of 16.50 in. If the trial and the true values agree, then the solution has been obtained; other-

wise, repeat as many cycles of computations as needed to reach the desired degree of precision between the trial and true values of e'.

The following table shows the progress of this procedure, starting with an initial assumed value of $c = 10.0$ in.:

Trial No.	Assume c	Trial a = 0.85c	Compute P'_u from Eq. 1	Compute Trial e'*
1	10.0	8.50	396	17.87
2	10.5	8.92	451	16.04
3	10.37	8.81	437	16.45
4	10.35	8.80	435	16.52

* From e' = right-hand side of Eq. 2 divided by P'_u.

The last trial results in an e' of 16.52 in., which is considered to be close enough to the true value of 16.50 in.

Alternatively, Eqs. 1 and 2 are combined into one equation by substituting (1) in (2) and noting $c = a/0.85$. The result of this, after some algebraic simplification, is

$$a^3 + 2a^2 + 223.6a - 2806 = 0 \qquad (3)$$

The procedure described in Appendix B may then be used to solve Eq. 3, which will be found to have two imaginary roots and a real root of $a = 8.80$ in. Hence $c = 10.35$ in., which agrees with the result of the iterative method above.

It remains now to verify the assumptions by computing the steel strains and comparing them with the yield strain of steel:

$$\epsilon_y = 0.00172 \text{ (as before)}$$
$$\epsilon_s = (0.003)(15.5 - 10.35)/10.35 = 0.00149 \quad < \epsilon_y$$
$$\epsilon'_s = (0.003)(10.35 - 2.50)/10.35 = 0.00228 \quad > \epsilon_y$$

These show that the assumptions made previously were correct. P'_u can then be computed from Eq. 1 or taken directly from the table given previously. Hence the ideal, short-column capacity load is:

$$P'_u = 61.2(8.80) + 93.2 - (395.0)\left(\frac{15.5 - 10.35}{10.35}\right) = \underline{435.2 \text{ kips}} \quad \text{Ans.}$$

Combined with the eccentricity of $e = 10.55$ in., this corresponds to a capacity moment:

$$M'_u = 435.2(10.55)(\tfrac{1}{12}) = \qquad \underline{382.6 \text{ kip-ft.}} \quad \text{Ans.}$$

EXAMPLE 4–6

Given the general data of Fig. 4–11, and that the load is applied at a distance of $y = 20$ in. "above" the mid-depth of the section.

Required to find the *ideal, short-column* capacity load, P'_u.

Solution. For $y = 20$ in., the load is at $e = 20.55$ in. from the plastic centroid, or $e' = 26.5$ in. from the centroid of the bottom bars. Assuming compression existing over only part of the section, the strains and forces are as indicated in Fig. 4–15b and c.

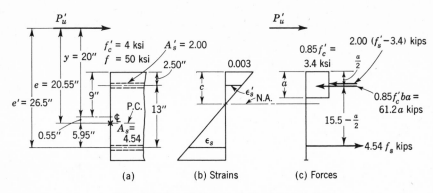

Fig. 4–15.   Column of Example 4–6.

Assuming a tensile failure, with the compression bars having yielded at ultimate load, the steel stresses are:

$$f_s = f'_s = f_y = 50 \text{ ksi}$$

Equilibrium considerations therefore give:

$$P'_u = 61.2a + 2.00(50 - 3.4) - 4.54(50)$$
$$= 61.2a + 93.2 - 227.0$$
$$= 61.2a - 133.8 \tag{1}$$
$$P'_u(26.5) = 61.2a(15.5 - a/2) + 93.2(13) \tag{2}$$

Substitution of Eq. 1 into Eq. 2, followed by transposition and simplification, yields the quadratic equation:

$$a^2 + 22a - 155.5 = 0 \tag{3}$$

Solving, one obtains $a = 5.63$ in., and $c = 5.63/0.85 = 6.62$ in.
The strains may be computed from Fig. 4–15b as:

$$\epsilon_s = (0.003)(15.5 - 6.62)/6.62 = 0.00402 \quad > \epsilon_y \text{ of } 0.00172$$
$$\epsilon'_s = (0.003)(6.62 - 2.50)/6.62 = 0.00187 \quad > \epsilon_y \text{ of } 0.00172$$

These justify the previous assumptions.
Therefore, from Eq. 1,

$$P'_u = 61.2(5.63) - 133.8 = \qquad \qquad \text{210.6 kips}\quad\text{Ans.}$$
$$M'_u = P'_u e = 210.6(20.55)(\tfrac{1}{12}) = \qquad \text{360.6 kip-ft.}\quad\text{Ans.}$$

EXAMPLE 4–7

Given the general data of Fig. 4–11.
Required to find the *ideal, short-column* capacity load for the balanced condition, and the corresponding eccentricity.
Solution. From Example 4–5, in which the section fails in compression, and Example 4–6, in which the failure is controlled by tension, it is obvious that an intermediate case exists in which at ultimate load extreme compressive concrete fibers reach the maximum strain of 0.003 simultaneously with the tensile steel reaching its yield strain, i.e., $\epsilon_s = \epsilon_y$. This is referred to as the *balanced condition* and occurs for a particular value of the load and eccentricity, denoted by P'_b and

e_b as shown in Fig. 4–16a. The neutral axis may be located by using the strains shown in (b), and its distance from the extreme fiber in compression denoted by c_b is given by:

$$\frac{c_b}{15.5} = \frac{0.003}{0.003 + \epsilon_y} = \frac{0.003}{0.003 + \dfrac{50}{29,000}} = \frac{87}{87 + 50}$$

or

$$c_b = 9.84 \text{ in.}$$

The corresponding stress block depth, a_b, is then:

$$a_b = k_1 c_b = 0.85(9.84) = 8.37 \text{ in.}$$

The strain in the top steel, ϵ'_s, may be found to be

$$\epsilon'_s = (0.003)\left(\frac{9.84 - 2.50}{9.84}\right) = 0.00224 \quad > \epsilon_y \text{ of } 0.00172$$

Hence the steel stresses in both the top and bottom bars are $f_s = f'_s = f_y = 50$ ksi. Summing up the forces shown in (c), one gets:

$$\begin{aligned} P'_b &= 61.2a_b + 2.00(f'_s - 3.4) - 227 \\ &= 61.2(8.37) + 2.00(50 - 3.4) - 227 \\ &= 512.0 + 93.2 - 227 = \hspace{2cm} \underline{378.4 \text{ kips}} \quad \text{Ans.} \end{aligned}$$

and taking moments about the centroid of the tensile bars, one gets:

$$P'_b(e'_b) = 512.0\left(15.5 - \frac{8.37}{2}\right) + 93.2(13) = 7005 \text{ kip-in.}$$

Dividing this moment by P'_b yields:

$$e'_b = 7005/378.4 = 18.51 \text{ in.}$$

from which the eccentricity with respect to the plastic centroid is found to be:

$$e_b = 18.51 - 5.95 = \hspace{2cm} \underline{12.56 \text{ in.}} \quad \text{Ans.}$$

And the corresponding value of M'_u denoted by M'_b, is then:

$$M'_b = P'_b e_b = (378.4)(12.56)/12 = \hspace{2cm} \underline{396.1 \text{ kip-ft.}} \quad \text{Ans.}$$

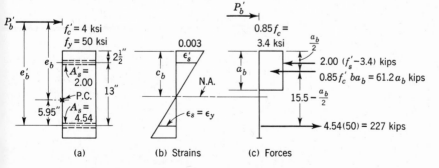

Fig. 4–16. Column of Example 4–7.

4–9. SUMMARY AND DISCUSSION OF SHORT-COLUMN EXAMPLES 4–2 THROUGH 4–7

The results of the investigation for the ideal, short-column ultimate capacity of the rectangular section of Arts. 4–6 and 4–8 are summarized in a table shown in Fig. 4–17a. From Examples 4–2 and 4–3 come the results for the two limiting cases of *centric loading only* and *pure flexure*. The results for the cases of intermediate eccentricities are taken from Examples 4–4 through 4–7, which include in particular those of the *balanced case* wherein the failure of the section is by simultaneous crushing of the concrete and the yielding of the tensile reinforcement. Other results given in the table have been obtained by calculations not shown herein but quite similar to those presented in the examples.

It is noted that, for small eccentricities, the neutral axis distance $c \geq t$, and compression exists over the entire section. The failure is necessarily controlled by compression. For larger eccentricities, the neutral axis lies within the section, i.e., $c < t$. Accordingly, tension exists over part of the section, and failure is controlled by either compression or yielding of the tensile reinforcement, with the balanced condition as the dividing case between these two modes of failure.

The matter of whether at ultimate load the compression reinforcement has yielded deserves a word of caution. The table of Fig. 4–17a reveals that, for eccentricities larger than that of the balanced case, the compression reinforcement may or may not have yielded, depending respectively on whether the eccentricity is moderately larger or very much larger than e_b. For eccentricities smaller than e_b, note that, at ultimate load, the compression reinforcement has yielded in all cases shown in the table. One must not draw the conclusion that this *always* happens for any section, nor that, by comparing the balanced eccentricity with a given eccentricity, the matter of compression reinforcement having yielded or not may be settled forthwith. The most that can be said is that, for any given section, as the eccentricity of the load decreases, the neutral axis moves farther away from the extreme compressive fiber, thereby increasing the strain in the compression reinforcement and the likelihood of causing it to yield. Accordingly, if for a given section it has been found that the compression reinforcement has yielded at ultimate load for a specific eccentricity, the only legitimate inference is that yielding of the compression reinforcement also occurs for all smaller eccentricities. Or, proceeding in the other direction, if it is established that, at ultimate load, the compression reinforcement in a given section has not yielded, then likewise it will not have yielded for larger eccentricities. In any event, for an investigation of a particular column, the state of stress in the compression reinforcement (and, for that matter, in all reinforcement) must be based on strain calculations.

Results from Example No.	Point on curve below	e in.	Ultimate capacity		At failure					Failure mode	
			P'_u, kips	M'_u, kip-ft.	Strains	N.A.	Stresses	A'_s yielded	A'_s not yielded	Comp.	Tens.
4-2	A	0.00	$\dfrac{P'_0}{1406}$	0		$c=\infty$	Compression over entire cross section	✓		✓	
4-4	1	0.55	1288	59		$c>t$		✓		✓	
*	2	2.06	1069	183		$c=t$		✓		✓	
*	3	5.55	691	320				✓		✓	
4-5	4	10.55	435	383				✓		✓	
4-7	B	$\dfrac{e_b}{12.56}$	$\dfrac{P'_b}{378}$	$\dfrac{M'_b}{396}$		N.A. $c<t$		✓		Balanced ✓	✓
4-6	5	20.55	211	361				✓			✓
*	6	30.55	129	328			Tension over part of cross section		✓		✓
4-3	C	∞	0	$\dfrac{M'_0}{261}$					✓		✓

*Calculations not shown

(a) Summary of results

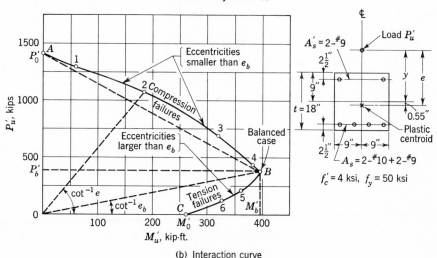

(b) Interaction curve

Fig. 4–17. Ideal, short-column strength—Examples 4–2 to 4–7.

It will be noted that, aside from the basic assumptions, all the calculations shown in the examples finally revolve around the equilibrium equations: one being the force equation and the other a moment equation. It may be generally shown, as is also revealed in part by the examples, that, except for the case in which the neutral axis distance c is given, assumed, or otherwise predetermined, the complexity of the equations to be solved in investigating a given column with reinforcement near two faces is indicated by the following:

1. In the centrically loaded case, P'_0 is obtained directly from the force-equilibrium equation, and the corresponding moment is, of course, zero.
2. For pure flexure, if both the tension and compression reinforcements have yielded, the two equations of equilibrium may be solved directly—the force equation yielding the stress block depth a, which upon substitution into the moment equation gives the value of M'_0. If *at least one* of the two bands of reinforcement is not yielding, the force-equilibrium equation will be quadratic.
3. For intermediate cases, with the exceptions noted below, when both the tensile and compression reinforcements have yielded, the two equations of equilibrium combine into a quadratic equation. And when *at least one* of the two bands of reinforcement is not yielding, then the two equations combine into a cubic equation. The *exceptions* are: (a) the balanced case, in which c_b is predetermined by strain requirements, and therefore the two equilibrium equations yield directly P'_b and M'_b, and hence e_b; (b) the case of large c when compression exists over the entire section, with $0.85c > t$, in which case the value of a is set equal to t, and the two equilibrium conditions will combine into a linear equation (see Example 4–4).

4–10. INTERACTION CURVES FOR COLUMNS

The results of the preceding examples may be more revealingly represented graphically, resulting in what is called an **interaction diagram.** As shown in Fig. 4–17b, the values of P'_u are plotted against the corresponding values of M'_u. The circled points correspond to the tabular data, but more points were used, based on calculations not shown here, in order to delineate the curve more accurately. Point A represents the centrically loaded case; point B represents the balanced case; and point C represents the case of pure bending.

Any point on such an interaction curve has coordinates representing the values of corresponding M'_u and P'_u. Accordingly, a radial line drawn from the origin O to any point on an interaction curve has a slope equal to the reciprocal of the eccentricity for the case represented by the point in question. For instance, the reciprocal of the slope of the radial line OB with respect to the M'_u-axis is equal to the e_b of the balanced case.

By reference to Fig. 4–17b, a number of interesting observations may be made:

1. Curve A-1-2-3-4-B represents the strength of the given section when it is governed by compression failure, corresponding to eccentricities smaller than e_b (except, of course, at the terminal point B where $e = e_b$). Curve B-5-6-C represents the column strength when it is governed by

yielding of the tensile reinforcement, corresponding to eccentricities larger than e_b (again, except at the terminal point B where $e = e_b$).

2. When $P'_u > P'_b$, the section fails by compression at an eccentricity $e < e_b$, but when $P'_u < P'_b$, the section fails by tensile yielding at an eccentricity $e > e_b$.   An alternative, equivalent statement is that, when a given $e < e_b$, the failure will be governed by compression at a load $P'_u > P'_b$, and that, when $e > e_b$, the failure will be by tensile yielding at a load $P'_u < P'_b$.

3. When the strength of the section is governed by compression, curve A-1-2-3-4-B shows that as P'_u increases, the corresponding M'_u (or e) decreases.

4. When the strength of the section is governed by yielding of the tensile reinforcement, curve B-5-6-C indicates that as P'_u increases, the corresponding failure M'_u also *increases*. This may appear at first illogical, but a little thought will substantiate this observation: a larger load P'_u decreases the tensile steel stress, and, if failure is to be initiated by yielding of the tensile steel, a larger M'_u may therefore be applied.

The importance of this observation may be illustrated by a hypothetical example: Suppose a given column section is being investigated for two loading conditions one of which produces P_1 and M_1, and the other produces P_2 and M_2, each set to be resisted by the section at one time, and suppose that $P_1 > P_2$ and $M_1 > M_2$. If the column fails by compression, then, by virtue of observation 3, the loading that produces P_1 and M_1 is more critical, and there will be no need to investigate the effects of the other loading.   On the other hand, if the column fails by yielding of the tensile steel, both loadings may have to be investigated.

5. It is sometimes proposed, for the sake of convenience, that, if a column fails by compression, the true interaction curve A-1-2-3-4-B be replaced by a straight line joining AB.   This line will always be conservative because of the shape of the true curve in this area.   If this assumption is accepted, then the ultimate strength may be shown to be given by:

$$P'_u = \frac{P'_0}{1 + \left(\dfrac{P'_0}{P'_b} - 1\right)\dfrac{e}{e_b}} \tag{4–3a}$$

or

$$P'_u = P'_0 - (P'_0 - P'_b)\frac{M'_u}{M'_b} \tag{4–3b}$$

To each given column section, there corresponds an interaction curve for its ideal, short-column ultimate capacity for uniaxial bending. Accordingly, for a section of given concrete dimensions, steel arrangement and location, and specifications regarding the materials, a family of inter-action curves exists for varying amounts of reinforcement.   For example,

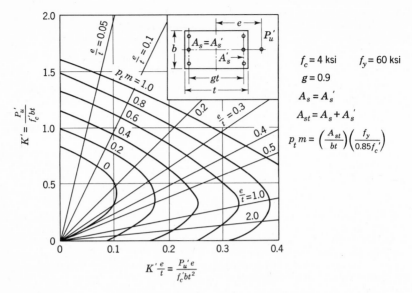

Fig. 4–18. Typical interaction diagram for ideal, short-column strength.

Fig. 4–18 shows the interaction diagram for a rectangular section with symmetrical reinforcement at two faces for a 4000-lb. concrete and 60,000-psi-yield-point steel, and with the distance between the centroids of the two groups of bars equal to $\frac{9}{10}$ of the overall depth. The quantities plotted in this diagram have been, as is usual, non-dimensionalized. The ideal ultimate capacity load and moment of such a section are then given by $P'_u = (K')f'_c bt$, and $M'_u = P'_u e$ or $K'(e/t)f'_c bt^2$. A radial line from the origin defines the eccentricity of the load as a fraction or multiple of the depth t.

Similar diagrams appear in Appendix C, and their use is described in detail in Section C of Chapter 5.

PRACTICE PROBLEMS

4–4. Using the general data of Examples 4–3 through 4–7, and $e = 5.55$ in. from the plastic centroid, verify the values of the ideal, short-column ultimate capacities as given in Fig. 4–17a.

4–5. On the assumptions that failure is governed by *tension* and that, at ultimate load, *yielding of the compressive reinforcement has taken place*, derive a general expression for the ideal, short-column ultimate capacity, P'_u, of a rectangular section with unequal reinforcement near two opposite faces as shown in Fig. 4–19. In addition to the symbols in Fig. 4–19, use the following notation: $p = A_s/bd$, $p' = A'_s/bd$, $m = f_y/0.85f'_c$, and $m' = m - 1$.

Ans. $P'_u = 0.85f'_c bd \times$

$$\left\{ (p'm' - pm) + \left(1 - \frac{e'}{d} \right) + \sqrt{ \left(1 - \frac{e'}{d} \right)^2 + 2 \left[\frac{e'}{d} (pm - p'm') + p'm' \left(1 - \frac{d'}{d} \right) \right] } \right\}$$

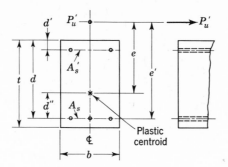

Fig. 4–19.   Problem 4–5.

4–6. A 14-by-20-in. rectangular column has a line of 3–#6 bars centered $2\frac{1}{2}$ in. from one of the 14-in. sides, and a line of 3–#9 bars centered $2\frac{1}{2}$ in. from the opposite side.   Using 4000-lb. concrete and 60,000-psi-yield-point steel, find for the balanced condition the ideal short-column ultimate capacity load, P'_b, and the corresponding eccentricity, e_b.   (NOTE: This is the same section used in Problem 4–2, which required the location of the plastic centroid of the section.)

4–11. RECTANGULAR SECTIONS WITH REINFORCEMENT NEAR FOUR FACES

When heavy bending exists, it is usually more economical to have all the reinforcement near the two most highly stressed faces.   However, in certain situations it may be more desirable to have bars placed near the other two faces as well.   For example, there may be bending moments in two directions, even though the two may not act simultaneously.   Also, for the case of light to moderate bending combined with axial loading, it is often better to have the steel placed more or less uniformly around the entire periphery of the section.   This contributes toward a better distribution of stresses, and often results in smaller concrete dimensions because of the clear spacing requirements for bars.

The inclusion of the effects of the intermediate "side" bars involves no new principles, but the analysis is largely a trial-and-error process, since, if the neutral axis should lie within the section, we do not even know between which rows of bars it will lie, let alone its exact location.   The following example will illustrate the process.

EXAMPLE 4–8

Given the column section of Fig. 4–20 and an eccentricity of 8 in., 4000-lb. concrete, and 50,000-psi-yield-point steel.

Required to find the ideal, short-column ultimate capacity.

Solution.   Assume that failure is initiated by yielding of Row 4 steel and that Row 1 steel has yielded at ultimate load.   Assume that the N.A. lies between Rows 2 and 3.   Then the strains and forces are as shown in Fig. 4–20b and c.

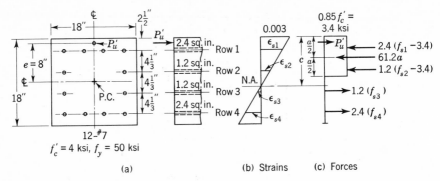

$f'_c = 4$ ksi, $f_y = 50$ ksi

(a)   (b) Strains   (c) Forces

Fig. 4–20.   Column with reinforcement near four faces.

The analysis may be performed by either solving a cubic equation (which is the result of combining the two equations of equilibrium) or dealing with the equilibrium equations as they stand and resorting to a trial-and-error process.   In either case, it is desirable to test *roughly* whether the assumption of the N.A. lying between the two central rows is reasonable.   For this purpose, suppose that the Rows 2 and 3 are ignored temporarily; the equilibrium equations would then be:

$$P'_u = 61.2a + 2.4(50 - 3.4) - 2.4(50) = 61.2a + 111.84 - 120$$
$$= 61.2a - 8.16$$

and

$$P'_u(14.5) = 61.2a(15.5 - 0.5a) + 111.84(13.0)$$

Combining the two equations, and simplifying, we get a quadratic equation:

$$a^2 - 2a - 51.36 = 0$$

whence $a = 8.24$, and $c = 9.69$.   So the assumption of the N.A. being between Rows 2 and 3 is probably fairly good for the given section.   Also, the strains in the two outer rows of bars may be tentatively checked:

$$\text{Row 1: } (0.003)\left(\frac{9.69 - 2.50}{9.69}\right) = 0.00223$$

$$\text{Row 4: } (0.003)\left(\frac{15.5 - 9.69}{9.69}\right) = 0.00180$$

Since both of these strains are larger than ϵ_y of 0.00172, Rows 1 and 4 have yielded as assumed if the intermediate bars are ignored.

Now, with the intermediate bars *included*, and from the strain diagram, the stresses in Rows 2 and 3 steel are:

$$f_{s2} = (29,000)(0.003)\left(\frac{c - 6.83}{c}\right) \text{ ksi}$$

$$f_{s3} = (29,000)(0.003)\left(\frac{11.17 - c}{c}\right) \text{ ksi}$$

and Rows 1 and 4 steel are assumed to be stressed to the yield point of 50 ksi.

Summing up the forces and their moments about the centroid of Row 4 bars,

$$P'_u = 61.2a + 2.4(50 - 3.4) + 1.2\left[87\left(\frac{c - 6.83}{c}\right) - 3.4\right]$$

$$- 1.2\left[87\left(\frac{11.17 - c}{c}\right)\right] - 2.4(50) \quad (1)$$

$$P'_u(14.5) = 61.2a(15.5 - 0.5a) + 2.4(50 - 3.4)(13.0)$$

$$+ 1.2\left[87\left(\frac{c - 6.83}{c}\right) - 3.4\right](8.67) - 1.2\left[87\left(\frac{11.17 - c}{c}\right)\right](4.33) \quad (2)$$

Substituting Eq. 1 into Eq. 2 and reducing to the simplest form results in the cubic equation:

$$a^3 - 2a^2 + 2.431a - 444.9 = 0 \quad (3)$$

Using the method of Appendix B, we obtain:

$$a = 8.24 \text{ in.} \quad \text{and} \quad c = 9.70 \text{ in.}$$

Now check strains and compute stresses: $\epsilon_y = 0.00172$

	Strains	Stresses
Row 1:	$(0.003)(9.70 - 2.5)/9.70 = 0.00223$ $(>\epsilon_y)$,	use $f_y = 50.00$ ksi
2:	$(0.003)(9.70 - 6.83)/9.70 = 0.00087$ $(<\epsilon_y)$, $\times\ 29{,}000 = 25.72$ ksi
3:	$(0.003)(11.17 - 9.70)/9.70 = 0.00045$ $(<\epsilon_y)$, $\times\ 29{,}000 = 13.14$ ksi
4:	$(0.003)(15.5 - 9.70)/9.70 = 0.00179$ $(>\epsilon_y)$,	use $f_y = 50.00$ ksi

Hence all the assumptions are justified.   Therefore:

$$P'_u = 61.2(8.24) + 2.4(50 - 3.4) + 1.2(25.72 - 3.4) - 1.2(13.14) - 2.4(50)$$
$$= 504.29 + 111.84 + 26.78 - 15.77 - 120.0 = \quad \underline{507 \text{ kips}} \quad \text{Ans.}$$

It may be shown that a trial-and-error process applied to Eqs. 1 and 2 will yield the same result.

4–12. CIRCULAR COLUMNS

Circular columns may be analyzed in the same way as rectangular columns.   The calculations will always involve the properties of circular segments, since the compressive zone of the concrete is a circular segment.

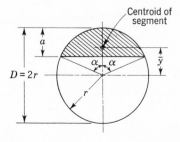

Fig. 4–21. Properties of circular segments.

It may be verified that for a segment of depth a of a circle of radius r, shown in Fig. 4–21, its area and centroidal distance from the center of the circle are given by the following equations:

$$\text{Area of segment} = r^2(\alpha - \sin \alpha \cos \alpha) \qquad (4\text{–}4a)$$

$$\text{Centroidal distance } \bar{y} = \tfrac{2}{3}r \left(\frac{\sin^3 \alpha}{\alpha - \sin \alpha \cos \alpha} \right) \qquad (4\text{–}4b)$$

where

$$\cos \alpha = 1 - a/r$$

These formulas are valid for $0 \leq \alpha \leq \pi$.

For example, for a segment of depth $a = 9.45$ in. of a circle of diameter $D = 2r = 20$ in., one obtains:

$$\cos \alpha = 1 - a/r = 1 - 9.45/10 = 0.055; \qquad \alpha = 1.516 \text{ radians}$$
$$\sin \alpha = 0.9985$$
$$\text{Area of segment} = (10)^2[1.516 - (0.9985)(0.055)] = 146 \text{ sq. in.}$$

Centroidal distance from the center of the circle is

$$\bar{y} = (\tfrac{2}{3})(10)\, \frac{(0.9985)^3}{1.516 - (0.9985)(0.055)} = 4.54 \text{ in.}$$

Alternately, Chart C–5 of Appendix C may be used. Thus, for $a/D = 9.45/20 = 0.472$, the coefficient for the segmental area is 0.365; therefore the area is $0.365(4)(10)^2 = 146$ sq. in. The coefficient for $\bar{y}$ is 0.454; therefore, $\bar{y} = 0.454(10) = 4.54$ in.

As in rectangular sections with intermediate "side" bars in addition to "end" bars, circular sections are analyzed by a process largely trial and error, unless the location of the neutral axis is definitely known for a given eccentricity. The following examples should be adequate to illustrate the procedure.

EXAMPLE 4–9

Given a circular column section of diameter $D = 20$ in. with 12–#9 bars arranged uniformly on a circle of diameter $D_s = 15$ in., as shown in Fig. 4–22, and a 4000-lb. concrete and 50,000-psi-yield-point steel.

Required to find, for the balanced condition, the ideal, short-column ultimate capacity P'_b, and the corresponding eccentricity e_b.

Solution. First, the neutral axis distance c_b for the balanced condition is computed by setting the steel strain in Row 7 equal to the yield strain, and by using the strain diagram (b) of Fig. 4–22:

$$c_b = \left(\frac{0.003}{0.003 + \epsilon_y} \right)(17.5) = \left(\frac{87}{87 + 50} \right)(17.5) = 11.11 \text{ in.}$$

from which the stress block depth is $a_b = 0.85(11.11) = 9.45$ in. This stress block acts over the shaded segment shown in (a), the area and the centroid of which may be determined by Eqs. 4–4 or by using Chart C–5 of Appendix C:

$$\text{Area of segment} = 146 \text{ sq. in.}, \quad \bar{y} = 4.54 \text{ in.}$$

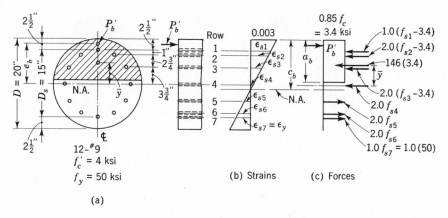

Fig. 4–22. Balanced condition for circular column.

The concrete force is then $0.85f'_c(146) = 3.4(146) = 496.4$ kips, acting at 4.54 in. from the column center.

The steel strains are found by using the simple geometry shown in the strain diagram (b); the steel stresses are then either equal to f_y or E_s times the strains, depending on whether the strains are larger or smaller than 0.00172. For bars which lie within the concrete stress block, deduct $0.85f'_c$ or 3.4 ksi from the computed stresses to make up for the use of the gross concrete area in computing the concrete force. Table 4–1 contains the evaluation of all the forces and their moments about the column center. Tensile forces are given a negative sign, and the lever arm of a force acting above the column center is positive.

Therefore,

$$P'_b = \underline{\hspace{1cm} 547 \text{ kips}} \quad \text{Ans.}$$
$$M'_b = {}^{4550}\!/_{12} = \underline{\hspace{1cm} 379 \text{ kip-ft.}} \quad \text{Ans.}$$
$$e_b = 4550/547.0 = \underline{\hspace{1cm} 8.32 \text{ in.}} \quad \text{Ans.}$$

Table 4–1. Calculations for Example 4–9

Item	Area, sq. in.	Strain, 10^{-3}		Stress, ksi	Force, kips	Distance from Center, in.	Moment About Center, kip-in.
Concrete	146			3.4	496.4	4.54	2254
Row 1	1.0	$\dfrac{3.00}{11.00}$	$(8.61) = 2.32$	$50.0 - 3.4 = 46.6$	46.6	7.50	350
2	2.0		$(7.61) = 2.05$	$50.0 - 3.4 = 46.6$	93.2	6.50	606
3	2.0		$(4.86) = 1.31$	$38.0 - 3.4 = 34.6$	69.2	3.75	260
4	2.0		$(1.11) = 0.30$	8.7	17.4	0	0
5	2.0		$(2.64) = 0.71$	20.6	−41.2	−3.75	155
6	2.0		$(5.39) = 1.46$	42.3	−84.6	−6.50	550
7	1.0		$(6.39) = 1.73$	50.0	−50.0	−7.50	375
				Sum	547.0		4550

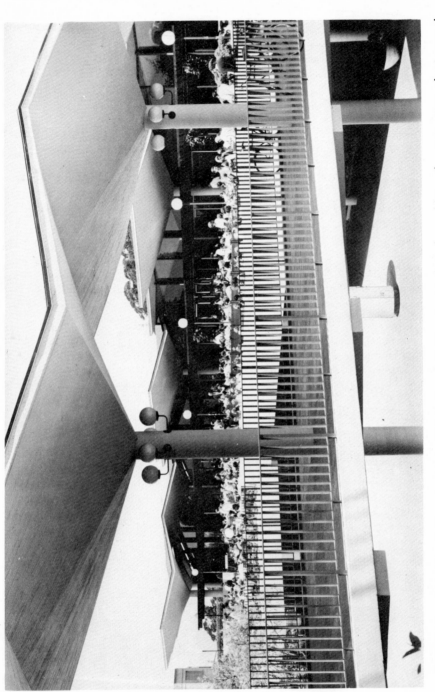

Plate 4-1. Concrete shell roof system, University of California at Berkeley. Note the two-story short round columns. (Courtesy of Portland Cement Association)

EXAMPLE 4–10

Given the circular column section of Example 4–9, and an eccentricity of $e = 13.2$ in.

Required to find the ideal, short-column capacity, P'_u.

Solution. Comparing the given eccentricity of 13.2 in. with the balanced eccentricity of 8.31 in. found in Example 4–9, it is obvious that the column here will fail by tension, and the neutral axis distance c will have to be smaller than c_b of 11.11 in. of the balanced case.   The shifting of the neutral axis toward the compressive face tends to increase the steel strains in the tension zone and decrease the steel strains in the compression zone, but it cannot be pre-ascertained how much the changes will be, that is, whether they are large enough to cause more rows of tensile steel to yield and fewer rows of compression steel to yield. It is probably best to attempt a trial-and-error solution from the very beginning, using an assumed value of c to start.

The first trial value of c assumed was 10.0 in.   For this c-value, strains can be calculated and all the forces found.   It can be shown, by calculations similar to those given in Example 4–9, that for $c = 10.0$ in. the trial $P'_u = 416$ kips and trial $e = 11.2$ in.   Since this trial e value did not agree with the prescribed value of 13.2 in., a few more c-values were tried.

In the final trial, $c = 9.41$ in., and $a = 0.85(9.41) = 8.00$ in.   The strain diagram and the forces are as shown in Fig. 4–23b and c.   The details of the computation are similar to those of Example 4–9.

At the end of the final cycle of calculations, the trial $P'_u = 349.6$ kips, and trial $M'_u = 4610$ kip-in., with the trial $e = 13.20$ in.   Since this agreed with the given e, the solution is:

$$P'_u = \qquad\qquad \underline{349 \text{ kips}} \quad \underline{\text{Ans.}}$$
$$M'_u = {}^{4610}\!/_{12} = \qquad \underline{384 \text{ kip-ft.}} \quad \underline{\text{Ans.}}$$

CIRCULAR AND TRIANGULAR COLUMN PROBLEMS

4–7. Take the column section of Example 4–10, and find the ideal short-column capacity moment for pure flexure, M'_0.   Try a c-value of 6.32 in.

Ans.   316 kip-ft.

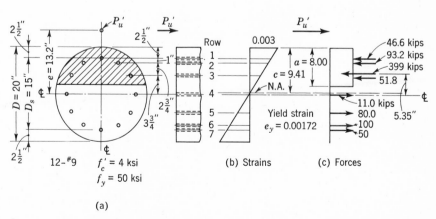

Fig. 4–23.   Investigation of a circular column—final trial.

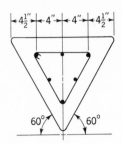

Fig. 4–24. Problem 4–8.

4–8. Given a column section in the shape of an equilateral triangle with 6–#9 bars arranged as shown in Fig. 4–24, with a 5000-lb. concrete ($k_1 = 0.80$) and 60,000 psi-yield-point steel. Find the ideal short-column capacity load for the balanced case.

4–13. EFFECT OF BARS APPROXIMATED BY THIN TUBULAR STEEL

When bars are placed more or less uniformly near the entire periphery of a rectangular column, or on a circle in a rectangular or circular column, it is sometimes convenient, for the purpose of facilitating analysis, to consider the individual bars as being replaced by a uniformly distributed thin steel tube of the same total area as the reinforcement. Even for rectangular columns with much heavier "end" reinforcement than "side" reinforcement, this approximation may be achieved by using different thicknesses for the end and side walls of the equivalent steel tube. Figure 4–25a shows the original bar arrangement and its approximating equivalent steel tube for a given rectangular section. If the original reinforcement is nearly uniformly distributed along the perimeter of the rectangle on which the bars are centered, the steel tube will have a uniform thickness given by dividing the total area of the reinforcement by the total perimeter; or the tube thickness may be made to vary from side to side to match the original bar arrangement. Views (b) show a circular section with bars uniformly placed on a circle of diameter gD, and the corresponding equivalent section with a steel ring of uniform thickness given by the total area of the reinforcement divided by πgD. Two possible strain patterns are shown in (c) and (d) by the dotted lines, respectively for the case of compression over the entire section and the case of tension over part of the section. Possible stress distributions in the tubular steel have been shown in bold lines superimposed on the strain diagram in (c) and (d).

The above approximation has certain advantages. If the approximation can be justifiably used in lieu of the individual bars, the analysis may be more easily formulated in equation form, which is better adapted for computer solution when a large number of similar problems with various combinations of input data have to be solved. Such a case develops

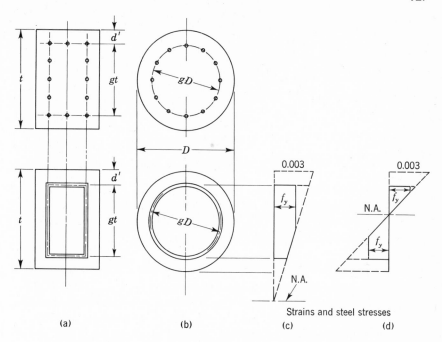

(a)   (b)   (c)   (d)

Fig. 4–25.   Thin tubular steel approximation for bars.

when design charts in the form of interaction diagrams have to be prepared to cover a wide range of parameters defining material properties, shapes of column sections, and so on.   Also, if the original bar arrangement is such that the bars are fairly uniformly distributed, the size, number, and pattern of individual bars do not become controlling factors in analysis, as long as the approximating steel tube has the same area as the original reinforcement.   Such an approach was adopted by ACI Committee 340 in its preparation of extensive column design tables and charts [5] for four types of sections with different combinations of f'_c, f_y, and values of g shown in Fig. 4–25.

The errors in the results obtained based on this approximation are usually of the order of magnitude [6] of 1 per cent or less when the total number of bars exceeds 8.   The larger the number of bars, the more nearly correct is the use of this approximation.   The errors are larger for smaller c-values and smaller for larger c-values.   When c is infinite, corresponding to the centrically loaded case, the error is zero.

4–14. ACI CODE SHORT-COLUMN STRENGTH FORMULAS

All the column investigations presented here so far are based on first principles and basic assumptions which are in accordance with those set forth in the ACI Code, specifically in Secs. 1503 and 1900(b).   In addition to these basic assumptions, the Code also provides a series of semi-empirical formulas which are intended to be used as guides in USD column design and investigation.   Most of the formulas given in Secs. 1902, 1903, and 1904 are somewhat approximate, and, more importantly, they involve one underlying assumption which limits the range of validity of those formulas: *the assumption that, at ultimate load, the compressive reinforcement has yielded.*   This, of course, is not always true, and conditions exist where substantial errors will result from an indiscriminate use of these formulas, as will be shown later in this article.   One who uses those formulas, therefore, must bear in mind that *the validity of these formulas is to be checked by strain computations.*

The Code strength formulas will now be presented together with comments.   The notation that has been used so far in this chapter is in accord with that of the Code; new symbols will be defined when first introduced. It should also be noted that the formulas given in the Code are for the *practical*, short-column strengths, that is, P_u, M_u, P_0, P_b, M_b, whereas here they have been converted to their corresponding expressions for the *ideal*, short-column strengths, P'_u, M'_u, P'_0, P'_b, M'_b, since it is desired to postpone a more thorough discussion of the understrength factor ϕ until later.

Rectangular Sections with Bars in One or Two Faces.   When the stress block depth $a \leq t$: Section 1902(a) gives the short-column capacity as

$$P'_u = P_u/\phi = [0.85f'_c ba + A'_s f_y - A_s f_s] \quad \text{[ACI Formula 19–1]}$$
$$P'_u e' = P_u e'/\phi = [0.85f'_c ba(d - a/2) + A'_s f_y(d - d')] \\ \text{[ACI Formula 19–2]}$$

By reference to Fig. 4–26, Formulas 19–1 and 19–2 will be recognized as merely equilibrium equations: (19–1) being the summation of the forces, and (19–2) being the summation of their moments about the centroid of the tensile reinforcement.   It is to be noted that in (19–1) and (19–2): (a) *the compressive reinforcement is assumed to have yielded at ulti-*

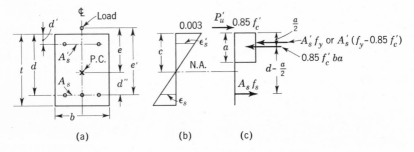

Fig. 4–26.   Column section notation for ACI formulas.

mate load; for this to be true, its strain ϵ'_s must be established to be larger than or equal to the yield strain ϵ_y; (b) the force in the yielding compression reinforcement is taken to be $A'_s f_y$, *ignoring the compression concrete displaced by A'_s.* If greater accuracy is desired, this displaced concrete effect may be introduced by substituting $A'_s(f_y - 0.85f'_c)$ for $A'_s f_y$.

For a balanced failure, the balanced neutral axis distance c_b may be found by using the strain diagram (b) of Fig. 4–26 and setting $\epsilon_s = \epsilon_y$, or

$$c_b = \frac{0.003}{0.003 + \epsilon_y} d = \frac{87,000}{87,000 + f_y} d$$

and the balanced stress block depth is $a_b = k_1 c_b$. Section 1902(b) then gives the formula for the balanced capacity P'_b as

$$P'_b = P_b/\phi = [0.85f'_c b a_b + A'_s f_y - A_s f_y]$$

which is derived from Formula 19–1 upon substitution of the expressions of c_b, a_b, and f_y for c, a, and f_s. The balanced moment capacity M'_b is given as

$$M'_b = P'_b e = M_b/\phi = P_b e/\phi = [0.85f'_c b a_b (d - d'' - \tfrac{1}{2}a_b) \\ + A'_s f_y (d - d' - d'') + A_s f_y d''] \quad \text{[ACI Formula 19–3]}$$

which is the sum of moments of the forces about the plastic centroid.

Again, these formulas for P'_b and M'_b *assume yielding A'_s* and *ignore the displaced concrete effect,* as noted for Formulas 19–1 and 19–2.

If failure is controlled by tension ($e > e_b$, and $P'_u < P'_b$ or $P_u < P_b$), Sec. 1902(c)1 gives the capacity P'_u as

$$P'_u = P_u/\phi = \left[0.85f'_c b d \left\{ p'm' - pm + \left(1 - \frac{e'}{d}\right) \right. \right.$$
$$\left. \left. + \sqrt{\left(1 - \frac{e'}{d}\right)^2 + 2\left[\left(\frac{e'}{d}\right)(pm - p'm') + p'm'\left(1 - \frac{d'}{d}\right)\right]} \right\} \right]$$
$$\text{[ACI Formula 19–4]}$$

in which

$$p = A_s/bd; \ p' = A'_s/bd; \ m = f_y/0.85f'_c; \ m' = m - 1$$

Formula 19–4 may be shown (see Problem 4–5) to have been derived by substituting f_s for f_y, and $A'_s(f_y - 0.85f'_c)$ for $A'_s f_y$ in Formulas 19–1 and 19–2, and solving the two resulting equations simultaneously. Accordingly, Formula 19–4 *does* take into account the compression concrete displaced by A'_s, as evidenced by the presence of m', but still assumes *yielding compression reinforcement.*

When $p' = p$, Formula 19–4 reduces to the formula for the case of symmetrical reinforcement in two faces:

$$P'_u = P_u/\phi = \left[0.85f'_cbd \left\{ -p + \left(1 - \frac{e'}{d} \right) \right. \right.$$
$$\left. \left. + \sqrt{\left(1 - \frac{e'}{d} \right)^2 + 2p \left[m' \left(1 - \frac{d'}{d} \right) + \frac{e'}{d} \right]} \right\} \right] \quad \text{[ACI Formula 19–5]}$$

When $p' = 0$, Formula 19–4 reduces to the formula for the case of no compression reinforcement:

$$P'_u = P_u/\phi = \left[0.85f'_cbd \left\{ -pm - \left(1 - \frac{e'}{d} \right) \right. \right.$$
$$\left. \left. + \sqrt{\left(1 - \frac{e'}{d} \right)^2 + 2\frac{e'pm}{d}} \right\} \right] \quad \text{[ACI Formula 19–6]}$$

If failure is controlled by compression ($e < e_b$, and $P'_u > P'_b$ or $P_u > P_b$), one first calculates the centrically loaded column capacity by

$$P'_0 = P_0/\phi = [0.85f'_c(A_g - A_{st}) + A_{st}f_y] \quad \text{[ACI Formula 19–7]}$$

and then, according to Sec. 1902(c)2, one assumes that the capacity varies linearly between the centrically loaded case and the balanced case, that is, the interaction curve within this range is approximated by a straight line, such as the dotted line AB in Fig. 4–17b. For this approximation, the following relations may be shown to be valid:

$$P'_u = \frac{P_u}{\phi} = \frac{P'_0}{1 + \left(\dfrac{P'_0}{P'_b} - 1 \right) \dfrac{e}{e_b}} = \frac{1}{\phi} \frac{P_0}{1 + \left(\dfrac{P_0}{P_b} - 1 \right) \dfrac{e}{e_b}}$$
$$\text{[ACI Formula 19–8]}$$

or,

$$P'_u = \frac{P_u}{\phi} = P'_0 - (P'_0 - P'_b)\frac{M'_u}{M'_b} = \frac{1}{\phi} \left[P_0 - (P_0 - P_b)\frac{M_u}{M_b} \right]$$
$$\text{[ACI Formula 19–9]}$$

The approximation represented by Formulas 19–8 and 19–9 is always conservative, as typified by straight line AB in Fig. 4–17b, *provided that the capacity for the balanced case is correctly calculated*. However, since the Code evaluation of P'_b and M'_b is based on Formulas 19–1 and 19–3, neither of which is correct for *all* conditions, the conservativeness of this approximation is not always assured.

The Code also gives the following formula for the case of symmetrical reinforcement in two faces of a rectangular section failing in compression:

$$P'_u = \frac{P_u}{\phi} = \left[\frac{A'_sf_y}{\dfrac{e}{d - d'} + 0.5} + \frac{f'_cbt}{\dfrac{3te}{d^2} + 1.18} \right] \quad \text{[ACI Formula 19–10]}$$

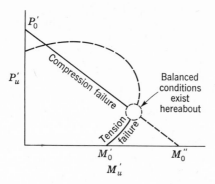

Fig. 4–27. Approximate interaction diagram based on Whitney and ACI formulas.

This formula, due to Whitney [7], is essentially similar to the straight line approximation of Formulas 19–8 and 19–9, but is somewhat easier to use. When $e = 0$, this formula reduces to

$$P'_u = P_u/\phi = 2A'_s f_y + 0.85 f'_c bt = A_{st} f_y + 0.85 f'_c bt$$

which is the value of P'_0 if the concrete area displaced by A_{st} is ignored. When $e = \infty$, Formula 19–10 yields

$$P'_u e = \lim_{e \to \infty} \left[\frac{A'_s f_y}{\dfrac{1}{d - d'} + \dfrac{0.5}{e}} + \frac{f'_c bt}{\dfrac{3t}{d^2} + \dfrac{1.18}{e}} \right] = A'_s f_y (d - d') + \tfrac{1}{3} f'_c bd^2$$

The term $(\tfrac{1}{3})f'_c bd^2$ is Whitney's expression for the ultimate capacity moment of a singly reinforced beam (i.e., without A'_s) failing in compression. Hence the above expression is Whitney's estimate of the ultimate capacity moment, M''_0, of a doubly reinforced beam if it could be made to fail in compression regardless of the amount of A_s that might be present, and it again assumes yielding compression reinforcement and ignores the displaced concrete effect. When plotted, Formula 19–10 gives a line (with a slight curvature, which may be considered negligible) as shown qualitatively in Fig. 4–27. It passes through P'_0 and M''_0, and passes near the balanced point, but only in certain cases does it pass exactly *through* the balanced point. Figure 4–27 also includes a line representing tension failure as given by ACI formulas.

Circular Sections with Bars Circularly Arranged. Section 1903(a) gives the following expressions for the capacity of circular columns:

When tension controls:

$$P'_u = P_u/\phi = \left\{ 0.85 f'_c D^2 \left[\sqrt{\left(\frac{0.85e}{D} - 0.38 \right)^2 + \frac{p_t m D_s}{2.5D}} \right. \right.$$
$$\left. \left. - \left(\frac{0.85e}{D} - 0.38 \right) \right] \right\} \qquad \text{[ACI Formula 19–11]}$$

When compression controls :

$$P'_u = P_u/\phi = \left[\frac{A_{st}f_y}{\dfrac{3e}{D_s} + 1} + \frac{A_g f'_c}{\dfrac{9.6De}{(0.8D + 0.67D_s)^2} + 1.18}\right]$$

[ACI Formula 19–12]

Both of these are due to Whitney [7]. The comments given above for corresponding expressions for rectangular sections apply equally here.[6] In the above formulas, D is the diameter of the circle through the centers of the bars, and p_t is A_{st}/A_g.

Comparison of ACI Formulas and Correctly Computed Results. It is interesting to compare the correctly computed results with those obtained by the ACI semiempirical formulas. Figure 4–28a shows, for the square column of Examples 4–2 to 4–7, the correctly computed interaction curve for its ideal, short-column strength represented by the bold lines ABC, and the interaction curve abc obtained by the ACI formulas without checking the strain compatibility. When failure is controlled by compression, curves AB and ab show that the errors from the use of ACI formulas are always conservative except near the balanced condition. When failure is by tension, curves BC and bc show that the errors are fairly small, though on the unsafe side.

Figure 4–28b shows a comparison for the circular column considered in Examples 4–8 and 4–10. The correctly computed interaction curve is shown by the bold curve ABC. The ACI interaction curve is obtained by first using ACI Formula 19–11 for tension failure, resulting in the curve *1-2-b-c*, and then using ACI Formula 19–12 for compression failure, resulting in the curve *a-2-b-d*. These two curves are found to intersect at two points, *2* and *b*. but the branch *1-2* has no physical meaning. Of the parts of the two curves that remain, the interaction curve for the strength when governed by compression is given by *a-2-b*, and that for the strength when governed by tension is given by *b-c*. The errors are seen to be quite large, and they exist on both the safe and unsafe sides.

The errors due to indiscriminate use of the Code formulas without verifying the strains tend to increase for one or a combination of the following: low g (where gt is the distance between A_s and A'_s for a rectangular section with bars in two faces, or $gD = D_s$ for a circular column), *large t or D, and high f_y.* So far as the effect of f_y is concerned, the ACI formulas normally give satisfactory results for $f_y = 40$ ksi; for $f_y = 50$ ksi, they are mostly but not always satisfactory; and for $f_y \geq 60$ ksi, significant errors are likely to result. Cohen [6] showed that the percentage errors may be as

---

[6] The same may be said for ACI Formulas 19–13 and 19–14 for square sections with bars arranged circularly; no further discussion of these formulas will be made herein.

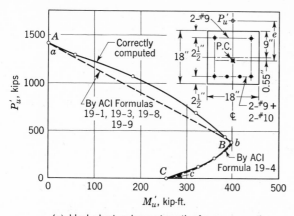

(a) Ideal, short–column strength of a square section

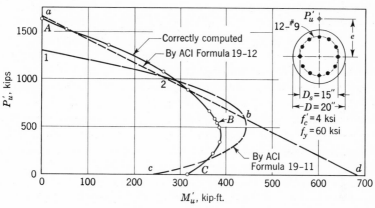

(b) Ideal, short–column strength of a circular section

Fig. 4–28. Comparison of ACI formulas with correctly computed results.

high as about 35 per cent on both the safe and unsafe sides, for an adverse combination of these factors.

4–15. BIAXIAL BENDING OF COLUMNS

Consider a rectangular section with one axis of symmetry, say the y-axis, as shown in Fig. 4–29. The x- and y-axes are then the principal axes of the section. Suppose an eccentric load P'_u acts on the section, with eccentricities e_x and e_y with respect to the axes x and y, respectively. If e_y is zero, then we have uniaxial bending, with the neutral axis parallel to the x-axis, but if neither e_x nor e_y is zero, we have biaxial bending plus

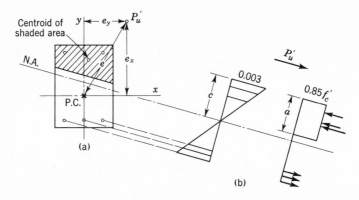

Fig. 4–29. Rectangular section in biaxial bending.

direct compression, and the neutral axis will be parallel to neither of the principal axes, x and y, nor will it be in general perpendicular to the line joining the load point and the plastic centroid. The analysis of such a section, while involving no new principles, requires an enormous amount of computation. For a given neutral axis location such as that shown in Fig. 4–29a, the strain diagram for the section in a direction perpendicular to the neutral axis may be drawn as shown in (b), and the equivalent stress block idea may still be applicable [9]. The concrete force on the shaded area acts through its centroid, and the various bar forces may be computed once their strains are determined by the strain diagram. Then three equilibrium equations may be written: one force equilibrium equation, and the other two, moment equilibrium equations, taken about the x- and y-axes, say. The solution of the three equations will yield the corresponding values of P'_u, e_x, and e_y, or $M'_{ux} = P'_u e_x$, and $M'_{uy} = P'_u e_y$.

As in uniaxial bending plus compression, an interaction diagram may be plotted relating P'_u, M'_{ux}, and M'_{uy} for any column. A typical interaction diagram for biaxial bending plus compression is shown in Fig. 4–30 for a rectangular section. Three orthogonal axes are chosen for the eccentric capacity load and corresponding moments about the x- and y-axes. The curve A-B_x-C_x is the interaction curve for compression plus uniaxial bending about the x-axis only; the curve A-B_y-C_y is that for compression plus uniaxial bending about the y-axis only; and the curve A-B-C is that for a specified combination of bending about both axes plus compression. Therefore, for biaxial bending plus compression, the interaction diagram is in the form of a surface, being the locus of all the individual interaction curves, and the coordinates of any point on this interaction surface are the corresponding values of P'_u, M'_{ux}, and M'_{uy}.

The true interaction surface is usually quite cumbersome to determine. Bresler [10] has proposed a simple, practical method to approximate this

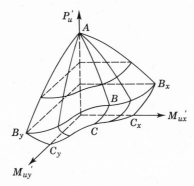

Fig. 4–30. Typical interaction surface for biaxial bending and compression.

surface, which may be expressed by the following formula:

$$1/P'_u = 1/P'_{ux} + 1/P'_{uy} - 1/P'_0 \qquad (4\text{–}5)$$

where P'_u = ideal, short-column ultimate load for biaxial bending with eccentricities e_x and e_y from the x- and y-axes

P'_{ux} = ideal, short-column ultimate load for uniaxial bending about x-axis only (with only e_x existing)

P'_{uy} = ideal, short-column ultimate load for uniaxial bending about y-axis only (with only e_y existing)

P'_0 = ideal, short-column ultimate load for centrically loaded column (when $e_x = e_y = 0$).

Equation 4–5 is satisfactory provided $P'_u \geq 0.10P'_0$. When biaxial bending exists together with an axial force smaller than $0.10P'_0$, Eq. 4–5 is not reliable, in which case it is sufficiently accurate and conservative to neglect the axial force entirely and to analyze the section for flexure only.

For circular sections with bars circularly and uniformly arranged, biaxial bending plus compression poses no difficulty, particularly if the bars are considered as being replaced by a thin steel tube. The two eccentricities may be combined to give a resultant eccentricity, and the column analysis reduces to that of uniaxial bending plus axial compression. Since the ultimate capacity load is the same for bending with respect to any diameter for a given eccentricity, the interaction diagram for a circular column is a surface of revolution generated by revolving around the P'_u axis the interaction curve for uniaxial bending.

EXAMPLE 4–11

Given the column sections of Examples 4–2 to 4–7, with eccentricities e_x of 10.55 in. and e_y of 8.52 in., as shown in Fig. 4–31, 4000-lb. concrete, and 50,000-psi-yield-point steel.

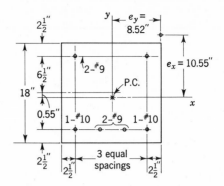

Fig. 4–31. Column under biaxial bending.

Required to find the ideal, short-column ultimate capacity load P'_u.

Solution. When $e_x = e_y = 0$, Example 4–2 shows that $P'_0 = 1406$ kips.

When $e_y = 0$, $e_x = 10.55$ in., the case reduces to that of Example 4–5, which shows an ideal, short-column ultimate capacity load of 435 kips. Hence, $P'_{ux} = 435$ kips.

When $e_x = 0$, $e_y = 8.52$ in., we have uniaxial bending about the y-axis in addition to compression, and it can be readily verified that the ideal, short-column ultimate capacity load for such a case is 460 kips. Therefore, $P'_{uy} = 460$ kips.

Therefore, according to Bresler's Eq. 4–5, the ultimate load for both eccentricities present is given by

$$1/P'_u = \frac{1}{435} + \frac{1}{460} - \frac{1}{1406} = 0.00376, \qquad \therefore \underline{P'_u = 266 \text{ kips}} \quad \underline{\text{Ans.}}$$

BIAXIAL BENDING PROBLEM

4–9. Take the column section and specifications used in Problems 4–2 and 4–6. What is the ideal, short-column ultimate capacity load for biaxial bending with eccentricities, e_x and e_y, equal to the balanced eccentricities for uniaxial bending only about the x- and y-axes, respectively?

CONTINUATION PROBLEMS

Unless otherwise noted, take 4000-lb. concrete, 50,000-psi-yield-point steel, 1-in. maximum aggregate size, and follow the ACI Code, USD, in performing the following solutions.

4–10. Given a round spiral column 26 in. in diameter containing 8–#11 bars on a $20\frac{1}{2}$-in. bar center diameter. It is required to determine:

    (a) Its ideal, short-column, centric capacity load P'_0.

    (b) Its ideal, short-column, ultimate capacity load P'_u at 8 in. eccentricity.

4–11. Design the required ACI spiral for the column of Problem 4–10.

4–12. Given a column 12 in. wide by 22 in. deep containing 1.43 sq. in. of compressive steel and 1.18 sq. in. of tensile steel along the 12-in. sides, both centered 2 in. from the outside.

    (a) Locate the plastic centroid of the section.

    (b) Determine its ideal, short-column, ultimate capacity load P'_u at 15 in. beyond its compression face.

QUESTIONS

    1. Define *pier, column, tied column, spiral column, lateral tie, spiral,* and *shell concrete.*

    2. What is the function of lateral ties?

3. Distinguish clearly between the performances of tied and spiral columns as load is increased.
4. Tell how to determine how many ties are necessary at a section of any given column.
5. Tell how to determine the spiral pitch in a given column.
6. Define the *plastic centroid* of a column section.
7. What is an interaction curve?
8. When is the failure of an eccentrically loaded column governed by compression?
9. Tell how to determine the "balanced eccentricity" of a given column section.
10. Is it always true that, if failure of a column is controlled by compression, its compression reinforcement has yielded? Is it true that, if compression exists over the entire cross section of a given column, its failure is always controlled by compression?

REFERENCES

1. SHANK, J. R. "The Mechanics of Plastic Flow of Concrete," *Proc. ACI*, 1936, Vol. 32, p. 149.
2. RICHART, F. E., and BROWN, R. L. "An Investigation of Reinforced Concrete Columns," *Bulletin No. 267*, University of Illinois Engineering Experiment Station, 1934.
3. AMERICAN CONCRETE INSTITUTE. "Commentary on Building Code Requirements for Reinforced Concrete (ACI 318-63)," *ACI·Publication SP-10*, 1965.
4. "Reinforced Concrete Column Investigation: Tentative Final Report of Committee 105," *Proc. ACI*, 1933, Vol. 29, pp. 275–282.
5. AMERICAN CONCRETE INSTITUTE. "Ultimate Strength Design of Reinforced Concrete Columns" (Interim Report of ACI Committee 340), *ACI Publication SP-7*, 1964.
6. EVERARD, N. J. "Evaluation of the ACI Code Equations for Ultimate Strength Design of Columns," *Proc. ACI*, 1965, Vol. 62, pp. 963–974.
7. WHITNEY, C. S. "Plastic Theory of Reinforced Concrete Design," *Trans. ASCE*, 1942, Vol. 107, pp. 251–326.
8. WHITNEY, C. S., and COHEN, E. "Guide for Ultimate Strength Design of Reinforced Concrete," *Proc. ACI*, 1956, Vol. 53, p. 455.
9. MATTOCK, A. J., and KRIZ, L. B. "Ultimate Strength of Nonrectangular Structural Concrete Members," *Proc. ACI*, 1961, Vol. 57, p. 737.
10. BRESLER, B. "Design Criteria for Reinforced Concrete Columns Under Axial Load and Biaxial Bending," *Proc. ACI*, 1960, Vol. 57, p. 481.

5

SLENDER COLUMNS UNDER AXIAL COMPRESSION AND BENDING

A. Slenderness Effects on Column Strength

5-1. INTRODUCTION

A **slender column** is one with cross-sectional dimensions which are small as compared to its length. As a measure of its slenderness, the **slenderness ratio,** h'/r, is generally used, where h' is its **effective length,** and r is the **radius of gyration** of the cross section. This effective length, h', is not always the same as the actual *unbraced length* of the column, h, and its value depends on the nature and degree of restraint present at the ends of the column. Such restraints may be *rotational* or *translational*, or both. Rotational restraints, as the name implies, prevent the column ends from rotating freely, and translational restraints prevent them from undergoing relative lateral movements, usually called *sidesway* in building columns.

A slender column may buckle under axial loads. The ultimate capacity load that has been computed so far for column sections of this text assumes short-column behavior; that is, it is computed on the assumption that buckling does not occur before the column is loaded to failure at the computed load level. However, a column may be so slender that it collapses through instability at a load materially smaller than the computed short-column ultimate capacity load. Furthermore, when a bending moment exists together with an axial load, it may become magnified due to the interaction of the axial load and the deflected shape of the column. This magnification varies very sensitively with the slenderness of the column.   Therefore an estimate of the slenderness effects on column strength is of extreme importance.

The slenderness effects are usually quite complex to evaluate; this is particularly so for reinforced concrete columns, made of two materials of which one, concrete, has inelastic characteristics and may be subject to tensile cracking.   The 1963 ACI Code provisions on columns are not yet entirely satisfactory, but they are much superior to those of previous editions, and until further research leads to the development of a more rational design procedure, they will serve as a much needed guide.

The ACI provisions on slenderness effects are given in Secs. 915 and 916.   It is well, however, first to discuss generally the various aspects of column behavior as affected by slenderness.   Such a discussion, although qualitative at best, and admittedly an oversimplification, will throw some light on the background of the Code provisions.

5–2. BUCKLING OF CENTRICALLY LOADED COLUMNS

Consider an ideal, centrically loaded column which has specified rotational and translational end restraints, as *schematically* represented by the springs in Fig. 5–1.   The column may be a part of a larger structure, and the end restraints may be supplied either by supports or by continuity with the rest of the structure.

Such a column may buckle elastically in the classical Euler-Engesser manner [1] when the axial load P reaches a critical value, P_{cr}.   This critical load is a function of the material properties, the cross-sectional properties, and the effective length h', and hence, the slenderness ratio h'/r.   For a given cross section of specified materials, the effective length h' depends on end restraints and also on the unbraced length h.   For a given set of end conditions, by varying h one obtains different h'/r values which yield different P_{cr} values.   If these P_{cr} values are plotted against the h'/r values, there results a curve somewhat like that shown in Fig. 5–2, in which it is seen to be intersecting a horizontal line representing the

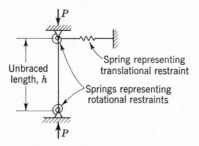

Fig. 5–1.   Centrically loaded column, schematic representation.

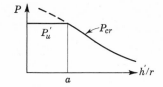

Fig. 5–2.   Relation between load and slenderness ratio.

computed ideal, short-column ultimate capacity load P'_u, at a particular value of $h'/r = a$.   Note that, for a column with $h'/r \leq a$, the capacity load is limited by P'_u; on the other hand, for a slender column with $h'/r > a$, the capacity load is limited by P_{cr}.

As to the effective length h', a few typical cases will illustrate how it is influenced by end conditions.[1]   Figure 5–3 shows ten typical cases of column buckling.   In the first five, sidesway is prevented; in the other five, sidesway is permitted.

Buckling Without Sidesway.   In Fig. 5–3a, a pin-ended column buckles into the shape shown with an effective length $h' = h$.   In (b), both ends are fixed against rotation; so the column buckles with two inflection points (I.P.) as shown, and the portion of the column between the I.P.'s behaves as a pin-ended column of length $h/2$.   Hence the effective length of the fixed-fixed column is $h' = h/2$.   In (c), we have a column rotationally restrained at both ends by the girders.   If both girders offer no rotational resistance whatever, then this case reduces to that of the pin-ended column of (a).   If both girders are infinitely rigid, this reduces to the case of the fixed-fixed column of (b).   Hence the column in (c) has two I.P.'s, the distance between which lies between the limits of h and $h/2$; that is, $h > h' > h/2$.   Case (d) shows a portal frame pinned at the lower ends of the columns and laterally braced against sidesway.   Besides the pinned end of the column, there is one inflection point somewhere along the length of the column, say, at h' above the lower end.   If the girder offers zero rotational resistance, this I.P. moves up to the top end of the column, and h' becomes h.   If the girder is infinitely rigid, then the column is fixed-hinged, and its effective length would be larger than the $h/2$ for the fixed-fixed column of (b).   Therefore, for some intermediate rigidity of the girder, the column will have an effective length h' between the limits of h and $h/2$.   In (e), the frame is similar to that in (d) except that the lower ends of the columns are fixed against rotation.   By similar reasoning, it may be concluded that $h > h' > h/2$.

Buckling With Sidesway.   Figure 5–3f shows a buckled cantilever column, the free end of which deflects laterally.   One may imagine that

---

[1] Reference 1 is recommended to the reader who wishes to probe further in this matter.

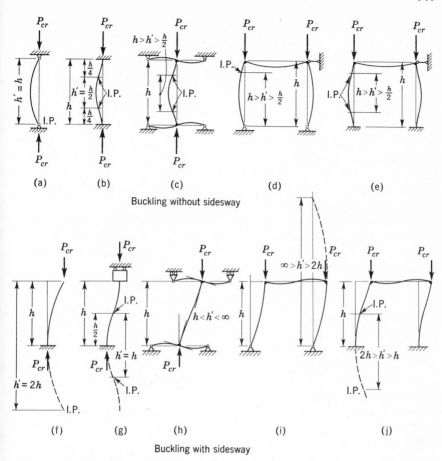

Fig. 5–3. Buckling shapes and effective lengths of centrically loaded columns.

the column behaves like one-half of a pin-ended column of which the other half is a mirror image about the fixed end. Hence, a cantilever column has an effective length $h' = 2h$. In (g) is shown a column fixed against rotation at both ends but not restrained against sidesway, which buckles into a shape having one I.P. at midlength. With a mirror image of this I.P. on the imaginary extension of the column, one finds the effective length to be $h' = h$. In (h), a column is restrained against rotation at both ends by the girders, but free to move laterally at the top by the rollers on the supports of the top girder. If both girders are infinitely rigid, the column is similar to that of (g), for which the effective length is h. If the girders are infinitely flexible, the column becomes pin-ended at both ends and yet can move sidewise—an obviously unstable case.

Hence, for case (h), $h < h' < \infty$. In (i) is shown a portal frame pinned at the supports but free to move laterally at the top. An infinitely flexible girder would transform the column into one having pinned ends and free to move; this is unstable, having an effective length of ∞. If the girder is infinitely rigid, each column, being hinged at one end and fixed at the other rotationally, but free to move sidewise at the top, has an effective length of $2h$, as in case (f). Hence, between these extremes, $\infty > h' > 2h$. In (j), with an infinitely flexible girder, the column would be similar to that of (f), for which the effective length is $2h$. With an infinitely rigid girder, the column would be like that of (g), for which the effective length is h. Hence for intermediate rigidity of the girder, the effective length lies between these limits; that is, $2h > h' > h$. In other words, the I.P. will always be within the upper half of the column.

Summarizing, it is noted that, for an ideal, centrically loaded column:

1. *Its strength is governed by P'_u only when its slenderness ratio h'/r is equal to or less than a certain limiting value; when h'/r exceeds this limiting value, the column strength is governed by its buckling load P_{cr}, which decreases with increasing h'/r.*
2. *Its effective length h' ranges from $h/2$ to h if the column is laterally braced, and from h to ∞ if it is not.*

5–3. BEAM-COLUMNS—INTRODUCTION

Article 5–2 discusses the buckling and the strength of centrically loaded columns, a limiting theoretical case seldom encountered in practice. Practically all columns carry some bending moments in addition to axial loads. These bending moments may be due to: lateral loads applied directly to the columns themselves; loads applied to the rest of the structure, of which the columns form a part; slight eccentricities of the axial loads; or initial column crookedness. In any event, some bending moments (often called **primary moments** to distinguish them from some other bending moments, as will be seen shortly) exist simultaneously with the axial loads. Such members, particularly when they are slender, are called **beam-columns.**

The primary moments in a beam-column may become magnified through the interaction between the axial loads and the deflections. If the member is stocky, or the axial loads small, this magnification is small and may usually be ignored, but if the member becomes slenderer, or the axial loads larger, this magnification increases very rapidly. And when the axial loads approach the critical P_{cr} of the member, the deflections and bending moments approach infinity. As in centrically loaded columns, this magnification of bending moments in beam-columns is influenced by the nature and degree of end restraints, rotational and translational.

Articles 5–4 and 5–5 contain descriptions of the behavior of some simple beam-columns as affected by end restraints.

5–4. BEHAVIOR OF BEAM-COLUMNS WITHOUT SIDESWAY

Consider a pin-ended column (Fig. 5–4a) subjected to axial loads $P < P_{cr}$ and two equal end moments, M_e, which, in the absence of the axial loads, would produce deflection y_i, bending the member into the shape of the dashed curve of single curvature. Without the influence of the axial loads, the bending moment at any point is given by the so-called **primary moment** M_i, which is everywhere equal to the end moments M_e, and is therefore represented by the rectangle in (b). Now, the axial loads interact with the initial deflection y_i, producing moment increments everywhere which lead to deflection increments everywhere. The latter, in turn interacting with the axial loads, lead to further moment increments, and thence deflection increments. A series of moment and deflection increments ensues until eventually there is reached a state of equilibrium in which the member, after having undergone a total deflection increment due to interaction, y_a, comes to rest in a position shown by the solid curve of (a), with a total deflection $y = y_i + y_a$. This state is reached only when the moment due to interaction, M_a, at any point is equal to the product of P and the *total* deflection y at the point. The **interaction moment** is as shown in (c). The final bending moment M is the sum of the primary and the interaction moments, and may be obtained by superposition of the moment diagrams of (b) and (c), resulting in the diagram of (d).

It is noted that the primary and interaction moments are additive everywhere, and each has its maximum at the midheight of the column. The maximum final moment $M_{\max}$ then also occurs there. It may be

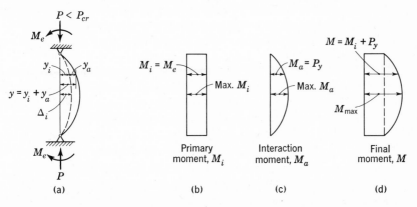

Fig. 5–4. Single-curvature bending of beam-column, without sideway.

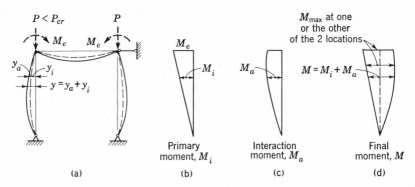

Fig. 5–5. Single-curvature bending of columns in hinged frame, without sidesway.

shown (e.g., Reference 2) for a prismatic, elastic beam-column of this type that, if the initial deflection at midheight is Δ_i, the maximum final moment will be

$$M_{\max} = M_e + \frac{P\Delta_i}{1 - P/P_{cr}} \qquad \text{(approximately)} \qquad (1)$$

The second term on the right side of Eq. 1 represents the magnification of bending moments, and P_{cr} is a function of h'/r, as explained in Art. 5–2. This magnification increases when P increases, and approaches infinity as P approaches P_{cr}.

A similar situation is shown in Fig. 5–5 in which the columns of a laterally braced, hinged frame are subject to axial loads $P < P_{cr}$ and moments M_e at the top ends of the columns. The primary moments bend the columns in single curvature, as shown by the dashed lines. Then interaction between the axial loads and the deflections brings the columns to their final position, indicated by the solid curves. Again, the primary and the interaction moments shown in (b) and (c) are additive everywhere. The final moment diagram of (d) is again obtained by superposition. The maximum final moment may occur at one or the other locations as indicated, but this location is close to the point of the maximum primary or maximum interaction moments. There can again be an appreciable magnification of moments.

When a hinged column under axial loads and equal end moments M_e is bent into a double-curvature curve as shown in Fig. 5–6a, it is seen that, at the ends, where the primary moment is maximum, the interaction moment is zero. The final moment diagram may look like that shown in (d), where the maximum moment remains at the ends, and is equal to M_e; which means that there is no magnification. Or, the maximum final moment may occur at a point slightly removed from the ends, as shown

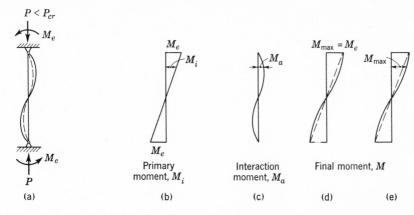

Fig. 5–6. Double-curvature bending of beam-column, without sidesway.

in (e), and its magnitude is just a little bit larger than M_e, since it can be shown that for an ideal, elastic beam-column, the total deflection y at any point is given by

$$y = \frac{y_i}{1 - P/4P_{cr}} \qquad \text{(approximately)} \qquad (2)$$

This indicates that the deflection amplification, and hence the moment amplification, are smaller than those indicated for the single-curvature bending of Fig. 5–4.

In conclusion, it may be stated that *if primary moments bend a beam-column into a single-curvature curve, the moments are significantly magnified, and the magnification increases with h'/r. If primary moments cause a double-curvature deflected shape, there is either no amplification of moments or comparatively less significant amplification.*

5–5. BEHAVIOR OF BEAM-COLUMNS WITH SIDESWAY

Consider a portal frame, either hinged as in Fig. 5–7a or fixed as in Fig. 5–8a. In either case the tendency to sway is not inhibited, and the columns are subjected to axial loads $P < P_{cr}$ plus some primary moments. The columns in the hinged frame first bend into single curvature under primary moments, and those of the fixed-ended frame bend into double curvature. The primary moments and interaction moments are shown in (b) and (c) of each figure. Note that, in each frame, the maximum primary and maximum interaction moments occur at the same point, and the moments are additive everywhere. From the nature of the moment diagrams shown in (b) and (c) of Fig. 5–7 or Fig. 5–8, the maximum final moment is the sum of the maximum primary and the maximum

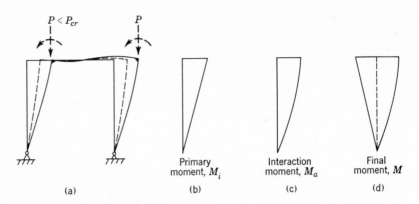

Fig. 5–7. Single-curvature bending of columns of hinged frame, with sidesway.

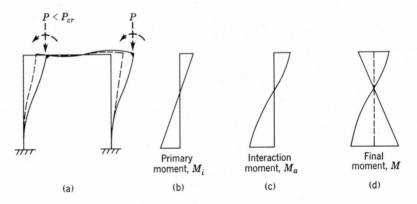

Fig. 5–8. Double-curvature bending of columns of fixed-ended frame, with sidesway.

interaction moments. Hence, it is concluded that *for beam-columns subject to sidesway, there is always substantial magnification of moments whether they deflect in single or double curvature under primary moments.*

5–6. BUCKLING AND BENDING OF COLUMNS—A SUMMARY AND ADDITIONAL REMARKS

The behavior of columns, as described in a rather oversimplified manner in Arts. 5–2 to 5–5, may be summarized, together with some additional comments, as follows:

Buckling. An ideal, centrically loaded slender column may buckle at a load, called the buckling or critical load, P_{cr}, unless yielding or failure should occur before it buckles. P_{cr} depends on the cross-sectional rigidity of the column and its effective length h' (Art. 5–2).

Effective Length h'.   The effective length depends on the nature and degree of end restraints (Art. 5–2):

   a. Without sidesway: $h/2 \leq h' \leq h$
   b. With sidesway: $\quad h \quad \leq h' \leq \infty$

In either case, h' is also a function of the rotational restraints at the ends.   Exact values of h' for various combinations of end rotational restraints may be obtained using the two nomographs of Fig. 5–9, wherein the end restraint is expressed by the parameter r', defined as:

$$r' \text{ at one end of a column} = \frac{\Sigma(\text{stiffnesses of columns})}{\Sigma(\text{stiffnesses of restraining members})}$$

the summation being taken for all members rigidly connected to that end and lying in the plane of buckling considered.

The *effective length parameter*, represented by the middle one of the three lines in each nomograph, when multiplied by the unbraced length h, gives the *effective length* h'.   These nomographs are based on formulas [1] derived for the elastic buckling of prismatic metal bars and are therefore necessarily approximate when applied to reinforced concrete columns.

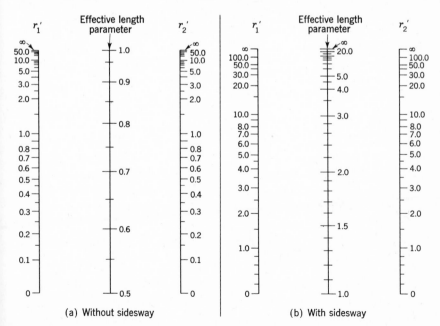

       (a) Without sidesway   (b) With sidesway

Fig. 5–9. Nomograph for effective length of slender columns.   (Courtesy of Column Research Council, Engineering Foundation)

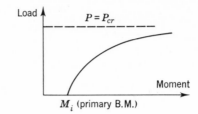

Fig. 5–10. Load-moment relation in beam-columns.

However, for design purposes, an *estimate* of the effective length may be all that is needed, and it is perhaps the best that *can* be realistically expected in view of the many intangible factors involved in practical situations.

Bending of Columns. In the classic Euler-Engesser buckling theory, it is assumed that the column remains straight during axial load application up to the point $P = P_{cr}$ whereupon buckling becomes imminent. This pattern is a theoretical one, and is realized only for ideal columns. A real column always carries some bending moment in addition to the axial load, whether due to load eccentricity or initial crookedness of the column; therefore it will not remain straight as the load increases. Instead, it behaves as a beam-column, which starts to bend as soon as the axial load and primary moment are applied, and due to their interaction, the bending moment may become magnified (Arts. 5–4 and 5–5). The load that can be put on a practical slender column is always smaller than P_{cr}, since it only approaches P_{cr} as a theoretical limit (see Fig. 5–10).

The increase in moments in a practical column depends on end restraints. When sidesway is prevented (Art. 5–4), the increase may be substantial for single-curvature bending under primary moments, or may be nil or moderate for double-curvature bending under primary moments.   When sidesway is not prevented (Art. 5–5), the moments are always substantially magnified for slender columns.

Adequate Lateral Bracing. It is noted that (except for the infrequent case of a single, isolated column), when sidesway occurs, it does so for an entire story or frame simultaneously, not for individual columns in the frame.   Sidesway of columns that are parts of structures may be prevented by (a) bracing against some immovable supports, (b) walls or partitions that are sufficiently strong and rigid in their own planes, (c) sufficiently strong and rigid utility cores, and (d) special bracings.

What constitutes *adequate* lateral bracing is a matter left to the engineer's judgment and discretion.   The present thinking seems to be [3, 4] that effective lateral stability is furnished by such bracing elements as are strong and rigid enough to resist, in addition to whatever loads are directly applied to them, a lateral force equal to at least 2 per cent of the total vertical load acting at the level of the structure for which the columns are being investigated.

5–7. ACI PROVISIONS FOR SLENDER COLUMNS— COMPRESSION FAILURE

With the background presented in the preceding articles on column behavior, it is now appropriate to study the ACI Code provisions. They are an outgrowth of a series of papers by Broms and Viest [5], and appear in Secs. 915 and 916 of the Code. Only columns whose failure is governed by compression are considered here; those failing by tension are presented in Art. 5–8.

The *unbraced length h* is as specified in Sec. 915(a). The *radius of gyration r* is that of the gross concrete section. For rectangular sections, $r = t/\sqrt{12} = 0.289t$, or approximately $0.30t$; for round sections, $r = 0.25D$.

Starting with the *ideal, short-column capacities* $(P'_u, M'_u, P'_0, P'_b, M'_b)$, the factor ϕ (0.75 for spiral and 0.70 for tied columns) is first applied to obtain the corresponding *practical, short-column capacities* $(P_u, M_u, P_0, P_b, M_b)$. Then R, a reduction factor for slenderness effects, is applied to obtain the corresponding *slender column capacities* $(P_{u,sl}, M_{u,sl}, P_{0,sl}, P_{b,sl}, M_{b,sl})$. That is,

$$P_{u,sl} = RP_u = R\phi P'_u$$
$$M_{u,sl} = RM_u = R\phi M'_u$$

and so on. The value of R to be used is given by a series of empirical formulas to be given below. However, for a given section and a value of R, the *reduction of the interaction curve* in the compression failure region from the ideal, short-column status through the practical, short-column status to the slender-column status may be illustrated by Fig. 5–11.

The curve A'-Q'-B' represents the interaction curve for the ideal, short-column strength in the compression zone failure. A point on this curve, such as Q', having an eccentricity e defined by the radial line OQ', has coordinates (P'_u, M'_u). To obtain its corresponding point Q for the practical, short column, multiply P'_u and M'_u by ϕ, resulting in $Q(P_u = \phi P'_u, M_u = \phi M'_u)$. And further multiplication by R gives the coordinates of the corresponding point q for the slender column as $(P_{u,sl} = RP_u, M_{u,sl} = RM_u)$. It is obvious that the three corresponding points, Q', Q, and q all lie on the same radial line of eccentricity e. By the same process, the curves A-Q-B and a-q-b are obtained.

It will be recalled that Sec. 1901(a) stipulates that all columns shall be designed for an eccentricity at least equal to 0.05 times the overall depth for spiral columns and 0.10 times the overall depth for tied columns. As shown in Fig. 5–11, this in effect chops off the top portion of each curve

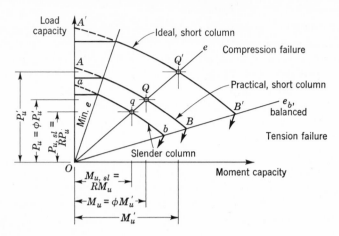

Fig. 5–11. Relation between short and slender column strengths in compression failure zone.

at its intersection with the radial line of minimum eccentricity, and replaces it with a horizontal line emanating from that intersection.

Columns Subject to No Sidesway and with Failure Governed by Compression. The effective length h' and the strength reduction factor R as provided by the Code are summarized in Table 5–1.

Columns Subject to Sidesway and with Failure Governed by Compression. Article 5–2 shows that $h \leq h' \leq \infty$, and the value of h' depends on end rotational restraints. The end rotational restraint is measured by a parameter r' defined by Eq. 5–1:

$$r' \text{ at one end of column} = \frac{\Sigma(\text{stiffnesses of columns})}{\Sigma(\text{stiffnesses of restraining members})}$$
$$= \frac{\Sigma(EI/h) \text{ of columns}}{\Sigma(EI/L) \text{ of restraining members}} \quad (5\text{–}1)$$

Table 5–1. ACI Provisions for Slenderness Effects for Columns with No Sidesway and Failure Governed by Compression

Effective Length, h'	Bending Under Primary Moment	Slenderness Ratio, h'/r	Strength Reduction Factor, R	ACI Code Formula	Section
$h' = h*$	Double curvature	$h'/r \leq 60$ $60 < h'/r \leq 100$ $100 < h'/r$	$R = 1.00$ $R = 1.32 - 0.006(h'/r) \leq 1$ Use beam–column analysis	9–2	916(a)1 916(d)
	Single curvature	All values	$R = 1.07 - 0.008(h'/r) \leq 1$	9–3	916(a)2

* Article 5–2 shows that $h/2 \leq h' \leq h$ and the theoretical value of h' is given by the nomograph (Fig. 5–9a). However, in the interest of simplicity, the ACI Code Sec. 915(c) adopts the conservative value of h for h' for all cases shown in Table 5–1.

in which the summation is taken over all members rigidly connected to that end and lying in the plane of bending being considered (see Art. 5–6).

For a *hinged* end, r' is theoretically ∞, but the Code considers an end as hinged if its $r' > 25$. For a *fixed* end, r' is theoretically zero, but the Code assigns it a value of 1.0.

The ACI expressions for the effective length h' and strength reduction factor R for columns with sidesway and failure governed by compression are summarized in Table 5–2.

Note especially the following with regard to Table 5–2:

1. For a column with one end fixed ($r' = 1.0$) and the other partially restrained, and bending with sidesway, use the formula for h' given in Table 5–2 for the case of both ends partially restrained, *unless* the ratio of the two r' values equals or exceeds 3, in which case, see the daggered footnote.

2. For a column with both ends fixed ($r' = 1.0$) and bending with sidesway, its effective length is $h' = h$.

3. For a column with one end fixed ($r' = 1.0$) and the other hinged ($r' > 25$), and bending with sidesway, its effective length is $h' = 2h$.

4. Columns with both ends hinged and undergoing sidesway are

Table 5–2. ACI Provisions for Slenderness Effects for Columns with Sidesway and Failure Governed by Compression

| Rotational Restraint | | | Strength Reduction Factor, R | | ACI Section Number |
End 1	End 2	Effective Length, h'	Sustained Load‡	Transient Load§	
Partial restraint r'_1	Partial restraint r'_2	$h' = h(0.78 + 0.22r')$† $\geq h$ where r' is the average of r'_1 and r'_2	$R = 1.07 - 0.008(h'/r) \leq 1$	$R = 1.18 - 0.009(h'/r) \leq 1$	915(d)3
Partial restraint r'_1	Hinged $r'_2 > 25$*	$h' = 2h(0.78 + 0.22r')2h$ where $r' = r_1$			915(d)2
Cantilever		$h' = 2h$			915(d)4

* Section 915(d)1.

† If the ratio r'_1/r'_2 or r'_2/r'_1 equals or exceeds 3, this formula is not satisfactory, in which event one should use the nomograph of Fig. 5–9b to obtain h'.

‡ ACI Formula 9–4.

§ ACI Formula 9–5.

unstable.   The reader is reminded that an end having its r' value larger than 25 is considered to be hinged.

5. In the formula for R for sustained loading, concrete creep has been taken into account.   Accordingly, for short-duration loads for which creep does not have time to develop, the Code has allowed a 10 per cent increase in the R value over that for sustained loading.

5–8. ACI PROVISIONS FOR SLENDER COLUMNS—TENSION FAILURE

Introduction.   It has been shown in Art. 5–7 that, for a column failing in compression, once the ϕ and R values are known, its strength—reduced for deviations from ideal conditions and for slenderness effects—may be determined in a straightforward manner, namely: by multiplying the ideal, short-column strength first by ϕ and then by R.   However, for failure by tension, the situation is not as simple.   First, a column subjected to pure flexure is in essence a beam, and if it fails in tension, no strength reduction need be made for its slenderness, unless there prevails a tendency of lateral buckling as in unsupported compression flanges of steel WF sections, a rather unlikely circumstance in ordinary concrete structures.   Accordingly, in the limiting case of pure flexure ($e = \infty$), R should appropriately be 1.0.   If the computed R value for compression failure is also 1.0, there is no question that the value of R for the entire tension failure zone should be uniformly 1.0.   But if the value of R for compression failure is, say, $R_c < 1.0$, the reduction factor R' for the tension failure zone bounded by the balanced case and the pure flexure case should increase from R_c for the balanced case more or less gradually to 1.0 for pure flexure.

Since the Code stipulates a value of ϕ, say, ϕ_c, equal to 0.70 and 0.75, respectively, for tied and spiral columns, and a value of ϕ equal to 0.9 for beams, a similar variation of ϕ is desirable in the tension failure zone. That is, if ϕ' is the proper value of ϕ for the tension failure zone, ϕ' should increase from ϕ_c at the balanced condition to 0.9 of the pure flexure case.

If both R' and ϕ' change gradually, between the limits described above, according to some continuous functions in the tension failure zone, then the reduction of the interaction curve from the ideal, short-column status to that of the slender column may be performed as shown qualitatively in Fig. 5–12a.   In that figure, curve ① is for the ideal, short-column strength.   The values of ϕ and R determined for compression failure are ϕ_c and R_c, and if these are applied to curve ①, curves ② and ③ would have been obtained.   Since $\phi = 0.9$ and $R = 1.0$ for pure flexure, the lower ends of both curves ② and ③ would have to be shifted to E.   If both ϕ and R are to change continuously in the tension failure zone from

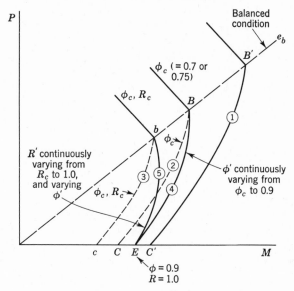

(a) Continuously varying ϕ and continuously varying R

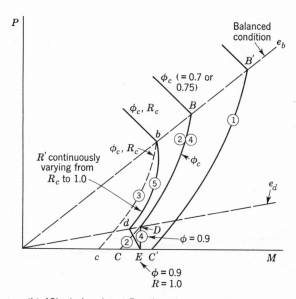

(b) ACI: ϕ changing at D and continuously varying R

Fig. 5–12. Effect of variable ϕ and R on interaction curves in tension failure zone.

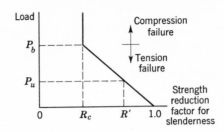

Fig. 5–13.   Reduction factor for tension failure.

the balanced condition to the pure flexure case, curves ④ and ⑤ would have been the result.

ACI Provisions.   Section 1901(c) provides that members subjected to *small* loads may be designed for the moment $P_u e$ alone, ignoring the axial load, as long as the resulting section has an axial capacity, P_b, greater than the axial load.   How *small* the axial load has to be for this to be permitted, the Code does not specify.

In Fig. 5–12b, curve ① is again the ideal, short-column interaction curve, and curves ② and ③ are obtained again, as in Fig. 5–12a, by applying the constant ϕ_c, and by further applying the constant R_c, respectively.   Section 1901(c) in effect produces an interaction curve as shown by ④, which is constructed as follows: From E (corresponding to zero axial load, and a value of M_u equal to $0.9M'_0$), draw a vertical line to intersect curve ② at D, which has an eccentricity of, say, e_d.   A section having a practical short-column moment capacity $0.9M'_0$ is considered to be safe as long as the applied load does not exceed that at D.   For axial loads larger than that at D, the practical short-column strength is given by BD, that is, coinciding with the top portion of curve ②, to which a constant ϕ_c value has been applied.   Therefore, for curve ④, the ϕ value is constant at ϕ_c for the top branch, and then changes abruptly at D to the constant value of 0.9 for the lower branch.   To establish this point D, the configuration of curve ① and thence curve ② must be available at least in the neighborhood of D.

For the variation of R in the tension failure zone, Sec. 916(b) provides that it should vary linearly with the axial load from its value at the balanced condition, computed for compression failure, to a value of 1.0 when the axial load is zero.   According to this provision, by reference to Fig. 5–13 it may be shown that if R' is the reduction factor for slenderness in the tension failure zone,

$$R' = 1.0 - (1.0 - R_c)(P_u/P_b) \qquad (5\text{-}2)$$

This may be approximated by the following equation [6]:

$$R' = 1.0 - (1.0 - R_c)(e_b/e) \qquad (5\text{-}3a)$$

When $R_c < 0.5$, use the following equation:

$$R' = 1.0 - 1.5(1.0 - R_c)(e_b/e) \qquad (5\text{--}3b)$$

With a linearly varying R' value, the slender-column strength for tension failure is then given by curve ⑤ in Fig. 5–12b, which is seen to consist of two parts: the curve bd, and the straight line dE, meeting at the division point d on the line of eccentricity e_d. The curved part bd is obtained by applying the variable R', computed for various eccentricities, to curve BD, and part dE is obtained by applying the variable R' to the straight line DE.

It is seen therefore that the ACI provisions for the tension failure zone of slender columns are unnecessarily complex. The discontinuity in the interaction curves, caused by Sec. 1901(c), is singularly distasteful. The reader is urged to pay special attention to the numerical examples given in Sections B and C of this chapter, which deal with the investigation and design of slender columns, particularly those governed by tension failure.

B. Ultimate Strength Investigation of Slender Columns

5–9. INTRODUCTION

Investigations of a given column may usually be reduced in the final analysis to the following types:

1. Given an eccentricity e, to find the capacity load, $P_{u,sl}$ (and/or the corresponding capacity moment, $M_{u,sl}$) that may be assigned to it.

2. Given a capacity load, $P_{u,sl}$, to find the eccentricity e (and/or the corresponding capacity moment, $M_{u,sl}$) that may be assigned to it.

Another possible type is: Given a capacity moment, $M_{u,sl}$, to find the corresponding capacity load, $P_{u,sl}$. This type of problem may admit of more than one applicable solution.

It is perhaps needless to add that in any case, the capacity moment $M_{u,sl}$ must not exceed $0.9M'_0$, nor should the capacity load exceed that associated with the minimum eccentricity, as stipulated in Sec. 1901(a) of the ACI Code.

The solution of such problems is presented with illustrative examples in Art. 5–10 for cases where an interaction curve or sufficient data for its construction are available, and in Art. 5–11 if such data are not available.

5–10. INVESTIGATION USING AN INTERACTION CURVE

When an interaction curve for investigating a given column is available, the solution is essentially graphical and extremely simple. The following procedure is a brief recapitulation of the more detailed discussion con-

Plate 5-1. The Lake Washington Bridge at Seattle, Washington. It is, in effect, a 1.3-mile floating highway. Closed reinforced concrete pontoons, securely anchored to the lake bottom, support the pavement. In the distance there is a 200-ft. pontoon drawspan, which retracts to allow large ships to pass.

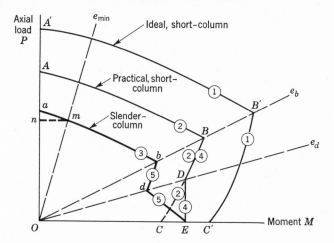

Fig. 5–14.   Investigation of columns using interaction curves.

tained in Arts. 5–7 and 5–8, to which the reader is referred for a thorough understanding.

Suppose the ideal short-column interaction curve ① of Fig. 5–14 is given for investigating a column. Multiply the coordinates of curve ① by the understrength ϕ (0.75 for spiral, 0.70 for tied, columns), and plot curve ②. On the moment axis, locate point E (representing zero axial load and a moment equal to $0.9M'_0$), and erect a vertical line to intersect curve ② at D. Draw the radial line e_d.

Next, for the compression failure zone, determine the slenderness strength reduction factor, R (Art. 5–7). Multiply the coordinates of curve ② in this zone by R and plot the results as curve ③. Draw the e_{min} line to intersect curve ③ at m, and draw the horizontal line nm.

For the region between the lines e_b and e_d, compute for selected eccentricities the values of R' (Eqs. 5–2, 5–3), and multiply the coordinates of B-D and plot the results as b-d. Join d and E by a straight line.

The bold line n-m-b-d-E then gives the slender-column strength. For any given eccentricity, any given capacity load, or any given capacity moment, the required solution may be found readily from this curve. Actually, when the failure is by compression, the curve n-m-b need not be drawn at all since the coordinates thereon are their corresponding coordinates on curve ① multiplied by a uniform constant (ϕR).

EXAMPLE 5–1

Column Investigation—Interaction Data Available

Given a building frame shown in elevation and plan in Fig. 5–15a; consider these cases: (a) the frame is laterally braced; (b) the frame is not laterally braced.

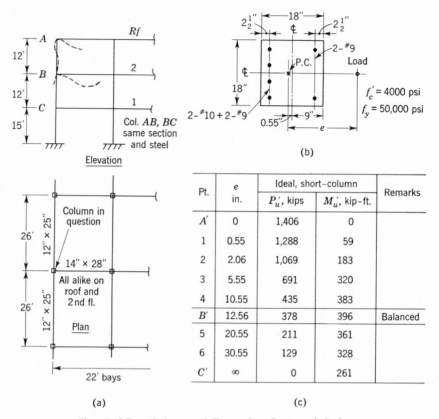

Fig. 5–15. Column of Examples 5–1 and 5–2.

The exterior roof column AB has a cross section and reinforcement as shown in Fig. 5–15b. Consider vertical loading only.

Required to find what load $P_{u,sl}$ may be assigned to the exterior roof column AB at level A for a given eccentricity e of 4.53 in., with interaction data as tabulated in Fig. 5–15c.

Solution. (NOTE: This is the same column section considered in Arts. 4–8 and 4–9.)

1. SHORT-COLUMN STRENGTH. It is seen that $e = 4.53$ in. lies between points *2* and *3* in the table of Fig. 5–15c; whence we conclude that *failure is by compression*, and since 4.53 in. is larger than the minimum e of $0.10(18) = 1.8$ in., the result is not modified by Sec. 1901(a). Plotting the interaction curve in the neighborhood of $e = 4.53$ in., and drawing a radial line for $e = 4.53$ in. to intersect it at Q', Fig. 5–16. Hence the ideal short-column $P'_u = 780$ kips, and the practical short-column $P_u = 0.7(780) = 546$ kips.

2. SLENDERNESS EFFECT. The unbraced length, $h = 12.0 - 2.33 = 9.67$ ft., where 2.33 ft. is the depth of the 14-by-28-in. girder. The radius of gyration, r, is $0.30(1.5) = 0.45$ ft. [Sec. 916(a)4].

(a) *Frame laterally braced.* Under gravity loading, column AB bends with a double curvature as shown in Fig. 5–15a. Therefore, with $h' = h$ (no sidesway), and $h'/r = 9.67/0.45 = 21.5$, Table 5–1 shows $R = 1.0$ for double-curvature bending.

Therefore, the slender-column capacity, $P_{u,sl} = 1.0(546) = $ 546 kips   Ans.

(b) *Frame laterally unbraced.*

At A,   girder stiffness $= \dfrac{1.17(2.33)^3/12}{22} = 0.056$ ft.³

column stiffness $= \dfrac{1.5(1.5)^3/12}{12} = 0.035$ ft.³ $\left.\right\}$ $r' = \dfrac{0.035}{0.056} = 0.63$

At B, there are two such columns and one girder, therefore $r' = 0.070/0.056 = 1.26$. The average of these values is $r' = 0.94$. Therefore according to Table 5–2, the effective length is given by

$$h' = h(0.78 + 0.22r') \geq h$$
$$= h(0.78 + 0.22 \times 0.94) = 0.99h$$

Therefore use

$$h' = h = 9.67 \text{ ft.}$$

and $h'/r = 21.5$ as in (b). The slenderness strength reduction factor is then

$$R = 1.07 - 0.008(h'/r) = 1.07 - 0.008(21.5) = 0.90$$

Accordingly, the slender-column load capacity is

$$P_{u,sl} = 0.90(546) = \hspace{3em} \text{491 kips} \quad \text{Ans.}$$

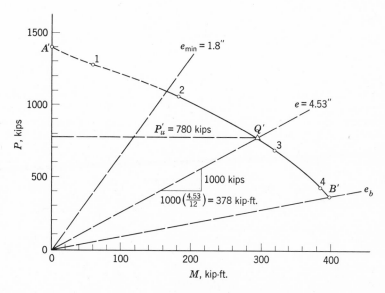

Fig. 5–16. Solution of Example 5–1.

EXAMPLE 5–2

Column Investigation—Interaction Data Available

Given the same column and data as in Example 5–1, and in Fig. 5–15.

Required to find, for both the laterally braced and unbraced conditions, the load capacity, $P_{u,sl}$, which may be assigned for a given eccentricity of (i) $e = 16.0$ in. and (ii) $e = 40.0$ in.

Solution. Since both eccentricities exceed e_b of 12.56 in., *failure by tension* is expected. The solution is presented in Fig. 5–17, and is obtained in the following manner:

(i) $e = 16.0$ in.   (ii) $e = 40.0$ in.

SHORT-COLUMN STRENGTH

Multiply the given P'_u, M'_u data for the ideal short column by a ϕ of 0.7, and plot the curve BC. From E on the moment axis, representing $0.9M'_0 = 0.9(261) = 235$ kip-ft., draw vertical line to intersect BC at D. This defines the cusp point in the resulting short-column interaction curve BDE.

(a) LATERALLY BRACED SLENDER-COLUMN STRENGTH

If failure were by compression, $h' = h = 9.67$ ft. Then $r = 0.45$ ft. and $h'/r = 21.5$, as in Example 5–1. Table 5–1 shows that for double-curvature bending and $h'/r \leq 60$, $R_c = 1.0$, which means that no reduction need be made for slenderness. Hence, the short-column strength curve BDE *is* the required strength curve.

The radial line of $e = 16.0$ in. inter-   The radial line of $e = 40.0$ in. intersects BDE at Q_{1a}, which gives the re-   sects BDE at Q_{2a}, which gives the required capacity: quired capacity:

$P_{u,sl} = P_u = $ 200 kips   Ans. $P_{u,sl} = P_u = $ 70 kips   Ans.

(b) LATERALLY UNBRACED SLENDER-COLUMN STRENGTH

For compression failure, as in Example 5–1, $h' = h(0.78 + 0.22r') \geq h$, where r' was found to be 0.94; $h' = h(0.78 + 0.22 \times 0.94) = 0.99h$. Hence, use $h' = h = 9.67$ ft. and $h'/r = 21.5$. The strength reduction factor for slenderness is $R_c = 1.07 - 0.008(h'/r) = 0.90$.

For tension failure, the reduction factor R' is given by $R' = 1 - (1 - R_c)(e_b/e)$ according to the ACI recommendation of linear variation of R' in the tension failure zone. Then between the radial lines e_b and e, R' values may be computed for different e values, and these when multiplied by the coordinates of curve BD give the required curve bd. Locate d and join d and E by a straight line. The complete curve bdE is the slender-column strength curve.

The intersection Q_{1b} of bdE with the   The intersection Q_{2b} of bdE with the
radial line $e = 16$ in. gives the required   radial line $e = 40$ in. gives the required
capacity: capacity:

$P_{u,sl} = $ 185 kips   Ans. $P_{u,sl} = $ 68 kips   Ans.

PRACTICE PROBLEM

5–1. Given a fixed-ended portal frame consisting of a 20-by-30-in. horizontal girder and 20-in. round spiral columns as shown in Fig. 5–18a. The columns have 12–#9 bars centered uniformly on a 15-in.-diameter circle, $f'_c = 4000$ psi, and $f_y = 60,000$ psi. The coordinates for the ideal, short-column strength are shown in the table of Fig. 5–18b. Assume that column AB is being investigated at A just below the girder for

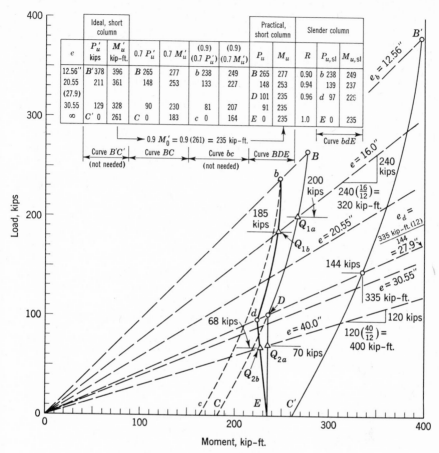

e	Ideal, short column						Practical, short column		Slender column		
	P_u' kips	M_u' kip-ft.	$0.7\,P_u'$	$0.7\,M_u'$	(0.9) $(0.7\,P_u')$	(0.9) $(0.7\,M_u')$	P_u	M_u	R	$P_{u,\text{sl}}$	$M_{u,\text{sl}}$
12.56″	B′378	396	B 265	277	b 238	249	B 265	277	0.90	b 238	249
20.55	211	361	148	253	133	227	148	253	0.94	139	237
(27.9)							D 101	235	0.96	d 97	225
30.55	129	328	90	230	81	207	91	235			
∞	C′ 0	261	C 0	183	c 0	164	E 0	235	1.0	E 0	235

$0.9\,M_0' = 0.9\,(261) = 235$ kip-ft.

Curve B′C′ (not needed) — Curve BC — Curve bc (not needed) — Curve BDE — Curve bdE

Fig. 5–17. Solution of Example 5–2.

some gravity loading. Consider the cases: (a) the frame is adequately braced; (b) the frame is not braced. It is required to find the slender-column capacity for each of the three eccentricities: (a) $e = 4.0$ in. (b) $e = 11.0$ in. (c) $e = 25$ in. (NOTE: For plotting the curves in the tension failure zone, use a scale no smaller than 1 in. = 100 kips, and 1 in. = 50 kip-ft.)

5–11. INVESTIGATION WITHOUT INTERACTION DATA

When complete interaction data are available, the investigation of a given column is usually quite simple, as shown in Art. 5–10. However, more often than not, such information is not available, and it may be that the problem at hand does not make it feasible to compile complete interaction data in advance. Under such circumstances, the analysis can become somewhat involved. It is appropriate therefore that some attention be given as to how best to deal with such situations, as described in Arts. 5–12 and 5–13. It is presumed in the discussions presented therein

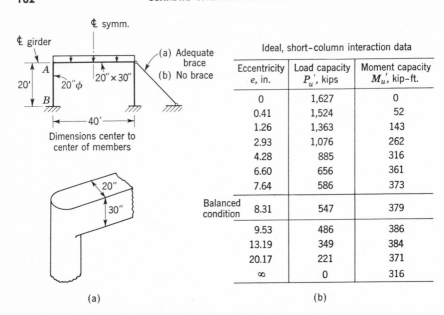

Ideal, short-column interaction data

Eccentricity e, in.	Load capacity $P_u{'}$, kips	Moment capacity $M_u{'}$, kip-ft.
0	1,627	0
0.41	1,524	52
1.26	1,363	143
2.93	1,076	262
4.28	885	316
6.60	656	361
7.64	586	373
Balanced condition 8.31	547	379
9.53	486	386
13.19	349	384
20.17	221	371
∞	0	316

(a)   (b)

Fig. 5–18.   Data for Problem 5–1.

that the reader is familiar with the determination of the following quantities for a given ideal, short-column section:

1. Capacities P'_b and M'_b and the associated e_b for the balanced condition.
2. Capacity M'_0 for pure flexure.
3. Capacities P'_u and M'_u for a given eccentricity e.
4. Eccentricity e or M'_u to be assigned for a given P'_u.

The reader may find it desirable to review Chapter 4 before proceeding
to the following articles.

5–12. SLENDER-COLUMN INVESTIGATION: GIVEN e, TO FIND $P_{u,sl}$

First, it must be determined whether, for the given eccentricity, the
column being investigated fails by compression or tension. This may be
done by first computing e_b for the section and then comparing it with the
given eccentricity e.

If $e < e_b$, **failure is by compression.** Next find the ideal, short-column
capacity, P'_u, for the given e. Then find ϕ and R and apply them to P'_u,
obtaining

$$P_{u,sl} = \phi R P'_u \qquad\qquad \text{Q.E.D.}$$

If $e > e_b$, **failure is by tension.** One must determine where the given
e radial line lies with respect to the e_d radial line (Fig. 5–19), which corresponds to the cusps d and D, but which is as yet undetermined. The
steps to follow are then:

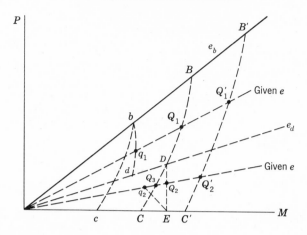

Fig. 5–19. Column investigation in tension failure zone.

1. Compute P'_u and M'_u for the given e; this yields one of the two locations marked Q'_1 and Q'_2.
2. Find $\phi M'_u$, resulting in either location Q_1 or Q_3.
3. Compute M'_0 and then $0.9M'_0$, which correspond respectively to C' and E.

Since D is directly above E, one may determine, by comparing $0.9M'_0$ with $\phi M'_u$, whether the given e gives Q_1 or Q_3, without actually locating D, in the following manner:

If $\phi M'_u > 0.9M'_0$, we have Q_1, which is above and to the right of D. Next determine the reduction factor R_c as if failure were by compression. Then compute for the given e the reduction factor R' for tension failure by $R' = 1 - (1 - R_c)(e_b/e)$. Since Q_1 is on the short-column strength curve BD, $P_u = \phi P'_u$. Hence, we apply R' to P_u, moving from Q_1 to q_1 on the slender-column strength curve bd, to obtain

$$P_{u,sl} = R'P_u = R'\phi P'_u \quad \text{Q.E.D.}$$

If $\phi M'_u < 0.9M'_0$, we have Q_3, which is below and to the left of D. Now Q_3 is on DC; therefore its corresponding position Q_2 on the straight line DE must be located, DE being the lower branch of the correct practical, short-column strength curve. Q_2 therefore gives P_u, which may be computed as

$$P_u = 0.9M'_0/\text{the given } e$$

Now find R_c as if failure were by compression, and then R' for tension failure by $R' = 1 - (1 - R_c)(e_b/e)$. Multiply P_u computed above by R', moving from Q_2 to q_2 on the straight branch dE of the slender-column curve, and one gets

$$P_{u,sl} = R'P_u = R'(0.9M_0/\text{given } e)$$
$$\text{Q.E.D.}$$

EXAMPLE 5–3

Column Investigation—Interaction Data Unavailable

Given the column and the data of Example 5–2 but without the interaction coordinates.

Required to find the load capacity $P_{u,sl}$ of the column AB for the laterally unbraced case if: (1) $e = 16.0$ in.; (2) $e = 40.0$ in.

Solution. STEP 1. Determine e_b of the balanced condition (see Example 4–7):

$$e_b = 12.56 \text{ in.}$$

STEP 2. Find M'_0 of the pure flexure case (Example 4–3):

$$M'_0 = 261 \text{ kip-ft.}$$

STEP 3. For the given eccentricities, find the ideal short-column P'_u, M'_u as follows:

(1) $e = 16.0$ in.; $e' = 21.95$ in. With tensile failure, $f_s = f_y$. Assume A'_s has yielded:

$$f'_s = f_y$$

The forces are then as shown in Fig. 5–20b, for which the equilibrium equations are:

$$P'_u = 61.2a + 93.2 - 227$$

$$P'_u(21.95) = 61.2a(15.5 - 0.5a) + 93.2(13.0)$$

Solving these two either by iteration or by solving the resultant quadratic equation, one gets:

$c = 8.07$ in. $a = 6.86$ in.
$P'_u = 286$ kips $M'_u = 381$ kip-ft.

These satisfy strain compatibility.

(2) $e = 40.0$ in.; $e' = 45.95$ in. With tensile failure, $f_s = f_y$. Assume A'_s has not yielded; hence

$$f'_s = 29,000(0.003)\left(\frac{c - 2.5}{c}\right)$$
$$= 87\left(1 - \frac{2.5}{c}\right)$$

The forces are then as shown in Fig. 5–20c, for which the equilibrium equations are:

$$P'_u = 61.2a + 2\left[87\left(1 - \frac{2.5}{c}\right) - 3.4\right] - 227$$

$$P'_u(45.95) = 61.2a(15.5 - 0.5a) + 2\left[87\left(1 - \frac{2.5}{c}\right) - 3.4\right](13.0)$$

Solving these two either by iteration or by solving the resultant cubic equation, one gets:

$c = 4.72$ in. $a = 4.01$ in.
$P'_u = 93$ kips $M'_u = 311$ kip-ft.

These satisfy strain compatibility.

STEP 4. Compare $\phi M'_u = 0.7M'_u$ with $0.9M'_0 = 0.9(261) = 235$ kip-ft.

$\phi M'_u = 0.7(381) = 266$ kip-ft.
> 235 kip-ft.

$\phi M'_u = 0.7(311) = 217$ kip-ft.
< 235 kip-ft.

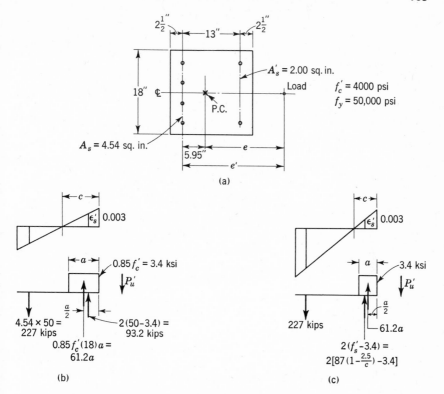

Fig. 5–20. Column of Example 5–3.

Therefore, the e radial line is above the cusp in the strength curves.

Hence, the short-column capacity is:

$$P_u = \phi P'_u = 0.7(286) = 200 \text{ kips}$$

Therefore the e radial line is below the cusp in the strength curves.

Hence the short-column P_u is *not* given by $\phi P'_u$, but is:

$$P_u = 0.9 M'_0/e = \frac{235(12)}{40.0} = 70 \text{ kips}$$

STEP 5. Find the reduction factor R' for the given e. As in Example 5–2, for compression failure in the unbraced case, h' is found to be equal to $h = 9.67$ ft., and $h'/r = 21.5$, and $R_c = 0.90$.

For tension failure with $e = 16.0$ in.,

$$R' = 1 - (1 - 0.90)\frac{12.56}{16} = 0.92$$

For tension failure with $e = 40.0$ in.,

$$R' = 1 - (1 - 0.90)\frac{12.56}{40} = 0.97$$

STEP 6. Find the required $P_{u,sl}$ as follows:

$$P_{u,sl} = R'P_u = 0.92(200) = \underline{\underline{184 \text{ kips}}} \quad \text{Ans.}$$

$$P_{u,sl} = R'P_u = 0.97(70) = \underline{\underline{68 \text{ kips}}} \quad \text{Ans.}$$

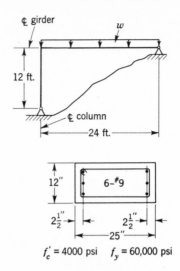

f'_c = 4000 psi f_y = 60,000 psi

Fig. 5–21.   Problem 5–2.

PRACTICE PROBLEM

5–2. The column of an L-shaped rigid frame has dimensions, reinforcement, and specifications as shown in Fig. 5–21.   Assume the vertical loading w on the girder to be sustained.

(a) Find the ultimate capacity of the column, $P_{u,sl}$ and $M_{u,sl}$, corresponding to an eccentricity

(i) $e = 5.00$ in.
(ii) $e = 41.14$ in.

(b) If, at service level, w consists of live load of 1.0 kip per ft. and dead load of 1.5 kip per ft. (including weight of the girder), both considered to be sustained, find whether the column has adequate ultimate capacity.

5–13. SLENDER-COLUMN INVESTIGATION: GIVEN $P_{u,sl}$, TO FIND e OR $M_{u,sl}$

This situation occurs less frequently than the one described in Art. 5–12 where it is required to find $P_{u,sl}$ if e is given.   The analysis is somewhat more troublesome, but may be handled in like manner.   A procedure is described below which usually works satisfactorily.

As in Art. 5–12, the first matter to decide is whether the given column fails in compression or tension.   The criterion is a comparison between the given and the balanced conditions.   For the ideal, short column, one finds P'_b for the balanced case, and then converts it to $P_{b,sl} = P'_b \phi R_c$ where ϕ is 0.75 or 0.70, respectively, for spiral or tied columns, and R_c is the reduction factor for slenderness for compression failure.

If $P_{u,sl} > P_{b,sl}$, **failure is by compression.**   One then converts the given

$P_{u,sl}$ to P'_u (that is, from the level of q_1 through Q_1 to Q'_1 in Fig. 5–22) by

$$P'_u = P_{u,sl}/\phi R_c$$

Then, for the given section find the eccentricity corresponding to P'_u. This is usually a trial-and-error process (see Example 5–4).

If $P_{u,sl} < P_{b,sl}$, failure is by tension. Here, again, one has to ascertain whether $P_{u,sl}$ is at the level of q_2 or q_3, that is, whether the required eccentricity is large enough so that Sec. 1901(c) may be taken advantage of. First, compute the reduction factor R' for the tension failure zone; since e is not known, find R' by $R' = 1 - (1 - R_c)(P_{u,sl}/P_{b,sl})$. Divide $P_{u,sl}$ by R' (that is, projecting from q_2 to Q_2 or q_3 to Q_3 as shown in Fig. 5–22).

Now, obtain $P_{u,sl}/R'\phi$. If the given $P_{u,sl}$ is at level q_2, this takes it to level Q'_2 on the ideal, short-column strength curve. If the given $P_{u,sl}$ is at level q_3, $P_{u,sl}/R'\phi$ will *not* convert it to the correct level Q'_3 on the ideal, short-column curve, but some level Q'_4 somewhat higher than Q'_3. The reason for this is that one gets to the correct level Q'_3 only by projecting from the level Q_5 through a division by ϕ, so that by going from Q_3 with a ϕ divisor, one obtains a higher level at Q'_4 which has its corresponding level Q_6 as its origin. Since we do not know at this stage whether we are at level q_2 or q_3, we have no way of telling whether $P_{u,sl}/R'\phi$ is the true P'_u for the given $P_{u,sl}$; accordingly, let us denote this by

$$\text{Tentative } P_u = P_{u,sl}/R'\phi$$

Next, for the given section, find the tentative M'_u and e corresponding to the tentative P'_u, and also M'_0 of the pure flexure case. Now multiply the tentative M'_u by ϕ (backing up from Q'_2 to Q_2, or from Q'_4 to Q_6), and compare it with $0.9M'_0$, which is represented by line DE.

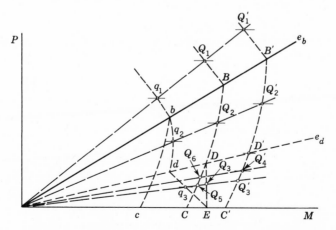

Fig. 5–22. Column investigation: Given $P_{u,sl}$, to find e.

If ϕ(tentative M'_u) $> 0.9M'_0$, we are on the upper branch BD of the practical short-column curve, which is related to the ideal short-column curve $B'D'$ by a simple factor ϕ. Hence, the tentative P'_u, and M'_u, and e computed previously, are the true P'_u, M'_u, and e values.

If ϕ(tentative M'_u) $< 0.9M'_0$, we have a point Q_6 to the left of the line DE. Since the shape of the interaction curve is usually such that point Q_5 corresponding to Q_3 is to the left of Q_6, the value of ϕ (the true M'_u at point Q'_3) would be smaller than ϕ(tentative M'_u), and hence even smaller than $0.9M'_0$. Hence by Sec. 1901(c), DE is the strength curve for the practical, short-column status. Therefore, the required eccentricity is

$$e = \frac{0.9M'_0}{P_{u,sl}/R'}$$

EXAMPLE 5–4

Column Investigation—Interaction Data Unavailable

Given the column and data of Example 5–2 but without the interaction data, and consider the laterally unbraced case only, for which $R_c = 0.9$.

Required to find the eccentricity e which may be assigned if the given slender-column capacity load $P_{u,sl}$ is (1) 491 kips, (2) 184 kips, and (3) 68 kips.

Solution. STEP 1. Determine the balanced condition: $P'_b = 378$ kips, $c_b = 9.84$ in., and $a_b = 8.37$ in. (from Example 4–7). Hence, for the balanced, slender column,

$$P_{b,sl} = \phi R_c P'_b$$
$$= 0.7(0.9)(378) = 238 \text{ kips}$$

(1) $P_{u,sl} = \textbf{491 kips}$
$$491 > 238$$
$$\therefore \textit{Compression failure}$$

STEP 2. Set $P'_u = P_{u,sl}/\phi R_c$:

$$P'_u = \frac{491}{0.7(0.9)} = 780 \text{ kips}$$

Find the corresponding e and M'_u: A_s has not yielded, and

$$f_s = 29,000(0.003)\left(\frac{15.5 - c}{c}\right)$$
$$= 87\left(\frac{15.5}{c} - 1\right) \text{ksi}$$

(2) $P_{u,sl} = \textbf{184 kips}$
$$184 < 238$$
$$\therefore \textit{Tension failure}$$

STEP 2. Obtain the factor R' and the tentative P'_u:

$$R' = 1 - (1 - R_c)(P_{u,sl}/P_{b,sl})$$
$$= 1 - (1 - 0.9)\frac{184}{238}$$
$$= 0.92$$

Tentative $P'_u = P_{u,sl}/\phi R'$
$$= \frac{184}{0.7(0.92)}$$
$$= 286 \text{ kips}$$

(3) $P_{u,sl} = \textbf{68 kips}$
$$68 < 238$$
$$\therefore \textit{Tension failure}$$

STEP 2. Obtain the factor R' and the tentative P'_u:

$$R' = 1 - (1 - 0.9)\frac{68}{238}$$
$$= 0.97$$

Tentative $P'_u = \frac{68}{0.7(0.97)}$
$$= 100 \text{ kips}$$

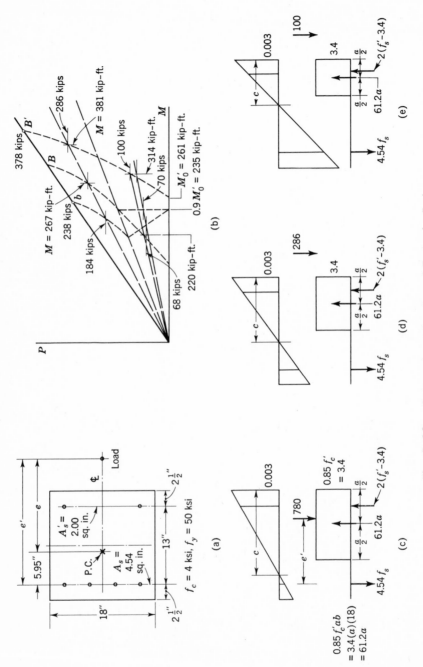

Fig. 5–23. Column investigation of Example 5–4.

Assume A'_s yielding: $f'_s = f_y = 50$ ksi. Referring to Fig. 5–23c, the equilibrium equations are:

$$780 = 61.2a + 93.2 - 4.54(87)\left(\frac{15.5}{c} - 1\right)$$

$$780e' = 61.2a\left(15.5 - \frac{a}{2}\right) + 93.2(13)$$

Solving the first equation, one obtains:

$c = 14.0$ in.
$a = 11.9$ in.

Strains show that A'_s has yielded as assumed.

With $a = 11.9$, the second equation above gives

$e' = 10.48$ in.
$e = e' - 5.95$
$ = 4.53$ in.   Ans.

For this tentative P'_u, determine the tentative e and M'_u.

Referring to Fig. 5–23d, with A_s yielding, and the assumption of yielding A'_s, that is:

$$f_s = f'_s = f_y = 50 \text{ ksi}$$

one writes the equations:

$$286 = 61.2a + 93.2 - 227$$

$$286(e') = 61.2a\left(15.5 - \frac{a}{2}\right) + 93.2(13)$$

Solving the first equation, one obtains:

$c = 8.07$ in.
$a = 6.86$ in.

These substantiate the assumption with regard to f'_s. Then the second of the above equations gives e' as 21.95 in. Hence,

Tentative $e = 16.0$ in.
Tentative $M'_u = (286)(16.0)/12$
$ = 381$ kip-ft.

For this tentative P'_u, determine the tentative e and M'_u.

Referring to Fig. 5–23e, with A_s yielding, and the assumption of elastic A'_s, that is:

$$f_s = f_y = 50 \text{ ksi}$$

$$f'_s = 87\left(1 - \frac{2.5}{c}\right) \text{ ksi}$$

one writes the equations:

$$100 = 61.2a + 2\left[87\left(1 - \frac{2.5}{c}\right) - 3.4\right] - 227$$

$$100e' = 61.2a\left(15.5 - \frac{a}{2}\right)$$
$$+ 2\left[87\left(1 - \frac{2.5}{c}\right) - 3.4\right](13)$$

Solving the first equation, one obtains:

$c = 4.81$ in.
$a = 4.09$ in.

These substantiate the assumption with regard to f'_s. Then the second of the above equations gives e' as 43.66 in. Hence,

Tentative $e = 37.71$ in.
Tentative $M'_u = (100)(37.71)/12$
$ = 314$ kip-ft.

STEP 3. Consider the pure flexure case (Example 4–3) to find

$$M'_0 = 261 \text{ kip-ft.}$$

Therefore, $0.9M'_0 = 0.9(261) = 235$ kip-ft. Now, compare this with ϕ(tentative M'_u) in the next step.

STEP 4.

$$\phi(\text{tentative } M'_u) = 0.7(381)$$
$$= 267 \text{ kip-ft.}$$

Since $267 > 235$, the given load is above the cusp in the strength curve, and the tentative values found above are the correct values.

Therefore the eccentricity is:

$$e = \qquad 16.0 \text{ in.} \quad \underline{\text{Ans.}}$$

STEP 4.

$$\phi(\text{tentative } M'_u) = 0.7(314)$$
$$= 220 \text{ kip-ft.}$$

Since $220 < 235$, the given load is below the cusp in the strength curve, and Sec. 1901(c) applies. Now the true practical, short-column capacity is:

$$P_u = P_{u,sl}/R' = 68/0.97$$
$$= 70 \text{ kips}$$

Therefore the eccentricity is:

$$e = 0.9M'_0/P_u$$
$$= 235(12)/70$$
$$= \qquad 40.2 \text{ in.} \quad \underline{\text{Ans.}}$$

PRACTICE PROBLEM

5–3. Given the rectangular tied column section of Fig. 5–24, 5000-lb. concrete, 50,000-psi-yield-point steel, and ACI Code, USD.

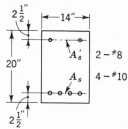

Fig. 5–24.   Problem 5–3.

(a) Show that: (i) the plastic centroid of the section is at 6.70 in. from the centroid of A_s; (ii) for pure flexure, the *ideal* moment capacity of the section, M'_0, is 331 kip-ft.; (iii) for the balanced condition, the *ideal, short-column* eccentric load capacity, P'_b, is 347 kips, at an eccentricity $e_b = 16.3$ in. from the plastic centroid.

(b) If the strength reduction factor for slenderness effects, R_c, is 0.8 when compression governs failure, find what eccentricity, e, may be assigned if (i) $P_{u,sl} = 400$ kips; (ii) $P_{u,sl} = 75$ kips.

C. Ultimate Strength Designing of Columns

5–14. INTRODUCTION

The discussion of columns presented so far has been concerned with their **investigation.**   In investigating a column of a given structure under a specified loading, one is given the load and bending moment in the column, P_{uf} and M_{uf} (hereafter referred to as the **load-factored** column load and bending moment), produced by an ultimate load on the structure equal to the given service loads augmented by the ACI load factors. Then, for the eccentricity $e = M_{uf}/P_{uf}$, one first determines the *ideal, short-column* capacity, P'_u, of the column section, which, when multiplied by the understrength factor ϕ, results in the *dependable, short-column* capacity, P_u.   Upon further multiplication by the strength reduction factor R to account for slenderness effects, one obtains the *slender-column* capacity, $P_{u,sl}$.   Finally, a comparison of the load-factored value P_{uf} and the slender-column capacity $P_{u,sl}$ yields a conclusion on the adequacy of the given column for the particular loading.

In **designing** a column for a set of given or previously computed load-factored P_{uf} and M_{uf} (or P_{uf} and its eccentricity e), the process is normally just the reverse of that of an investigation.   Then it is required to find the concrete dimensions and reinforcement of the column section such that its *slender-column* capacity $P_{u,sl}$ is at least equal to the *load-factored* P_{uf}.   Stated alternately, the problem is to find a column section such that its ideal, short-column capacity P'_u is at least equal to the *load-factored* P_{uf} divided by the factors ϕ and R, that is:

$$\text{Required ideal, short-column } P'_u = \frac{\text{load-factored } P_{uf}}{\phi R} \qquad (5\text{–}4)$$

Now, while ϕ is predetermined (0.75 for spiral, 0.70 for tied, columns), the factor R depends on the column dimensions, which are yet unknown at this stage. The concrete dimensions affect the slenderness ratio h'/r and the all-important eccentricity parameter, e/t or e/D, where t is the overall depth of a rectangular section and D is the overall diameter of a round section. This parameter, e/t or e/D, determines whether failure of a section is controlled by tension or compression. If failure is controlled by compression, the minimum eccentricity clause of Sec. 1901(a) may dictate the design, as for columns with light or zero bending. If failure is controlled by tension, further complication may arise due to the provision contained in Sec. 1901(c) of the Code which applies to columns subjected to heavy bending.[2] In any event, to obtain the required ideal, short-column capacity P'_u, the value of R (or concrete dimensions) in Eq. 5–4 would have to be guessed or estimated.

Accordingly, column designing is essentially a trial-and-error process. To start, one assumes the mode of failure and a value of R, the overall dimensions of the section, the eccentricity parameter, e/t or e/D, the approximate steel percentage, or a combination thereof. The designing then proceeds by successive revision until the desired section is obtained.

Column designing is obviously usually more time-consuming, although no more complex in principle, than straightforward investigation. Practical column designing will undoubtedly be based on charts, tables, or other design aids. However, few design aids cover all situations, and the designer must be familiar with basic principles which are the only recourse for unusual cases. For this reason, emphasis in the remainder of the chapter is placed on the application of basic principles, except near the end of the chapter where some discussion of the use of design aids is given.

5–15. CENTRICALLY OR NEARLY CENTRICALLY LOADED COLUMNS

Truly centrically loaded columns are extremely rare, particularly in reinforced concrete structures, which by their very nature are rigidly connected frames in which all members are subject to some bending. Furthermore, initial crookedness, however slight, is virtually unavoidable in real columns. Hence, Code Sec. 1901(a) stipulates that all columns based on USD be designed for a minimum eccentricity, e, equal to 0.05 and 0.10 times the overall depth of the section for spiral and tied columns, respectively.

However, cases do frequently occur in which the *computed* moments in columns are either zero or negligibly small. An example is an interior

---

[2] The reader who finds this obscure should review Arts. 5–7 through 5–13.

column of a building frame without sidesway and supporting identical and symmetrically loaded bays on both sides of the column. Nevertheless, such columns are still to be designed for the minimum eccentricity as described above.

The longitudinal reinforcing bars in a centrically or nearly centrically loaded column of rectangular cross section are usually made symmetrical about the center line, whether they are placed near two opposite faces, or nearly uniformly distributed on a circle, or near its four faces. Round sections, of course, nearly always have their reinforcing bars spaced uniformly near the circumference.

Failure of column sections designed for the ACI minimum eccentricity is always controlled by compression. Therefore, to evaluate the strength reduction factor R for slenderness effects, Sec. 916(a) applies; its provisions are summarized in Table 5–1 when sidesway is prevented, and in Table 5–2 when sidesway is not prevented. Attention should be drawn to Sec. 916(c) and the following comments when these two tables are applied to the design of columns for minimum eccentricity.

When there is sidesway, there is no question that Table 5–2 applies. When there is no sidesway, Table 5–1 applies, but two situations may arise to dictate whether there is double- or single-curvature bending. First, if the initial computed eccentricities at both ends of a column are not zero but are simply smaller than the minimum, then the actual bending pattern may be easily determined from the nature of the end moments, and the proper R may be selected from Table 5–1. The second situation is that in which the column moments either have not been considered or have been shown by computation to be zero at one or both ends of the column. For this case, Sec. 916(c)2 requires that the R factor for the single-curvature bending of Table 5–1 be chosen, provided that there is no sidesway.[3]

5–16. DESIGN OF A RECTANGULAR TIED COLUMN FOR ACI MINIMUM ECCENTRICITY

It was stated in Art. 5–15 that the ACI Code provides that all USD columns subjected to small or zero bending moments are to be designed for a minimum eccentricity equal to 0.05 and 0.10 times the overall depth of the section for spiral and tied columns, respectively. This article develops an approximate procedure to expedite the designing of such rectangular tied sections; in Art. 5–17 we develop a similar procedure for round, spiral columns with minimum eccentricity.

[3] According to Reference 6, this is based on the assumption that the initial crookedness of the real column has a single-curvature shape.

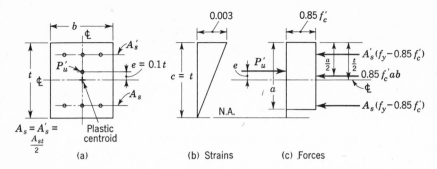

Fig. 5–25. Symmetrical rectangular tied column with minimum eccentricity.

The procedure described here involves finding approximately an increased fictitious, equivalent centric load, which is so obtained that if it is used for designing a centrically loaded section, the resulting section will have the required capacity associated with the ACI minimum eccentricity.

Consider a rectangular tied column section bt having equal areas of reinforcement A_s and A'_s at the two opposite faces, $A_s = A'_s = A_{st}/2$, as shown in Fig. 5–25a. This section is to have an ideal, short-column capacity equal to P'_u at an eccentricity $e = 0.10t$. Let P'_0 be the ideal, short-column capacity of the same section if it were loaded truly centrically.

To find the relation between P'_u and P'_0, the following assumptions are made for the section being loaded with the minimum eccentricity of $0.10t$:

1. The strain diagram is a single triangle covering the entire depth of the section. That is, the neutral axis distance $c = t$, as shown in Fig. 5–25b, and the stress block depth $a = k_1 c = k_1 t$. For the minimum eccentricity of $0.10t$ considered, this assumption is nearly correct, as may be verified for any rectangular section (for instance, see Fig. 4–17 for a typical example).
2. Both A'_s and A_s have yielded. For A'_s, this assumption is valid, whereas for A_s it is not correct, as the strains in A_s are likely to be small in view of the assumed triangular strain distribution.
3. A_s lies within the stress block depth a.

Based on these assumptions, the forces on the section will then be as shown in Fig. 5–25c, in which the concrete area in compression displaced by the reinforcement is taken into account. Summing up the forces, one obtains:

$$P'_u = 0.85f'_c ab + A'_s(f_y - 0.85f'_c) + A_s(f_y - 0.85f'_c)$$

or,

$$P'_u = 0.85f'_c(k_1 t)b + A_{st}(f_y - 0.85f'_c) \qquad (1)$$

Summing up the moments of the forces about the plastic centroid and assuming equal lever arms for the forces in A'_s and A_s, one gets:

$$P'_u e = 0.85 f'_c ab \left(\frac{t}{2} - \frac{a}{2} \right)$$

or,

$$P'_u (0.10t) = \tfrac{1}{2}(0.85 f'_c)(k_1 t) b(t - k_1 t) \qquad (2)$$

Now, if the same section were loaded centrically, its capacity would be

$$P'_0 = 0.85 f'_c bt + A_{st}(f_y - 0.85 f'_c) \qquad (3)$$

Combining Eqs. 1 and 2, one gets

$$A_{st}(f_y - 0.85 f'_c) = P'_u - 0.85 f'_c k_1 bt = \frac{1}{0.1t} \frac{0.85 f'_c k_1 bt}{2}(t - k_1 t) - 0.85 f'_c k_1 bt$$

$$= 0.85 f'_c k_1 bt[5(1 - k_1) - 1] = 0.85 f'_c k_1 bt(4 - 5k_1) \qquad (4)$$

Substitution of this expression in Eq. 3 yields

$$P'_0 = 0.85 f'_c bt + 0.85 f'_c k_1 bt(4 - 5k_1)$$
$$= 0.85 f'_c k_1 bt[(1/k_1) + (4 - 5k_1)]$$

and

$$P'_u = 0.85 f'_c k_1 bt + 0.85 f'_c k_1 bt(4 - 5k_1)$$
$$= 0.85 f'_c k_1 bt(5 - 5k_1)$$

Dividing P'_0 by P'_u and letting the ratio be B, one gets:

$$B = \frac{P'_0}{P'_u} = \frac{(1/k_1) + 4 - 5k_1}{5(1 - k_1)} \qquad (5)$$

This quantity B may be considered as a sort of magnification factor which, when multiplied by the required capacity P'_u at the minimum eccentricity of $0.10t$, gives the required equivalent centric load capacity P'_0. According to Eq. 5, B is a function of k_1 which in turn is a function of f'_c. For f'_c of 4, 5, and 6 ksi, k_1 is 0.85, 0.80, and 0.75, and B is 1.24, 1.25, and 1.27, respectively. Hence as a function of f'_c, B varies only over a very narrow range, and averages to 1.25.

On the other hand, the theoretically correct B must be also a function of f_y, p_t (the total steel percentage), and gt (the distance between the two rows of reinforcement). In the derivation of Eq. 5, these factors have been ignored. Assumption 2 corresponds to A_s being stressed to f_y, whereas its actual stress may be much smaller. Accordingly, the theoretically correct value of B is likely to be a bit larger than the approximate value of 1.25 for higher f_y and larger p_t. A little reflection will show that the value of B tends to decrease with increase of the value of g. An examination of available interaction curves for rectangular sections with reinforcement at two faces reveals that, for the range of f_y from 40 to 60 ksi, $p_t m$ ($m = f_y/0.85f'_c$) from 0 to 1.0, and g from 0.6 to 0.9, the theoretically correct B ranges from 1.22 to 1.29 and, within this range, tends to increase with increasing f_y, increasing $p_t m$, and decreasing g. It seems then that a conservative yet simple value of B for practical design is 1.30 unless f_y should exceed 60 ksi significantly.

The same idea may be extended to rectangular sections with reinforcement distributed near four faces. A similar examination of available interaction curves for such sections shows a range of B from 1.25 to 1.35 with similar tendency in its variation as a function of f_y, $p_t m$, and g. Hence a practical value of B will be conservatively 1.35 for many cases with f_y not exceeding 60 ksi.

The value of B recommended above may appear to be crude and arbitrary, but it gives satisfactory results. In any event, its use is merely to expedite design, and once a section has been chosen based on the equivalent centric load, it should be investigated to see if it indeed furnishes the required capacity at the minimum ACI eccentricity. An example is given below.

EXAMPLE 5–5

Given a *laterally braced* column having an unsupported length of 10 ft. and undergoing *double-curvature* bending under *service* axial loads of 400 kips dead, 250 kips live, and a bending moment of 60 kip-ft. live. Take 4000-lb. concrete and 60,000-psi-yield-point steel.

Required to design a square tied column (a) with reinforcement near two faces; (b) with reinforcement distributed near four faces. In either case, the reinforcement is to be centered 3 in. from the nearest face.

Solution. Applying the ACI load factors, the *load-factored* ultimate load and moment are:

	Axial load	Moment
Dead	1.5(400) = 600	
Live	1.8(250) = 450	1.8(60) = 108
Total	P_{uf} = 1050 kips	M_{uf} = 108 kip-ft.

Eccentricity $e = 108(12)/1050 = 1.23$ in.

Assuming an 18-in. depth, the radius of gyration is $r \cong 0.3t = 0.3(18) = 5.4$ in., and minimum eccentricity $e = 0.1(18) = 1.8$ in., which is larger than the computed e of 1.23 in. Therefore the column is to be designed for minimum e.

For failure controlled by compression without sidesway, the effective length $h' = h = 10$ ft. (see Table 5–1), and $h'/r = (10)(12)/5.4 = 22.2$, which is smaller than than 60. Hence, according to Table 5–1, the strength reduction factor R for slenderness is 1.0 for double-curvature bending.

The required *slender-column* capacity at minimum eccentricity, $P_{u,sl}$, is set equal to P_{uf}, or 1050 kips. Hence the required *ideal, short-column* capacity is

$$P'_u = P_{u,sl}/\phi R = 1050/(0.7)(1) = 1500 \text{ kips}$$

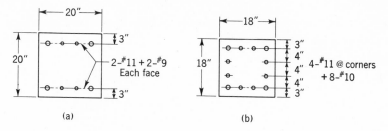

Fig. 5–26. Columns of Example 5–5.

(a) **Design with reinforcement near two faces.** Adopting $B = 1.30$, the required equivalent centric load capacity is

$$P'_0 = BP'_u = 1.30(1500) = 1950 \text{ kips}$$

Now, design a section for this load applied centrically. It can be verified that an 18-in. square section will result in overcrowding the bars at two faces. *Try a 20-in. square section.* This will change h'/r, but R remains at 1.0. The force on the concrete area $= 0.85f'_c bt = 0.85(4)(20)(20) = 1360$ kips. The force to be carried by reinforcement $= 1950 - 1360 = 590$ kips.

At an effective steel stress of $(f_y - 0.85f'_c) = 60 - 0.85(4) = 56.6$ ksi, the required total steel area is $A_{st} = 590/56.6 = 10.43$ sq. in., or $A_s = A'_s = 5.22$ sq. in.

Try 2–$\#11 + 2$–$\#9 = 5.12$ sq. in. each face, as shown in Fig. 5–26a. Upon investigation, it can be shown that for the minimum eccentricity $e = 2$ in., the neutral axis $c = 20.62$ in., A'_s has yielded and A_s has not, and the ideal, short-column capacity furnished by the section is

$$P'_u = 1542 \text{ kips}$$

which when multiplied by ϕ and R gives the slender-column capacity of the section chosen at the minimum e as

$$P_{u,sl} = 1542(0.7)(1.0) = 1080 \text{ kips}$$

This is slightly larger than the load-factored P_{uf} of 1050 kips. Hence the section chosen is satisfactory.

<u>Use 20 in. square column, 2–#11 + 2–#9 each face.</u>　<u>Ans.</u>

(b) **Design with reinforcement near four faces.** Adopting a value of B of 1.35,

$$P'_0 = 1.35(1500) = 2025 \text{ kips}$$

Try an 18-in. square section.

Force on the concrete area $= 0.85(4)(18)(18) = 1102$ kips
Force to be carried by reinforcement $= 2025 - 1102 = 923$ kips
Required steel area, $A_{st} = 923/56.6 = 16.31$ sq. in.

Try 4–$\#11 + 8$–$\#10 = 16.40$ sq. in., as shown in Fig. 5–26b. It may be verified that at the minimum $e = 1.8$ in., the neutral axis distance is $c = 18.03$ in., and the ideal, short-column capacity of the section is $P'_u = 1545$ kips. The corresponding slender-column capacity is $P_{u,sl} = 1545(0.7)(1.0) = 1082$ kips. This is slightly larger than the load-factored P_{uf} of 1050 kips; hence the section chosen is satisfactory.

<u>Use 18 in. square column, 4–#11 + 8–#10</u>　<u>Ans.</u>

5-17. DESIGN OF A CIRCULAR SPIRAL COLUMN FOR ACI MINIMUM ECCENTRICITY

The idea presented in Art. 5–16 of finding an equivalent centric load to expedite the design of a rectangular tied column for minimum eccentricity may be extended to circular spiral columns, the only difference being that the ACI minimum eccentricity for spiral columns is 0.05 times the overall depth.

For the circular section subjected to P'_u applied eccentrically at $e = 0.05D$ as shown in Fig. 5–27a, the same assumptions as in Art. 5–16 are made, namely: (1) the strain distribution is triangular as shown in (b); (2) all reinforcement has yielded; (3) all reinforcement lies within the stress block depth. The stress block acts over a circular segment of area A with its centroid at $\bar{y}$ from the center of the section, as shown in (a).

Based on these assumptions, the forces on the section are as shown in (c). Equilibrium of the forces requires

$$P'_u = 0.85 f'_c A + A_{sf}(f_y - 0.85 f'_c) \tag{1}$$

and taking moments about the center of the section,

$$P'_u(0.05D) = 0.85 f'_c A \bar{y} \tag{2}$$

Now, if there were no eccentricity, the centric load capacity of the section would be

$$P'_0 = 0.85 f'_c A_g + A_{st}(f_y - 0.85 f'_c) \tag{3}$$

in which A_g is the gross area of the entire section.

It may be shown that by similar operations on Eqs. 1 through 3 to those described in Art. 5–16, the factor B is given by

$$B = \frac{P'_0}{P'_u} = \frac{0.05\left(\dfrac{A_g}{A} - 1\right) + \dfrac{\bar{y}}{D}}{\dfrac{\bar{y}}{D}} \tag{4}$$

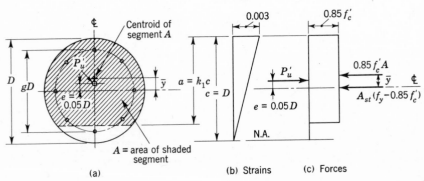

Fig. 5–27. Circular spiral column with minimum eccentricity.

For f'_c of 4, 5, and 6 ksi, k_1 is 0.85, 0.80, 0.75; A is $0.712D^2$, $0.674D^2$, $0.632D^2$; and $\bar{y}$ is $0.0427D$, $0.0633D$, and $0.0857D$, respectively.[4] Equation 4 then gives the value of B respectively as 1.12, 1.13 and 1.14, indicating that as a function of f'_c, B varies within a very narrow range. However, here again, it should be mentioned that Eq. 4 is not theoretically correct, and in this connection, the comments given in Art. 5–16 apply. The correct B tends to be increasingly larger for higher f_y, larger p_t, and smaller g. A survey of interaction curves for circular spiral columns shows that for the range of f_y from 40 to 60 ksi, $p_t m$ ($m = f_y/ 0.85f'_c$) from 0 to 1.0, and g from 0.6 to 0.9, the correct B ranges from 1.12 to 1.21. A good, simple value of B to use seems to be 1.20 for f_y up to 60 ksi.

EXAMPLE 5–6

Given a *laterally braced* column having an unsupported length of 10 ft. and subjected to *service* axial loads of 500 kips dead and 300 kips live, with zero computed bending moment. Take 4000-lb. concrete and 60,000-psi-yield-point steel.

Required to design a circular spiral column with longitudinal reinforcement centered on a circle 3 in. inside the circumference.

Solution. Applying the ACI load factors:

$$P_{uf} = 1.5(500) + 1.8(300) = 1290 \text{ kips}$$

There being no moment, the required slender-column capacity at the minimum $e = 0.05D$ is 1290 kips. Section 916(c)2 requires the column to be designed for the laterally braced, single-curvature bending case, for which $R = 1.07 - 0.008(h'/r)$ for failure controlled by compression (see Table 5–1).

Try 18-in. round. $h' = h = 10$ ft., $r = 0.25D = 0.25(18) = 4.5$ in.

$$h'/r = 10(12)/4.5 = 26.7$$
$$R = 1.07 - 0.008(26.7) = 0.86, \quad \text{and} \quad \phi = 0.75$$

Hence the required ideal, short-column capacity is

$$P'_u = 1290/(0.75)(0.86) = 2000 \text{ kips}$$

and the required equivalent centric load capacity, using a value of $B = 1.20$, is

$$P'_0 = 1.20(2000) = 2400 \text{ kips}$$

Gross area of concrete $A_g = (\pi/4)(18)(18) = 254.5$ sq. in., and the force on this area is $0.85f'_c A_g = 0.85(4)(254.5) = 865$ kips. This leaves $(2400 - 865) = 1535$ kips for the reinforcement, which is stressed to $(f_y - 0.85f'_c) = 60 - 0.85(4) = 56.6$ ksi. Hence the required $A_{st} = 1535/56.6 = 27.10$ sq. in., and the corresponding steel percentage $= 27.10/254.5 = 10.7$ per cent, which is far too high. <u>N.G.</u>

Try 24-in. round. $r = 0.25(24) = 6$ in., $h'/r = 10(12)/6 = 20.0$.

$$R = 1.07 - 0.008(20.0) = 0.91 \text{ and } \phi = 0.75 \text{ as before}$$

---

[4] The properties of circular segments are given in Appendix C, Chart C–5.

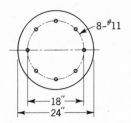

Fig. 5–28.   Example 5–6.

Hence $P'_u = 1290/(0.75)(0.91) = 1890$ kips, and the required equivalent centric load capacity is

$$P'_0 = 1.20(1890) = 2268 \text{ kips}$$
$$A_g = (\pi/4)(24)(24) = 452.4 \text{ sq. in.}$$
$$0.85f'_c A_g = 0.85(4)(452.4) = 1538 \text{ kips}$$
$$\text{Force in steel} = 2268 - 1538 = 730 \text{ kips}$$
$$\text{Required steel area} = 730/56.6 = 13.0 \text{ sq. in.}$$

Try 8–#11 = 12.48 sq. in., as shown in Fig. 5–28. It may be verified that, at the minimum eccentricity $e = 0.05(24) = 1.2$ in., the section has a neutral axis distance c of 25.40 in., and the corresponding ideal, short-column capacity furnished is $P'_u = 1962$ kips, which, when multiplied by $\phi R = (0.75)(0.91)$, gives a furnished slender-column capacity $P_{u,sl} = 1339$ kips. This is slightly larger than the load-factored P_{uf} of 1290 kips; hence the section designed is satisfactory.

Use 24-in. round, 8–#11.   Ans.

SLENDER-COLUMN DESIGN PROBLEMS

5–4. Design a *laterally braced*, square tied column with reinforcement distributed along the four faces and centered $2\frac{1}{2}$ in. therefrom. It is subjected to *service* axial loads of 200 kips dead, and 150 kips live, with no computed bending moment. Design for minimum eccentricity and consider the bending pattern as being single-curvature. Take 5000-lb. concrete, 50,000-psi-yield-point steel, and $h = 10$ ft.

5–5. Same data as in Problem 5–4, but design a circular spiral column to match.

5–18. RECTANGULAR COLUMNS SUBJECTED TO HEAVY BENDING— APPROXIMATE PROCEDURE FOR DESIGNING OF REINFORCEMENT NEAR TWO BENDING FACES

This article presents a procedure for designing the reinforcement near the bending faces of a rectangular column which is subject to heavy bending. The method involves the idea of **axial load transfer**. In it, the eccentric load is initially "transferred" to the position of the tensile reinforcement; that is, it is imagined to be replaced by its statical equivalent: the combination of a bending moment about, and an axial load through, the centroid of the tensile reinforcement. The designing consists in first considering the bending moment alone, and determining the areas of reinforcement at the two bending faces of the section as for a doubly reinforced beam. Then, the axial load alone is considered, and is assumed to stress solely and compressively the reinforcement near the face which was in tension due to the moment alone. The combination of the steel areas found for the two cases is assumed to yield the final required steel areas.

The load-transfer part of the procedure is theoretically legitimate whereas the designing part is only approximate, and its accuracy deteriorates with decreasing eccentricity of the load. However, for columns subject to heavy bending, it works quite well. For columns subject to light to moderate bending, it is *not* recommended. In any event, an investigation should properly follow the designing. In subsequent articles a theoretically correct, flexible and more sophisticated procedure, called the Mörsch procedure, will be described. It is applicable to rectangular sections with reinforcement near two opposite faces and subject to either light or heavy bending.

EXAMPLE 5–7

Given an 18-in. square column which is to have an *ideal, short-column* capacity, P'_u, equal to 215 kips total, acting at 19 in. from the center line of the section. Take 4000-lb. concrete and 50,000-psi-yield-point steel.

Required to design the reinforcement, to be centered $2\frac{1}{2}$ in. from the two bending faces.

Solution. *Axial load transfer.* Referring to Fig. 5–29a, the axial load of 215 kips is transferred to the centroid of A_s plus a moment equal to 215(25.5) or 5483 kip-in.

Designing double-reinforcement for 5483 kip-in. Referring to Fig. 5–29b, first find the single flexural reinforcement area A_1. To preclude compression failure, this steel percentage is not to exceed the ACI maximum, which is equal to 0.75 times the balanced steel percentage [Sec. 1601(b)], or

$$0.75\left(0.85k_1\frac{f'_c}{f_y}\frac{87,000}{87,000+f_y}\right) = 0.75(0.85)(0.85)\left(\frac{4}{50}\right)\left(\frac{87}{87+50}\right) = 2.75\%$$

Therefore $A_1 = 2.75\%(18)(15.5) = 7.67$ sq. in.

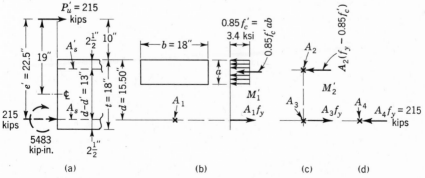

Fig. 5–29. Rectangular column subject to heavy bending.

The tensile steel force is

$$T'_1 = A_1 f_y = 7.67(50) = 384 \text{ kips}$$

The stress block depth is

$$a = 384/(0.85f'_c b)$$
$$= 384/(3.4)(18) = 6.27 \text{ in.}$$

The resisting moment is

$$M'_1 = 384\left(15.5 - \frac{6.27}{2}\right) = 4747 \text{ kip-in.}$$

The remaining moment is

$$M'_2 = 5483 - 4747 = 736 \text{ kip-in.}$$

Steel couple. To account for the compression concrete area displaced by the compression reinforcement, the area A_2 is stressed to $(f_y - 0.85f'_c)$ whereas the area A_3, being in the tension zone, is stressed to f_y, as shown in (c). Hence, A_2 and A_3 are not equal unless the effect of the displaced concrete is ignored.

$$A_2 = \frac{M'_2}{(d - d')(f_y - 0.85f'_c)} = \frac{736}{(46.6)(13)} = 1.22 \text{ sq. in.}$$
$$A_3 = \frac{M'_2}{f_y(d - d')} = \frac{736}{(50)(13)} = 1.13 \text{ sq. in.}$$

Effect of axial load: Figure 5–29d shows that the tensile steel equivalent of the 215-kip load is

$$A_4 = {}^{215}\!/_{50} = 4.30 \text{ sq. in.}$$

Hence, the final steel areas are

$$A'_s \text{ in "top"} = A_2 = 1.22 \text{ sq. in.}$$
$$A_s \text{ in "bottom"} = A_1 + A_3 - A_4 = 4.50 \text{ sq. in.}$$

Use 3–#6 in "top" and 2–#10 + 2–#9 in "bottom" (Fig. 5–30).   **Ans.**

Investigation: Using a procedure similar to Example 4–6, it may be shown that for the reinforcement designed, with $e' = 25.50$ in., the section has an *ideal, short-*

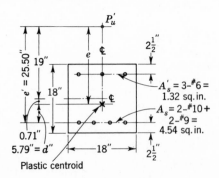

Fig. 5–30. Example 5–7.

column capacity

$$P'_u = 217 \text{ kips} \qquad \text{(furnished)}$$

for which the neutral axis distance is $c = 7.35$ in. and all steel has yielded. This capacity compares satisfactorily with the required 215 kips.

Comments. (1) For cases of large eccentricities, economy usually dictates an unsymmetrical arrangement of the reinforcement. However, as long as heavy bending is present, the procedure may also be used for designing symmetrical reinforcement, as illustrated in the following article, and indeed for designing some unsymmetrical arrangement other than that in the present example.

(2) In order not to obscure the main issue involved in this example, it was merely stated that the section was to have an *ideal, short-column* capacity P'_u of 215 kips. This value was actually precalculated on the basis of certain data which were deliberately withheld temporarily, and which may now be given together with the additional calculations as follows:

Additional data. At the eccentricity indicated previously, the *service* axial loads are 19 kips dead, and 55 kips live, and for the 18-in. dimensions given, the reduction factor for slenderness $R = 0.8$ if compression should govern failure.

Additional calculations. The *load-factored* value of the column load is

$$P_{uf} = 1.5(19) + 1.8(55) = 128 \text{ kips}$$

The true eccentricity e of this load referred to the plastic centroid is not exactly the same as the given distance of 19 in. except for symmetrical reinforcement, but is likely to have the same order of magnitude. Since the eccentricity is large, it is reasonable to assume that tension controls failure, for which case the reduction factor for slenderness is given approximately by Eq. 5–3a as:

$$R' = 1 - (1 - R)(e_b/e) \qquad \text{not to exceed 1.0} \qquad (5\text{--}3a)$$

where e_b is the *balanced* eccentricity and e is the eccentricity of the given loading. But both e_b and e are not known prior to the designing of the reinforcement. So, to get the designing started, R' is estimated to be about 0.85; this is slightly smaller than the average of the given R of 0.8 for compression failure and the value of 1.0 for the case of pure flexure. Assuming that the understrength factor ϕ remains at the nominal value of 0.7 for tied columns (which is equivalent to assuming that the prevailing eccentricity is not large enough to bring Sec. 1901(c) of the ACI Code into force),[5] the required *ideal, short-column* capacity is:

$$P'_u = P_{uf}/(\phi R') = 128/(0.7)(0.85) = 215 \text{ kips}, \text{ } estimated$$

This value is the same as that which was *posed* as given information, but in reality is no better than an estimate. Accordingly, after the tentative designing has been done, resulting in the reinforcement as shown in Fig. 5–30, the value of R' is to be recomputed, the assumption regarding Sec. 1901(c) is to be verified, and finally, the furnished *slender-column capacity* of the section is to be evaluated and compared with the *load-factored* P_{uf}.

By calculations similar to those of Example 4–2 for centric loading, Example 4–3 for pure flexure, and Example 4–7 for balanced failure, the section having the

---

[5] The reader is referred to the extended discussions in Arts. 5–8 through 5–13 for clarification on the complications engendered by Sec. 1901(c) in the tension failure zones of column interaction diagrams.

Table 5–3. Column Investigation, Example 5–7

Point in Fig. 5–31	Loading	Eccentricity, e, in.	Neutral Axis Distance, c, in.	A'_s Yields	A_s Yields	P'_u, kips	M'_u, kip-ft.
—	Centric	0	∞	Yes	Yes	P.C. 0.71 in. below ℄ $d'' = 5.79$ in.	
B'	Balanced	e_b, 13.25	9.84	Yes	Yes	P'_b, 346	M'_b, 4586
Q'	Given	19.71	7.35	Yes	Yes	217	4277
C'	Pure flexure	∞	3.72	No	Yes	0	M'_0, 3129

tentatively chosen reinforcement of Fig. 5–30 may be investigated, and the results obtained (together with those previously obtained for the prevailing loading), all computed on the *ideal, short-column* basis, are as shown in Table 5–3.

Although a graphical solution is not being sought here, Fig. 5–31 serves to clarify subsequent calculations. Curve $B'Q'C'$ represents the ideal, short-column interaction relation. It is desired to proceed from Q' to Q on the dependable short-column curve, and thence to q on the slender-column curve. To find whether Q is affected by the "intrusion" of Sec. 1901(c), which is represented by the vertical DE:

$$D \text{ or } E: 0.9M'_0 = 0.9(3129) = 2816 \text{ kip-in.}$$
$$Q: 0.7M'_u = 0.7(4277) = 2994 \text{ kip-in.}$$

Hence Q is above and to the right of DE, and is not affected by Sec. 1901(c), and ϕ remains at 0.7 as assumed.

The slenderness effect is given by

$$R' = 1 - (1 - R)(e_b/e) = 1 - (1 - 0.8)(13.25/19.71) = 0.87$$

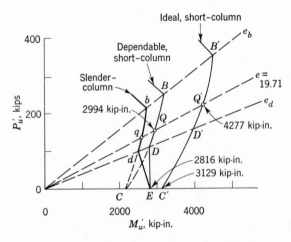

Fig. 5–31. Tension failure zone of interaction diagram—Example 5–7.

Therefore, the slender-column capacity at $e = 19.71$ in. (represented by point q) is

$$P_{u,sl} = P'_u(\phi R') = 217(0.7)(0.87) = 132 \text{ kips} > P_{uf} \text{ of } 128 \text{ kips} \qquad \text{O.K.}$$

5–19. RECTANGULAR COLUMNS SUBJECTED TO HEAVY BENDING— APPROXIMATE PROCEDURE FOR DESIGNING REINFORCEMENT NEAR TWO BENDING FACES, WITH VARIATIONS

The reinforcement determined ($A'_s = 1.22$ and $A_s = 4.50$ sq. in., totaling 5.72 sq. in.) for the required capacity P'_u of 215 kips in Example 5–7 is by no means the only solution. It is possible to obtain other solutions by varying the initial tensile steel amount A_1 from 7.67 sq. in., and proceeding in precisely the same fashion. For instance, the following calculations yield equally valid results (within the limitation imposed by the approximate nature of the procedure), disregarding the question of economy in the reinforcement.

Case 1—nearly symmetrical reinforcement. Suppose the initial tensile steel amount A_1 is made exactly equal to A_4, the "tensile steel equivalent" of the 215-kip compressive load, that is,

$$A_1 = A_4 = 4.30 \text{ sq. in.}$$

Then, in the singly-reinforced part,

Tensile steel force, $T'_1 = 4.30(50) = 215$ kips
Stress block depth, $a = 215/(0.85)(4)(18) = 3.51$ in.

$$\text{Resisting moment, } M'_1 = 215\left(15.5 - \frac{3.51}{2}\right) = 2954 \text{ kip-in.}$$

Remaining moment, $M'_2 = 5483 - 2954 = 2529$ kip-in.

In the steel couple,

$$A_2 = 2529/(13)[50 - 0.85(4)] = 4.17 \text{ sq. in. in top}$$
$$A_3 = 2529/(13)(50) \qquad\qquad = 3.89 \text{ sq. in. in bottom}$$

Hence, the final reinforcement areas are

$$A'_s = A_2 \qquad\qquad\qquad = 4.17 \text{ sq. in. in top}$$
$$A_s = A_1 + A_3 - A_4 = A_3 = \underline{3.89 \text{ sq. in. in bottom}}$$
$$\text{Total } A_{st} = \underline{8.06 \text{ sq. in.}} \qquad \text{Ans.}$$

Comments. (a) The slight dissymmetry in the above reinforcement stems from the effect of the displaced concrete area by compression reinforcement. If this effect were ignored, symmetry would result, and all the areas A_2, A_4, A_s, and A'_s would each equal 3.89 sq. in. It is possible, as illustrated in Case 2 given below, to obtain symmetry without discarding this effect, as is consistent with all of our column calculations.

(b) The pattern of dissymmetry in the foregoing reinforcement (heavier compressive steel than tensile steel) is just opposite to that in Example 5–7. This is seen to result in larger total steel area. In general, for heavy bending, economy in steel weight is obtained with the pattern of dissymmetry of Example 5–7, and it worsens as this pattern changes and switches over, through the one of symmetry, to that obtained herein. This will be demonstrated in Case 2 which follows.

Case 2—symmetrical reinforcement. If it is desired to obtain symmetry in the reinforcement, yet still retaining the effect of displaced concrete by the compression steel, one needs only adjust slightly the initial tensile steel area A_1 from its value of 4.30 sq. in. of Case 1. The proper amount of A_1 may be obtained, if desired, by a formal approach (not shown here), in which A_1 as an unknown is substituted in all the expressions similar to the numerical manipulations, resulting finally in a quadratic equation, whereby A_1 may be solved explicitly. However, a trial-and-error solution is just as efficient.

An examination of Example 5–7 and Case 1 will show that the correct A_1 to yield symmetry in the final steel content should be slightly larger than 4.30 sq. in. of Case 1. A first-trial A_1-value may then be assumed, and calculations similar to those of Case 1 can be performed, and repeated for successively revised A_1-values, until the desired symmetry of final reinforcement is attained. Table 5–4 summarizes the results so obtained, starting with trial $A_1 = 4.50$.

The last line of Table 5–4 gives a close-enough symmetry in the reinforcement. Hence: Use 4–#9 in top and in bottom.   Ans.

It may be verified, in the manner of Example 5–7, that the section with this reinforcement has an *ideal, short-column* capacity of $P'_u = 216$ kips at the eccentricity e of 19 in. (as compared with the estimated value of 215 kips). Also, with the balanced eccentricity, $e_b = 9.98$ in., R' may be

Table 5–4. Alternate Solutions to Example 5–7

Singly Reinforced					Steel Couple		Tensile Steel Equivalent of Axial Load	Final Reinforcement	
Tensile Steel A_1	Tensile Steel Force T'_1	Stress Block Depth a	Resisting Moment M'_1	Remaining Moment M'_2	Top A_2	Bottom A_3	A_4	Top $A'_s = A_2$	Bottom $A_s = A_1 + A_3 - A_4$
4.50	225	3.68	3074	2409	3.98	3.71 ⎫		⎧ 3.98	3.91
4.54	227	3.71	3099	2384	3.94	3.67 ⎬ 4.30		⎨ 3.94	3.91
4.58	229	3.74	3121	2362	3.90	3.63 ⎭		⎩ 3.90	3.91

found to be 0.90; Sec. 1901(c) will be found to be inapplicable, and hence ϕ remains at 0.7. Accordingly, the furnished *slender-column* capacity of the section is $P_{u,sl} = 136$ kips, versus the load-factored P_{uf} of 128 kips.

HEAVY BENDING DESIGN PROBLEMS

5–6. This problem is the same as Example 5–7 except that the *service* axial loads are 10 kips dead, 35 kips live, acting at 36 in. from the centerline of the section. Find the unsymmetrical reinforcement as in Example 5–7. (*Hint:* Due to the much larger eccentricity, Sec. 1901(c) of the ACI Code may come into play, and also, the slenderness strength reduction factor R' is likely to be larger than in that example.)

5–7. A 16-in. square tied column is eccentrically loaded 4 in. outside one face thereof. The column is to have an *ideal, short-column* capacity, associated with this eccentricity, equal to 200 kips. It is required to calculate the necessary symmetrical reinforcement, centered $2\frac{1}{2}$ in. from the bending faces. Take 3000-lb. concrete and 50,000-psi-yield-point steel.

5–20. MÖRSCH PROCEDURE FOR DESIGNING REINFORCEMENT NEAR TWO BENDING FACES OF RECTANGULAR COLUMNS— INTRODUCTION

The axial load transfer procedure of Arts. 5–18 and 5–19 for designing rectangular columns with reinforcement near their two bending faces is approximate, and works satisfactorily only for columns subject to heavy bending. As was pointed out therein, there is nothing wrong with replacing an eccentric load by an axial load through, and a moment about, the centroid of the tensile steel since the two force systems are statically equivalent. Actually, the eccentric load may be similarly "transferred" to some point other than the centroid of the tensile steel. However, in the *designing* phase of that procedure, errors were introduced, in that the transferred axial load was assumed to be resisted entirely by the tensile steel, and that the final steel amounts were assumed to be the simple algebraic sum of this steel amount and those required for the transferred bending moment alone. Strictly speaking, these assumptions violate the equilibrium conditions for all the external and internal forces on the column section although the errors are small for large eccentricities of the load. Moreover, it was assumed therein that all the reinforcement had yielded, which may not always be valid. Therefore, it was emphasized that the design procedure of Arts. 5–18 and 5–19 should be used for heavy bending only, and the results subjected to an investigation.

A theoretically correct procedure is that originated by Mörsch [7], and later extended and improved upon by Chambaud and Lebelle [8]. An English description thereof first appeared in the book by Granholm [9]. Hereafter referred to as the Mörsch procedure, it is very simple to use and offers great flexibility in designing. The practicing engineer will find it easily adaptable to the construction of design charts.

The description of the Mörsch procedure presented here differs from the original version in that the latter was aimed primarily to effect a graphical solution, whereas here, while retaining essentially the same basic ideas, the treatment is analytical. The graphical means is used solely to clarify the exposition qualitatively. Also, the original version considers only the case of tension existing over part of a column section, whereas here, consideration has been extended to include additionally the case of compression over the entire cross section. Thus the procedure may be applied to the entire range of light through heavy bending cases. The effect of the concrete area displaced by compression reinforcement, ignored in the original treatment, is included here. The following articles contain the details of the Mörsch procedure, using a notation more in accord with the usage in this country.

5–21. MÖRSCH PROCEDURE—CASE I: TENSION OVER PART OF THE CROSS SECTION

This article presents the Mörsch procedure for heavy through moderate bending cases in which tension exists over part of the cross section under consideration. It should be noted that failure of such a section may be controlled by either tension or compression depending on the eccentricity of the load. (See Fig. 4–17 for examples of typical situations that fall into this category.)

Consider a rectangular section b by t having reinforcements A_s and A'_s, and subjected to an eccentric load P'_u on the ideal, short-column level as shown in Fig. 5–32. The eccentricity of the load is e from the plastic centroid (P.C.), e' from the centroid of A_s, and e'' from the centroid of A'_s. (Note that e'' is positive as shown; that is, if P'_u is between A'_s and P.C., e'' becomes negative.) The problem is to determine the required amounts

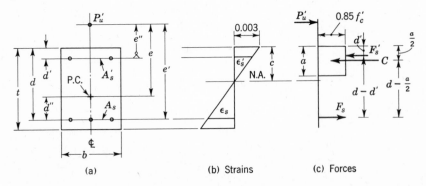

(a)   (b) Strains   (c) Forces

Fig. 5–32. Mörsch procedure—Case I: Tension over part of the cross section.

of A_s and A'_s, all other data being given and b, t, d, and d' being known or assumed.

Strains.   From the geometry of the strain diagram shown in Fig. 5–32b, the steel strains may be found to be:

$$\left.\begin{array}{l} \text{Compression steel strain, } \epsilon'_s = 0.003 \left(\dfrac{c - d'}{c}\right) \\[2mm] \text{Tension steel strain, } \qquad \epsilon_s = 0.003 \left(\dfrac{d - c}{c}\right) \end{array}\right\} \qquad \text{(I)}$$

Forces.   The external load P'_u and the resisting forces of the section are as shown in Fig. 5–32c.   If the stresses in A'_s and A_s are respectively f'_s and f_s, and if the effect of concrete area displaced by A'_s is considered, the resisting forces are:

$$\left.\begin{array}{ll} \text{Compressive force in concrete, } & C = 0.85f'_c ab \\ \text{Compressive force in } A'_s, & F'_s = A'_s(f'_s - 0.85f'_c) \\ \text{Tensile force in } A_s, & F_s = A_s f_s \end{array}\right\} \qquad \text{(II)}$$

Now, introduce two *steel factors*, r'_s and r_s, which are defined as follows:

$$\left.\begin{array}{l} r'_s = \dfrac{A'_s}{bd}\dfrac{f'_s - 0.85f'_c}{0.85f'_c} = p'\dfrac{f'_s - 0.85f_c}{0.85f_c} \\[3mm] r_s = \dfrac{A_s}{bd}\dfrac{f_s}{0.85f'_c} \qquad = p\dfrac{f_s}{0.85f'_c} \end{array}\right\} \qquad \text{(5–5)}$$

in which $p' = A'_s/bd$ and $p = A_s/bd$, as defined in the usual way.

The expressions for the resisting forces may now be rewritten as

$$\left.\begin{array}{ll} \text{Compressive force in concrete, } & C = 0.85f'_c ab \\ \text{Compressive force in } A'_s, & F'_s = 0.85f'_c r'_s bd \\ \text{Tensile force in } A_s, & F_s = 0.85f'_c r_s bd \end{array}\right\} \qquad \text{(5–6)}$$

Equilibrium.   The conditions of equilibrium for all the forces on the section may be stated in various ways.   Instead of the usual force equilibrium equation plus a moment equilibrium equation, equilibrium may be specified by two moment equations referred to the centroids of A_s and A'_s, respectively.   Thus,

Moments about A_s:

$$\begin{aligned} M_s = P'_u e' &= C\left(d - \frac{a}{2}\right) + F'_s(d - d') \\[2mm] &= 0.85f'_c ab\left(d - \frac{a}{2}\right) + 0.85f'_c r'_s bd(d - d') \\[2mm] &= 0.85f'_c bd^2\left[\frac{a}{d}\left(1 - \frac{1}{2}\frac{a}{d}\right) + r'_s\left(1 - \frac{d'}{d}\right)\right] \qquad \text{(III)} \end{aligned}$$

Moments about A'_s:

$$M'_s = P'_u e'' = F_s(d - d') - C\left(\frac{a}{2} - d'\right)$$

$$= 0.85f'_c r_s bd(d - d') - 0.85f'_c ab\left(\frac{a}{2} - d'\right)$$

$$= 0.85f'_c bd^2\left[r_s\left(1 - \frac{d'}{d}\right) - \frac{a}{d}\left(\frac{1}{2}\frac{a}{d} - \frac{d'}{d}\right)\right] \qquad \text{(IV)}$$

Dividing both sides of the foregoing equations by $(0.85f'_c bd^2)$ and introducing the symbols K_s and K'_s, one obtains

$$\frac{M_s}{0.85f'_c bd^2} = \frac{P'_u e'}{0.85f'_c bd^2} = K_s = r'_s\left(1 - \frac{d'}{d}\right) + \frac{a}{d}\left(1 - \frac{1}{2}\frac{a}{d}\right) \qquad \text{(5-7a)}$$

$$\frac{M'_s}{0.85f'_c bd^2} = \frac{P'_u e''}{0.85f'_c bd^2} = K'_s = r_s\left(1 - \frac{d'}{d}\right) - \frac{a}{d}\left(\frac{1}{2}\frac{a}{d} - \frac{d'}{d}\right) \qquad \text{(5-7b)}$$

Equations 5–7 are nothing but equilibrium equations expressed in dimensionless form. In these equations, the quantities K_s and K'_s can be easily computed from the given load P'_u and its eccentricities e' and e''; so for a given d'/d ratio, three unknowns remain, viz.: a/d, r'_s, and r_s. For a selected value of a/d, the required values of r'_s and r_s may be computed from Eqs. 5–7, and the required steel percentages, p' and p, may then be computed from Eqs. 5–5 if f'_s and f_s have been calculated from the strains given by Eqs. I. Theoretically, with the three unknowns, a/d, r'_s, and r_s in the two equations of 5–7, there are an infinite number of solutions possible for a given d'/d ratio.

Graphically, each of the Eqs. 5–7 may be represented by a *family* of curves for a given d'/d ratio and different K_s and K'_s values. The family of solid-line curves in the *qualitative* plot of Fig. 5–33 represents Eq. 5–7a which relates r'_s and a/d for different K_s values, and the family of dashed-line curves represents Eq. 5–7b, which relates r_s and a/d for different K'_s values. (Note that K'_s may be negative since e'' may be negative, which happens when the load is between A'_s and P.C.)

Limits for validity of Eqs. 5–7. Equations 5–7 are derived for the strain pattern of Fig. 5–32b with the neutral axis lying between the centroids of A'_s and A_s. Further, the neutral axis must not coincide precisely with the centroid of either A'_s or A_s in order that f'_s or f_s does not become zero and A'_s or A_s does not become infinite. Accordingly, for Eqs. 5–7 to be valid, the following condition must be satisfied:

$$d' < c < d \qquad \text{or} \qquad \frac{d'}{d} < \frac{c}{d} < 1$$

Since $c = a/k_1$, this condition may be stated as

$$k_1\frac{d'}{d} < \frac{a}{d} < k_1 \qquad \text{(5-8)}$$

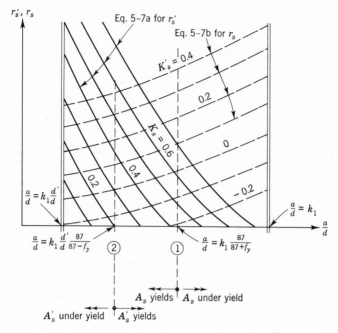

Fig. 5–33. Mörsch procedure—Case I: Tension over part of the cross section; relation between r'_s, r_s, and a/d for a given d'/d and different K_s and K'_s values (*no-scale, qualitative plot*).

These two limiting values of a/d are represented in Fig. 5–33 by the double vertical lines which chop off the families of curves at both ends, and within the boundaries of these lines, Eqs. 5–7 are valid.

Limits on a/d for steel yielding. The steel stresses, f_s and f'_s, depend on the strains ϵ_s and ϵ'_s, which in turn depend on c and hence on a. Therefore, there are limits on c/d or a/d in order that $f_s = f_y$ or $f'_s = f_y$.

Tensile steel A_s. Suppose $\epsilon_s \geq \epsilon_y$. Then $0.003(d - c)/c \geq f_y/E_s$, giving $d/c \geq (f_y/0.003E_s) + 1$. Thus $c/d \leq 0.003E_s/(0.003E_s + f_y)$. With $E_s = 29{,}000$ ksi and f_y expressed in ksi units, this may be stated as

$$\frac{c}{d} \leq \frac{87}{87 + f_y}$$

or

$$\frac{a}{d} \leq k_1 \frac{87}{87 + f_y} \tag{5-9a}$$

If this is satisfied, then A_s yields, and

$$f_s = f_y \tag{5-9b}$$

If

$$\frac{a}{d} > k_1 \frac{87}{87 + f_y} \tag{5-9c}$$

then A_s has not yielded, and its stress is given by

$$f_s = E_s \epsilon_s = 29{,}000(0.003) \left(\frac{d - c}{c} \right) = 87 \left(\frac{1}{c/d} - 1 \right) = 87 \left(\frac{k_1}{a/d} - 1 \right)$$
$$(5\text{–}9\text{d})$$

The dotted vertical line ① in Fig. 5–33 represents this limiting a/d value: a/d values to its left correspond to A_s yielding, and those to its right correspond to A_s under yield.

Compression steel A'_s. The limiting a/d value for A'_s yielding may be similarly derived. Thus for $\epsilon'_s \geq \epsilon_y$, $0.003(c - d')/c \geq f_y/E_s$, which leads to $1 - (f_y/0.003E_s) \geq d'/c$. Therefore,

$$\frac{c/d}{d'/d} \geq \frac{0.003E_s}{0.003E_s - f_y}$$

and again with $E_s = 29{,}000$ ksi and f_y expressed in ksi units,

$$\frac{c}{d} \geq \frac{d'}{d} \frac{87}{87 - f_y}$$

or

$$\frac{a}{d} \geq k_1 \frac{d'}{d} \frac{87}{87 - f_y} \qquad (5\text{–}10\text{a})$$

for which A'_s yields, and

$$f'_s = f_y \qquad (5\text{–}10\text{b})$$

If

$$\frac{a}{d} < k_1 \frac{d'}{d} \frac{87}{87 - f_y} \qquad (5\text{–}10\text{c})$$

then A'_s has not yielded, and its stress is

$$f'_s = E_s \epsilon'_s = 29{,}000(0.003) \left(\frac{c - d'}{c} \right) = 87 \left(1 - \frac{d'/d}{c/d} \right)$$
$$= 87 \left(1 - k_1 \frac{d'/d}{a/d} \right) \quad (5\text{–}10\text{d})$$

The dotted vertical line ② in Fig. 5–33 represents this limiting a/d value for compression steel: those a/d values to its right correspond to A'_s yielding and those to its left correspond to A'_s under yield.

If a designer should desire both reinforcements to yield, all he needs to do is to select a value of a/d which lies within the range bounded by the two limiting lines ① and ②.

Summary of necessary calculations. The necessary calculations in the Mörsch procedure may be very easily and systematically performed. Summarizing, the following steps of calculations may be enumerated:

   1. Calculate d'/d. Calculate the moments of the external load P'_u about the centroids of A_s and A'_s, resulting in M_s and M'_s. Divide them by

$(0.85f'_cbd^2)$ to yield K_s and K'_s. Substitute K_s, K'_s, and d'/d in Eqs. 5–7, leaving a/d, r'_s, and r_s as unknowns.

2. By Eq. 5–8, find the limits on a/d to validate Eqs. 5–7.
3. By Eqs. 5–9 and 5–10, find the limits on a/d for yielding of the steels.
4. Select an a/d value, and enter Eqs. 5–7 to compute r'_s and r_s.
5. With the selected a/d value, the steel stresses f_s and f'_s may be determined by Eqs. 5–9 and 5–10. With the values of r'_s and r_s found in the foregoing step, the required steel percentages, p' and p, are found from Eqs. 5–5. On multiplication by bd, one obtains the required A'_s and A_s.

Comments. The development of the Mörsch procedure has been presented in general terms, resulting in a number of non-dimensional equations in a form readily applicable to numerical computations. However, the reader should not feel obliged to become slavishly bound to these equations, but on the contrary, he should be prepared to derive them step by step for any specific numerical problem. The details of the general development presented should not obscure the fact that the procedure involves nothing more profound than two moment equilibrium equations about the reinforcement centroids, and two steel parameters r'_s and r_s defined in the manner of Eqs. 5–5. As Eqs. 5–5 show, these two parameters r'_s and r_s are nothing more than the steel percentages p' and p, each multiplied by the corresponding ratio of what might be considered as "the effective steel stress" to "the effective concrete stress."

Furthermore, it is not necessary to use the non-dimensional form of calculations presented in the foregoing discussion. For a given set of numerical data, it may be just as simple, for instance, to use a instead of a/d in the calculations.

EXAMPLE 5–8

Given the 18-in. square column of Fig. 5–34a which is to have an *ideal, short-column* capacity P'_u equal to 215 kips total, acting at 19 in. from the center line of the section. Take 4000-lb. concrete and 50,000-psi-yield-point steel. (This example is the same as Example 5–7 except that the Mörsch procedure is to be used.)

Required to design the reinforcement, to be centered $2\frac{1}{2}$ in. from the two bending faces.

Solution.

$$P'_u = 215 \text{ kips} \qquad f'_c = 4 \text{ ksi}$$
$$e' = 25.5 \text{ in.} \qquad k_1 = 0.85$$
$$e'' = 12.5 \text{ in.} \qquad 0.85f'_c = 3.4 \text{ ksi}$$
$$d'/d = 2.5/15.5 = 0.1613 \qquad 0.85f'_cbd^2 = 3.4(18)(15.5)^2 = 14{,}703 \text{ kip-in.}$$
$$1 - d'/d = 0.8387 \qquad f_y = 50 \text{ ksi}$$

Non-dimensional moment of P'_u:

About A_s: $K_s = P'_u e'/0.85f'_cbd^2 = (215)(25.5)/14{,}703 = 0.3729$
About A'_s: $K'_s = P'_u e''/0.85f'_cbd^2 = (215)(12.5)/14{,}703 = 0.1828$

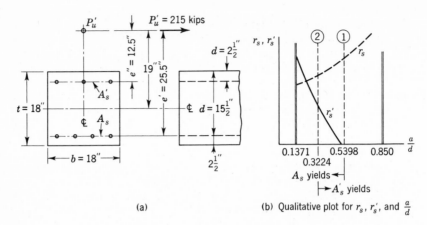

(a)

(b) Qualitative plot for r_s, r'_s, and $\frac{a}{d}$

Fig. 5–34.   Column of Example 5–8.

Non-dimensional moment equilibrium equations. From Eqs. 5–7, substituting K_s, K'_s, and d'/d:

$$0.3729 = r'_s(0.8387) + \frac{a}{d}\left(1 - \frac{1}{2}\frac{a}{d}\right)$$

$$0.1828 = r_s(0.8387) - \frac{a}{d}\left(\frac{1}{2}\frac{a}{d} - 0.1613\right)$$

or,

$$r'_s = \frac{1}{0.8387}\left[0.3729 - \frac{a}{d}\left(1 - \frac{1}{2}\frac{a}{d}\right)\right] \tag{1}$$

$$r_s = \frac{1}{0.8387}\left[0.1828 + \frac{a}{d}\left(\frac{1}{2}\frac{a}{d} - 0.1613\right)\right] \tag{2}$$

in which r'_s and r_s are related respectively to p' and p by Eqs. 5–5, which may be written as

$$p' = r'_s\left(\frac{0.85f'_c}{f'_s - 0.85f'_c}\right) = r'_s\left(\frac{3.4}{f'_s - 3.4}\right) \tag{3}$$

$$p = r_s\left(\frac{0.85f'_c}{f_s}\right) = r_s\left(\frac{3.4}{f_s}\right) \tag{4}$$

Limits for validity of equations. Equation 5–8 stipulates

$$k_1\frac{d'}{d} < \frac{a}{d} < k_1, \quad \text{or,} \quad 0.1371 = 0.85(0.1613) < \frac{a}{d} < 0.85$$

These are represented by the double vertical lines in Fig. 5–34b.

Limit for tensile steel yielding. From Eqs. 5–9, $f_s = f_y = 50$ ksi, if

$$\frac{a}{d} \leq k_1\left(\frac{87}{87 + f_y}\right), \quad \text{or,} \quad \frac{a}{d} \leq 0.85\left(\frac{87}{87 + 50}\right) = 0.5398$$

Otherwise,

$$f_s = 87\left(\frac{k_1}{a/d} - 1\right) = 87\left(\frac{0.85}{a/d} - 1\right)$$

This limit is represented by vertical line ① in Fig. 5–34b.
Limit for compression steel yielding. From Eqs. 5–10, $f'_s = f_y = 50$ ksi, if

$$\frac{a}{d} \geq k_1 \frac{d'}{d} \left(\frac{87}{87 - f_y} \right), \quad \text{or,} \quad \frac{a}{d} \geq 0.85(0.1613) \left(\frac{87}{87 - 50} \right) = 0.3224$$

Otherwise,

$$f'_s = 87 \left(1 - k_1 \frac{d'/d}{a/d} \right) = 87 \left(1 - 0.85 \frac{0.1613}{a/d} \right) = 87 \left(1 - \frac{0.1371}{a/d} \right)$$

This limit is represented by vertical line ② in Fig. 5–34b.
Select a/d. If a/d is taken to be 0.400, both A_s and A'_s yield and $f_s = f'_s = 50$ ksi. From Eqs. 1 and 2, the r'_s and r_s values are

$$r'_s = \frac{1}{0.8387} \left[0.3729 - (0.400) \left(1 - \frac{0.400}{2} \right) \right] = 0.0631$$

$$r_s = \frac{1}{0.8387} \left[0.1828 + (0.400) \left(\frac{0.400}{2} - 0.1613 \right) \right] = 0.2364$$

From Eqs. 3 and 4, the steel percentages p' and p are

$$p' = 0.0631 \left(\frac{3.4}{50 - 3.4} \right) = 0.460\%$$

$$p = 0.2364 \left(\frac{3.4}{50} \right) = 1.61\%$$

Therefore, the steel amounts are

$$A'_s = 0.460\% \ (18)(15.5) = 1.28 \text{ sq. in.}$$
$$A_s = 1.61\% \ (18)(15.5) = 4.49 \text{ sq. in.}$$

Use 3–#6 compressive steel and 2–#10 + 2–#9 tensile steel.   Ans.

This is not the only possible solution. Table 5–5 contains the above solution and others which were obtained in exactly the same manner. Note that it also contains a symmetrical reinforcement design, which was arrived at by trial and error.

MÖRSCH PROCEDURE—CASE I PROBLEMS

5–8. Solve Problem 5–6, using the Mörsch procedure for tension over part of the column section.

5–9. Solve Problem 5–7, using the Mörsch procedure for tension over part of the column section.

5–22. MÖRSCH PROCEDURE—CASE II: COMPRESSION OVER ENTIRE CROSS SECTION

The procedure described in Art. 5–21 for the case of tension existing over part of a column section may be easily extended to that of compression over the entire cross section, which occurs for moderate through small load eccentricities.

Table 5–5. Summary of Solutions of Example 5–8

$\dfrac{a}{d}$	r'_s (Eq. 1)	r_s (Eq. 2)	$f'_s = 87\left(1 - \dfrac{0.1371}{a/d}\right) \le 50$ ksi	$f_s = 87\left(\dfrac{0.85}{a/d} - 1\right) \le 50$ ksi	$p' = r'_s\left(\dfrac{3.4}{f'_s - 3.4}\right)$	$p = r_s\left(\dfrac{3.4}{f_s}\right)$	A'_s sq. in.	A_s sq. in.
0.400	0.0631	0.2364	50	50	0.460%	1.61%	1.28	4.49
0.350	0.1003	0.2237	50	50	0.732	1.52	2.04	4.24
0.300	0.1406	0.2139	47.24	50	1.09	1.45	3.04	4.06
0.250	0.1838	0.2071	39.29	50	1.74	1.41	4.86	3.93
0.271	0.1653	0.2096	42.99	50	1.42	1.43	3.96	3.98

Figure 5–35a shows a rectangular section b by t having reinforcement A'_s and A_s near the two bending faces. The eccentric load P'_u is located at e from the plastic centroid (P.C.), at e' from the centroid of A_s, and at e'' from that of A'_s. (Note that the distance e'' is taken positive as shown.) For compression to exist over the entire cross section, the neutral axis must not lie within the section, as shown in the strain diagram of Fig. 5–35b. Both A'_s and A_s will be compressive, and their strains are, respectively,

$$\left.\begin{array}{l} \text{Strain in } A'_s, \ \epsilon'_s = 0.003\left(\dfrac{c - d'}{c}\right) \\[2mm] \text{Strain in } A_s, \ \ \epsilon_s = 0.003\left(\dfrac{c - d}{c}\right) \end{array}\right\}$$

For this Case II to prevail, the neutral axis distance, c, and the stress block depth, a, must lie within certain limits. For the neutral axis not lying within the section, $c \ge t$, or $c/d \ge t/d$. Therefore $a/d \ge k_1(t/d)$, provided that a equals k_1c and is no larger than t; if k_1c is larger than t, a should be set equal to t and will no longer be related to c via the factor k_1. Hence the limits on c and a are given by:

$$\frac{c}{d} \ge \frac{t}{d} \tag{5–11a}$$

$$k_1\left(\frac{t}{d}\right) \le \frac{a}{d} \le \frac{t}{d} \tag{5–11b}$$

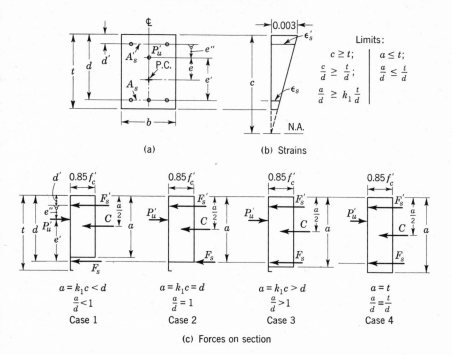

Fig. 5–35. Mörsch procedure—Case II: Compression over entire cross section.

Within these general limits, four situations may develop, depending on the stress block depth, a, relative to d and t.   As depicted in Fig. 5–35c, the stress block is above A_s in Case 1; it is as deep as d in Case 2; it is deeper than d but within the overall depth t in Case 3; and in Case 4 which occurs when $k_1 c > t$, the stress block depth a attains its maximum value equal to t.

Resisting forces.   The compressive force in concrete is

$$C = 0.85 f'_c ab$$

where

$$a = k_1 c \leq t$$

The compressive force in A'_s, allowing for the effect of the displaced concrete area, is

$$F'_s = A'_s(f'_s - 0.85 f'_c)$$

In computing the compressive force F_s in A_s, it is assumed that, for Case 1, A_s lies entirely outside the stress block and hence no concrete area is displaced thereby; for Case 2, the effect of displaced concrete area equal to half of A_s is accounted for; and for Cases 3 and 4, a displaced concrete area equal to the full amount of A_s is considered. Hence for the four cases, the force F_s is given by:

$$\text{Case 1:} \quad F_s = A_s F_s$$

$$\text{Case 2:} \quad F_s = \frac{A_s}{2} f_s + \frac{A_s}{2}(f_s - 0.85f'_c) = A_s\left(f_s - \frac{1}{2}0.85f'_c\right)$$

$$\text{Cases 3 and 4:} \quad F_s = A_s(f_s - 0.85f'_c)$$

Now introduce symbols r'_s and r_s, defined as follows:

$$\left.\begin{aligned}
r'_s &= \frac{A'_s}{bd}\frac{f'_s - 0.85f'_c}{0.85f'_c} &&= p'\frac{f'_s - 0.85f'_c}{0.85f'_c} \\
r_s &= \frac{A_s}{bd}\frac{f_s}{0.85f'_c} &&= p\frac{f_s}{0.85f'_c} &&\text{(Case 1)} \\
r_s &= \frac{A_s f_s - \frac{1}{2}(0.85f'_c)}{bd} \frac{}{0.85f'_c} &&= p\frac{f_s - \frac{1}{2}(0.85f'_c)}{0.85f'_c} &&\text{(Case 2)} \\
r_s &= \frac{A_s f_s - 0.85f'_c}{bd} \frac{}{0.85f'_c} &&= p\frac{f_s - 0.85f'_c}{0.85f'_c} &&\text{(Cases 3 and 4)}
\end{aligned}\right\} \quad (5\text{-}12)$$

With these symbols, all the resisting forces may now be concisely given as:

$$\left.\begin{aligned}
&\text{Compressive force in concrete,} && C = 0.85f'_c ab \\
&\text{Compressive force in } A'_s, && F'_s = 0.85f'_c r'_s bd \\
&\text{Compressive force in } A_s, && F_s = 0.85f'_c r_s bd
\end{aligned}\right\} \quad (5\text{-}13)$$

Equilibrium. Taking moments of the load and all the resisting forces of the section about the centroids of A_s and A'_s, one obtains

$$\text{About } A_s: \quad M_s = P'_u e' = C\left(d - \frac{a}{2}\right) + F'_s(d - d')$$

$$= 0.85f'_c ab\left(d - \frac{a}{2}\right) + 0.85f'_c r'_s bd(d - d')$$

$$= 0.85f'_c bd^2\left[\frac{a}{d}\left(1 - \frac{1}{2}\frac{a}{d}\right) + r'_s\left(1 - \frac{d'}{d}\right)\right]$$

$$\text{About } A'_s: \quad M'_s = P'_u e'' = C\left(\frac{a}{2} - d'\right) + F_s(d - d')$$

$$= 0.85f'_c ab\left(\frac{a}{2} - d'\right) + 0.85f'_c r_s bd(d - d')$$

$$= 0.85f'_c bd^2\left[\frac{a}{d}\left(\frac{1}{2}\frac{a}{d} - \frac{d'}{d}\right) + r_s\left(1 - \frac{d'}{d}\right)\right]$$

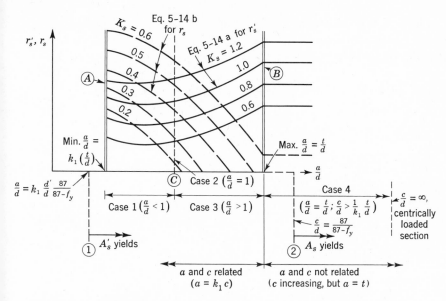

Fig. 5–36. Mörsch procedure—Case II: Compression over entire cross section; relation between r'_s, r_s, and a/d for a given d'/d and different K_s and K'_s values *(no-scale, qualitative plot)*.

Dividing both sides of the foregoing equations by $(0.85f'_c bd^2)$ and introducing the symbols K_s and K'_s, one obtains the non-dimensional equations of equilibrium:

$$\frac{M_s}{0.85f'_c bd^2} = \frac{P'_u e'}{0.85f'_c bd^2} = K_s = r'_s\left(1 - \frac{d'}{d}\right) + \frac{a}{d}\left(1 - \frac{1}{2}\frac{a}{d}\right) \quad (5\text{–}14a)$$

$$\frac{M'_s}{0.85f'_c bd^2} = \frac{P'_u e''}{0.85f'_c bd^2} = K'_s = r_s\left(1 - \frac{d'}{d}\right) + \frac{a}{d}\left(\frac{1}{2}\frac{a}{d} - \frac{d'}{d}\right) \quad (5\text{–}14b)$$

For a given d'/d value, Eqs. 5–14 may be represented graphically by two families of curves as shown in the qualitative plot of Fig. 5–36. These curves are truncated on the left by the double vertical line Ⓐ representing the minimum $a/d = k_1(t/d)$. On the right, they intersect (unless already cut off by the horizontal axis) with the double vertical line Ⓑ, at which a/d attains its maximum value of t/d.

To the *left* of line Ⓑ lie Cases 1 through 3, for which **a and c are related,** that is, $a = k_1 c$, or $a/d = k_1(c/d)$. The vertical line Ⓒ represents $a/d = 1$, and hence corresponds to Case 2. The region between lines Ⓐ and Ⓒ corresponds to Case 1, for which $a/d < 1$; but if the minimum $a/d = k_1(t/d)$ of line Ⓐ is larger than the $a/d = 1$ of line Ⓒ, Case 1 would be nonexistent. Case 3, for which $t/d > a/d > 1$, falls between lines Ⓒ and Ⓑ.

To the *right* of Ⓑ is Case 4, for which **a and c are not related,** because, while c may increase, a remains constant at the value of t, that is, $c/d >$ $(1/k_1)(t/d)$, but $a/d = t/d$. Therefore, from Eqs. 5–14, it is obvious that for constant $a/d = t/d$, r'_s and r_s have unique values for a given combination of d'/d, K_s, and K'_s values. In other words, the curves shown in Fig. 5–36, unless they have already been cut off by the horizontal axis, become horizontal after intersecting line Ⓑ, and will remain so throughout the region to right of line Ⓑ up to the limit of $c/d = \infty$, which corresponds to the theoretical centrically-loaded condition.

Limit for A'_s yielding. If $\epsilon'_s \geq \epsilon_y$, then $0.003(c - d')/c \geq f_y/E_s$. Therefore, $1 - (f_y/0.003E_s) \geq d'/c$. Hence,

$$\frac{c/d}{d'/d} \geq \frac{0.003E_s}{0.003E_s - f_y}$$

If $E_s = 29,000$ ksi and f_y is expressed in ksi units,

$$\frac{c}{d} \geq \frac{d'}{d} \frac{87}{87 - f_y} \tag{5–15a}$$

If $k_1 c \geq t$, and $a = k_1 c$, this condition may be stated in terms of a/d as

$$\frac{a}{d} \geq k_1 \frac{d'}{d} \frac{87}{87 - f_y} \tag{5–15b}$$

If Eq. 5–15a or 5–15b is valid, then A'_s has yielded, and its stress is

$$f'_s = f_y \tag{5–15c}$$

On the other hand, if

$$\frac{c}{d} < \frac{d'}{d} \frac{87}{87 - f_y} \tag{5–15d}$$

or, alternately in terms of a/d, if

$$\frac{a}{d} < k_1 \frac{d'}{d} \frac{87}{87 - f_y} \tag{5–15e}$$

then A'_s is elastic, and its stress is given by

$$f'_s = E_s\epsilon'_s = 29,000(0.003)\left(\frac{c - d'}{c}\right) = 87\left(1 - \frac{d'/d}{c/d}\right) \tag{5–15f}$$

or, alternately by

$$f'_s = 87\left(1 - k_1 \frac{d'/d}{a/d}\right) \tag{5–15g}$$

This limit is represented by dotted line ① in Fig. 5–36, and for most cases, is to the left of and beyond the limiting boundary line Ⓐ, indicating that A'_s has yielded for the range of a/d under consideration.

Limit for A_s yielding. If $\epsilon_s \geq \epsilon_y$, then $0.003(c - d)/c \geq f_y/E_s$. Therefore, $1 - (f_y/0.003E_s) \geq d/c$. With $E_s = 29,000$ ksi and f_y expressed in ksi units, this may be stated as

$$\frac{c}{d} \geq \frac{87}{87 - f_y} \tag{5-16a}$$

for which A_s has yielded and its stress is therefore

$$f_s = f_y \tag{5-16b}$$

This limit may be represented by line ② in Fig. 5–36, which always lies to the right of line Ⓑ.

If

$$\frac{c}{d} < \frac{87}{87 - f_y} \tag{5-16c}$$

then A_s is elastic, and its stress is

$$f_s = E_s\epsilon_s = (29,000)(0.003)\left(\frac{c - d}{c}\right) = 87\left(1 - \frac{1}{c/d}\right) \tag{5-16d}$$

If, *and only if*, $a = k_1 c \leq t$, then this stress may be alternately expressed as

$$f_s = 87\left(1 - \frac{k_1}{a/d}\right) \tag{5-16e}$$

All the relations necessary for the Mörsch procedure for compression over the entire cross section of a column have now been developed. The following example illustrates the application of this procedure to a numerical problem.

EXAMPLE 5–9

Given the 20-in. square column section of Fig. 5–37 which is to have an *ideal, short-column* capacity of P'_u equal to 1500 kips, acting at 2 in. from the center line of the section. Take 4000-lb. concrete and 60,000-psi-yield-point steel.

Required to design the reinforcement, to be centered 3 in. from the two bending faces, using the Mörsch procedure and assuming that compression exists over the entire cross section.

Solution.

$P'_u = 1500$ kips	$f'_c = 4$ ksi
$e' = 9.00$ in.	$k_1 = 0.85$
$e'' = 5.00$ in.	$0.85f'_c = 3.4$ ksi
$d'/d = 3.0/17.0 = 0.1765$	$0.85f'_cbd^2 = 3.4(20)(17)^2 = 19,650$ kip-in.
$1 - d'/d = 0.8235$	$f_y = 60$ ksi

Non-dimensional moment of P'_u.

About A_s: $K_s = P'_ue'/0.85f'_cbd^2 = 1500(9)/19,650 = 0.6870$
About A'_s: $K'_s = P'_ue''/0.85f'_cbd^2 = 1500(5)/19,650 = 0.3816$

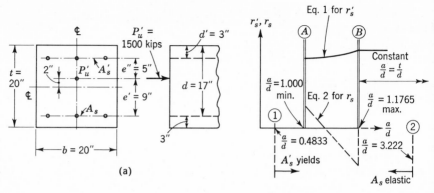

Fig. 5–37. Column of Example 5–9.

Non-dimensional moment equilibrium equations. From Eqs. 5–14 and substituting K_s, K'_s, and d'/d:

$$0.6870 = r'_s(0.8235) + \frac{a}{d}\left(1 - \frac{1}{2}\frac{a}{d}\right)$$

$$0.3816 = r_s(0.8235) + \frac{a}{d}\left(\frac{1}{2}\frac{a}{d} - 0.1765\right)$$

or,

$$r'_s = \frac{1}{0.8235}\left[0.6870 - \frac{a}{d}\left(1 - \frac{1}{2}\frac{a}{d}\right)\right] \qquad (1)$$

$$r_s = \frac{1}{0.8235}\left[0.3816 - \frac{a}{d}\left(\frac{1}{2}\frac{a}{d} - 0.1765\right)\right] \qquad (2)$$

These equations are subject to the limitations as set forth in Eqs. 5–11, that is:

$$\frac{c}{d} \geq \frac{t}{d} = \frac{20}{17} = 1.1765 \qquad (3)$$

$$k_1\left(\frac{t}{d}\right) \leq \frac{a}{d} \leq \frac{t}{d} \quad \text{or} \quad 1.000 = 0.85\left(\frac{20}{17}\right) \leq \frac{a}{d} \leq \frac{20}{17} = 1.1765 \qquad (4)$$

The limits on a/d as given by Eq. 4 are shown by the vertical lines Ⓐ and Ⓑ in Fig. 5–37b. Note that the permissible a/d values lie within a very narrow range. The relations between r'_s, r_s, and the steel percentages p', p are, from Eqs. 5–12:

$$p' = r'_s\left(\frac{0.85f'_c}{f'_s - 0.85f'_c}\right) \quad = r'_s\left(\frac{3.4}{f'_s - 3.4}\right) \qquad (5)$$

$$\left.\begin{aligned}
p &= r_s\left(\frac{0.85f'_c}{f_s}\right) &&= r_s\left(\frac{3.4}{f_s}\right) &&\text{(for } a/d < 1) \\
p &= r_s\left[\frac{0.85f'_c}{f_s - (\tfrac{1}{2})(0.85f'_c)}\right] &&= r_s\left(\frac{3.4}{f_s - 1.7}\right) &&\text{(for } a/d = 1) \\
p &= r_s\left(\frac{0.85f'_c}{f_s - 0.85f'_c}\right) &&= r_s\left(\frac{3.4}{f_s - 3.4}\right) &&\text{(for } a/d > 1)
\end{aligned}\right\} \qquad (6)$$

Limit for A'_s yielding. Equation 5–15b specifies that for A'_s yielding, a/d must be such that

$$\frac{a}{d} \geq k_1 \frac{d'}{d} \frac{87}{87 - f_y} = 0.85 \left(\frac{3}{17}\right) \left(\frac{87}{87 - 60}\right) = 0.4833$$

This is represented by line ① in Fig. 5–37b. It is seen that for all permissible a/d values, A'_s yields and $f'_s = f_y = 60$ ksi.

Limit for A_s yielding. From Eq. 5–16a, this limit is

$$\frac{c}{d} \geq \frac{87}{87 - f_y} = \frac{87}{87 - 60} = 3.222 \tag{7}$$

and it is represented by line ② in Fig. 5–37b. It is seen that it lies to the right of line ⑧ and in a region in which a/d is constant at its maximum value of 1.1765.

To the left of line ②, A_s is elastic. Its stress for a/d values between lines ⓐ and ⑧ is, from Eq. 5–16:

$$f_s = 87 \left(1 - \frac{k_1}{a/d}\right) = 87 \left(1 - \frac{0.85}{a/d}\right) \tag{8}$$

and for c/d values between lines ⑧ and ② it is given by Eq. 5–16d as

$$f_s = 87 \left(1 - \frac{1}{c/d}\right) \tag{9}$$

Select a/d. In order to reveal the effect of varying a/d value on the required steel content, more than one solution was performed. The results of these solutions are presented in Table 5–6 in the order of increasing a/d values although the actual sequence of computations is as indicated by the numbers in the first column.

In Table 5–6, line 1 was first obtained, using the minimum a/d value of 1.000, which is seen to result in A'_s of 4.64 sq. in. and A_s of 7.19 sq. in. Next, the maximum a/d value of 1.1765 was used, resulting in line 2 which shows that r_s becomes negative; this means a negative A_s unless A_s is allowed to become tensile, obviously an unacceptable solution. The same is true for line 3 with $a/d = 1.100$.

Lines 4, 5, and 6 were next computed, using a/d equal to 1.05, 1.025, and 1.020, respectively. Comparing the results obtained so far, it is interesting to note that A'_s changes but slightly whereas A_s is extremely sensitive to changes in a/d. Between lines 6 and 5, it is seen that A'_s practically remains constant at 4.65 sq. in.

Table 5–6. Solutions of Example 5–9

Line	a/d	r'_s (Eq. 1)	r_s (Eq. 2)	f'_s, ksi	f'_s, ksi (Eq. 8)	p' (Eq. 5)	p (Eq. 6)	A'_s, sq. in.	A_s, sq. in.
1	1.000	0.2271	0.07055		13.05	1.36%	2.11%	4.64	7.19
6	1.020	0.2273	0.05027		14.50	1.37	1.54	4.65	5.24
7	1.024	0.2274	0.04614		14.78	1.37	1.38	4.65	4.69
5	1.025	0.2274	0.04517	60	14.85	1.37	1.34	4.65	4.56
4	1.050	0.2285	0.01906		16.57	1.37	0.49	4.67	1.67
3	1.100	0.2332	Negative						
2	1.176	0.2460	Negative						

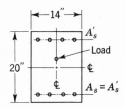

Fig. 5–38.   Column of Problem 5–10.

whereas A_s changes from 5.24 to 4.56 sq. in. corresponding to a change in a/d from 1.020 to 1.025.   It is obvious that an a/d value between 1.020 and 1.025 may be found to give $A'_s = A_s = 4.65$ sq. in.   If one is interested in this particular a/d value, one may find this by interpolation and trial-and-error; the results of such a process are shown in line 7 for a/d of 1.024, giving A'_s of 4.65 and A_s of 4.69, which is a practically close enough agreement.   If a designer is interested only in getting a symmetrical reinforcement pattern, and not in the precise value of a/d that will yield it, he need go no further than line 6 and simply settle on the required steel amounts as $A'_s = A_s = 4.65$ sq. in.

MÖRSCH PROCEDURE—CASE II PROBLEM

5-10. Given the 14-by-20-in. rectangular tied column of Fig. 5–38 which at *service level* is subject to an axial load of 160 kips dead, and 200 kips live, plus a bending moment about the center line of the section of 30 kip-ft. dead, and 40 kip-ft. live. The understrength factor is $\phi = 0.70$, and the reduction factor for slenderness is $R = 0.80$ for compression failure.   Take 4000-lb. concrete and 60,000-psi-yield-point steel.   Using the Mörsch procedure and assuming compression existing over the entire section, design the symmetrical reinforcement, to be centered $2\frac{1}{2}$ in. from the two bending faces.

5–23. MÖRSCH PROCEDURE—FURTHER REMARKS

For the 20-in. square column section of Example 5–9, which was designed using Case II of the Mörsch procedure on the assumption that compression existed over the entire cross section, suppose now that the load P'_u of 1500 kips were to act at 3 in., instead of the original 2-in. distance, from the centerline of the section, all other data being unaltered. Then, the eccentricities of the load from A_s and A'_s would be respectively

$$e' = 10.0 \text{ in.} \quad \text{and} \quad e'' = 4.00 \text{ in.}$$

and the non-dimensional moments of the load about A_s and A'_s would be

$$K_s = P'_u e'/0.85 f'_c b d^2 = (1500)(10.0)/19{,}650 = 0.7634$$
$$K'_s = P'_u e''/0.85 f'_c b d^2 = (1500)(4.00)/19{,}650 = 0.3053$$

Accordingly, the non-dimensional moment equilibrium equations would be

$$r'_s = \frac{1}{0.8235}\left[0.7634 - \frac{a}{d}\left(1 - \frac{1}{2}\frac{a}{d}\right)\right]$$

$$r_s = \frac{1}{0.8235}\left[0.3053 - \frac{a}{d}\left(\frac{1}{2}\frac{a}{d} - 0.1765\right)\right]$$

It would then be found that within the permissible range of a/d = 1.000 and a/d = 1.1765, r_s is negative for *all* a/d values. This indicates that for the 20-by-20-in. concrete dimensions adopted, compression could *not* exist over the entire cross section as assumed. The designer would then have the choice of either (1) retaining the 20-in. dimensions but switching to calculations for Case I with tension over part of the section, or (2) retaining the Case II assumption but reducing the concrete dimensions. Similar techniques are to be adopted when a similar situation develops in a trial design using Case I assumption.

For the sake of completeness, the Mörsch procedure has been developed here for both Cases I and II; however, it should be pointed out that the range of application of Case I is much wider than Case II. Case II usually applies only to cases of very light bending, and its range of applicability is further narrowed down by the ACI minimum eccentricity provision.

5–24. USE OF COLUMN DESIGN AIDS

In a practical design office where a large number of columns often have to be proportioned, design aids in the form of tables and charts become virtually indispensable. Many such aids have been published by various agencies, such as the American Concrete Institute, the Portland Cement Association, and the Concrete Reinforcing Steel Institute. Such tables or charts, naturally, cover only the most common and routine types of sections, and unusual column sections will have to be dealt with individually from basic principles.

One of such design aids is the *ACI Publication SP-7* [10], which contains a number of tables and some 120 charts for different concrete strengths and steel yield strengths. To illustrate their use, 16 charts thereof have been excerpted and presented throughout Appendix C. These charts are plotted for $f'_c \leq 4$ ksi and $f_y = 60$ ksi, and for four types of sections, viz.: Charts C–1 for round spiral sections; Charts C–2 for square spiral sections with bars arranged on a circle; Charts C–3 for rectangular tied sections with symmetrical reinforcement near the two bending faces; and Charts C–4 for rectangular tied sections with reinforcement near all the four faces.

The computations on which these charts are based have been prepared in accordance with the basic assumptions of ACI Sec. 1503, and the steel stresses used are compatible with the strains. Also, the effect of concrete area displaced by compression reinforcement has been included. The only approximation introduced in these computations is that all reinforcing bars have been considered to be replaced by thin tubular steel rings of equivalent area, as described in Art. 4–13. The reader is referred thereto for a more detailed discussion of the errors involved in such an

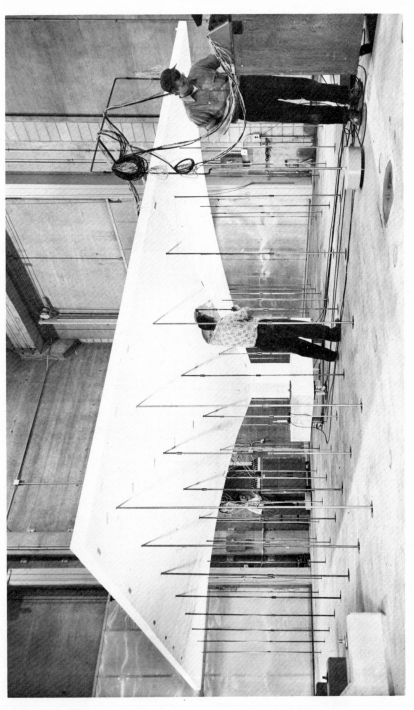

Plate 5-2. Test of a hyperbolic paraboloid shell at the research and development laboratories of the Portland Cement Association, Skokie, Illinois.

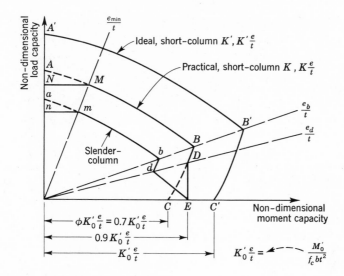

Fig. 5–39. Typical non-dimensional interaction curves for rectangular tied column section for a given g and $p_t m$.

approximation; it suffices to say here that the magnitude of such errors is of the order of 1 per cent or less.

These ACI charts are in the form of interaction curves, plotted on a dimensionless basis. The notation used therein is identical to what has been used herein so far. Besides the symbols which are defined in the charts in a self-explanatory way, the following may be recapitulated: A_{st} = total area of longitudinal reinforcement; A_g = gross concrete area of section; $p_t = A_{st}/A_g$; and $m = f_y/0.85f'_c$.

It is to be noted that the charts give *primarily* the **practical, short-column** strengths as expressed by the dimensionless parameters:

$$K = \frac{P_u}{f'_c D^2} \text{ and } K\frac{e}{D} = \frac{P_u e}{f'_c D^3} = \frac{M_u}{f'_c D^3} \quad \text{for round sections}$$

or,

$$K = \frac{P_u}{f'_c bt} \text{ and } K\frac{e}{t} = \frac{P_u e}{f'_c bt^2} = \frac{M_u}{f'_c bt^2} \quad \text{for rectangular sections}$$

These K and $K(e/t)$ or $K(e/D)$ values have been obtained by multiplying the corresponding values of K' and $K'(e/t)$ or $K'(e/D)$ for the *ideal, short-column* level by the understrength factor ϕ (equal to 0.70 for tied and 0.75 for spiral sections), *uniformly* for *all* values of e/t or e/D with no regard to the minimum eccentricity requirement of Sec. 1901(a) or to Sec. 1901(c) for very light bending. To clarify, refer to Fig. 5–39, which shows the non-dimensional strength curves of a rectangular tied column section for a given g and $p_t m$. $A'B'C'$ represents the *ideal, short-column* strength; C' corresponds to the pure moment capacity given by the parameter $K'_0(e/t) = M'_0/f'_c bt^2$.   The curve $AMBDC$ typifies the curves to be found in the Charts of Appendix C, and it is obtained from $A'B'C'$ by a multiplication by ϕ of 0.70.   Hence C corresponds to a pure moment capacity given by $0.70(K'_0)(e/t)$.   Curve $AMBDC$ is to be modified at the upper end by the horizontal line MN which is located by the e_{min}/t line, and necessitated by Sec. 1901(a), and at the lower end by the vertical DE, E being at $0.9(K'_0)(e/t)$ as stipulated by Sec. 1901(c).   Hence the complete strength curve is given by $NMBDE$ for the *practical, short-column* level, and by $nmbdE$ for the *slender-column* level.   The radial line defining the balanced eccentricity e_b/t is not expressly shown in the charts of Appendix C, but the value of e_b/t is given by a small diagram which accompanies each chart.   Neither is the e_d/t radial line shown on these charts.   It will have to be located by the user when an occasion for its use arises.   (See Example 5–11.)

The reader who finds the foregoing discussion difficult is invited to review Arts. 5–8 through 5–10 before proceeding with the numerical examples of the following article.

5–25. NUMERICAL EXAMPLES OF COLUMN DESIGNING BY CHARTS

This article presents three numerical examples to illustrate column designing by the use of the charts of Appendix C: Example 5–10 deals with column designing in the compression failure zone; Example 5–11 takes it into the tension failure zone in which ACI Sec. 1901(c) may come into play; and Example 5–12 involves the designing of a column subject to biaxial bending.

EXAMPLE 5–10

Given the column AB of a *laterally unbraced* building frame as shown in Fig. 5–40a.   The floor girders at level A and the column above AB have already been

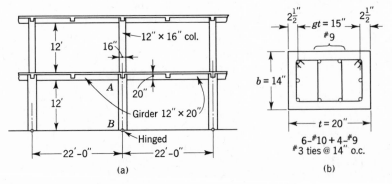

Fig. 5–40. Column of Example 5–10.

designed and have cross-sectional dimensions as indicated. Prior analysis of the frame for two loadings showed that column AB is subject to a resultant axial load and bending moment whose load-factored values are:

	Loading (1)	Loading (2)
Axial load P_{uf}	560 kips	508 kips
Moment M_{uf} about column ₵	0	104 kip-ft.

Take 4000-lb. concrete and 60,000-psi-yield-point steel.

Required to design AB as a rectangular tied column with reinforcement centered $2\frac{1}{2}$ in. from the four faces.

Solution. *Assume AB has a 14-by-20-in. section.*

$b = 14$ in., $t = 20$ in., $g\,t = 15$ in., therefore $g = {}^{15}\!/_{20} = 0.75$. $f'_c bt = (4)(14)(20)$ $= 1120$ kips.

The required *slender-column* capacities equal the load-factored values:

Loading (1)	Loading (2)
$P_{u,sl} = P_{uf} = 560$ kips	$P_{u,sl} = P_{uf} = 508$ kips
$M_{u,sl} = M_{uf} = 0$	$M_{u,sl} = M_{uf} = 104$ kip-ft.
$e = 0$	$e = 104(12)/508 = 2.46$ in.
Use min. $e/t = 0.1$	$e/t = 2.46/20 = 0.123$

Charts C–4b and C–4c show that, for both these loadings, e_b/t is larger than e/t. Therefore, compression controls failure.

Slenderness effect.   The strength reduction factor R is calculated according to Table 5–2 of Art. 5–7, which pertains to columns subject to sidesway and compression failure. AB has an unsupported length of $h = 12.0$ ft. = 144 in., and is partially restrained at A and hinged at B.

$$\text{End } A\!: \text{Stiffness of } AB = \frac{14(20)^3}{12}\,\frac{1}{(12)(12)} = 64.8 \text{ in.}^3$$

$$\text{Stiffness of each girder} = \frac{12(20)^3}{12}\,\frac{1}{(22)(12)} = 30.3 \text{ in.}^3$$

$$\text{Stiffness of column above} = \frac{12(16)^3}{12}\,\frac{1}{(12)(12)} = 28.4 \text{ in.}^3$$

Therefore,

$$r'_1 = \Sigma(\text{Column stiffness})/\Sigma(\text{Stiffness of restraining members})$$
$$= (64.8 + 28.4)/(2)(30.3) = 1.54$$

Hence, the effective length is

$$h' = 2h(0.78 + 0.22r') \geq 2h, \text{ where } r' = r'_1$$

or,

$$h' = (288)[0.78 + (0.22)(1.54)] = 322 \text{ in.}$$

The radius of gyration is

$$r \cong 0.30t = 0.3(20) = 6.00 \text{ in.}$$

Slenderness ratio,

$$h'/r = 322/6.00 = 53.7$$

Hence, the strength reduction factor is

$$R = 1.07 - 0.008(h'/r) \leq 1$$
$$= 1.07 - 0.008(53.7) = 0.64$$

Therefore the required *practical, short-column* capacity is $P_u = P_{u,sl}/R$ and the corresponding non-dimensional parameter is $K = P_u/f'_c bt$; their values for the two loadings are:

Loading (1)	Loading (2)
$P_u = 560/0.64 = 875$ kips	$P_u = 508/0.64 = 794$ kips
$K = 875/1120 = 0.781$, and $e/t = 0.1$	$K = 794/1120 = 0.709$, and $e/t = 0.123$

Entering Charts C–4b and C–4c with the above values as arguments, and interpolating between g of 0.70 and 0.80, one finds the required $p_t m$ as:

g	$p_t m$		g	$p_t m$
0.70	0.74		0.70	0.57
0.80	0.70		0.80	0.53
0.75	0.72		0.75	0.55

Therefore, loading (1) governs, and requires $p_t m$ of 0.72.

$$m = f_y/0.85f'_c = 60/(0.85)(4) = 17.6$$
$$p_t = 0.72/17.6 = 4.08\%$$
Required $A_s = 4.08\%(14)(20) = 11.42$ sq. in.
Use 14-by-20-in. section, 6–#10 + 4–#9 = 11.62 sq. in.,
and #3 ties at 14 in. on centers (Fig. 5–40b).　　Ans.

EXAMPLE 5–11

Given the same column AB and data of Example 5–10, except that in addition to loadings (1) and (2), the column must also be adequate for a loading (3) which produces an axial load and a bending moment about the column centerline, whose *load-factored* values are: $P_{uf} = 100$ kips, and $M_{uf} = 333$ kip-ft.

Required to design AB to match.

Solution. The designing of Example 5–10 for loadings (1) and (2) resulted in a 14-by-20-in. section, a required $p_t m$ of 0.72, and the reduction factor for slenderness, $R_c = 0.64$ for compression failure.

Loading (3)

$$P_{u,sl} = 100 \text{ kips}; \quad M_{u,sl} = 333 \text{ kip-ft.}$$
$$e = 333(12)/100 = 40 \text{ in.}; \quad e/t = {}^{40}\!/_{20} = 2.00$$

By reference to Charts C–4b and C–4c, this e/t is larger than $e_b t$ for $p_t m$ up to 1.0. Hence, tension controls failure for this loading.

Slenderness effect. The reduction factor R' is not known at this stage. *Estimate $R' = 0.82$*, which is the average of 1.0 for pure bending and the R_c of 0.64.

Therefore, estimated *practical short-column* capacity required is

$$P_u = 100/0.82 = 122 \text{ kips}$$

and

$$K = P_u/f'_c bt = {}^{122}\!/_{1120} = 0.109; \quad K(e/t) = 0.109(2.00) = 0.218$$

Now *check on R'.* With the above values as arguments, enter Charts C–4b and C–4c to find p_tm, and then interpolate between g of 0.70 and 0.80:

g	p_tm	
0.7	1.07	(out of range of Chart C-4b slightly; so this value was extrapolated)
0.8	0.89	
0.75	0.98	(by interpolation)

With p_tm at 0.98, enter Charts C–4b and C–4c to find e_b/t of 0.84 for $g = 0.70$ and 0.80 for $g = 0.80$. Hence for $g = 0.75$, $e_b/t = 0.82$.

Revised $R' = 1 - (1 - R_c)(e_b/t)/(e/t) = 1 - (1 - 0.64)(0.82/2.00) = 0.85$
Revised $P_u = 100/0.85 = 118$ kips
Revised $K = {}^{118}\!/_{1120} = 0.105$, and $K(e/t) = 0.105(2.00) = 0.210$

With these revised values, re-enter Charts C–4b and C–4c and interpolate to obtain $p_tm = 0.96$ for $g = 0.75$, and thence $e_b/t = 0.81$. Hence $R' = 0.85$ which agrees with the last R' value used.

Does Sec. 1901(c) apply? If Sec. 1901(c) does not apply, the required p_tm is 0.96 as determined above. If it applies, the required p_tm would be smaller than 0.96. To settle this question, perform the following operation: Take the $K(e/t)$ value of 0.210 which corresponds to the required p_tm of 0.96, and multiply it by $\phi/0.9$ to yield a quantity, say x. Thus,

$$x = 0.210(\phi/0.9) = 0.210(0.7/0.9) = 0.163$$

Now use this x value as argument for $K(e/t)$ together with $K = 0$ (i.e., pure bending), enter Charts C–4b and C–4c, find p_tm for g of 0.7 and 0.8, and interpolate for $g = 0.75$ to find p_tm of 0.81. For distinction in reference, call this p_tm as $(p_tm)_x$. If $(p_tm)_x$ is larger than 0.96, then Sec. 1901(c) does *not* apply; otherwise, Sec. 1901(c) applies, and the true required p_tm is equal to $(p_tm)_x$. In the present case, $(p_tm)_x$ of 0.81 is smaller than 0.96; therefore Sec. 1901(c) applies, and the required p_tm is 0.81. This of course will change R' again, but usually not appreciably; a re-examination on R' may always be made, however, as follows: Enter the charts with $p_tm = 0.81$ to find e_b/t of 0.74 and 0.70 for g of 0.70 and 0.80; hence, for g of 0.75, $e_b/t = 0.72$, and $R' = 1 - (1 - 0.64)(0.72/2.00) = 0.87$, which differs only slightly from the R' of 0.85 used.

With $p_tm = 0.81$, $m = 60/(0.85)(4) = 17.6$, the required $p_t = 0.81/17.6 = 4.60\%$ and $A_{st} = 4.60\%(14)(20) = 12.89$ sq. in. Obviously, loading (3) governs.

Use 14-by-20 in. section, 4–#11 + 6–#10 = 13.86 sq. in.,
and #3 ties at 14 in. on centers (Fig. 5–41a).   **Ans.**

Comments. The rationale behind the foregoing technique to decide whether or not Sec. 1901(c) applies may be explained by reference to Fig. 5–41b. It was found that with e/t of 2.00 and $K(e/t)$ of 0.210, a value of p_tm of 0.96 was required; this is represented by point q on curve Cq. Now, if Sec. 1901(c) applies, the required $(p_tm)_x$ must be smaller than 0.96, and its strength curve would be above Cq, such as that indicated by $C_xD_xH_x$. Suppose C_x has an abscissa of x; its corresponding point on the ideal, short-column strength curve, C'_x, would have an abscissa of x/ϕ or $x/0.7$. If this is multiplied by 0.9 to yield $(x/\phi)(0.9)$ and if a vertical is erected at point E_x with abscissa of $(x/\phi)(0.9)$, the curve $E_xD_xH_x$

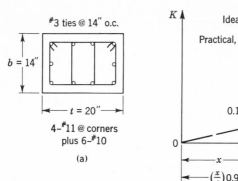

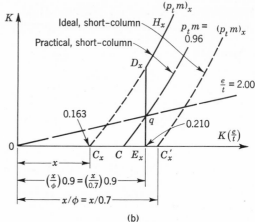

Fig. 5–41.   Column of Example 5–11.

would be the correct *practical, short-column* curve for $(p_t m)_x$. Suppose the vertical $E_x D_x$ is made to pass through point q which has an abscissa of 0.210; then

$$\frac{x}{\phi}(0.9) = 0.210$$

or

$$x = 0.210\left(\frac{\phi}{0.9}\right) = 0.210\left(\frac{0.7}{0.9}\right) = 0.163$$

So now, with $K(e/t)$ set equal to 0.163 and $K = 0$, one finds the required $(p_t m)_x$ to be 0.81. Since this is smaller than 0.96, we indeed have a situation as depicted.

EXAMPLE 5–12

Given a row of columns of a three-story, *laterally unbraced* building frame as shown in Fig. 5–42. The roof column has already been designed and is 14 in. square. The column AB and that below it are assumed to be respectively 22 in. and 24 in. square. The floors at levels A and B have also been designed, and each floor thereat has a total stiffness (I/L) of 51.4 in.³ about the x axis, and 71.8 in.³ about the y-axis. Prior analysis of the frame has shown that under two different loadings, the column AB is subject to *load-factored* axial loads and bending moments about the x- and y-axes as follows:

Load-factored values = Slender-column capacities required

Level	Loading (1)			Loading (2)		
	$P_{u,sl}$	$M_{x,sl}$	$M_{y,sl}$	$P_{u,sl}$	$M_{x,sl}$	$M_{y,sl}$
A	305 kips	310 kip-ft.	0	228 kips	184 kip-ft.	73 kip-ft.
B	312	185	0	312	116	43

Take 4000-lb. concrete and 60,000-psi-yield-point steel.

Required to design AB as a 22-in. square spiral column with bars centered on a 17-in. diameter circle.

Solution.

Properties of column AB

$t = 22$ in., $gt = 17$ in., and $g = {}^{17}\!/_{22} = 0.77$. Therefore interpolate between Charts C-2b and C-2c.

$$\text{Radius of gyration, } r = t/\sqrt{12} = 22/\sqrt{12} = 6.36 \text{ in.}$$
$$m = f_y/0.85f'_c = 60/(0185)(4) = 17.6$$
$$f'_c t^2 = (4)(22)^2 = 1936 \text{ kips}$$

Column AB is partially restrained at both ends and is subject to sidesway. According to Table 5-2 of Art. 5-7, the reduction factor R_c for *compression failure* may be calculated as follows:

	About x-axis	About y-axis
At A, $r'_A = \dfrac{\Sigma(I/h \text{ of col.})}{\Sigma(I/L \text{ of floor})} = \dfrac{28.6 + 173}{51.4} = 3.92$		$\dfrac{28.6 + 173}{71.8} = 2.81$
At B, $r'_B = \dfrac{\Sigma(I/h \text{ of col.})}{\Sigma(I/L \text{ of floor})} = \dfrac{173 + 165}{51.4} = 6.58$		$\dfrac{173 + 165}{71.8} = 4.71$
Average	$r' = 5.25$	$r' = 3.76$
Effective $h' = h(0.78 + 0.22r') \geq h$		
$= 113[0.78 + 0.22(5.25)] \quad = 219 \text{ in.}$		$113[0.78 + 0.22(3.76)] = 182 \text{ in.}$
Slenderness ratio, $h'/r = 219/6.36 \quad = 34$		$182/6.36 = 29$
Reduction factor, $R_c = 1.07 - 0.008(h'/r)$		
$= 1.07 - 0.008(34) = 0.80$		$1.07 - 0.008(29) = 0.84$

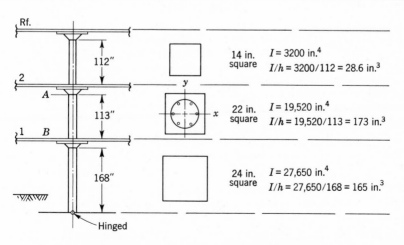

Rf.

112″

2

A

113″

1 B

168″

Hinged

y

x

14 in. square $I = 3200$ in.^{4}
$I/h = 3200/112 = 28.6$ in.^{3}

22 in. square $I = 19{,}520$ in.^{4}
$I/h = 19{,}520/113 = 173$ in.^{3}

24 in. square $I = 27{,}650$ in.^{4}
$I/h = 27{,}650/168 = 165$ in.^{3}

Fig. 5–42. Columns of Example 5–12.

Loading (1).   Uniaxial bending about x-axis only

LEVEL A

$$P_{u,sl} = 305 \text{ kips}, M_{x,sl} = 310 \text{ kip-ft.}, e_x = 310(12)/305 = 12.2 \text{ in.}$$
$$e_x/t = 12.2/22 = 0.554 > 0.05 \text{ minimum}$$

Charts C–2b and C–2c show that e_b/t averages about 0.50 between $p_t m$ of 0.0 and 1.0.   Assume a tensile failure, and estimate $R' = 0.85$.   Hence, the required *practical, short-column* capacity, and the corresponding non-dimensional parameters are:

$$P_u = P_{u,sl}/R' = 305/0.85 = 359 \text{ kips}$$
$$K = P_u/f'_c t^2 = {}^{359}\!/_{1936} = 0.185$$
$$K(e_x/t) = 0.185(0.554) = 0.102$$

Entering the charts with these as arguments to find $p_t m$ for g of 0.7 and 0.8, and interpolating for g of 0.77, one finds the required $p_t m$ to be 0.24.   Using the charts again, one finds that for $g = 0.77$ and $p_t m = 0.24$, the e_b/t value is 0.37, which is smaller than e_x/t of 0.554, and hence confirms the tensile failure assumption.

CHECK R': $R' = 1 - (1 - R_c)[(e_b/t)/(e_x/t)] = 1 - (1 - 0.80)(0.37/0.554) = 0.87$ versus 0.85 estimated.   With the revised R' of 0.87, repeat the same calculations to obtain:

$$P_u = 305/0.87 = 351 \text{ kips}$$
$$K = {}^{351}\!/_{1936} = 0.181$$
$$K(e_x/t) = 0.181(0.554) = 0.100$$

Entering the charts with K of 0.181 and $K(e_x/t)$ of 0.100, one finds the revised value of $p_t m$ to be 0.22.   The corresponding e_b/t value may be found from the charts to be substantially the same as its previous value of 0.37.   Hence R' of 0.87 stands, and the required $p_t m$ is 0.22, tentatively.   Now, a check should be made to see whether Sec. 1901(c) would intrude, thereby reducing the required $p_t m$ value from 0.22.

CHECK WHETHER SEC. 1901(c) APPLIES: Using the same technique as described in Example 5–11, take $K(e_x/t)$ of 0.100 and multiply it by $\phi/0.9$ to get $0.100(0.75)/0.9 = 0.084$.   This, together with $K = 0$, gives a $(p_t m)_x$ of 0.34.   Since $0.34 > 0.22$, Sec. 1901(c) does not apply.   Therefore,

Required $p_t m = 0.22$ at A.

LEVEL B

$$P_{u,sl} = 312 \text{ kips}, M_{x,sl} = 185 \text{ kip-ft.}, e_x = 185(12)/312 = 7.11 \text{ in.}$$
$$e_x/t = 7.11/22 = 0.323 > 0.05 \text{ minimum}$$

Assume compression failure, $R_c = 0.80$.   Hence,

$$P_u = 312/0.80 = 390 \text{ kips}$$
$$K = {}^{390}\!/_{1936} = 0.201$$
$$K(e_x/t) = 0.201(0.323) = 0.065$$

Entering the charts of Appendix C, one finds that the required $p_t m$ is smaller than the value corresponding to the minimum p_t of 1 per cent, specified in Sec. 913(a).   Also, the corresponding e_b/t may be found to be larger than e_x/t of 0.332, thus confirming the assumption of compression failure.   Therefore, use the minimum $p_t m = 1\%(17.6) = 0.176$.

Required $p_t m = 0.176$ at B.

Of the required $p_t m$ values at A and B, obviously that at A, 0.22, governs.

Hence for loading (1), the required $p_t = 0.22/m = 0.22/m = 0.22/17.6 = 1.25\%$, and $A_{st} = 1.25\%(22)^2 = 6.05$ sq. in.

<u>Try 6–#9 bars.</u>

<u>Loading (2).　Biaxial bending</u>

Biaxial bending exists at both levels A and B. The Bresler approximate formula for biaxial bending, Eq. 4–5 of Art. 4–14, is:

$$\frac{1}{P'_u} \cong \frac{1}{P'_{ux}} + \frac{1}{P'_{uy}} - \frac{1}{P'_0} \tag{4–5}$$

In Eq. 4–5, P'_u is the capacity for biaxial bending with eccentricities e_x and e_y; P'_{ux} is that for bending about x-axis alone $(e_y = 0)$; P'_{uy} is that for bending about y-axis alone $(e_x = 0)$; and P'_0 is the centrically loaded capacity $(e_x = e_y = 0)$, all these being the *ideal, short-column* capacities. If all the capacities are divided by $f'_c t^2$, this formula may be written non-dimensionally as:

$$\frac{1}{K'} \cong \frac{1}{K'_x} + \frac{1}{K'_y} - \frac{1}{K'_0} \tag{1}$$

where $K' = P'_u/f'_c t^2$, $K'_x = P'_{ux}/f'_c t^2$, $K'_y = P'_{uy}/f'_c t^2$, and $K'_0 = P'_0/f'_c t^2$. Assuming a uniform value of ϕ, Eq. 1 for the *ideal, short-column* status may be converted to one for the *practical, short-column* status as:

$$\frac{1}{K} \cong \frac{1}{K_x} + \frac{1}{K_y} - \frac{1}{K_0} \tag{2}$$

where $K = P_u/f'_c t^2$, $K_x = P_{ux}/f'_c t^2$, $K_y = P_{uy}/f'_c t^2$, and $K_0 = P_0/f'_c t^2$.

Let $K_{sl} = P_{u,sl}/f'_c t^2 = RK$, in which R is the reduction factor for slenderness for *biaxial bending*. Equation 2 may then be rewritten for the *slender-column* status as:

$$\frac{1}{K_{sl}} \cong \frac{1}{R}\left(\frac{1}{K_x} + \frac{1}{K_y} - \frac{1}{K_0}\right) \tag{3}$$

The difficulty with Eq. 3 is that we do not know how to determine R for biaxial bending. In the interest of simplicity, Eq. 3 is approximated by

$$\frac{1}{K_{sl}} \cong \frac{1}{R_x K_x} + \frac{1}{R_y K_y} - \frac{1}{R_0 K_0} \tag{4}$$

in which R_x, R_y, and R_0 are the reduction factors for bending about x-axis alone, bending about y-axis alone, and for no bending, respectively.

Equation 4 may now be used to investigate column AB for loading (2).

LEVEL A

The required slender-column capacities are:

$$P_{u,sl} = 228 \text{ kips}; \; M_{x,sl} = 184 \text{ kip-ft.}; \; M_{y,sl} = 73 \text{ kip-ft.}$$

The trial 6–#9 reinforcement corresponds to:

$$p_t m = 0.22; \; e_b/t = 0.37$$
Compression failure, $R_c = 0.80$, about x-axis
Compression failure, $R_c = 0.84$, about y-axis

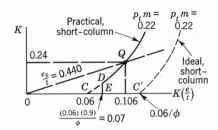

Fig. 5–43. Example 5–12, loading 2, level A, uniaxial bending about x-axis.

No BENDING ($e_x = e_y = 0$): Taking R_0 conservatively equal to the smaller of the two R_c values, that is, 0.80, and using Charts C–2b and C–2c, one finds that:

$$\text{Furnished } K_0 = 0.78$$

BENDING ABOUT x-AXIS ALONE ($e_y = 0$):

$$e_x/t = 184(12)/(228)(22) = 0.440$$

Since this is larger than e_b/t of 0.37, there is tension failure, and

$$R_x = 1 - (1 - 0.80)(0.37/0.44) = 0.83$$

From the charts again, with $p_t m$ of 0.22 and e_x/t of 0.440, one finds that:

$$\text{Furnished } K_x = 0.24, \text{ and corresponding } K_x(e_x/t) = 0.106$$

This is represented by point Q on the practical short-column strength curve of Fig. 5–43. We do not as yet know whether Sec. 1901(c) applies; hence it is necessary to perform the following check.

Check if Sec. 1901(c) applies. By means of the charts, one finds that point C in Fig. 5–43 has an abscissa of 0.06. The corresponding point C' for the ideal, short-column status will then have an abscissa equal to $0.06/\phi$. Therefore, point E, at which the vertical representing Sec. 1901(c) is to be drawn, has an abscissa equal to $(0.9)(0.6)/\phi$, or $(0.9)(0.06)/0.75 = 0.07$. Since this is smaller than the abscissa of Q, 0.106, therefore Sec. 1901(c) does not apply, and the previously computed K_x of 0.24 stands.

BENDING ABOUT y-AXIS ALONE ($e_x = 0$):

$$e_y/t = 73(12)/(228)(22) = 0.175$$

Since this is smaller than e_b/t of 0.37, we have compression failure, for which $R_y = R_c = 0.84$. Entering the charts with $p_t m$ of 0.22 and e_y/t of 0.175, one finds that:

$$\text{Furnished } K_y = 0.50$$

BIAXIAL BENDING: Now, substituting the values of K_0, K_x, and K_y, and the corresponding R values in Eq. 4, one obtains:

$$\frac{1}{K_{sl}} \cong \frac{1}{(0.24)(0.83)} + \frac{1}{(0.50)(0.84)} - \frac{1}{(0.78)(0.80)} = 5.80$$

from which,

Furnished K_{sl} = 1/5.80 = 0.172

Furnished $P_{u,sl} = K_{sl}(f'_c l^2)$ = 0.172(1936) = 333 kips

This is larger than the required $P_{u,sl}$ of 228 kips.   O.K.

LEVEL B

The required slender-column capacities are:

$P_{u,sl}$ = 312 kips; $M_{x,sl}$ = 116 kip-ft.; $M_{y,sl}$ = 43 kip-ft.

By calculations similar to those performed at level A, the following results are obtained:

NO BENDING ($e_x = e_y = 0$): $K_0 = 0.78; R_0 = 0.80$

BENDING ABOUT x-AXIS ALONE ($e_y = 0$): e_x/t = 0.203; $K_x = 0.46; R_x = 0.80$

BENDING ABOUT y-AXIS ALONE ($e_x = 0$): e_y/t = 0.075; $K_y = 0.65; R_y = 0.85$

BIAXIAL BENDING: Equation 4 gives

$$\frac{1}{K_{sl}} \cong \frac{1}{(0.46)(0.80)} + \frac{1}{(0.65)(0.85)} - \frac{1}{(0.78)(0.80)} = 2.95$$

from which,

Furnished K_{sl} = 1/2.95 = 0.339

Furnished $P_{u,sl}$ = 0.339(1936) = 657 kips

This is larger than the required $P_{u,sl}$ of 312 kips.   O.K.

Therefore, the trial reinforcement designed for loading (1) is satisfactory.

Use 22-in. square section, 6–#9 bars, and ⅝ in.

round spirals at 2-in. pitch.   Ans.

Comment. In the column designing of this example, no live load reductions were made. For multistory buildings other than heavy industrial ones, such reductions are usually permitted. For permissible reductions of the live loads tributary to multistory columns, see Appendix F.

COLUMN CHART PROBLEMS

5–11. Using the charts of Appendix C, re-solve Problem 5–10.

5–12. Given column AB of a *laterally unbraced* frame of Fig. 5–44. The column

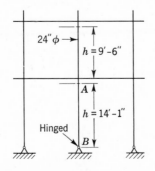

Fig. 5–44. Problems 5–12 and 5–13.

above AB is 24 in. round and has an unsupported height of 9 ft. 6 in. The floor supported by AB has a *total* stiffness at A of $I/L = 103$ in.[3] AB is hinged at the lower end and has an unsupported length of 14 ft. 1 in. Analysis of the frame has shown that under two different loadings, column AB is subject to *load-factored* axial loads and bending moments about its center line as follows:

	Loading (1)	Loading (2)
P_{uf}	968 kips	801 kips
M_{uf}	0	97 kip-ft.

Take 4000-lb. concrete and 60,000-psi-yield-point steel. Using the charts of Appendix C, design AB as a round spiral column with an overall diameter of 26 in. and the bars centered on a 21-in.-diameter circle.

5-13. Take the column AB of Problem 5-12 and the same data except that AB is subject to *one loading only* which produces *load-factored* P_{uf} of 400 kips and M_{uf} of 868 kip-ft., and it is to be 30-in. round spiral column with bars centered on a 25-in.-diameter circle.

REVIEW PROBLEMS

Unless otherwise noted, take 4000-lb. concrete, 60,000-psi-yield-point steel, 1-in. maximum aggregate size, and follow the ACI Code, USD, in performing the following solutions.

5-14. A cantilevered round spiral column is 18 in. in diameter and 15 ft. long. At its free end, there act a vertical centric load of 220 kips plus a horizontal load of 2.5 kips, both being *load-factored* values. Design the longitudinal reinforcement.

5-15. A 12-ft.-long column, 12 in. wide by 22 in. deep, carries a load of 120 kips (load-factored) applied 26 in. from its central axis, or 15 in. beyond its face. The column bends in double curvature without sidesway. Using the axial load transfer method, find the unequal amounts of longitudinal reinforcement along each of the 12-in. sides, assuming bar centers $2\frac{1}{2}$ in. from the outside.

5-16. Re-solve Problem 5-15, but using symmetrical longitudinal reinforcement along the 12-in. sides.

5-17. Re-solve Problem 5-15, using the Mörsch procedure.

5-18. Re-solve Problem 5-16, using the Mörsch procedure.

5-19. Re-solve Problem 5-16, using the column charts of Appendix C.

QUESTIONS

1. Define the *effective length of a column, slenderness ratio,* and *sidesway.*
2. What is the effective length of a cantilever column?
3. Define *primary* and *interaction moments* in a beam-column.
4. When a column bends in single curvature without sidesway, is there any magnification of the primary bending moments?
5. What constitutes adequate lateral bracing of a column?
6. What is the purpose of the ACI minimum eccentricity requirement in column designing?
7. What limitations, if any, are there to the "axial load transfer" method of designing rectangular columns?
8. Tell how to design symmetrical reinforcement near two faces of a rectangular column section using the "axial load transfer" method.
9. Answer Question 8 using the Mörsch procedure.
10. Suppose that in the Mörsch procedure, the r'_s value turns out to be negative for *all* permissible a/d values. What does this mean?

REFERENCES

1. COLUMN RESEARCH COUNCIL OF ENGINEERING FOUNDATION. *Guide to Design Criteria for Metal Compression Members* (2d ed.). New York: John Wiley & Sons, Inc., 1966.
2. TIMOSHENKO, S. P., and GERE, J. M. *Theory of Elastic Stability* (2d ed.). New York: McGraw-Hill Book Co., Inc., 1961.
3. ZUK, W. "Lateral Bracing Forces on Beams and Columns," *Journal of Engineering Mechanics Division, Proc. ASCE*, 1956, Vol. 82, No. E.M. 3.
4. WINTER, G. "Lateral Bracing of Columns and Beams," *Journal of Structural Division, Proc. ASCE*, 1958, Vol. 84, No. ST 2.
5. BROMS, B., and VIEST, I. M. "Long Reinforced Concrete Columns: A Symposium," *Trans. ASCE*, 1961, Vol. 126, Part II, pp. 309–395.
6. AMERICAN CONCRETE INSTITUTE. "Commentary on Building Code Requirements for Reinforced Concrete (ACI 318-63)," *ACI Publication SP-10*, 1965.
7. MÖRSCH, E. *Der Eisenbetonbau.* Stuttgart: 1926.
8. CHAMBAUD, R., and LEBELLE, P. *Formulaire de Béton armé.* Paris: 1953.
9. GRANHOLM, R. H. *A General Flexural Theory of Reinforced Concrete.* New York: John Wiley & Sons, Inc., 1965.
10. AMERICAN CONCRETE INSTITUTE. "Ultimate Strength Design of Reinforced Concrete Columns: Interim Report of ACI Committee 340," *ACI Publication SP-7*, 1964.

6

ONE-WAY SLAB, BEAM, AND GIRDER FLOORS

6–1. TYPES OF FLOOR AND ROOF SYSTEMS

In reinforced concrete buildings, a floor or roof usually consists of a slab appropriately supported so as to effect a successful, efficient, and economical transfer of the floor or roof loads to the columns, and thence to the foundation via the footings. The slab may be supported:

1. By a system of reinforced concrete beams and girders (precast or, more often, poured monolithically with the slab) which in turn are supported on columns.
2. On masonry or reinforced concrete walls.
3. Directly on columns.

In some buildings, a floor may consist of a concrete slab supported on structural steel beams. Our discussion will be limited to the construction in which the slab is poured monolithically with the supporting beams and girders or, in the absence of the beams and girders, with the supporting columns.

Some of the common types of such monolithic construction are shown in Fig. 6–1. Illustration (a) shows what is called the **slab, beam, and girder system,** in which each of the slabs has its principal reinforcement placed in one direction only (shown by the arrows), and hence is called a **one-way slab.** A variation of this construction is shown in (b), in which the intermediate floor beams of (a) have been dispensed with, and the one-way slabs have longer span lengths. In (c) is shown a slab with principal reinforcement in both directions, called a **two-way slab.** When the slab is supported directly on columns without beams or girders, it is called a **flat slab.** An example of flat slab is shown in (d), in which the slab is thickened around the columns, and the columns are enlarged at

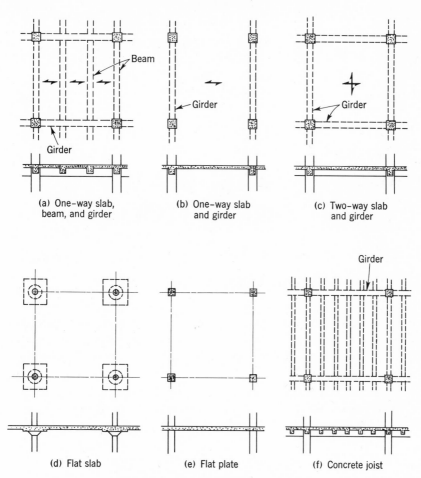

(a) One-way slab, beam, and girder

(b) One-way slab and girder

(c) Two-way slab and girder

(d) Flat slab

(e) Flat plate

(f) Concrete joist

Fig. 6–1.   Types of floor systems.

their tops.   The thickened part of the flat slab is called the *drop panel,* and the enlarged part of the columns is called the *column capital.*   A flat slab may also be constructed without drop panels.   Sometimes, the column capitals may be omitted when the loads are light, resulting in what is called **flat plate** as shown in (e), which may be with or without drop panels.   Of course, the flat slab or the flat plate is really no more flat than the one-way or two-way slab, but the terminology is in accord with customary usage in this country.   The **concrete joist system** is one in which the solid slab is replaced by a series of fairly closely spaced beams called **joists.**   These joists may run in one direction only such as shown in (f), or in both directions, resulting in a waffle-like floor.

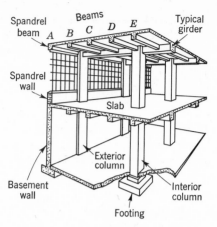

Fig. 6–2.   Slab, beam, and girder skeleton construction.

This chapter deals with one-way slab, beam, and girder floors.   Two-way slabs and flat slabs will be taken up in Chapter 7.   Figure 6–2 illustrates the kind of **skeleton construction** considered herein.   The relatively thin walls and partitions above ground are supported story by story, through girders, by a forest of columns.   It should be clearly distinguished from the older **wall bearing construction** still used for low buildings, in which all or most of the weight of the structure is supported by thick bearing walls.

The term **girder** is here applied to horizontal beam-like members extending from column to column, as distinguished from **beams,** which typically extend from girder to girder.

6–2. ANALYSIS OF SLABS

Slabs have been analyzed as elastic plates made of isotropic and homogeneous material [1].   The results of such analysis have been found to furnish a fairly satisfactory guide for most present-day *working stress* designing of reinforced concrete slabs.   It is to be noted that, before cracking, concrete behaves in much the same way as an isotropic and elastic material.   Once it is cracked, and strains get into the inelastic region, the elastic plate theory strictly does not apply, and the results obtained therefrom are subject to modification.

Accordingly, a more rational analysis used with *ultimate strength* proportioning of slabs is one which is based on their behavior at failure, taking into account the inelastic redistribution of forces throughout the entire floor system.   Such a design approach is called *limit design,* and one of the theories applicable to slabs is the *yield-line theory* of Johansen [2].

The ACI Code, on the other hand, permits the coupling of ultimate strength proportioning of members with the forces determined primarily from elastic analyses, modified in certain instances to approximate limit design. This coupling obviously contains an inconsistency, but is considered to be conservative and practically expedient in view of the limited amount of research findings now available along the lines of limit design, and the relative lack of familiarity of designers with them.

Except for slabs of unusual shapes, support conditions and loads, the simplified design procedures and the approximate coefficients for design moments and shears given in the ACI Code will usually be found satisfactory for most buildings.

6–3. BEHAVIOR OF ONE-WAY SLABS

Although only one-way slabs will be discussed in this chapter, it should be emphasized at this time that one-way slabs are really very special cases of two-way slabs. Consider, for instance, a simply supported and nearly square panel shown in Fig. 6–3a. Under transverse loads, the panel will deflect into a dish shape, as indicated by the contour lines and the side views. Obviously, if the panel is square and the support conditions are identical along the four edges, bending of about equal amount takes place in each direction. On the other hand, a very narrow, long panel as shown in (b) will deflect into the shape of a trough, in which most of the bending takes place in the short direction, except near the ends where some bending takes place in the long direction as well. It is usually assumed that when the ratio of the long side to the short side of a slab panel is at least 2, the panel may be designed as if all the bending took place in the short direction, and the steel located accordingly. But this does not mean that a slab *so designed,* and hence *called* a one-way slab, is throughout its domain entirely free of some two-way action. The ACI Code therefore, in its Methods 2 and 3 of two-way slab design (described in Chapter 7), contains a discerning clause requiring adequate

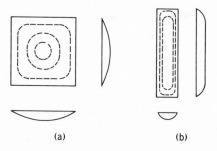

(a)   (b)

Fig. 6–3. Bending of slabs.

reinforcing in the long direction of any slab supported along its four edges even though the ratio of long side to short side of the panel may be ≥ 2, and with principal steel spanning the short direction.

6–4. CONTINUITY IN CONCRETE STRUCTURES

Since most slabs and beams are continuous members, and most girders are parts of the entire building frame, a review of statically indeterminate structural theory is highly pertinent and strongly recommended for the student at this time, before he gets involved with various design ramifications and practical considerations. There are a number of methods for analyzing statically indeterminate structures, but the much-used *moment distribution* procedure is probably the most efficient technique for flexural members, and should be thoroughly mastered by the student.

For the purpose of review, a numerical example illustrating moment distribution is presented in Appendix D. For a fuller treatment of the subject, the reader is referred to Reference 3.

A. Design Moments and Shears

6–5. SLABS SUPPORTED ON BEAMS, OR BEAMS SUPPORTED ON GIRDERS

This article describes first the general procedure of analysis to determine the maximum moments and shears for designing continuous slabs or beams. Then, the ACI simplified procedure will be discussed. Finally, a set of recommended coefficients for design moments will be given.

1. **General Procedure of Analysis.** Suppose the continuous slab or beam shown in Fig. 6–4a is subject to uniformly distributed dead and live loads. One may assume knife-edge non-yielding supports at the center lines of the supporting beams. This assumption ignores the torsional rigidity of the supporting beams, the effect of their widths, as well as any deflections they themselves undergo. As regards loading, the dead load is, of course, always present on all spans. The live load may be placed anywhere to produce the maximum possible effects. In bridges, it is usual to consider the possibility of live load on part of a span, but in building structures, it is more customary to consider the entire span to be either with or without live load.

Consider the span AB, for instance. The loading patterns to produce the maximum bending moments and shears are as shown in Fig. 6–4d.

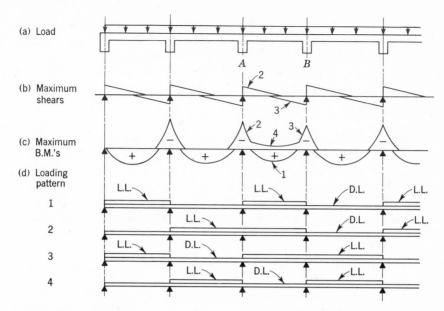

Fig. 6–4. Analysis of continuous slabs or beams. (Note that the moment diagrams are shown above in *inverted positions* principally to facilitate the visualization of the tensile steel locations. For reinforced concrete members, such orientation advantageously puts the moment curves along the side of the members where tensile reinforcement is needed. Refer also to Fig. G–1 of Appendix G.)

In loading pattern 1, the live load acts on span AB and on every alternate span therefrom, producing the *maximum positive bending moment in the interior of span* AB. Part of the moment diagram for this loading is shown by the curve marked *1* in (c).

As shown in loading pattern 2, by placing live load on the two spans adjacent to support A and on every alternate span therefrom, one obtains the *maximum negative bending moment over support* A. As shown by curve *2* in (c), this moment decreases very rapidly with the distance away from the support. This loading also produces the *maximum shears* on each side of support A. Curve *2* in (b) shows the maximum shear to the right of A.

Similarly, by loading the spans adjacent to support B and every alternate span therefrom as shown by loading pattern 3, one obtains the *maximum negative bending moment at support* B and the *maximum shears* on each side of B. The corresponding shear and moment diagrams are partially represented by the curves *3* in (b) and (c).

Normally, the foregoing loading patterns are all that one needs to consider for any span. However, if the live load is significantly larger than the dead load, and/or if the span under consideration is much shorter than its adjacent spans, a reversal in sign of the design bending moment in the interior of the span may occur. In that case, loading pattern 4 should also be investigated, which shows no live load on the span in question, but full live load on every alternate span therefrom. This produces the *minimum positive bending moment in the interior of span AB*. If this is positive, loading pattern 1 producing the maximum positive moment will govern the design. But if this turns out to be negative, as shown by curve *4* in (c), then it should be included in the designing of the span.

After the shears and moments for each loading pattern for all the spans have been calculated and plotted, one obtains the shear and moment **envelopes** as shown in Fig. 6–4b and c. The design negative moments and shears at the *faces of supports* may then be found by statics once the support widths are known.

For USD, both dead and live service loads are to be multiplied by the ACI load factors (1.5 for dead and 1.8 for live loads) in analyzing the foregoing loading patterns. Any reasonable assumptions may be made for computing the relative flexural stiffnesses of the members as long as they are consistent throughout the analysis. Usually, the reinforcement may be neglected in estimating the I values. In a beam which acts technically as a rectangular beam in one part and as a T-beam in another, the average I-value is sometimes used.

2. ACI Simplified Procedure of Analysis. The general procedure of analysis just described can become quite tedious for a multi-span continuous slab or beam. A slight simplification permitted by the ACI Code, Sec. 905(a)2, is that "consideration may be limited to combinations of dead load on all spans with full live load on two adjacent spans and with full live load on alternate spans." A further simplification may be obtained by utilizing the ACI Code, Sec. 2103(a)2, in connection with the elastic analysis of flat slabs. This provision permits one to assume that in determining the bending at any given support, the slab or beam in question is fixed at any support at two spans therefrom, provided that the slab or beam continues beyond that point. If both Secs. 905(a)2 and 2103(a)2 are adopted, the approximate loading patterns shown in Fig. 6–5 may be used for span AB in lieu of the corresponding and more accurate ones of Fig. 6–4. In this fashion, one need not have to deal with more than five spans at the most, at any one time.

3. Recommended Moment Coefficients for Slabs and Beams—Equal Spans and Uniform Loads. The procedure described in the two preceding parts of this article is generally applicable to any continuous slabs or beams having different span lengths, and loads other than uniformly dis-

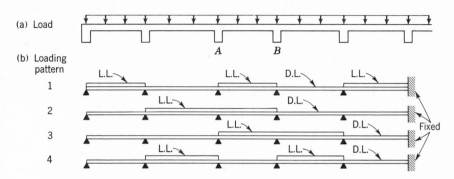

Fig. 6–5. ACI simplified analysis of continuous slabs or beams.

tributed ones. In buildings, the slabs and beams often have equal spans and uniform loads only. Their designing may be greatly facilitated by the coefficients presented in Fig. 6–6. These coefficients have been calculated by applying the general procedure of analysis of Part 1 to continuous systems of several equal spans, uniformly loaded according to the live-load criteria of Fig. 6–4. Detailed calculations are not shown here, but the sample calculations presented in Appendix D for the four-span case, together with a summary of the results thereof given in Table D–1, are typical.

The entries in the upper table of Fig. 6–6 have been taken directly from tables similar to Table D–1. For the minimum positive bending moments at the two quarter-points of each span, the *algebraic minimum* values from tables similar to Table D–1 have been used.

The values in the upper table of Fig. 6–6 are therefore coefficients of $w_D L^2$ and $w_L L^2$ for dead and live load moments, respectively. Ruling out the two-span and three-span systems shown therein, it is noted that there is no appreciable variation in the columns of these coefficients. Hence, the maximum values in the columns have been underscored, except in those for the minimum positive bending moments, in which the *algebraic minimum* values have been underscored. Using these underscored values, the *weighted combined coefficients* for use with *total* dead load plus live load have been computed for ratios of live to dead load from 0 through 5, and the results are shown in the lower table of Fig. 6–6. For example, the underscored coefficients for the maximum positive moment near the center of the end span are 0.078 for dead load and 0.100 for live load. For a live to dead load ratio of 2, the weighted combined coefficient is $[(0.078)(1) + (0.100)(2)]/(1 + 2)$, or 0.093, to be used with $(w_D + w_L)(L)^2$. For ratios of live to dead load not shown in this table, similar calculations may be easily made, or a simple interpolation may be employed if the particular ratio of live to dead load lies within the range of the table.

No. of spans	End span: Max. pos. B.M. near midspan		End span: Min. pos. B.M. — Midspan		End span: Min. pos. B.M. — $\frac{1}{4}$-pt.		First interior support: max. neg. B.M.		Interior spans: Max. pos. B.M. near midspan		Interior spans: Min. pos. B.M. — Midspan		Interior spans: Min. pos. B.M. — $\frac{1}{4}$-pt.		Typical interior support: max. neg. B.M.	
	D.L.	L.L.	D.L.	L.L.	D.L.	L.L.	D.L.	L.L.	D.L.	L.L.	D.L.	L.L.	D.L.	L.L.	D.L.	L.L.
2	0.070	0.096	0.063	−0.031	0.000	−0.047	−0.125	−0.125	—	—	—	—	—	—	—	—
3	0.080	0.101	0.075	−0.025	0.019	−0.037	−0.100	−0.117	0.025	0.075	0.025	−0.050	−0.006	−0.050	—	—
4	0.077	0.100	0.072	−0.027	0.013	−0.040	−0.107	−0.121	0.036	0.081	0.036	−0.045	−0.004	−0.049	−0.071	−0.107
5	0.078	0.100	0.072	−0.026	0.015	−0.039	−0.105	−0.119	0.046	0.086	0.033	−0.046	−0.005	−0.050	−0.079	−0.111
6 or more	0.078	0.100	0.072	−0.026	0.015	−0.040	−0.106	−0.120	0.043	0.084	0.034	−0.046	−0.005	−0.050	−0.087	−0.115

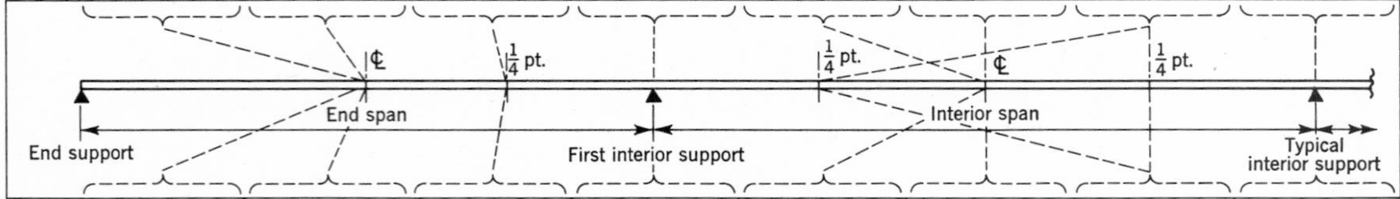

Ratio $\frac{L.L.}{D.L.}$	End span: Max. pos. B.M. near midspan	End span: Min. pos. B.M. Midspan	End span: Min. pos. B.M. $\frac{1}{4}$-pt.	First interior support	Interior spans: Max. pos. B.M. near midspan	Interior spans: Min. pos. B.M. Midspan	Interior spans: Min. pos. B.M. $\frac{1}{4}$-pt.	Typical interior support
0	0.078	0.072	0.013	−0.107	0.046	0.033	−0.005	−0.087
0.5	0.085	0.039	−0.004	−0.112	0.059	0.007	−0.020	−0.096
1	0.089	0.023	−0.014	−0.114	0.066	−0.007	−0.028	−0.101
2	0.093	0.006	−0.022	−0.116	0.073	−0.020	−0.035	−0.106
3	0.094	−0.002	−0.027	−0.117	0.076	−0.026	−0.039	−0.108
4	0.096	−0.007	−0.029	−0.118	0.078	−0.030	−0.041	−0.109
5	0.096	−0.011	−0.031	−0.119	0.079	−0.033	−0.043	−0.110

Max. B.M. coefficients for combined D.L. + L.L. designing
(4 or more equal spans, uniformly distributed load)

Fig. 6–6. Moment coefficients for continuous slabs and beams.

6–6. BEAMS OR GIRDERS RIGIDLY FRAMED INTO COLUMNS

Beams or girders rigidly framed into columns may have their moments and shears determined as described in Part 1 of Art. 6–5. However, column stiffness would now enter the analyses, as well as loading patterns involving floors other than that in question. While the shear and moment envelopes would look essentially similar to those shown in Fig. 6–4b and c, the necessary work to arrive at these is often quite excessive. So far as the maximum bending moments in the columns are concerned, the correct loading patterns are as shown in Appendix E, again requiring extensive calculations.

ACI Simplified Procedure of Analysis.   The ACI Code again permits certain simplifications in frame analysis for gravity loading. The student is here again referred to Secs. 905(a) and 2103(a)2 thereof, and also to Sec. 914.   By assuming the far ends of all the columns above and below the floor in question as fixed, the involvement with the other floors is eliminated.   Accordingly, the loading patterns in this simplified procedure are as shown in Fig. 6–7, in which AB is the span in question.   As shown therein, loading pattern 1 produces the maximum positive moment in AB.   Loading patterns 2 and 3 produce respectively the maximum negative moments at ends A and B as well as the maximum shears thereat. Loading pattern 4 produces the minimum positive moment in the interior of AB.   Loading patterns 1 and 4 will also give the maximum effects of unbalanced floor loads in the columns above and below A and B, as required by Sec. 914.

To facilitate frame designing, the practical designer will undoubtedly resort to tables similar to those of Fig. 6–6.   Reference 4 contains such design aids covering a wide variety of loadings, ratios of column to girder stiffnesses, ratios of live to dead loads, and different adjacent span lengths.

6–7. ACI MOMENT AND SHEAR COEFFICIENTS FOR LIMITED CONDITIONS

In lieu of more accurate analyses, many designers often obtain maximum moments and shears produced by gravity loading on slabs, beams, or girders by using the coefficients given in Sec. 904(c).   These coefficients are shown schematically in Fig. 6–8.   The use of these coefficients is subject to the following limitations:

1. Approximately equal spans (the longer of the two adjacent spans not to exceed the shorter by more than 20% of the longer).
2. Uniformly distributed loads where the ratio of live to dead loads does not exceed 3 (in USD, where the ratio of 1.8 times live load to 1.5 times dead load does not exceed 3).

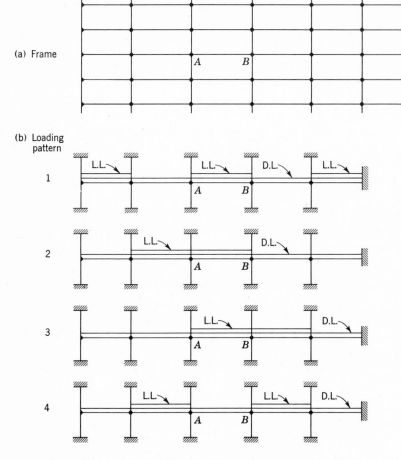

Fig. 6–7. ACI simplified frame analysis for gravity loading.

It is to be noted that these coefficients should not be used indiscriminately. On the other hand, one may use them at least as a guide to preliminary design, and resort later to a more precise investigation.

6–8. LATERAL FORCES

When lateral forces (such as wind or earthquake forces) on a building frame have to be considered, one may no longer isolate one floor at a time and analyze it independently of the others as was done in the simplified procedure of Art. 6–6. Instead, the entire building frame must be considered as a whole. The *portal method* and the *cantilever method* are sometimes used to analyze such a frame. Although crude, they are useful tools, at least in preliminary designing because of their simplicity and because they do not require prior knowledge of the cross-sectional dimensions of the members.

The so-called "exact analysis" of building frames subject to wind or earthquake forces, as usually performed, is really not exact, since wind gusts or earthquake forces are time-dependent phenomena. Unless the dynamic behavior of the structure is considered, any other kind of analysis is at best quasi-static, and may give results that are quite misleading despite the semblance to "exactness" in the static analysis.

B. Design Considerations for One-Way Slab, Beam, and Girder Floors

The following articles regarding practical design details of one-way slabs and the supporting beams and girders as well as certain ACI Code requirements may be found helpful.

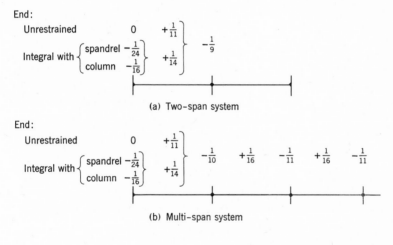

(a) Two-span system

(b) Multi-span system

(c) For slabs with 10 ft. span or less, or for beams and girders where ratio of sum of column stiffnesses to beam stiffness exceeds 8 at each end

Notes:

1. L' = clear span for positive B.M. and shear, or the average of the two adjacent clear spans for negative B.M.

2. All value shown are B.M. coefficients of wL'^2

3. Shear in end members at the first interior support = (1.15) $(wL'/2)$

4. Shear at all other supports = $(wL'/2)$

Fig. 6–8. ACI coefficients [Sec. 904(c)].

Plate 6–1.   Precast rigid frame factory building in England.   The *gable frames* were cast in three pieces, there being a single-lap, bolted concrete splice in the vicinity of the contraflexure point, underneath the glass roof sections shown.   Note the tapered, rigidly connected column portion of the frames.

6–9. SLAB THICKNESS

1. Unless deflections are computed, the minimum thickness of one-way slabs of normal-weight concrete should be as stipulated in Sec. 909(b), part of which is given below:

Simply supported	$L/25$
One end continuous	$L/30$
Both ends continuous	$L/35$
Cantilever	$L/12$

Except for the concrete joist type of construction, the minimum thickness of solid slabs in the United States is, for practical reasons, $3\frac{1}{2}$ in.

2. Slab thicknesses are usually given in $\frac{1}{2}$-in. multiples, although some designers may wish to use $\frac{1}{4}$-in. multiples for slabs less than 6 in. thick.

3. If not dictated by considerations other than strength, the slab thickness is usually governed by flexure, seldom by diagonal tension, although the latter should always be checked.   Since stirrups are very awkward in slabs except in very thick ones, the thickness should normally be so chosen that no web reinforcement is required.

4. Slabs are usually designed as singly reinforced members except thick ones wherein compression reinforcement may be properly tied without difficulty.

5. If possible, a uniform slab thickness should be planned for throughout all spans as it facilitates the simplicity and reuse of the formwork. For nearly equal span lengths, the largest bending moment usually occurs at the first interior support, so the end span thickness may be maintained throughout the system and the interior spans become more lightly reinforced. On the other hand, overall economy may be achieved by using a thinner slab largely dictated by the interior spans and by reinforcing the end spans more heavily. Making the end spans shorter than the rest is structurally sound if architecturally acceptable.

6–10. SLAB REINFORCING

1. Minimum Principal Reinforcement. The minimum amount of principal reinforcement [Sec. 911(b)] should not be less than the minimum shrinkage and temperature steel content (see next item). Also, Sec. 804(c) requires that the center-to-center spacing of principal reinforcing bars should not be more than $3t$ nor more than 18 in. Some such limitation is necessary in order to insure slab action, reduce cracking, and provide for the possibility of high local concentration of load. The occurrence of the latter would tend to punch out a frustum of concrete, largely through diagonal tension failure, as pictured in Fig. 6–9. With suitably limited bar spacings, there would remain at least some principal reinforcing bars in the frustum. Referring to Fig. 6–9, it is seen that the spacing of the bars should not exceed s which is equal to $(q + 2d \cot \beta)$. If β is 45°, and the load concentration is distributed over a width $q = d$, then s equals $3d$. Preferably, principal bars should not be farther apart than, say, $2\frac{1}{2}d$.

2. Shrinkage and Temperature Reinforcement. Slabs with one-way principal reinforcement require *shrinkage and temperature* (S & T) reinforcement normal thereto to resist the concrete tensile stresses caused by the shrinkage of the concrete, and/or by temperature changes. Most of

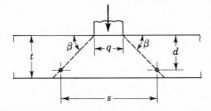

Fig. 6–9.   Maximum spacing of principal reinforcing bars.

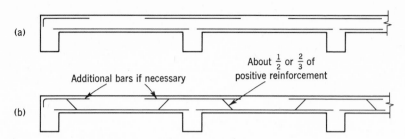

Fig. 6–10.   Arrangement of reinforcement.

the shrinkage takes place in the first few months after placing, but may recur after a re-wetting.   The S & T reinforcement also serves admirably to space and hold the principal reinforcement in place.   The minimum amount of S & T reinforcement is stipulated in ACI Sec. 807 in terms of slab thickness, t, as follows:

Slabs where plain bars are used	0.25% bt
Slabs where deformed bars having f_y < 60 ksi are used	0.20% bt
Slabs where deformed bars having f_y = 60 ksi or welded wire fabric having welded intersections not farther apart in the direction of stress than 12 in.	0.18% bt

Also, the spacing of S & T reinforcement must not exceed $5t$ or 18 in.

3. Spandrel Effect.   A spandrel beam at the exterior end of a slab is often stiffer than the interior floor beams, either by virtue of its larger size or because of its relative inability to rotate as much, if buried in masonry.   Hence some negative steel in the top of the slab at such points goes a long way toward preventing unsightly top tensile cracking. Design for $(\frac{1}{24})(w)(L')^2$ per Sec. 904(c).

4. Arrangement of Principal Reinforcement.   One has the choice of using all straight bars alone (Fig. 6–10a), or some bent bars (Fig. 6–10b). The all-straight bar arrangement uses a bit less steel, but more supporting chairs.   The bent-bar arrangement involves a little more cost in bending but permits easier positioning and placement of the top steel.   If bent bars are used, one should check whether extra top steel is needed in addition to the bent-up bars at the exterior end of the end span in order to cover the entire region of the negative bending moment thereat.

5. Additional Top Reinforcement in the Flange of a Girder.   When a girder is parallel to the principal reinforcement of an adjacent one-way slab, part of the slab near the girder is already working in compression. Therefore, *if the girder is designed as a T-beam* in its positive moment region by using a part of the already stressed slab as its flange, the flange portion of the tee should be additionally reinforced in some fashion.   In a situation like this, as pictured in Fig. 6–11, Sec. 906(e) provides that rein-

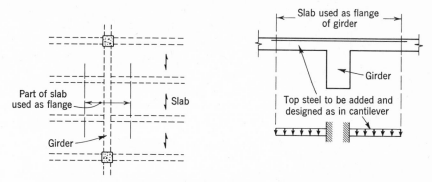

Fig. 6–11.   Additional top reinforcement across a girder.

forcement should be added at the top of the flange, and transversely to the girder to resist a bending moment in the flange acting as a cantilever and carrying the load on the portion of the slab required for the flange of the T-beam.   The maximum spacing of such bars is $5t$ or 18 in., whichever is the smaller.

However, it is emphasized that *even if the girder is not designed as a T-beam,* some top negative steel across the girder is desirable in order to take care of two-way action thereat in the adjacent one-way slabs, as described more fully in the next item.

6. Additional Top Reinforcement Across Short Edges of One-Way Slab Panels. When the ratio of the long to the short span of a slab panel is equal to 2 or larger, the panel is usually designed as a one-way slab with principal reinforcement in the short direction.   However, as explained in Art. 6–3, some two-way action exists near the ends of the long span in such panels.   Therefore, some top negative steel is desirable thereat, as shown in Fig. 6–12.   The absence of this reinforcement will not, of course, result in structural failure of the slab since the slab has been designed to carry all the load in the short direction, but may lead to cracking of the top of the slab near the girders.

The moments for designing this reinforcement are highly indeterminate. To avoid extensive analysis, the approximate average moment coefficients given in Table 6–1 may be found helpful.   These coefficients are based on Method 2 for two-way slab design given in Appendix A, Sec. A2002 of the ACI Code; their derivation is quite simple.[1]   However, since two way

[1] The moment coefficients of the ACI Method 2 of two-way slabs appear in Table 7–1 of this text.   The last column thereof gives the long-span mid-strip negative moment coefficients, C, of wS^2.   The corresponding column-strip moment coefficients are taken to be $\frac{2}{3}$ of C on the average.   This assumes a distribution of moments along the short edge as shown in Fig. 6–13.   If C_{av} is the average moment coefficient for the entire

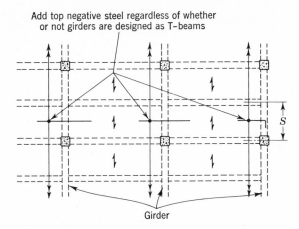

Add top negative steel regardless of whether
or not girders are designed as T–beams

Girder

Fig. 6–12.   Additional top steel in long span of one-way slabs.

Table 6–1. Approximate Coefficients, C_{av}, **of** wS^2 **for Negative B.M. in Long Span of One-Way Slabs**

w = uniform load per unit area S = short span length

Average long-span negative B.M. = $C_{av}wS^2$, per unit length of short edge

Edge Conditions of Slabs	Slab Continuous Across Short Edge	Slab Discontinuous Across Short Edge
Case 1—Interior panels	−0.028	—
Case 2—One edge discontinuous	−0.034	−0.018
Case 3—Two edges discontinuous	−0.041	−0.021
Case 4—Three edges discontinuous	−0.048	−0.024
Case 5—Four edges discontinuous	—	−0.028

slabs are not taken up in this text until Chapter 7, the student is requested to take for granted at this time that these are reasonable values, postponing a closer examination of the derivation until after he has studied Chapter 7.

Note that, in applying the coefficients of Table 6–1, the *short* span length S is used in computing the long-span moment in question, where S is the center to center distance between supports or the clear span plus

short edge, its value may be found by equating the areas of the trapezoid and the rectangle. Thus,

$$C_{av}S = CS - (S/4)(\tfrac{2}{3})(C)$$

from which $C_{av} = (\tfrac{5}{6})(C)$. Hence the values given in Table 6–1 are simply $\tfrac{5}{6}$ of those in the last column of Table 7–1.

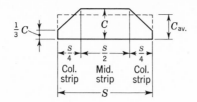

Fig. 6–13. Distribution of long-span negative bending moment along short edge.

twice the slab thickness, whichever is smaller.   Also, where the negative moment on one side of a support is less than 80 per cent of that on the other side, two-thirds of the difference should be distributed in proportion to the relative stiffness of the slabs.

The top bars in question need not be very long; their extension into each adjacent panel for a distance equal to about $\frac{1}{5}$ of the long span is usually adequate.

7. Splices in Reinforcement.   The number of spans over which a bottom bar can be extended depends on the bar lengths available, which may be from 35 to 60 ft., depending on shipping and handling facilities. If splices are used, they must be explicitly indicated on the design drawings, and must conform to the requirements stated in detail in Sec. 805. Briefly, the essential requirements for splicing given therein are as follows:

1. *Tensile reinforcement splicing* [Sec. 805(b)].
   a. Lapped splices in tension are not allowed for bars larger than #11.
   b. Avoid splices at points of maximum tensile stress.
   c. Any splice must be able to transfer the entire computed stress from bar to bar without exceeding $\frac{3}{4}$ of the permissible bond values, u_u.
   d. The lap length for deformed bars must not be less than 12 in., nor less than:

   > 24 bar diameters for f_y of 40 ksi
   > 30 bar diameters for f_y of 50 ksi
   > 36 bar diameters for f_y of 60 ksi

2. *Compression reinforcement splicing.*
   a. For bars larger than #11, welded splices should preferably be used.
   b. Where lapped splices are used, the minimum lap length for deformed bars [Sec. 805(c)] is:

   > For f'_c of 3 ksi or more, 12 in. or
   > 20 bar diameters for f_y of 50 ksi or less
   > 24 bar diameters for f_y of 60 ksi
   > 30 bar diameters for f_y of 75 ksi
   > For f'_c less than 3 ksi, the above values
   > are to be increased by one-third.

6–11. FLOOR FRAMING LAYOUTS

Before any detailed designing can proceed, a decision must be made as to the general layout, especially regarding the location of the columns. Generally, the simplest arrangement is best. The owner usually wants as few columns as possible, but the decision should be made by the architect after the structural engineer has shown him by rapid preliminary calculations what structural sacrifices are involved in a given proposal, and what alternate layout would be the most economical. To do this the engineer may study several typical slab, beam, and girder arrangements similar to Fig. 6–2, recognizing that extensive thick solid slabs are uneconomical; that for light loads such slab spans may be 12 ft. or more, for heavy ones perhaps 6 to 7 ft.; that beams and girders of more than 20- to 25-ft. span tend to have depths which encroach upon headroom; that when the column spacings are unequal in the two directions it will usually be better to run the girders in the short direction; and that heavy concentrated loads near the center of long spans should be avoided.

EXAMPLE 6–1

The Design of an Industrial Building

Following preliminary studies, it is required to design a three-story manufacturing and storage building according to the floor plan and section shown on Calculation Sheet 1. Other data and the USD specifications of the ACI Code are shown on Sheet 2 for ready reference.

The comments in the following articles are presented to elucidate certain details of design shown on the remaining Calculation Sheets, and also to describe alternate techniques or details. Throughout the design, a tabular bookkeeping system of recording calculations has been adopted as much as possible. Because of its efficiency and availability for presenting an overall picture of the structure being considered, it is much favored by many designers, particularly when working with continuous structures.

The Design of Floor Slabs

(Calculation Sheets 3 Through 5)

6–12. Slab Thickness (Sheet 3)

First, a sketch of slabs *S1* and *S2*, taken as a continuous beam 1 ft. in width, was drawn, showing the span lengths and the loads. The clear span lengths were obtained by assuming a 12-in. beam width.[2] The weight of the slab was estimated, subject to later revision. For USD, the

---

[2] It is advisable to underestimate the width of supporting members, as this will result in conservatively higher values of slab shear and bending moments which will not need to be revised later on.

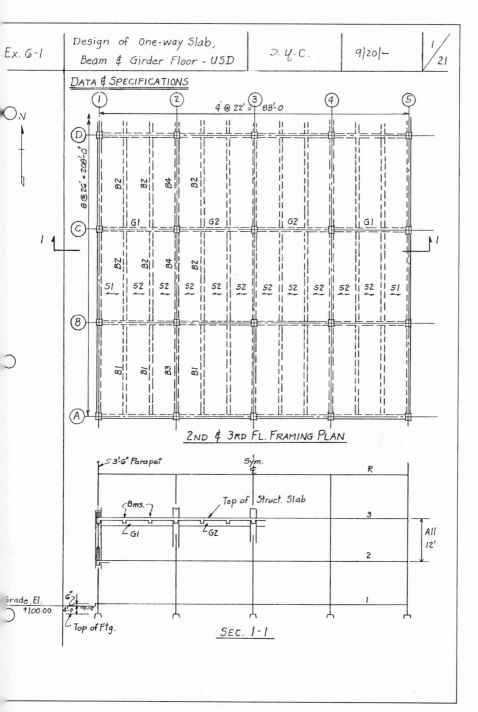

Ex. 6-1 | Design of One-way Slab, Beam & Girder Floor - USD | D. Y. C. | 9|20|– | 1/21

DATA & SPECIFICATIONS

4 @ 22' = 88'-0

8 @ 26' = 208'-0"

B2 B2 B4 B2

G1 G2 G2 G1

B2 B2 B4 B2

S1 S2 S2 S2 S2 S2 S2 S2 S2 S2 S2 S1

B1 B1 B3 B1

2ND & 3RD FL. FRAMING PLAN

S 3'-6" Parapet

Sym. ℄

R

Bms.

Top of Struct. Slab

G1 G2

3

All 12'

2

Grade El.
+100.00

Top of Ftg.

1

SEC. 1-1

loads were augmented by load factors of 1.5 and 1.8 for dead and live loads respectively.

As the ratio of 1.8(L.L.)/1.5(D.L.) = 7.2 exceeds 3, the ACI moment coefficients of Sec. 904 (given in Art. 6–7) were, strictly, not applicable. Also, as this ratio of 7.2 was outside the range of the lower table of Fig. 6–6 in Art. 6–5, the moment coefficients were determined by using the values underscored in the upper table thereof. For example, the coefficient for the maximum negative moment over the first interior support was obtained as follows:

$$\frac{1.0(\text{D.L. coef.}) + 7.2(\text{L.L. coef.})}{8.2} = \frac{1.0(-0.107) + 7.2(-0.121)}{8.2} = -0.119$$

Coefficients for moments at other sections were similarly calculated.

The moments were then obtained by multiplying the coefficients by wL^2. The maximum negative moments at the center of supports were then reduced to those at the faces thereof by statics. This calculation is explained in the inset on the right margin near the middle of Sheet 3, which shows that

$$M \text{ (at face of support)} = M \text{ (at center of support)} + \frac{Va}{2} - \frac{w}{2}\left(\frac{a}{2}\right)^2$$

Other designers may prefer to obtain this moment by using

$$M \text{ (at face of support)} = M \text{ (at center of support)} + \frac{Va}{3}$$

An explanation of the above calculation may be found in Reference 5.

Of the moments determined, the maximum value was seen to occur near midspan of *S1*, which was then used to find the required effective depth d and overall thickness t. The calculations show that the required t of 2.75 in. was smaller than the minimum t of 2.93 in. for stiffness and the practical minimum t of $3\frac{1}{2}$ in. Taking a t of $3\frac{1}{2}$ in., the slab was checked for diagonal tension, before proceeding to the designing of reinforcement, by comparing the concrete shear capacity, $V_c = v_c bd = 2\phi \sqrt{f'_c}\, bd$, with the maximum shear V_u at the critical section which is at d from the face of the interior support of the end span.

6–13. SLAB REINFORCEMENT (Sheets 4 and 5)

For the designing of the **principal reinforcement,** the previously determined load-factored moments were summarized in a line marked M_{uf} on Sheet 4. At the exterior end of the end span *S1*, a moment of $wL'^2/24$, where L' is the clear span, was arbitrarily introduced to account for the spandrel effect. With $\phi = 0.9$, $b = 12$ in., and $d = 2.50$ in., the values

| Ex. 6-1 | Data & Spec. (concl.) | J. Y. C. | 9/20/— | 2/21 |

DATA & SPEC. (cont.)

Loads : __L.L.__ Heavy manufacturing & storage @ 300 #/□' on floors.
50 #/□' on roof.

      __D.L.__ ½" wearing surface concrete on top of floor structural slab @
6 #/□' additional on floors and not counted for strength
[Sec. 907(b)]. (All subsequent slab designing refers to the
structural slab.)
Roofing & finish = 20 #/□' on roof.

__Concrete__ : $f_c' = 4,000$ psi $k_1 = 0.85$

__Steel__ : A305, $f_y = 40,000$ psi for floors and roof.
$f_y = 60,000$ " for columns.

__Spec.__ : ACI - __USD.__

__Flexure__ [Sec. 1504(b)]: $\phi = 0.9$
[Sec. 1601(b)]: $p_{max.} = 0.75\left[0.85\,k_1\,\dfrac{f_c'}{f_y}\,\dfrac{87,000}{87,000+f_y}\right]$

$$= 0.75\left[0.85(0.85)\left(\tfrac{4}{40}\right)\left(\tfrac{87}{127}\right)\right]$$

$$= 3.71\% \text{ , singly-reinforced rectangular section.}$$

[Sec. 911(a)]: Min. $p = 200/f_y = 0.2/40 = 0.5\%$ (Beams & girders)
[Sec. 911(b) & Sec. 807]:
        Min. $p = 0.2\%$ bt (Slabs)

[Sec. 1507]: Deflection check req'd. if p, $(p-p')$, or (p_w-p_f)
exceeds $0.18\,f_c'/f_y = 0.18(4)/40 = 1.8\%$

__Diagonal Tension__ [Sec. 1504(b)] : $\phi = 0.85$
    [Sec. 1701(c)] : $v_c = 2\phi\sqrt{f_c'} = 2(0.85)\sqrt{4000} = 0.108$ ksi
    [Sec. 1705(b)] : v_u max. $= 10\,\phi\sqrt{f_c'}$ $= 0.538$ "
    [Sec. 1706(a)] : $6\,\phi\sqrt{f_c'}$ $= 0.323$ "
        Max. vert. stirrup spacing $= d/2$ if $v_u \le 0.323$ ksi
        "   "   " $= d/4$ if $v_u > 0.323$ "
    [Sec. 1706(b)]: Min. web reinf. $A_v = 0.15\%$ bs.

__Bond & Anchorage__ [Sec. 1504(b)] : $\phi = 0.85$

    [Sec. 1801(c)1]:
      Top bars, $u_u = 6.7\sqrt{f_c'}/D = 0.423/D$ ksi, or 0.560 ksi
      Other bars, $u_u = 9.5\sqrt{f_c'}/D = 0.601/D$ ", or 0.800 "

$R = M_{uf}/\phi bd^2$ at the various sections were calculated. Using the USD Beam Chart A–1 of Appendix A, the required p, and hence A_s, were easily determined.

It is seen that because of the heavy live load relative to the dead load, there was a reversal in the moments in the interior of all spans, requiring top steel in addition to the usual bottom steel for positive moment thereat. Using an all-straight bar arrangement, the selected sizes of bars and their spacings were as shown in the sketch marked *"Use A_s,"* on Sheet 4. All the bottom bars were extended at each end 6 in. beyond the faces of supports. The top bars at the exterior end were anchored 9 in. into the support. All the top bars over the interior supports were extended to midspan of adjacent slabs and adequately lapped thereat. This steel arrangement, although slightly wasteful, was adopted because of its simplicity. An alternative arrangement would be to use bent-up bars plus additional top bars, some of which may be cut off at points where they are no longer needed. This alternative arrangement was later used for the floor beams *B1* and *B2*, and as will be seen then, it entails a great deal more calculation.

The **shrinkage and temperature reinforcement** was then designed as a straight percentage of (*bt*), subject to the maximum spacing requirement of 5*t* or 18 in.

Flexural bond stress was then checked at the faces of all supports and was found to be satisfactory. It should be mentioned that by virtue of Sec. 1801(c), this step was really unnecessary since all the bars used here had either end anchorage equal to at least 1.25 times that required, or lap lengths specified for tensile splices and long enough to develop the bar forces at $\frac{3}{4}$ of the nominal permissible bond stress u_u.

Long-span top negative steel was provided, as shown on Sheet 5, to prevent potential cracks due to two-way action. The reader is referred to Part 6 of Art. 6–10 for designing such reinforcement. The lengths of the bars across the interior girders were arbitrarily estimated at about $\frac{1}{5}$ of the sum of the long span lengths of the adjacent slab panels. The bars near the exterior griders were extended roughly $\frac{1}{5}$ of the clear span into the adjacent slab and were anchored 9 in. in the spandrel girder.

ONE-WAY SLAB DESIGN PROBLEMS

6–1. Same as Example 6–1 except that the beams are spaced 11 ft. center to center instead of 7 ft. 4 in. Completely design the floor slab system.

6–2. Given a three-story building with the typical floor framing plan and section as shown in Fig. 6–14. The *service* loads are:

Live load: Floor—80 psf
              Stair—100 psf
Dead load: Floor—Partition 20 psf
               —Finish   10
               —Ceiling   20
            Stair—Finish   10 psf

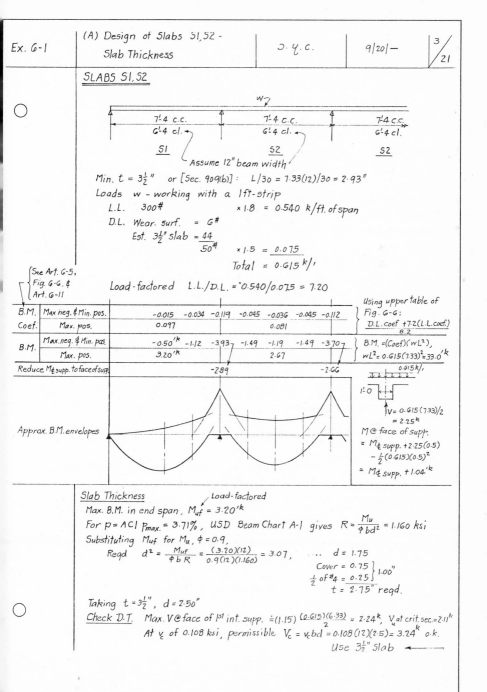

| Ex. 6-1 | (A) Design of Slabs S1,S2 -
Slab Thickness | ↄ. Ƴ. C. | 9/20/— | 3/21 |

SLABS S1,S2

```
                    w ↗
  ▽━━━━━━━━━━━━━▲━━━━━━━━━━━━━▲━━━━━━━━━━━━━▲
    7'-4 c.c.         7'-4 c.c.         7'-4 c.c.
    6'-4 cl.↰         6'-4 cl.↰         6'-4 cl.
      S1                 S2                S2
         ↳ Assume 12" beam width ↲
```

Min. $t = 3\frac{1}{2}''$ or [Sec. 909(b)] : $L/30 = 7.33(12)/30 = 2.93''$

Loads w - working with a 1ft-strip

     L.L.   300#   × 1.8 = 0.540 $k/ft.$ of span

     D.L. Wear. surf. = 6#

        Est. $3\frac{1}{2}''$ slab = $\dfrac{44}{50^{\#}}$

                   × 1.5 = $\underline{0.075}$

                Total = 0.615 $k/'$

{ See Art. 6-5, Fig. 6-6, & Art. 6-11

Load-factored   L.L./D.L. = 0.540/0.075 = 7.20

B.M. Coef.	Max neg. & Min. pos.	-0.015	-0.034	-0.119	-0.045	-0.036	-0.045	-0.112
	Max. pos.	0.097				0.081		
B.M.	Max.neg. & Min. pos.	-0.50'k	-1.12	-3.93⤻	-1.49	-1.19	-1.49	-3.70⤻
	Max. pos.	3.20'k				2.67		
Reduce M⌷ supp. to face of supp			-2.89				-2.66	

Using upper table of Fig. 6-6:

$$\dfrac{D.L.\,coef + 7.2(L.L.coef.)}{8.2}$$

B.M. = (Coef.)(wL²),
$wL^2 = 0.615(7.33)^2 = 33.0'^k$

Approx. B.M. envelopes

```
    0.615k/'
  ↓↓↓↓↓↓↓
  1'-0 ├──┤
       └──┘
```

↧V = 0.615 (7.33)/2
     = 2.25^k

M @ face of supp.
= M⌷ supp. + 2.25(0.5)
   − $\frac{1}{2}$(0.615)(0.5)²
= M⌷ supp. + 1.04'^{k}

Slab Thickness

Max. B.M. in end span, M_{uf} = 3.20'^{k} (Load-factored)

For $p = ACI\ p_{max}$ = 3.71%, USD Beam Chart A-1 gives $R = \dfrac{M_u}{\phi bd^2}$ = 1.160 ksi

Substituting M_{uf} for M_u, $\phi = 0.9$,

   Reqd $d^2 = \dfrac{M_{uf}}{\phi b R} = \dfrac{(3.20)(12)}{0.9(12)(1.160)}$ = 3.07,   ... $d = 1.75$

                       Cover = 0.75 ⎱ 1.00"
                  $\frac{1}{2}$ of #4 = 0.25 ⎰
                    $t = \underline{2.75''}$ reqd.

Taking $t = 3\frac{1}{2}''$, $d = 2.50''$

Check D.T.   Max. V @ face of 1st int. supp. ≐ (1.15) $\dfrac{(0.615)(6.33)}{2}$ = 2.24^k, V_u at crit.sec.=2.11^k

At v_c of 0.108 ksi, permissible $V_c = v_c bd$ = 0.108 (12)(2.5) = 3.24^k o.k.

                   Use $3\frac{1}{2}''$ slab ⟵

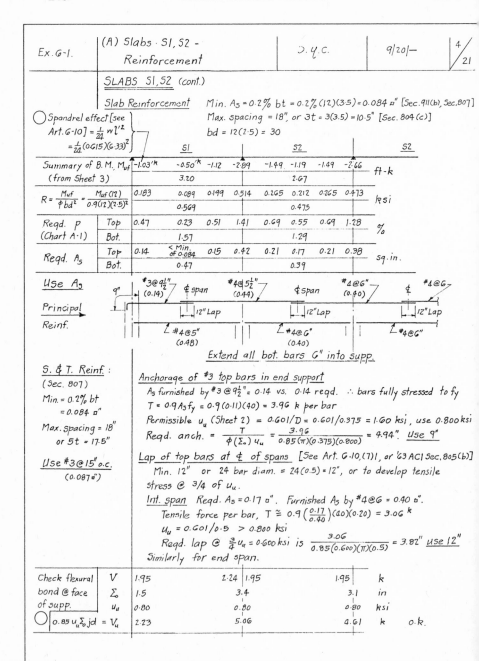

Ex. 6-1.	(A) Slabs · S1, S2 - Reinforcement	D. Y. C.	9/20/—	4/21

SLABS S1, S2 (cont.)

Slab Reinforcement   Min. $A_s = 0.2\% \, bt = 0.2\% (12)(3.5) = 0.084 \, \square''$ [Sec. 911(b), Sec. 807]

○ Spandrel effect [see   Max. spacing = 18", or $3t = 3(3.5) = 10.5''$ [Sec. 804(c)]

Art. 6-10] $= \frac{1}{24} w l'^2$ $bd = 12(2.5) = 30$

$= \frac{1}{24}(0.615)(6.33)^2$

		S1		S2			S2	
Summary of B.M. M_{uf} (from Sheet 3)		-1.03'k -0.50'k 3.20	-1.12 -2.89	-1.49 -1.19 2.67	-1.49 -2.66			ft-k
$R = \frac{M_{uf}}{\phi b d^2} = \frac{M_{uf}(12)}{0.9(12)(2.5)^2}$		0.183 0.089 0.569	0.199 0.514	0.265 0.212 0.475	0.265 0.473			ksi
Reqd. p (Chart A·1)	Top	0.47 0.23	0.51 1.41	0.69 0.55	0.69 1.28			%
	Bot.	1.57		1.29				
Reqd. A_s	Top	0.14 < Min. of 0.084	0.15 0.42	0.21 0.17	0.21 0.38			sq. in.
	Bot.	0.47		0.39				

Use A_s

Principal Reinf.

9"

#3@9½" (0.14)   ₵ span   #4@5½" (0.44)   ₵ span   #4@6" (0.40)   ₵   #4@6

12" Lap   12" Lap   12" Lap

#4@5" (0.48)   #4@6" (0.40)   #4@6"

Extend all bot. bars 6" into supp.

S. & T. Reinf. :

(Sec. 807)

Min. = 0.2% bt
= 0.084 □"

Max. spacing = 18"
or 5t = 17.5"

Use #3@15" o.c.
(0.087 □")

Anchorage of #3 top bars in end support

A_s furnished by #3 @ 9½" = 0.14 vs. 0.14 reqd. ∴ bars fully stressed to f_y

$T = 0.9 A_s f_y = 0.9(0.11)(40) = 3.96$ k per bar

Permissible u_u (Sheet 2) = 0.601/D = 0.601/0.375 = 1.60 ksi, use 0.800 ksi

Reqd. anch. = $\frac{T}{\phi(\Sigma_o) u_u} = \frac{3.96}{0.85(\pi)(0.375)(0.800)} = 4.94''$. Use 9"

Lap of top bars at ₵ of spans   [See Art. 6-10,(1)], or '63 ACI Sec. 805(b)]

Min. 12" or 24 bar diam. = 24(0.5) = 12", or to develop tensile stress @ 3/4 of u_u.

Int. span. Reqd. $A_s = 0.17$ □". Furnished A_s by #4@6 = 0.40 □".

Tensile force per bar, $T \cong 0.9 \left(\frac{0.17}{0.40} \right)(40)(0.20) = 3.06$ k

$u_u = 0.601/0.5 > 0.800$ ksi

Reqd. lap @ $\frac{3}{4} u_u = 0.600$ ksi is $\frac{3.06}{0.85(0.600)(\pi)(0.5)} = 3.82''$ use 12"

Similarly for end span.

Check flexural bond @ face of supp. ○ $0.85 u_u \Sigma_o jd = V_u$	V	1.95	2.24 1.95	1.95	k
	Σ_o	1.5	3.4	3.1	in
	u_u	0.80	0.80	0.80	ksi
		2.23	5.06	4.61	k o.k.

Ex. 6-1	(A) Slabs S1,S2 (concl.) - Additional Top Steel (N-S)	つ. 4. C.	9/20/—	5/21

SLABS S1,S2 (cont.)

Additional Top Steel Across Short Edges of Slab Panels [Refer to Art. 6-10]

S = c. to c. short span = $7'-4''$,
or S = clear short span plus $2(t)$
    $= (6'-4'') + 7''$ $= 6'-11''$, governs.
$w = 0.615$ k/ft. (Sheet 3)

Moment coef. of wS^2 @ different locations corresponding to the support conditions shown are taken from Table 6-1 of Art. 6-10.
In slab panels S1 & across col. line B:
$\frac{0.034}{0.041} > 80\%$. No distrib. needed, [Sec. A2002(b)].
Use 0.041 for designing
In slab panels S2 & across col. line B
$\frac{0.028}{0.034} > 80\%$ No distrib.
Use 0.034 for designing

Giving the preferential placement to short span #4 bars, & assuming #3 bars for long span, the eff. depth for the latter is:
$d = 3.50 - 0.75 - 0.50 - 0.19 = 2.06''$
Max. spacing = 18'' or 3t = 10.5''   (Sheet 3)
$bd = 12(2.06) = 24.72$ □''

Min $A_s = 0.084$ □'' (Sheet 3),
$wS^2 = 0.615 (6.93)^2 = 29.54$ 'k,

B.M. coef.	B.M. M_{ut}	$R = \frac{M_{uf}}{\phi bd^2}$	Reqd. p, Chart A-1	Reqd. A_s	Use A_s	
0.018	0.53'k	0.139 ksi	0.35%	0.09 □''	Bars a : #3 @ $10\frac{1}{2}''$ = 0.130 □	Anch. 9'' ⌐ 4'.9
0.021	0.62	0.162	0.42	0.10	'' ''	Face of girder
0.028	0.83	0.217	0.56	0.14	Bars b : #3 @ $9\frac{1}{2}''$ = 0.14	
0.034	1.00	0.262	0.69	0.17	Bars c : #3 @ 8'' = 0.17	5'.3 / 5'.3
0.041	1.21	0.317	0.84	0.21	Bars d : #3 @ 6'' = 0.22	₵ Girder

$\frac{1}{5}(26') = 5.2'$
use 5'.3

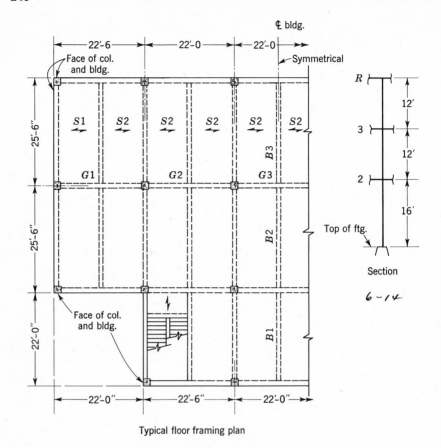

Typical floor framing plan

Fig. 6–14.   Problem 6–2.

Take 4000-lb. concrete and 60,000-psi-yield-point steel for columns and 50,000-psi-yield-point steel for other members, and the ACI Code, USD.   Completely design the floor slabs *S1* and *S2*.

The Design of Floor Beams

(Calculation Sheets 6 Through 13)

6–14. PRELIMINARY DESIGN

First a sketch is made on Calculation Sheet 6 of the beams *B1* and *B2*, showing the center to center spans and clear spans (estimating the widths of the supporting girders).   The floor area tributary to the beams being known, the loads from the slabs may be calculated readily.   The weight of the beam stems is unknown at this time and should be estimated, sub-

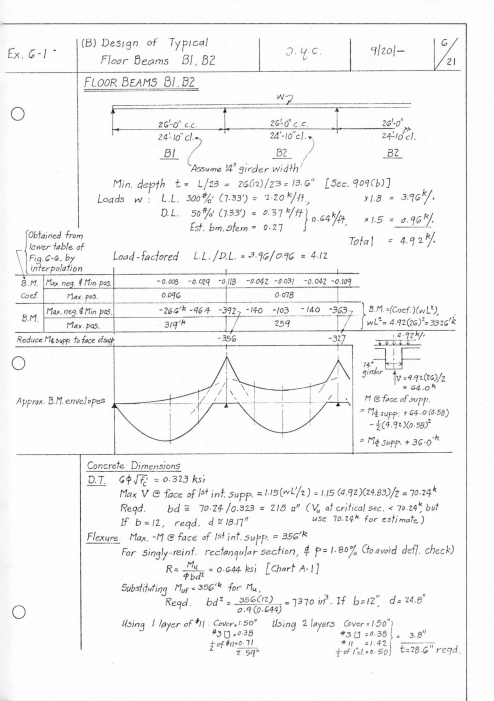

| Ex. 6-1 · | (B) Design of Typical
Floor Beams B1, B2 | J.Y.C. | 9/20/— | G/21 |

FLOOR BEAMS B1, B2

w→

26'-0" c.c.   26'-0" c.c.   26'-0"
24'-10" cl.   24'-10" cl.   24'-10" cl.

B1   B2   B2

'Assume 14" girder width'

Min. depth t = L/23 = 26(12)/23 = 13.6" [Sec. 909(b)]

Loads w : L.L. 300#/□' (7.33') = 2.20 k/ft.,   ×1.8 = 3.96 k/.
          D.L. 50#/□' (7.33') = 0.37 k/ft, } 0.64 k/ft, ×1.5 = 0.96 k/.
          Est. bm. stem = 0.27

Total = 4.92 k/.

Obtained from lower table of Fig. 6-6, by interpolation

Load-factored   L.L./D.L. = 3.96/0.96 = 4.12

B.M.	Max. neg. & Min. pos.	−0.008	−0.029	−0.118	−0.042	−0.031	−0.042	−0.109	
Coef.	Max. pos.	0.096			0.078				
B.M.	Max. neg. & Min. pos.	−26.6'k	−96.4	−392	−140	−103	−140	−363	B.M.=(Coef.)(wL²),
	Max. pos.	319'k			259				wL²= 4.92(26)²=3326'k

Reduce M @ supp. to face of supp.   −356   −327

Approx. B.M. envelopes

14" girder

V = 4.92(26)/2 = 64.0 k

M @ face of supp.
= M₵ supp. + 64.0(0.58)
− ½(4.92)(0.58)²

= M₵ supp. + 36.0'k

Concrete Dimensions

D.T. $6\phi\sqrt{f_c'}$ = 0.323 ksi

Max V @ face of 1st int. supp. = 1.15(wL'/2) = 1.15(4.92)(24.83)/2 = 70.24 k

Reqd.   bd ≅ 70.24/0.323 = 218 □"   (V_u at critical sec. < 70.24k, but use 70.24k for estimate)

If b = 12, reqd. d ≅ 18.17"

Flexure   Max. −M @ face of 1st int. supp. = 356'k

For singly-reinf. rectangular section, & p = 1.80% (to avoid defl. check)

$$R = \frac{M_u}{\phi bd^2} = 0.644 \text{ ksi} \text{[Chart A-1]}$$

Substituting M_uf = 356'k for M_u,

Reqd. $bd^2 = \frac{356(12)}{0.9(0.644)} = 7370 \text{ in}^3$. If b=12", d= 24.8"

Using 1 layer of #11 : Cover = 1.50"   Using 2 layers Cover = 1.50"
#3 □ = 0.38   #3 □ = 0.38
½ of #11 = 0.71   #11 = 1.42   } = 3.8"
‾‾‾‾‾‾‾‾‾‾   ½ of 1"cl. = 0.50   ‾‾‾‾‾‾‾‾‾‾
2.59"   t = 28.6" reqd.

ject to later revision. Experienced designers can often make this estimate fairly accurately. In the absence of other data, an estimated depth of 1 in. per ft. of span may sometimes be used as a crude but reasonable guide for a moderately reinforced beam. For a beam designed on the basis of ultimate strength concepts, the depth may be somewhat smaller than this, depending on, among other things, how high a steel percentage the designer wishes to use as long as tensile failure is assured, assuming that diagonal tension or stiffness of the beam does not govern the design. In any event, some preliminary calculations would prove very helpful. Such calculations need not be very accurate and need be carried only far enough to reveal the approximate concrete dimensions and probable steel arrangement (whether one layer or more of bars are required) that might eventually be used. This way, drastic revision of design calculations may be avoided and the little effort in this preliminary work would prove well spent indeed.

Whether in the preliminary or the final design stage, the beam size cannot be ascertained without consideration of the reinforcement. If headroom or other architectural considerations do not prevail, the size of a continuous beam is usually controlled by three factors:

1. Diagonal tension at the critical sections for maximum shear.
2. Maximum negative moments over supports.
3. Maximum positive moments near the center of spans.

Item 3 above is usually less critical than item 2 since the maximum positive moment in a span is most frequently smaller than those at its ends, and also, if necessary, the center portion of the beam may be designed as a T-beam. In the negative moment region, the section is rectangular, and here the designer has to decide (a) whether he will adopt dimensions for a singly or doubly reinforced section, (b) what steel percentage, whether p or $p - p'$, he wishes to use. The two considerations are, of course, interrelated. If deflection calculations are to be avoided, the steel percentage should be kept below $0.18f_c/f_y$ [Sec. 1507(a)]. On the other hand, if one wants to have the slimmest section, the doubly reinforced section combined with the maximum permissible steel percentage to ensure tensile failure should be adopted, at the expense of having to make deflection calculations. Similarly, if one does not want to have any web reinforcement at all, the dimensions chosen should be such that the computed v_u at the critical section does not exceed $2\phi \sqrt{f'_c}$ [Sec. 1701(c)]. Or, one may wish to have a v_u value at the limit of $10\phi \sqrt{f'_c}$ [Sec. 1705(b)], and requiring rather heavy web reinforcement. Usually, it is economical to choose dimensions such that the critical v_u lies somewhere between the two limits, say at about $6\phi \sqrt{f'_c}$, and requiring some but not heavy web reinforcement—unless other requirements prevail.

For the present example, it will be assumed that the design is to be made requiring no deflection calculations (limiting the steel percentage to $0.18 f'_c/f_y$), allowing compression reinforcement at the supports if necessary, letting the critical v_u be near $6\phi \sqrt{f'_c}$, and using part of the slab as a T-flange in the positive moment regions if necessary. With these decided on, the following preliminary calculations have been made:

$$\begin{array}{l} \text{Live load} \quad 300\# \ (7.33) \cong 2.2 \text{ kips/ft.} \quad \overset{\text{L/F}}{\times} 1.8 \cong 4.0 \\ \left. \begin{array}{l} \text{Dead load} \quad 50\# \ (7.33) \cong 0.4 \text{ kips/ft.} \\ \quad\quad \text{Stem} \quad\quad\quad \cong 0.3 \\ \left(\begin{array}{l} \text{12 by 26 section} \\ \text{12 by 22} \pm \text{ stem} \end{array}\right) \end{array} \right\} \times 1.5 \cong 1.1 \\ \quad\quad\quad\quad\quad\quad\quad\quad\quad\quad\quad\quad\quad \text{Total} \cong 5.1 \text{ kips/ft.} \end{array}$$

Clear span = 25 ft. $\pm$

Maximum shear at first interior support, $V \cong (1.2\pm)(5.1)(25\!\!\!/2) = 77$ kips.

At critical section, $V_u \cong 77 - (5.1)(22\!\!\!/12) = 68$ kips.

At $v_u = 6\phi \sqrt{f'_c} \cong 0.32$ ksi, the required bd for diagonal tension is $68/0.32 \cong 220$ sq. in.

Using the ACI coefficients (Art. 6–7), the maximum negative moment at the first interior support is

$$(1\!\!\!/10)(w)(L')^2 = (1\!\!\!/10)(5.1)(25)^2 \cong 320 \text{ kip-ft.}$$

Limiting the steel percentage to $1.8(f'_c/f_y) = 1.8\%$, and using Chart A–1:

$$R = M_u/\phi bd^2 \cong 0.64 \text{ ksi}$$

If the section is singly reinforced at the first interior support, the required $bd^2 = 320(12)/(0.9)(0.64) \cong 6700$ in.[3] If $b = 12$ in., d would be roughly 24 in., and $A_s = 1.8\%(12)(24) \cong 5.2$ sq. in., which would probably require two layers of bars. Adding about 4 in. to the d of 24 in., the total depth t required would be about 28 in.

If the section is doubly reinforced, t may be less. Taking $t = 24$ in., the effective depth would be $d \cong 20$ in., and the (bd) furnished would be $(12)(20) = 240$ sq. in., which is O.K. for diagonal tension. Hence,

$$\begin{array}{ll} M_{u1} = 0.64(0.9)(12)(20)^2/12 \cong 230 \text{ kip-ft.} \\ M_{u2} = 320 - 230 \quad\quad\quad\quad \cong \ 90 \text{ kip-ft.} \end{array}$$

$$A_{s1} = 1.8\%(12)(20) \quad\quad\quad\quad\quad\quad\quad\quad \cong 4.3 \text{ sq. in.}$$
$$A'_s = M_{u2}/\phi f_y(d - d') = (90)(12)/(0.9)(40)(20 - 4) \cong 1.9$$

$$A_s \cong 6.2 \text{ sq. in.}$$
$$\text{(2 layers)}$$

The steel contents elsewhere may be found very roughly by proportion:

End span: maximum positive $M \cong (\tfrac{1}{14})(w)(L')^2$

$$A_s \cong (6.2)(^{10}\!\!/_{14}) = 4.4 \text{ sq. in.}$$

Interior spans: maximum positive $M \cong (\tfrac{1}{16})(w)(L')^2$
$$A_s \cong (6.2)(^{10}\!\!/_{16}) = 3.9 \text{ sq. in.}$$

Utilizing these rough calculations, the stem weight may now be estimated using a tentative beam size of say, 12 by 25 in., with two layers of bars over the interior supports and in the maximum positive moment regions, and one layer of bars elsewhere. If any revision is needed, it will likely not be drastic.

6–15. BEAM SIZE (Sheet 6)

Based on the preliminary studies of the foregoing article, the more refined calculations shown on Sheet 6 were next made.

The moments were determined by multiplying (wL^2) by coefficients taken from the lower table of Fig. 6–6 (Art. 6–5). The maximum negative moments at the center of supports were again reduced to the faces thereof.

The effective depths d for one and two layers of bars were computed, assuming #3 stirrups and conservatively, #11 bars. Finally, the 12-by-25-in. beam size was chosen, using compression reinforcement over the interior supports.

6–16. BEAM REINFORCEMENT (Sheets 7 Through 9)

The load-factored moments at the various sections were then summarized in the line entitled M_{uf} on Sheet 7. The spandrel effect at the face of the end support was estimated arbitrarily at $(\tfrac{1}{24})(w)(L')^2$. With $\phi = 0.9$, $b = 12$ in., and $d = 21.2$ in. for two layers of bars, or 22.4 in. for one, the values of $M_{uf}/\phi bd^2$ were easily computed.

At the typical interior supports B and C, the double reinforcement was determined as shown in the lower half of Sheet 7. In the interior of the spans, the beams were designed as T-sections for maximum positive moments and the steel contents were obtained as shown on Sheet 8. Elsewhere, the beams act as singly-reinforced rectangular sections, for which the required steel percentages were obtained directly from the USD Beam Chart A–1.

The bars chosen are shown in the sketch on Sheet 9. They consist of straight and truss bars (with 60° bends) in the bottom of each span, and additional top bars over the supports. The top support bars were

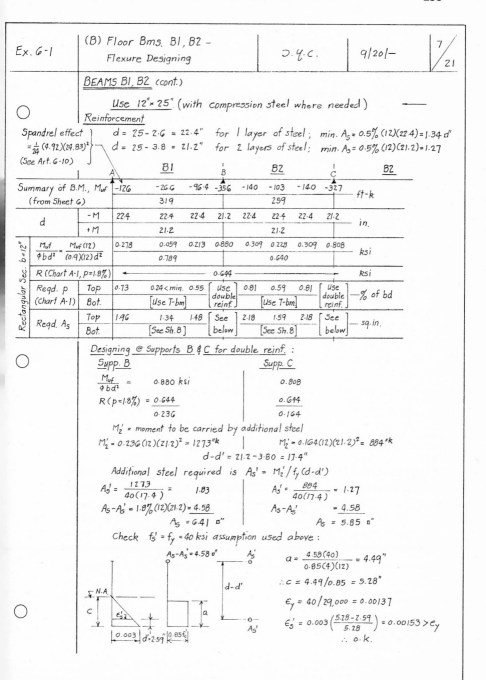

| Ex. 6-1 | (B) Floor Bms. B1, B2 – Flexure Designing | | D. Y. C. | 9/20/– | 7/21 |

BEAMS B1, B2 (cont.)

Use 12"× 25" (with compression steel where needed)
Reinforcement

Spandrel effect $= \frac{1}{24}(4.92)(24.83)^2$ (See Art. 6-10)

$d = 25 - 2.6 = 22.4"$ for 1 layer of steel ;   min. $A_s = 0.5\% (12)(22.4) = 1.34$ ◻'

$d = 25 - 3.8 = 21.2"$ for 2 layers of steel;   min. $A_s = 0.5\% (12)(21.2) = 1.27$

			A	B1		B	B2		C	B2
Summary of B.M., M_{uf} (from Sheet 6)			-126	-26.6		-356	-140	-103 -140	-327	ft-k
				319	-96.4		259			
d	-M		22.4	22.4	22.4	21.2	22.4	22.4	22.4	21.2	in.
	+M			21.2			21.2			
$\frac{M_{uf}}{\phi bd^2} = \frac{M_{uf}(12)}{(0.9)(12)d^2}$			0.278	0.059	0.213	0.880	0.309	0.228	0.309	0.808	ksi
				0.789			0.640			
R (Chart A-1, p=1.8%)			◄——————— 0.644 ———————►							ksi
Reqd. p (chart A-1)	Top		0.73	0.24 < min.	0.55	Use double reinf.	0.81	0.59	0.81	Use double reinf.	—% of bd
	Bot.			[Use T-bm]			[Use T-bm]			
Reqd. A_s	Top		1.96	1.34	1.48	See below	2.18	1.59	2.18	See below	sq. in.
	Bot.			[See Sh.8]			[See Sh.8]			

(left margin, rotated): Rectangular Sec. b = 12"

Designing @ Supports B & C for double reinf. :

Supp. B	Supp. C
$\frac{M_{uf}}{\phi bd^2} =$ 0.880 ksi	0.808
R (p=1.8%) = 0.644	0.644
0.236	0.164

M_2' = moment to be carried by additional steel

$M_2' = 0.236(12)(21.2)^2 = 1273"^k$ | $M_2' = 0.164(12)(21.2)^2 = 884"^k$

$$d-d' = 21.2 - 3.80 = 17.4"$$

Additional steel required is $A_s' = M_2'/f_y(d-d')$

$A_s' = \frac{1273}{40(17.4)} = 1.83$ | $A_s' = \frac{884}{40(17.4)} = 1.27$

$A_s - A_s' = 1.8\%(12)(21.2) = 4.58$ | $A_s - A_s' = 4.58$

$A_s = 6.41$ ◻" | $A_s = 5.85$ ◻"

Check $f_s' = f_y = 40$ ksi assumption used above :

$A_s - A_s' = 4.58$ ◻"

$a = \frac{4.58(40)}{0.85(4)(12)} = 4.49"$

$\therefore c = 4.49/0.85 = 5.28"$

$\epsilon_y = 40/29,000 = 0.00137$

$\epsilon_s' = 0.003\left(\frac{5.28 - 2.59}{5.28}\right) = 0.00153 > \epsilon_y$

$\therefore$ o.k.

extended to and lapped at the centers of the adjacent spans to provide for the reversals in moments produced thereat by the heavy live loading.

It will be noted that in this sketch, all the dimensions have been left blank. These dimensions have to do with the location of the bend-up (or bend-down) points of the truss bars, the cut-off points, the anchorage lengths, and the lap lengths. These details must be worked out carefully; the following article is devoted to this important matter. The reader should be aware of the tentative nature of the bars chosen and shown on Sheet 9, and of the possibility that some revision may be found necessary later on.

6–17. DETAILS OF BEAM REINFORCEMENT (Sheets 9 Through 12)

Under normal circumstances (uniform loads on approximately equal spans, relatively light live loads), the bending details for reinforcement in concrete structures have been more or less standardized in the United States. Figure 6–15, for instance, shows the detailing standards for beams as recommended in Reference 6.

For the present problem, however, since the live load is so very much heavier than the dead load, the detailing standards shown in Fig. 6–15 may or may not be satisfactory. Accordingly, additional calculations are needed.

Bend-up and Bend-down Points. Theoretically the truss bars may be bent up where they are no longer needed for positive moments. Also, they should reach the top of the beam where they are expected to act as tensile reinforcement for the negative moments. Therefore, the location of the bend-up points must be worked out together with their corresponding bend-down points. Specifically, points a, b, f, l, and i in the sketch of Sheet 9 are to be paired respectively with points c, d, g, m, and j. To determine the theoretical location of these points, the capacity of the beam at those points and the moment envelope must first be determined.

1. **Beam capacity.** The capacity of the beam at those points must be based on the area of the bars that continue beyond them. For instance,

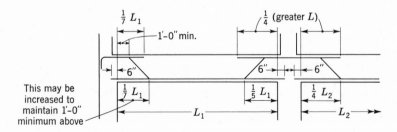

Fig. 6–15. Standard beam detail.

| Ex. 6-1 | (B) Floor Beams B1, B2 - Flexure Designing | Ͻ. Ψ. c. | 9/20/— | 8/21 |

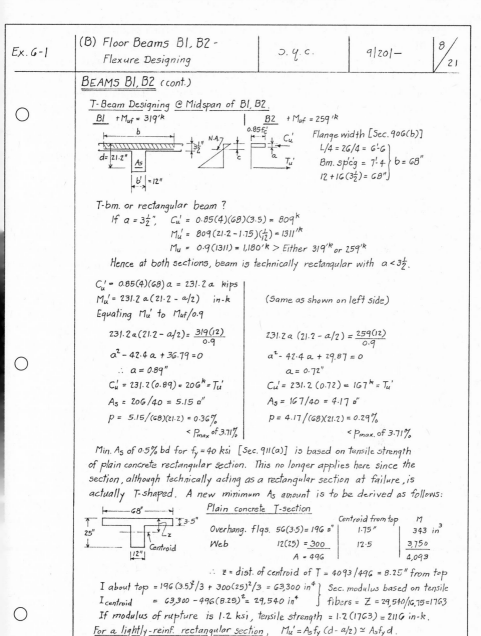

BEAMS B1, B2 (cont.)

T-Beam Designing @ Midspan of B1, B2.

B1 $+M_{uf} = 319'^k$ B2 $+M_{uf} = 259'^k$

Flange width [Sec. 906(b)]

$L/4 = 26/4 = 6'-6$
Bm. sp'cg = 7'-4 $\}$ b = 68"
$12 + 16(3\frac{1}{2}) = 68"$

T-bm. or rectangular beam ?

If $a = 3\frac{1}{2}"$, $C_u' = 0.85(4)(68)(3.5) = 809^k$

$M_u' = 809(21.2 - 1.75)(\frac{1}{12}) = 1311'^k$

$M_u = 0.9(1311) = 1,180'^k >$ Either $319'^k$ or $259'^k$

Hence at both sections, beam is technically rectangular with $a < 3\frac{1}{2}$.

$C_u' = 0.85(4)(68)a = 231.2 a$ kips

$M_u' = 231.2 a(21.2 - a/2)$ in-k   (Same as shown on left side)

Equating M_u' to $M_{uf}/0.9$

$231.2 a(21.2 - a/2) = \dfrac{319(12)}{0.9}$ $231.2 a (21.2 - a/2) = \dfrac{259(12)}{0.9}$

$a^2 - 42.4 a + 36.79 = 0$ $a^2 - 42.4 a + 29.87 = 0$

$\therefore a = 0.89"$ $a = 0.72"$

$C_u' = 231.2(0.89) = 206^k = T_u'$ $C_u' = 231.2(0.72) = 167^k = T_u'$

$A_s = 206/40 = 5.15 \,\square"$ $A_s = 167/40 = 4.17 \,\square"$

$p = 5.15/(68)(21.2) = 0.36\%$ $p = 4.17/(68)(21.2) = 0.29\%$

$< p_{max}$ of 3.71% $< p_{max}$ of 3.71%

Min. A_s of 0.5% bd for $f_y = 40$ ksi [Sec. 911(a)] is based on tensile strength of plain concrete rectangular section. This no longer applies here since the section, although technically acting as a rectangular section at failure, is actually T-shaped. A new minimum A_s amount is to be derived as follows:

Plain concrete T-section

		Centroid from top	M
Overhang. flgs.	$56(3.5) = 196 \,\square"$	1.75"	343 in^3
Web	$12(25) = \underline{300}$	12.5	$\underline{3,750}$
	A = 496		4,093

$\therefore \bar{z} =$ dist. of centroid of T = 4093/496 = 8.25" from top

I about top = $196(3.5)^2/3 + 300(25)^2/3 = 63,300 \,in^4$ $\}$ Sec. modulus based on tensile

$I_{centroid} = 63,300 - 496(8.25)^2 = 29,540 \,in^4$ $\}$ fibers = $Z = 29,540/16.75 = 1763$

If modulus of rupture is 1.2 ksi, tensile strength = 1.2 (1763) = 2116 in-k.

For a lightly-reinf. rectangular section, $M_u' = A_s f_y (d - a/2) \simeq A_s f_y d$.

Equating the two values, $A_s = 2116/(40)(21.2) = 2.50 \,\square" < 5.15$ or 4.17   o.K.

referring to the sketch on Sheet 9, to locate the bend-up point b for the 2–#9 truss bars, the beam capacity is to be based on the area of the continuing 4–#8 straight bars. Similarly, to locate point d, the area of the 2–#11 top bars plus the 2–#8 truss bars bent up from the adjacent span should be used. Similar calculations were made for the other points, and the results have been summarized in the table at the bottom of Sheet 9.

2. **Moment envelope.** If the beams in question were such as to require from the very beginning a complete analysis for maximum moments, we would have, at this stage, complete information regarding the moment envelope. But with the use of maximum moment coefficients, such as those in the ACI Code or those in Fig. 6–6, we do not have adequate information for constructing the moment envelope, since the coefficients given are only the maximum values at critical sections, and we do not have the concurrent support moments to enable us to determine the complete moment diagrams. Under these circumstances, the designer may revert to a more complete analysis, or try to make the best of the dilemma by determining the moment curves approximately. One of such approximations is described herewith.

First, the simple beam moments were determined for dead load alone and for total dead plus live loads as shown near the bottom of Sheet 9.

Interior span. The maximum positive moment of 259 kip-ft. occurred under loading 1 shown on Sheet 10. The simple beam moment for dead plus live load being 416 kip-ft. at midspan, the support moments, assumed to be equal, were therefore found to be each equal to $-(416 - 259) = -157$ kip-ft. The moment curve may then be drawn easily.

The minimum positive moment of -103 kip-ft. occurred when there was only dead load on the span, as shown in loading 2 of Sheet 10. Since the simple beam moment for dead load alone was 81 kip-ft. at midspan, the two end moments were each $-(81 + 103) = -194$ kip-ft., and the moment curve would follow immediately.

For the maximum negative moment of -363 kip-ft. over the left support of the interior span, loading 5 was used. Here, however, the right support moment was not known. Nevertheless, it is reasonable to assume that under dead load alone on all spans, the two support moments are nearly equal. For live loads patterned as in loading 5, the right support moment usually ranges from about 20 to 40 per cent of the left support moment. The higher limit of this range tends to move the inflection point away from the left support and to result in generally larger negative moments in its neighborhood, and it was therefore used. To determine the combined dead and live moment at the right support, we need to retrace the steps which had been used to compute the maximum negative moment at the left support. Using the underscored coefficients in the upper table of Fig. 6–6, calculations were made as shown on Sheet 10, resulting in a right support moment of -180 kip-ft.

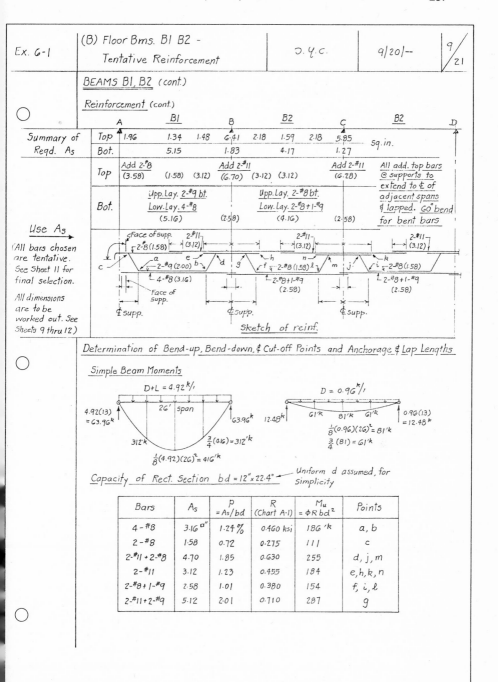

| Ex. 6-1 | (B) Floor Bms. B1 B2 - Tentative Reinforcement | O. Y. C. | 9/20/-- | 9/21 |

BEAMS B1, B2 (cont.)

Reinforcement (cont.)

		A	B1	B	B2	C	B2	D
Summary of Reqd. As	Top	1.96	1.34 1.48	6.41 2.18	1.59 2.18	5.85	sq. in.	
	Bot.		5.15	1.83	4.17	1.27		

Top	Add 2-"8 (3.58) (1.58) (3.12) Add 2-#11 (6.70) (3.12) (3.12) Add 2-#11 (6.28) All add. top bars @ supports to extend to ¢ of adjacent spans & lapped. 60° bend for bent bars
Bot.	Upp.Lay. 2-#9 bt. Low.Lay. 4-#8 (5.16) (7.58) Upp.Lay. 2-#8 bt. Low.Lay. 2-#8+1-#9 (4.16) (2.58)

Use As

(All bars chosen are tentative. See Sheet 11 for final selection.

All dimensions are to be worked out. See Sheets 9 thru 12.)

Sketch of reinf.

Determination of Bend-up, Bend-down, & Cut-off Points and Anchorage & Lap Lengths

Simple Beam Moments

D+L = 4.92 k/ʹ

4.92(13) = 63.96ᵏ   26ʹ span   63.96ᵏ

312ᵏ   ¾(416)=312ᵏ

⅛(4.92)(26)² = 416ᵏ

D = 0.96 k/ʹ

61ᵏ   81ᵏ   61ᵏ   0.96(13) = 12.48ᵏ

12.48ᵏ   ⅛(0.96)(26)² = 81ᵏ

¾(81) = 61ᵏ

Capacity of Rect. Section   bd = 12" x 22.4" ← Uniform d assumed, for Simplicity

Bars	As	p = As/bd	R (Chart A-1)	Mu = ΦR bd²	Points
4 - #8	3.16 ᵈ''	1.24 %	0.460 ksi	186 'ᵏ	a, b
2 - #8	1.58	0.72	0.275	111	c
2-#11 + 2-#8	4.70	1.85	0.630	255	d, j, m
2-#11	3.12	1.23	0.455	184	e, h, k, n
2-#8 + 1-#9	2.58	1.01	0.380	154	f, i, l
2-#11+2-#9	5.12	2.01	0.710	287	g

| Ex. 6-1 | (B) Floor Bms B1, B2 - Checkerboard L.L. | Ͻ.Ҷ.C. | 9/20/— | 10/21 |

<u>BEAMS B1, B2</u> (cont.)

<u>Reinforcement</u> (cont.)

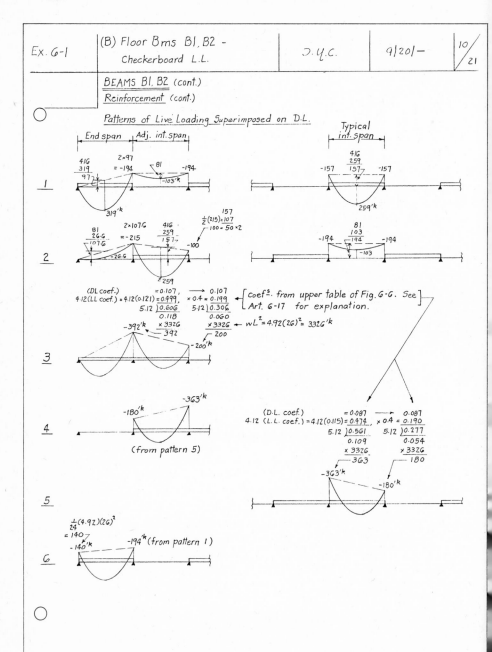

Patterns of Live Loading Superimposed on D.L.

Coef⁵. from upper table of Fig. 6-6. See Art. 6-17 for explanation.

$wL^2 = 4.92(26)^2 = 3326'^k$

(from pattern 5)

(from pattern 1)

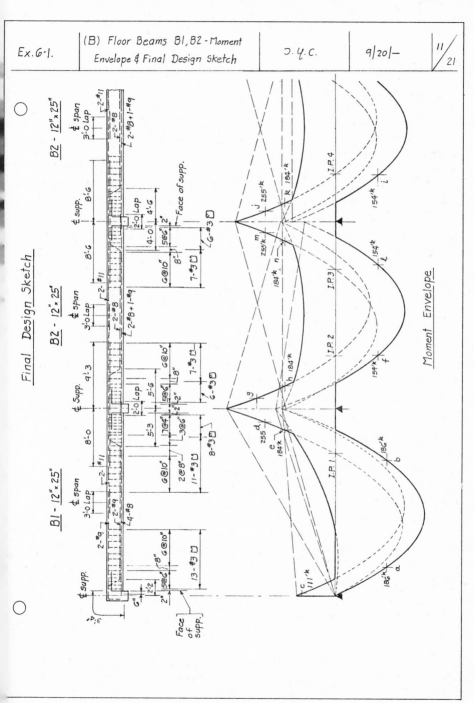

| Ex.6-1. | (B) Floor Beams B1,B2 - Moment Envelope & Final Design Sketch | J.Y.C. | 9/20/— | 11/21 |

End span and adjacent interior span. Similar calculations were made for these spans as for the typical interior span except that the end support was assumed to be hinged. For the spandrel effect shown in loading pattern 6, the negative spandrel moment of $(\frac{1}{24})(w)(L)^2$ was imposed on the moment curve for pattern 1. This of course is not correct but was adopted as an expedient step.

By superposing all the moment curves of Sheet 10, the final moment envelope shown on Sheet 11 was obtained. The theoretical location of the bend points was then obtained from the moment envelope, and their distances from the center of the adjacent supports were listed in the first table of Sheet 12. According to ACI Sec. 918(b), the required location of these points is to be beyond the theoretical location for a distance equal to 12 bar diameters or the depth d; this calculation has been included in the same table. The distances of the actual bend-up points from the center of their adjacent supports were then selected. By subtracting from these distances the horizontal projection of the bent portion of the bars, equal to $(21.2 - 2.6)(\tan 30°)/12 = 0.89$ ft., the corresponding bend-down points were located. It was then noted that the points a and c could not be satisfactorily reconciled. Hence, although the 2–#9 bars in the end span were still bent up at a, they were not counted as resisting the spandrel moment, and the 2–#8 top bars originally chosen for the end support were revised to 2–#9.

Cut-off Points. The truss bars may be stopped some distance beyond the supports. Since these bars were primarily for the negative support moments, the inflection points (I.P.) were first located using the moment envelope of Sheet 11, and the bars were then carried beyond these points for a distance equal to $\frac{1}{16}$ of the clear span or the depth d. These calculations were summarized in the second table of Sheet 12.

Anchorage and Lap Lengths. These calculations have been shown on Sheet 12 and are almost self-explanatory.

The final design sketch on Sheet 11 shows the details of the reinforcement adopted.

6–18. WEB REINFORCEMENT AND FLEXURAL BOND (Sheet 13)

The designing of web reinforcement follows the concepts described in Chapter 3 and needs no further explanation, except to point out that near the interior supports where compression reinforcement was required, ties instead of stirrups were used, per ACI Sec. 806(c).

The last part of Sheet 13 indicates that a flexural bond check was unnecessary since all tensile bars have been either given adequate anchorage equal to more than 25 per cent over that required, or adequately lapped as for tensile splices.

Ex. 6-1	(B) Floor Beams B1, B2 – Location of Bend-up & Cut-off Points, Etc.	⊃. Y. C.	9/20/–	12/21

BEAMS B1, B2 (cont.)

(Refer to Sheets 9 & 11)

Reinforcement – *Bend-up & Cut-off Points and Anchorage & Lap Lengths* (cont.)

	Distance from ℄ of adjacent support								
Bend-up point	Theoretical location	Subtract	Reqd. dist. to be not more than	Bend-down point	Theoretical location	Add	Reqd. dist. to be not less than	Adopted location of bend-up pt.	Corresp. location of bend-down pt.	Remarks
a	3.98'	12 bar diam. or d = 21.2" = 1.77' d governs in all cases. [Sec. 918(b)]	2.21'	c	0.48'	12 bar diam. or d = 1.77' d governs in all cases [Sec. 918(b)]	2.25'	2'-2"	1.28' < 2.25	Ignore contribution of bent bars. Revise 2-#8 to 2-#9
b	7.02'		5.25'	d	1.84'		3.61'	5'-3"	4.36'	
f	7.33'		5.56'	g	1.56'		3.33'	5'-6"	4.61'	
l	5.53'		3.76'	m	1.61'		3.38	4'-0"	3.11'	A little shy. Say, o.k.
i	6.47'		4.70'	j	1.61'		3.38	4'-6"	3.61'	

	Distance from ℄ of support			
Cut-off point	Location of I.P. for max. neg. supp. B.M.	Add	Reqd. distance	Use
e	I.P.1 - 6.13'	[Sec. 918(e)] $\frac{1}{16}$ (24.83) = 1.55' or d = 1.77' d governs	7.90'	8'-0"
h	I.P.2 - 7.37'		9.14'	9'-3"
n	I.P.3 - 6.64'		8.41'	8'-6"
k	I.P.4 - 6.64'		8.41'	8'-6"

Anchorage

At end support A : Top bars 2-#9

$u_u = 0.423/D = 0.423/1.13 = 0.382$ ksi

Reqd. anch. $a = \dfrac{0.9 A_s f_y}{0.85 \, u_u \, \Sigma_o}$

[Sec. 1801(c)] $= \dfrac{0.9(1.00)(40)}{0.85(0.382)(3.54)}$

$= 31.3''$

Increase to $1.25(31.3) = 39.1''$ Use 3'-4"

thereby eliminating flex. bond check.

Bot. bars   6" into end supp.

Lap lengths for top bars @ ℄ of spans [Sec. 805(b)]

Min. = 12" 24 bar diam., or length to develop bar force at 3/4 of u_u.

Span B1   2-#9 = 2.00 ◻",   24D = 27.1", $\frac{3}{4} u_u = \frac{3}{4} \frac{0.423}{1.13} = 0.281$ ksi

2-#11 = 3.12 ◻",   24D = 33.8", $\frac{3}{4} u_u = \frac{3}{4} \frac{0.423}{1.41} = 0.225$ "

Reqd. $A_s = 1.34$ ◻"

Based on 2-#9, force per bar, $T_u \cong 0.9 A_s f_y \left(\frac{1.34}{2.00}\right) = 0.9(1.00)(40)\left(\frac{1.34}{2.00}\right) = 24.1^k$

Reqd. length = 24.1/(0.85)(0.281)(3.54) = 28.5"

Based on 2-#11, $T_u \cong 0.9(1.56)(40)\left(\frac{1.34}{3.12}\right) = 24.1^k$ per bar

Reqd. length = 24.1/(0.85)(0.225)(4.43) = 28.4"   Use 3'-0"

Span B2   2-#11 = 3.12   }   24D = 33.8, $\frac{3}{4} u_u = 0.225$ ksi

2-#11 = 3.12   } $T_u \cong 0.9(1.56)(40)\left(\frac{1.59}{3.12}\right) = 28.6^k$

Reqd $A_s = 1.59$ Reqd. length = 28.6/(0.85)(0.225)(4.43) = 33.8"   Use 3'-0"

Lap lengths for bottom bars as compression reinf. at supports [Sec. 805(c)]

Min. = 12" or 20 bar diam. #9 bars ∴ 20(1.13) = 22.6"   Use 2'-0"

FLOOR BEAM DESIGN PROBLEMS

6-3. Following up Problem 6-1, completely design the corresponding typical floor beams *B1* and *B2*.

6-4. Following up Problem 6-2, completely design the floor beams *B1*, *B2*, and *B3* shown on the floor framing plan of Fig. 6-14.

The Design of Girders

(Calculation Sheets 14 Through 20)

6–19. GIRDERS AS RIGID FRAME MEMBERS

Calculation Sheet 14 shows the third-floor interior girders as members of a rigid frame. As they support concentrated loads in addition to uniform loads, the bending moment coefficients given in Fig. 6–6 or in Sec. 904(c) do not apply, and a frame analysis is therefore in order. For gravity loading, the frame analysis may be executed using the ACI simplified procedure (described here in Art. 6–6), in which the far ends of all the columns above and below the floor in question are assumed to be fixed.

In such an analysis, the weight of the girders first has to be estimated, and more importantly, the relative stiffnesses of the girders and the columns must be known or estimated. An experienced designer can often make fairly good guesses of these values, but rough preliminary calculations will always furnish close estimates thereof and eliminate drastic revisions later on.

6–20. PRELIMINARY GIRDER DESIGN

The comments given in Art. 6–14 regarding beam designing apply equally well to girder designing. Additionally, the following remarks will be found pertinent.

Approximate Loading. Each girder at its third point carries concentrated loads coming from the reactions of the beams at the ends of their *clear* spans. In addition, each girder supports a uniform load consisting of its own weight and the live load directly over its width. The concentrated loads may be estimated by computing the beam reactions on the basis of their *center-to-center* span lengths. In view of the heavy concentrated loads, the effect of the uniform load is likely to be small, and may therefore be neglected in preliminary calculations. Accordingly, the girders are *approximately loaded* as shown in Fig. 6–16a.

Diagonal Tension. The maximum shear will occur in the end span near the first interior column, and may be estimated to be roughly 1.2 times the simple-beam shear thereat, or 1.2(128) = 154 kips. Taking $v_u = 6\phi \sqrt{f'_c} \cong 0.32$ ksi, the required (bd) is roughly $(154/0.32) \cong$ 480 sq. in. If $b = 14$ in., the required d is about 34 in.

Ex. 6-1	(B) Floor Beams B1, B2 (concl.) Web Reinforcement.	つ. 4. c.	9/20/—	13/21

BEAMS B1, B2 (cont.)

Web Reinforcement   (Constant d = 21.2" used throughout)

	A	B1	B	B2	C	B2
		$10\,\phi\sqrt{f'_c} = 0.538$ ksi,	$\times (12)(21.2) = 136.9^k$			
		$6\,\phi\sqrt{f'_c} = 0.323$,	$\times (12)(21.2) = 82.2$			
		$2\,\phi\sqrt{f'_c} = 0.108$,	$\times (12)(21.2) = 27.5 = V_c$			
Shear @ face of supp.		$61.1^k = \dfrac{4.92(24.83)}{12}$, $1.15(61.1)=70.2^k$	61.1^k		61.1^k	
$V_u =$ Shear on critical sec. at d of 1.77' from face of supp.		52.4^k	61.5	52.4	52.4	$< 136.9^k$ o.k. [Sec.1705(b)] < 82.2 Max. $s = \dfrac{d}{2} = 10.6"$ [Sec.1706(a)]
V_c		27.5^k	27.5	27.5	27.5	Min. A_v @ $s=10$ $= 0.15\%$ bs [Sec.1706(b)] $= 0.15\%\,(12)(10) = 0.18\,\square"$
$V_u' = V_u - V_c$		24.9^k	34.0	24.9	24.9	

Web reinforced region	A	B1	B	B2	C	B2
From crit. sec.		5.06'	6.91	5.06	5.06	
From face of supp.		6.83'	8.68	6.83	6.83	
Add d [Sec.1702(a)]		1.77'	1.77	1.77	1.77	
Total distance from face of supp.		8.60'	10.45	8.60	8.60	

Use → web reinforcement	A	B1	B	B2	C	B2
		#3 ⊐, 1@2"	#3 ⊐, 1@2"	Ea. End : #3⊐, 1@2"	#3⊐, 1@8"	#3 stirrups or ties
		5@6"	7@4"		5@6"	$\phi A_v f_y d$
		1@8"	#3 ⊐ 3@6"		6@10	$= 0.85(0.22)(40)(21.2)$
		6@10"	2@8" [Sec.806(c)]			$= 159$ in-k
			6@10"			

Flexural Bond

At end supp. A

(See Sheet 12)   Top 2-#9 bars : Left anch. > 1.25 reqd. anch.

Right ends adequately lapped with top bars from supp. B.

∴ No check necessary.

At supp. B

Top 2-#11 bars : Both ends adequately lapped with top bars from adj. supp.

(See Sheet 11)   Bent bars : 2-#8 cut off @ e, & 2-#9 cut off @ h, both passing the I.P.'s for adequate distance. Furthermore :

Theor. dist. of e = 2.89' ; $0.8\,u_u = 0.8\,(0.423/1.00) = 0.338$ ksi

Length to develop bar force = $0.9(40)(0.79)/0.85(0.338)(3.14) = 31.5"$

Furnished length = (8'-0) -(2.89) = 5.11' > 31.5".

Similarly for the cut-off at h.   ∴ No check necessary.

At other supp.   Same conclusions as at supp. B prevail.

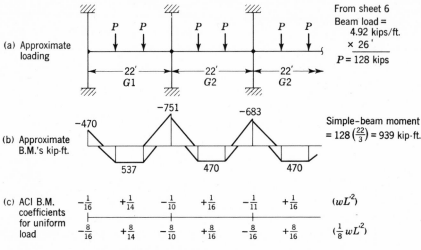

Fig. 6–16.   Preliminary girder designing.

Flexure.   For uniform load only, the ACI bending moment coefficients of wL'^2 (where L' is the clear span length) are as shown in the top line of Fig. 6–16c, and their values expressed in terms of the simple-beam moment of $(\frac{1}{8})(wL'^2)$ are as shown in the bottom line thereof.   Because of the concentrated loads, these coefficients are strictly not applicable to the girders.   But for preliminary design purposes, one may assume that the ratios of the girder moments to the simple-beam moment are substantially the same for concentrated and for uniform loads.   The simple-beam moment due to concentrated loads of 128 kips each at the third points of a 22-ft. span is $128(22)/3 = 939$ kip-ft.   Hence, the girder moments produced by the concentrated loads may be obtained approximately by multiplying 939 kip-ft. by the coefficients given in the bottom line of Fig. 6–16c, and the results are as shown in (b).   With the girder moments estimated, one may now evaluate the approximate concrete dimensions and steel contents for flexure.

In figuring the effective depth for negative girder moments, one should be aware of the presence of the top bars in the intersecting beams, and hence the need of placing the girder top steel to clear the beam top steel, as shown in Fig. 6–17.   In figuring the effective depth for positive girder moments, this complication will not arise if, as is usual, the beams are shallower than the girder.

Referring to Fig. 6–16b, it is seen that the maximum negative girder moment is 751 kip-ft. at the first interior column.   Limiting the steel percentage to $1.8(f'_c/f_y) = 1.8$ per cent so that no deflection check will

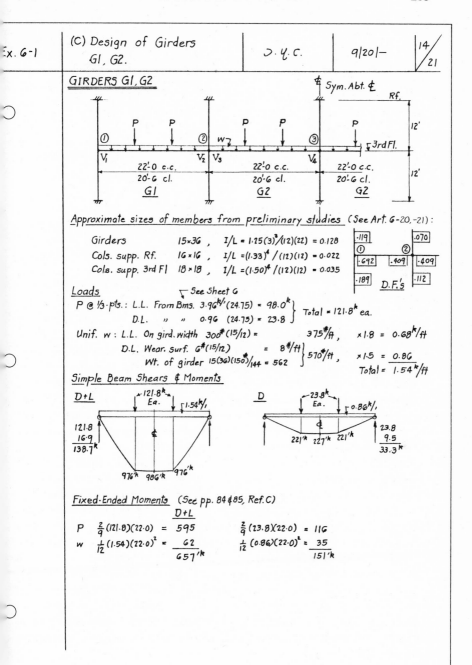

| Ex. 6-1 | (C) Design of Girders
GI, G2. | ⊃. Ψ. C. | 9/20/– | 14/21 |

GIRDERS GI, G2

⊄ Sym. Abt. ⊄

Rf.

① P P ② w⌐ P P ③ P

V_1 V_2 V_3 V_4 ⌐3rd Fl.

12'

22'-0 c.c.   22'-0 c.c.   22'-0 c.c.
20'-6 cl.   20'-6 cl.   20'-6 cl.
GI   **G2**   **G2**

12'

Approximate sizes of members from preliminary studies (See Art. 6-20, -21):

Girders   15×36 , $I/L = 1.25(3)^3/(12)(22) = 0.128$

Cols. supp. Rf.   16×16 , $I/L = (1.33)^4/(12)(12) = 0.022$

Cols. supp. 3rd Fl   18×18 , $I/L = (1.50)^4/(12)(12) = 0.035$

.119		.070
①		②
.692	.409	.409
.189		.112

D.F.'s

Loads   ⌐ See Sheet 6

P @ ⅓-pts.: L.L. From Bms. $3.96^{k/'}(24.75) = 98.0^k$ ⎫ Total = 121.8^k ea.

         D.L. ''   '' $0.96 (24.75) = 23.8$ ⎭

Unif. w : L.L. On gird. width 300# (15/12) =   375#/ft ,   ×1.8 = 0.68^{k}/ft

         D.L. Wear. surf. 6#(15/12)   =   8#/ft ⎫ 570#/ft ,   ×1.5 = 0.86

         Wt. of girder $15(36)(150)/144 = 562$ ⎭   Total = 1.54^k/ft

Simple Beam Shears & Moments

D+L   ⌐121.8ᵏ   **D**   -23.8ᵏ
              Ea. ⌐1.54ᵏ/'   Ea. ⌐0.86ᵏ/'

121.8   23.8
16.9   ⊄   221'ᵏ 227'ᵏ 221'ᵏ   9.5
138.7ᵏ   33.3ᵏ

    976'ᵏ 986'ᵏ 976'ᵏ

Fixed-Ended Moments (See pp. 84 & 85, Ref. C)

          D+L

P $\frac{2}{9}(121.8)(22.0) = 595$ $\frac{2}{9}(23.8)(22.0) = 116$

w $\frac{1}{12}(1.54)(22.0)^2 = \underline{62}$ $\frac{1}{12}(0.86)(22.0)^2 = \underline{35}$

                    657'ᵏ   151'ᵏ

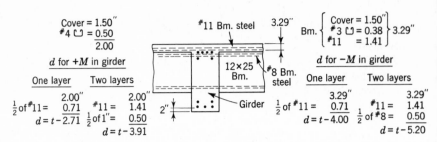

Fig. 6–17. Intersection between girder and beams.

be necessary, and using Chart A–1, one finds

$$R = M_u/\phi b d^2 = 0.644 \text{ ksi}$$

If the girder is singly reinforced thereat, the required $bd^2 = (751)(12)/(0.9)(0.644) = 15,550$ in.[3] If $b = 14$ in., the required d would be 33.3 in., and allowing two layers of tensile bars, the required overall depth would be $t = 33.3 + 5.20 = 38.5$ in. If the girder is doubly reinforced thereat, t may be less. Taking $t = 36$ in., the effective depth would be $d = 30.8$ in. The furnished (bd) would be $(14)(30.8) = 431$ sq. in. which would make v_u slightly larger than $6\phi \sqrt{f'_c}$ at the first interior column but still less than the maximum permissible value of $10\phi \sqrt{f'_c}$.

The maximum positive moments of 537 kip-ft. in the end span and 470 kip-ft. in the interior spans will not be critical since the slab is always available to act as T-flanges if needed. The minimum positive moments are not given by the approximate ACI coefficients, but they would not govern the design anyway.

The conclusion of the foregoing rough calculations is then that a 14-by-36-in. girder section would be satisfactory, using two layers of tensile bars plus some compression reinforcement where needed at the interior supports; using two layers of tensile bars at the maximum positive moment sections; and using one layer of tensile bars elsewhere. In the final decision, a 15-by-36-in. section was selected on which basis the more refined calculations were started.

6–21. PRELIMINARY COLUMN DESIGN

Now that the tentative girder dimensions were decided on, the next step was to estimate the column dimensions. In an actual design job in practice, the design of the roof would have been complete by this time, furnishing some information regarding the dimensions of the roof beams and girders, the loads transmitted to the roof columns, and possibly even the roof column dimensions. For the present example, the following information is assumed to be part of the given data:

Roof loads:

Live load $\qquad$ (50 psf)(22)(26)(1.8) = 52 kips

Dead load

| Roofing and finish | 20 |
| 3½-in. slab | 44 |
| Stem of 12-by-20-in. beams: 206 plf/7.33 = 29 |
| Stem of 12-by-24-in. gird.: 256 plf/26.0 = 10 |

(103 psf)(22)(26)(1.5) = 89

16-in. square roof column = (2.7)(1.5) = 4

Total P_{uf} on roof column $\qquad$ = 145 kips

Based on the final design calculations for the slabs and beams and the preliminary calculations for the girders, the floor loads may be estimated as follows:

Floor loads:

Live load $\qquad$ (300 psf)(22)(26)(1.8) = 309 kips

Dead load

| Wearing surface | 6 |
| 3½-in. slab | 44 |
| Stem of 12-by-25-in. beams: 269 plf/7.33 = 37 |
| Stem of 15-by-36-in. gird.: 508 plf/26.0 = 20 |

(107 psf)(22)(26)(1.5) = 92

Total, per floor $\qquad$ = 401 kips

In order for the column steel to clear the steel in the beams and girders, the columns supporting the third floor should be a few inches wider than the girders, and were assumed to be roughly 18 in. square. Those supporting the second floor were tentatively assumed to be 24 in. square. The preliminary column design may then proceed according to the tabular calculations shown in Fig. 6–18. First, the reduction factors R for slenderness effects were evaluated. These do not differ from their final values given on the bottom half of Calculation Sheet 20, to which the reader is referred for the details of their calculations.

Although the interior columns may be subject to bending due to unbalanced live loading on any floor, their sizes are most probably governed by the maximum axial loads produced by loading all floors and bays simultaneously. The bending that accompanies the latter loading is likely to be small. Hence, the tentative column sizes will be determined for the estimated maximum axial loads with the ACI minimum eccentricity of $0.10t$ for tied columns. As shown in Fig. 6–18, the maximum axial loads P_{uf} were then computed, from which the required ideal,

Rf 12×24 gird.	R	P_{uf}	$P'_u =$ $P_{uf}/\phi R$	Equiv. P'_0 = 1.35 P'_u	$0.85 f'_c\, bt$	$A_{st} = \dfrac{P'_0 - 0.85 f'_c\, bt}{f_y - 0.85 f'_c}$
12' 16×16 col.	0.87	Rf 141				
3 ↓ 15×36 gird.		Col. 4	145	238	321	870	Min. A_{st}
12' 18×18 col. (?)	0.84	Fl. 401				
2 ↓ 15×36 gird.		Col. 5	551	937	1270	1100	3.00 sq. in. Use min. A_{st}
16½' 24×24 col. (?)	0.64	Fl. 401				
		Col. 12	964	2150	2900	1960	16.6 sq. in.: $p \cong 2.9\%$

Fig. 6–18. Preliminary column designing.

short-column capacity loads $P'_u = P_{uf}/\phi R$ were readily obtained. The equivalent centrically loaded capacity P'_0, as described in Art. 5–16, was then estimated to be 1.35 times P'_u. Finally, the required steel contents were computed in the last column of Fig. 6–18. It is seen that in the upper two stories, the columns needed only the minimum areas of reinforcement, indicating that their dimensions might be reduced if desired. However, in order to avoid congestion of the vertical and horizontal bars at the three-way intersection of the beams, girders and columns, the tentative column sizes were retained.

6–22. FRAME ANALYSIS (Sheets 14 Through 17)

Using the approximate dimensions of the girders and columns just determined, a frame analysis based on the moment distribution procedure may now begin. Sheet 14 shows the determination of the loads on the girders, the relative stiffnesses of all the members and their distribution factors, the fixed-end moments, and the simple-beam shears and moments.

Three loadings were considered:

Loading 1 (Sheet 15). So far as the girders are concerned, this loading produced (a) the maximum positive moments in the first and third spans, (b) the minimum positive in the second and fourth spans, (c) the maximum shear V_1 in the end span at the exterior column, and (d) the maximum negative end moment at the exterior column. With the moments determined at the ends of each girder span (shown by the circled values on Sheet 15), the girder bending moments were easily

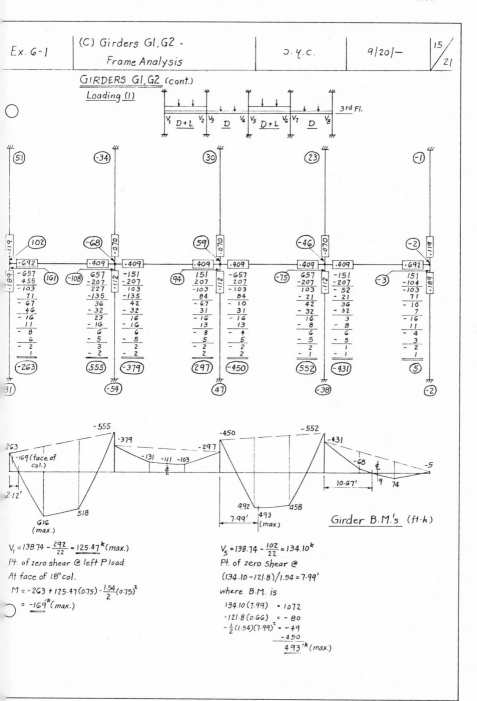

| Ex. 6-1 | (C) Girders G1,G2 - Frame Analysis | | Ɔ. Ɏ. C. | 9/20/— | 15/21 |

GIRDERS G1,G2 (cont.)

Loading (1)

3rd Fl.

V_1 D+L V_2 V_3 D V_4 V_5 D+L V_6 V_7 D V_8

Girder B.M.'s (ft·k)

$V_1 = 138.74 - \dfrac{292}{22} = 125.47^k (max.)$

Pt. of zero shear @ left P load.

At face of 18" col.

$M = -263 + 125.47(0.75) - \dfrac{1.54}{2}(0.75)^2$

$= -169^{'k} (max.)$

$V_5 = 138.74 - \dfrac{102}{22} = 134.10^k$

Pt. of zero shear @

$(134.10 - 121.8)/1.54 = 7.99'$

where B.M. is

134.10(7.99) = 1072

−121.8(0.66) = −80

$-\frac{1}{2}(1.54)(7.99)^2 = -49$

−450

$\overline{493^{'k}(max.)}$

obtained by statics, either by calculation or graphically by superposing the end moments on the simple-beam moment diagrams.

Loading 1 also produced the maximum column moments due to unbalanced live loads. The column moments were obtained quite easily from the *distributed* moments in the girders. For example, the moment of 102 kip-ft. at the bottom of the left exterior column supporting the roof was obtained as follows:

The sum of the distributed moments in the girder at the joint thereat is $(455 + 71 + 46 + 11 + 6 + 1) = 590$. This, when multiplied by the ratio of the distribution factor of the column in question (0.119) to that of the girder (0.692), gives

$$590(0.119)/0.692 = 102 \text{ kip-ft.}$$

At the top end of this column, the moment is simply one-half of 102 or 51 kip-ft.

The column moments elsewhere were determined in a similar fashion.

Loading 2 (Sheet 16). This loading produced (a) the maximum negative moments in the left two spans at the first row of interior columns, and (b) the maximum shears V_2 and V_3.

Loading 3 (Sheet 17). This loading produced (a) the maximum negative moments in the second and third spans at the central row of columns, and (b) the maximum shears V_4 and V_5. As the system was symmetrical about the center line of the frame, only one-half of the frame needed to be analyzed.

6–23. GIRDER DESIGNING (Sheets 18 Through 20)

The designing of the girders is similar in principle to that of the beams, and the calculations presented on these sheets are almost self-explanatory. As shown on Sheet 19, a straight-bar arrangement was chosen. If it is desired to bend some of the bars, the necessary additional calculations would be similar to those made for the beams *B1* and *B2*.

The Design of Interior Columns

(Calculation Sheets 20 and 21)

6–24. INTERIOR COLUMN DESIGNING

To illustrate column designing, a typical interior column supporting the third floor was considered. Based on the assumed column dimensions, the strength reduction factors R for slenderness effects were first computed, assuming the frame to be laterally unbraced. The roof and

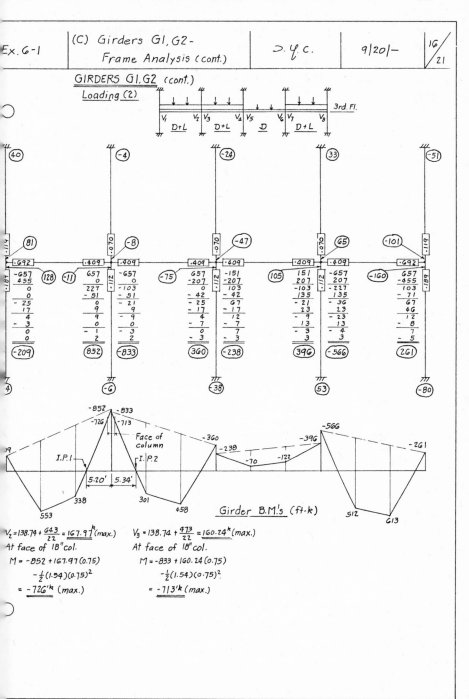

| Ex. 6-1 | (C) Girders G1, G2 – Frame Analysis (cont.) | Ɔ. Ɏ. C. | 9/20/– | 16/21 |

GIRDERS G1, G2 (cont.)

Loading (2)

$V_2 = 138.74 + \frac{643}{22} = 167.97^k$ (max.)

At face of 18" col.

$M = -852 + 167.97 (0.75)$

$\quad -\frac{1}{2}(1.54)(0.75)^2$

$\quad = -726'^k$ (max.)

$V_3 = 138.74 + \frac{473}{22} = 160.24^k$ (max.)

At face of 18" col.

$M = -833 + 160.24 (0.75)$

$\quad -\frac{1}{2}(1.54)(0.75)^2$

$\quad = -713'^k$ (max.)

Girder B.M.'s (ft-k)

| Ex. 6-1 | (C) Girders G1, G2 – Frame Analysis (concl.) | Ɔ.Ч.C. | 9/20/– | 17/21 |

GIRDERS G1, G2 (cont.)

Loading (3)

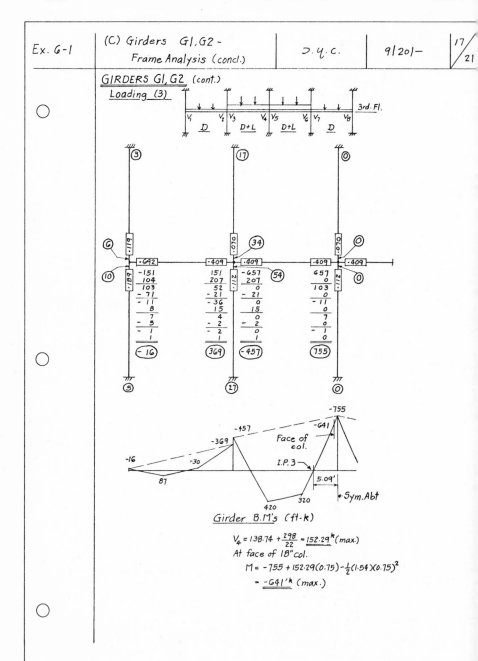

Girder B.M's (ft·k)

$$V_4 = 138.74 + \frac{298}{22} = 152.29^k (max.)$$

At face of 18" col.

$$M = -755 + 152.29(0.75) - \tfrac{1}{2}(1.54)(0.75)^2$$

$$= -641'^k (max.)$$

| Ex. 6-1 | (C) Girders G1,G2 – Concrete Dimensions. | ⊃. 4. C. | 9/20/– | 18/21 |

GIRDERS G1, G2 (cont.)

Concrete Dimensions

D.T. $6\phi\sqrt{f_c'} = 0.323$ ksi

Max. V is V_2 of loading(2) $= 167.97^k$ @ ₵ of col.

At crit. sec. located $d \cong 30''$ from face of col., $V_u = 167.97 - 1.54(0.75 + 2.50)$

$\cong 163^k$

Reqd. $bd = \dfrac{163}{0.323} = 505$ □″.   If $b = 15''$, $d = 33.7''$ reqd. for $v_u = 6\phi\sqrt{f_c'}$

Flexure

Max. -M at face of 1st int. col. $= 726'^k$, loading (2)

For singly-reinf. rect. section ⨍ $p = 1.80\%$, $R = M_u/\phi bd^2 = 0.644$ ksi (Chart A·1)

Reqd. $bd^2 = \dfrac{726(12)}{0.9(0.644)} = 15,030$ in³   If $b = 15''$, $d = 31.7''$

$\dfrac{+\ 5.2''}{t = 36.9''}$ reqd.

∴ Use 15″ x 36″ (with comp. steel where needed) ⟵

Eff. depth

Neg. M : 2 layers tensile bars :   Cover   1.50″⎫
                                    #3 bm. □ = 0.38 ⎬ 3.29″
                                    #11 bm bars = 1.41
                                    #11 gdr. ″ = 1.41
                                    ½ of #8 = 0.50
                                    $d = 36 - \overline{5.20''} = 30.8''$

                    1 layer tensile bars :   3.29
                                    ½ of #11 = 0.71
                                    $d = 36 - \overline{4.00} = 32.0''$

                    1 layer comp. bars where used :   Cover = 1.50 ⎫
                                    #4 stir. = 0.50 ⎬ $2.71'' = d'$
                                    ½ of #11 = 0.71 ⎭

Pos. M : 2 layers tensile bars: Cover = 1.50
                                    #4 stir. = 0.50
                                    #11 = 1.41
                                    ½ of 1″ = 0.50
                                    $d = 36 - \overline{3.91''} = 32.1''$

                    1 layer tensile bars : $d = 36 - 2.71 = 33.3''$

Reinforcement

At 1st int. support, $-M = 726'^k$, $b = 15''$, $d = 30.8''$, $d' = 2.71''$

$M_{uf}/\phi bd^2 = 0.680$ ksi

$R(p = 1.9\%) = \dfrac{0.644}{0.036}$ $A_s - A_s' = 1.8\%(15)(30.8) = 8.32$ □″

$M_2' = 0.036(15)(30.8)^2 = 512''^k$, $A_s' = \dfrac{512}{40(30.8-2.71)} = \dfrac{0.46}{8.78}$ □″ $= A_s$

Check $a = \dfrac{8.32(40)}{0.85(4)(15)} = 6.53''$ $\epsilon_y = 40/29,000 = 0.00137$
ϵ_s'

        $c = 6.53/0.85 = 7.68''$ $\epsilon_s' = 0.003\ \dfrac{7.68-2.71}{7.68} = 0.00194 > \epsilon_y$ o.k.

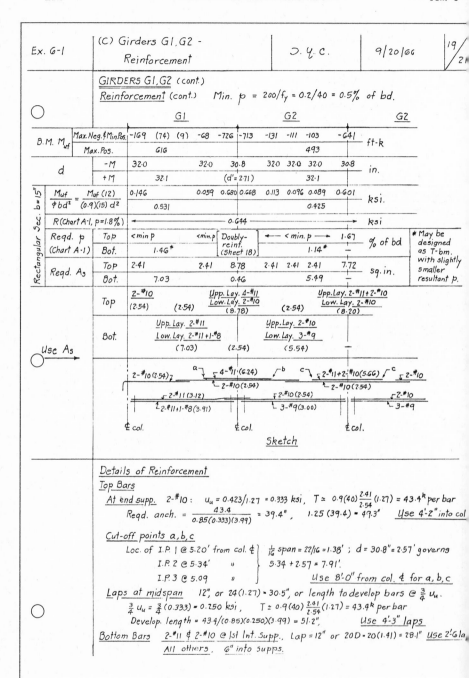

| Ex. 6-1 | (C) Girders G1,G2 - Reinforcement | ⊃. 𝒴. C. | 9/20/66 | 19/2 |

GIRDERS G1,G2 (cont.)

Reinforcement (cont.)　　Min. p = 200/f_y = 0.2/40 = 0.5% of bd.

		G1		G2			G2	
B.M. M_{uf}	Max.Neg.&Min.Pos.	-169	(74) (9) -68 -726	-713	-131 -111 -103	-641	ft-k
	Max.Pos.	616			493		
d	-M	32.0	32.0　30.8	32.0 32.0 32.0	30.8	in.
	+M	32.1	(d'=2.71)	32.1		

Rectangular Sec. b=15"

$\dfrac{M_{uf}}{\phi bd^2} = \dfrac{M_{uf}(12)}{(0.9)(15) d^2}$	0.146	0.059 0.680 0.668	0.113 0.096 0.089	0.601	ksi.
	0.531		0.425		
R(Chart A-1, p=1.8%)	←—————— 0.644 ——————→				ksi
Reqd. p (Chart A-1)	Top	< min p	< min.p	Doubly- reinf. (Sheet 18)	←— < min. p —→ 1.67	% of bd	* May be designed as T-bm. with slightly smaller resultant p.
	Bot.	1.46*			1.14*	
Reqd. A_s	Top	2.41	2.41 8.78	2.41 2.41 2.41	7.72	sq. in.
	Bot.	7.03	0.46	5.49		

Use A_s →

	Top	2-#10 (2.54)　(2.54)	Upp.Lay. 4-#11 Low.Lay. 2-#10 (8.78) (2.54)	Upp.Lay. 2-#11+2-#10 Low.Lay. 2-#10 (8.20)
	Bot.	Upp.Lay. 2-#11 Low.Lay. 2-#11+1-#8 (7.03) (2.54)	Upp.Lay. 2-#10 Low.Lay. 3-#9 (5.54)	

Sketch

Details of Reinforcement

Top Bars

At end supp.　2-#10 :　u_u = 0.423/1.27 = 0.333 ksi,　T ≈ 0.9(40)$\dfrac{2.41}{2.54}$(1.27) = 43.4^k per bar

Reqd. anch. = $\dfrac{43.4}{0.85(0.333)(3.99)}$ = 39.4",　1.25 (39.4) = 49.3"　Use 4'-2" into col

Cut-off points a,b,c

Loc. of I.P. 1 @ 5.20' from col. ₵ ⎤　$\frac{1}{16}$ span = 22/16 = 1.38' ; d = 30.8" = 2.57' governs

I.P. 2 @ 5.34'　"　⎬　5.34 + 2.57 = 7.91'.

I.P. 3 @ 5.09　"　⎦　　　Use 8'-0" from col. ₵ for a,b,c

Laps at midspan　12", or 24(1.27) = 30.5", or length to develop bars @ $\frac{3}{4}$ u_u.

$\frac{3}{4}$ u_u = $\frac{3}{4}$ (0.333) = 0.250 ksi,　T ≈ 0.9(40)$\dfrac{2.41}{2.54}$(1.27) = 43.4^k per bar

Develop. length = 43.4/(0.85)(0.250)(3.99) = 51.2",　Use 4'-3" laps

Bottom Bars　2-#11 & 2-#10 @ 1st Int. Supp., Lap = 12" or 20D = 20(1.41) = 28.1" Use 2'-6 lap

All others. 6" into supps.

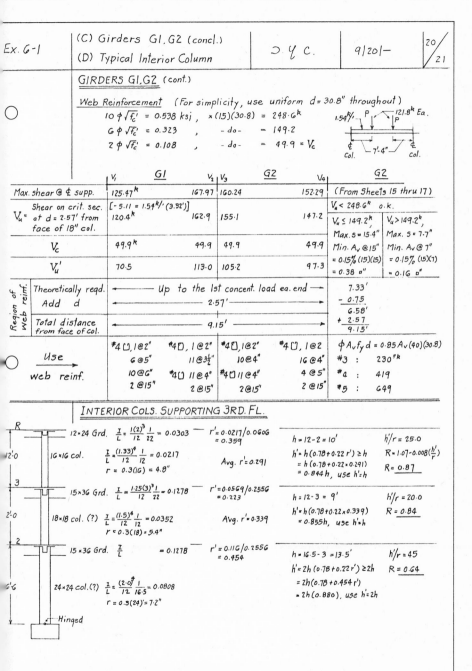

| Ex. 6-1 | (C) Girders G1,G2 (concl.)
 (D) Typical Interior Column | ⊃ Ч C. | 9/20/— | 20/21 |

GIRDERS G1,G2 (cont.)

Web Reinforcement (For simplicity, use uniform d = 30.8" throughout)

$$10 \, \phi \sqrt{f_c'} = 0.538 \text{ ksi}, \quad \times (15)(30.8) = 248.6^k$$
$$6 \, \phi \sqrt{f_c'} = 0.323, \quad - do - \ = 149.2$$
$$2 \, \phi \sqrt{f_c'} = 0.108, \quad - do - \ = 49.9 = V_c$$

1.54 k/'   P   121.8 k Ea.   P

₵ Col. — 7'-4" — ₵ Col.

	V_1	**G1**	V_2	V_3	**G2**	V_4	**G2**
Max. shear @ ₵ supp.	125.47 k		167.97	160.24		152.29	(From Sheets 15 thru 17)
$V_u =$ Shear on crit. sec. at d = 2.57' from face of 18" col.	[−5.11 = 1.54 k/' (3.32')] 120.4 k		162.9	155.1		147.2	$V_u < 248.6^k$ o.k.
V_c	49.9 k		49.9	49.9		49.9	$V_u \le 149.2^k$ | $V_u > 149.2^k$ Max. s = 15.4" | Max. s = 7.7" Min. A_v @15" | Min. A_v @ 7" = 0.15% (15)(15) | = 0.15% (15)(7)
V_u'	70.5		113.0	105.2		97.3	= 0.38 □" | = 0.16 □"

Region of web reinf.	Theoretically reqd.	← Up to the 1st concent. load ea. end →					7.33'
	Add d	← 2.57' →					− 0.75 6.58'
	Total distance from face of col.	← 9.15' →					+ 2.57 9.15'

| Use web reinf. | #4 ⊔,1@2"
 6 @5"
 10 @6"
 2 @15" | #4 ⊔, 1@2"
 11 @3½"
 #4 ⊔ 11 @4"
 2 @15" | #4 ⊔,1@2"
 10 @4"
 #4 ⊔ 11 @4"
 2@15" | #4 ⊔, 1@2
 16 @4"
 4 @5"
 2 @15" | $\phi A_v f_y d = 0.85 A_v (40)(30.8)$
 #3 : 230"k
 #4 : 419
 #5 : 649 |

INTERIOR COLS. SUPPORTING 3RD. FL.

R

12'-0

3

2'-0

2

6'-6

12×24 Grd. $\dfrac{I}{L} = \dfrac{1(2)^3}{12} \cdot \dfrac{1}{22} = 0.0303$ $r' = 0.0217/0.0606 = 0.359$

16×16 col. $\dfrac{I}{L} = \dfrac{(1.33)^4}{12} \cdot \dfrac{1}{12} = 0.0217$ Avg. r' = 0.291 <br> r = 0.3(16) = 4.8"

h = 12−2 = 10'   h'/r = 25.0 <br> h' = h(0.78 + 0.22 r') ≥ h   R = 1.07−0.008(h'/r)
 = h (0.78 + 0.22 · 0.291)   R = 0.87
 = 0.844h, use h'=h

15×36 Grd. $\dfrac{I}{L} = \dfrac{1.25(3)^3}{12} \cdot \dfrac{1}{22} = 0.1278$ $r' = 0.0569/0.2556 = 0.223$

18×18 col. (?) $\dfrac{I}{L} = \dfrac{(1.5)^4}{12} \cdot \dfrac{1}{12} = 0.0352$ Avg. r' = 0.339 <br> r = 0.3(18) = 5.4"

h = 12−3 = 9'   h'/r = 20.0 <br> h' = h(0.78 + 0.22×0.339)   R = 0.84
 = 0.855h, use h'=h

15×36 Grd. $\dfrac{I}{L}$ = 0.1278 $r' = 0.116/0.2556 = 0.454$

24×24 col.(?) $\dfrac{I}{L} = \dfrac{(2.0)^4}{12} \cdot \dfrac{1}{16.5} = 0.0808$
 r = 0.3(24) = 7.2"

h = 16.5−3 = 13.5'   h'/r = 45 <br> h' = 2h (0.78 + 0.22 r') ≥ 2h   R = 0.64
 = 2h(0.78 + 0.454 r')
 = 2h(0.880), use h'=2h

Hinged

| Ex. 6-1 | (D) Typical Interior Column | ⌐ U. C. | 9/20/— | 21/2 |

INT. COLS. SUPPORTING 3RD FL.

Rf Loads

L.L.

D.L. Rfg. & fin. $20^{\#/\square'}$

$3\frac{1}{2}"$ slab   44

Stem of 12×20 bms $206^{\#/'} \div 7.33' = 29$

Stem of 12×24 grds. $256^{\#/'} \div 26' = 10$

$50^{\#/\square'} \times 22 \times 26 = 28.6^k, \times 1.8 = 52^k$ D+L $= 141^k$

$103^{\#/\square'} \times 22 \times 26 = 58.9^k, \times 1.5 = 89^k$ $D+\frac{1}{2}L = 115^k$

Rf. col. $= 2.7^k, \times 1.5 = 4^k$

Fl. Loads

L.L.

D.L. Wear. surf. $\square^{\#/\square'}$

$3\frac{1}{2}"$ slab   44

Stem of 12×25 bms $269^{\#/'} \div 7.33' = 37$

Stem of 15×36 grds. $508 \div 26 = 20$

$300^{\#/\square'} \times 22 \times 26 = 171.6^k, \times 1.8 = 309^k$ D+L $= 401^k$

$107^{\#/\square'} \times 22 \times 26 = 61.2, \times 1.5 = 92^k$ $D+\frac{1}{2}L = 247^k$

3rd Fl. col. $= 3.0^k \times 1.5 = 5^k$

2nd Fl. col. $= 8.1^k \times 1.5 = 12^k$

Design col. supp. 3rd Fl. based on:

3rd ⌐ ℄ Grd. ⌐ $108'^k$

T $-88'^k$

12'

B

2nd ℄ Grd. ⌐ $54'^k$

Col. B.M.
due to unbal.
L.L. on 3rd Fl.
(See Sheet 15)

$g = 13/18 = 0.72$

$f_c' = 4$ ksi

$f_y = 60$

$f_c' bt = 4(18)^2 = 1296^k$

$m = f_y / 0.85 f_c'$

   $= 17.6$

Min. $P_t m = 1\% (17.6)$

   $= 0.176$

Loading (1)

Rf. fully loaded

D+L 141^k

Rf. col.   4

3rd Fl. with unbal. L.L.

$D+\frac{1}{2}L$ 247

Level T, $P_{uf} = 392^k$

$M_{uf} = 88'^k$

$e = 2.69"$

$e/t = 0.15$

$R = 0.84$

$P_u = 467^k$

$K = P_u/f_c' bt = 0.360$

$P_t m < min.$

$P_t = 1\%$

Loading (2)

Rf fully loaded

D+L 141^k

Rf. col.   4

3rd Fl. fully loaded

D+L.   401

3rd Fl. col.   5

Level B, $P_{uf} = 551^k$

& Min. $\frac{e}{t} = 0.1$

$e/t = 0.10$

$R = 0.84$

$P_u = 656^k$

$K = 0.506$

$P_t m < min.$

$P_t = 1\%$

Enter Charts C-4b, -4c & interpolate

$A_{st} = 1\% (18)(18) = 3.24 \,\square"$

Use 18" sq.   4-#9   ⟵

#3 ties @ 18" o.c.

floor loads were next computed; these were substantially mere reproductions of the preliminary calculations given in Art. 6–21.

This column was designed for two loadings:

Loading 1, in which the roof was fully loaded and the third floor was subject to unbalanced live loads. The column bending moments were taken from Sheet 15, the values used being the maximum ones in the interior columns. The designing was performed at level marked T on Sheet 21, just below the third-floor girders.

Loading 2, in which both the roof and the third floor were fully loaded. The column moments were either those at the first row of interior columns from the left on Sheet 16, or those at the central row of columns on Sheet 17. In either case, the ACI minimum eccentricity of $0.10t$ governed. The designing for this loading was performed at level B of the column.

The main reinforcement chosen was that which corresponds to the ACI minimum p of 1 per cent.

GIRDER DESIGN PROBLEMS

6–5. Following up Problem 6–3, completely design the girders *G1* and *G2*, and a typical interior column supporting the third floor, using the following additional data for the roof:

Live load at 30 psf
Dead load due to roofing and finish of 20 psf, 4½-in. slab, 12-by-22-in. beams, and 13-by-26-in. girders

6–6. Following up Problem 6–4, completely design the girders *G1*, *G2*, and *G3* and a typical interior column supporting the girders *G2* and *G3* at the third floor, using the same additional data for the roof as given in Problem 6–5.

6–25. SUMMARY OF FLOOR DESIGNING

Floors to carry moderate to heavy loadings, with rectangular bays between columns, may be designed using beams and girders. The girders should preferably extend in the shorter direction. The slabs will be pronouncedly rectangular and should have one-way steel in the shorter direction. If the beams are omitted, the resulting slabs must be designed with two-way reinforcement, as in Chapter 7.

The probability of loaded and unloaded continuous spans of live load throughout has led to the use of convenient arbitrary bending moment coefficients. The novice will do well to study the underlying mechanics thereof before blindly accepting published coefficients. When span lengths differ widely, moment distribution studies for maximum bending moments should be made, employing the aforementioned equal-span loading criteria as guides.

In designing for floor continuity, it is probably best to use center to center spans and story heights in the determination of the bending moments, but to use the decreased value at the face of the support for

Plate 6–2. Self-supporting reinforced concrete spiral stairs, Port Museum, The Hague, Netherlands.   (Photograph by G. T. Hamer.)   See also V. R. Bergman, "Helicoidal Staircases of Reinforced Concrete," *Proc. ACI,* 1956, Vol. 53, pp. 403–412; and A. C. Scordelis, "Internal Forces in Uniformly Loaded Helicoidal Girders," *Proc. ACI,* 1960, Vol. 56, pp. 1013–1026.

the design negative bending moment, as has been done throughout the present designing.

Whether to use the thicker exterior slab thickness throughout a floor to save formwork depends partly upon the width of the structure. A structure with a preponderance of interior spans should ordinarily not be so designed. Alternate schemes should be worked out and costs compared.

The designer's choice of flexural steel bar size should be made in conjunction with the selection of the span-to-span bent-up bar arrangement. In slabs it is often convenient to bend up half the positive steel although an all-straight bar arrangement may be alternately used, as shown in Fig. 6–10a. Furthermore, in beam and girder design, four bars of some size at the center of the span should be considered early, since, if necessary, three of them may be bent up [ACI Sec. 918(f)], unless more than one layer of bars are anticipated.

Since all the girders extend from column to column, their design involves *rigid frame* action. In calculating relative stiffnesses I/L, it is customary, convenient, and in accordance with test results to use the plain concrete section in calculating moment of inertia. If, as in the present case, the slab has already been relied upon for flexure in the direction of the girder, the girder should be designed as a rectangular beam. If the girder is designed as a T-beam, its flange must be additionally reinforced [Sec. 906(e)].

All reinforced concrete flexural members must be examined for four strength factors, namely, *bending* over a span, *diagonal tension* in the concrete, *flexural bond* of the concrete to the steel and *anchorage* of the ends of the bars against slippage. However, the flexural bond check may be omitted if the anchorage or *development* length provided at the ends of the bars exceeds that required at the basic permissible bond stress by 25% [ACI Sec. 1801(c)].

REVIEW PROBLEMS

6–7. A five-span continuous beam consists of center-to-center spans, L, as follows: 24 ft., 20 ft., 24 ft., 20 ft., and 24 ft. Consider the ends hinged. The *service* loads are 1 kip per ft. live and 2 kips per ft. dead. Apply the ACI load factors, and calculate the maximum dead load plus live load bending moments, both positive and negative. Assuming all supports 12 in. wide, reduce the maximum negative support moments to the faces thereof. Also calculate the maximum dead load plus live load shears at the faces of all the supports.

Tabulate a comparison of the results with ACI Sec. 904(c) and Fig. 6–8 of this text, and discuss.

6–8. Redesign the structure of Example 6–1 on the same 22-by-26-ft. column centers, but with the girders spanning the 26-ft. direction. Tabulate a comparison of the two designs.

QUESTIONS

1. Distinguish clearly between skeleton and wall bearing building construction.

2. State the loading criteria for (a) maximum positive and (b) maximum negative bending moment in a continuous beam or slab.

3. What is meant by the term *spandrel effect?*

4. What is meant by the term *bending moment envelope?*

5. Describe how to terminate both the top and bottom slab reinforcement at the end of a floor system using deformed bars.

6. Tell in how many ways the locations of the inflection points in a continuous slab or beam are useful.

7. Why were the floor girders in Example 6–1 designed as elements of a continuous frame while the slabs and beams were not?

8. Can the interior columns of continuous equal-span rigid frames be designed for axial load only? Tell why. What about the exterior columns?

REFERENCES

1. WESTERGAARD, H. M. "Formulas for the Design of Rectangular Floor Slabs and the Supporting Girders," *Proc. ACI*, 1926, Vol. 22, pp. 26–43.

2. JOHANSEN, K. W. *Yield-Line Theory.* (English translation.) London: Cement. & Concrete Association, 1962.

3. CROSS, HARDY, and MORGAN, N. D. *Continuous Frames of Reinforced Concrete.* New York: John Wiley & Sons, Inc., 1932.

4. AMERICAN CONCRETE INSTITUTE. "Reinforced Concrete Design Handbook, Working Stress Method," *ACI Publication SP-3*, 1965.

5. PORTLAND CEMENT ASSOCIATION. *Continuity in Concrete Building Frames.* Chicago: The Association.

6. AMERICAN CONCRETE INSTITUTE. "Manual of Standard Practice for Detailing Reinforced Concrete Structures," *ACI Standard 315-65*, 1965.

7

TWO-WAY SLABS AND FLAT SLABS

Thus far, rectangular floor or roof slabs with flexure steel in only one direction, called *one-way slabs*, have been considered. If the slabs are square, or approximately so, it is more economical to run the steel in both horizontal directions. Such slabs are of two types, depending on how they are supported. When the slabs are *directly supported along all four edges*, as by girders extending between columns, they are called **two-way slabs.** Figure 7–1 is an illustration thereof.

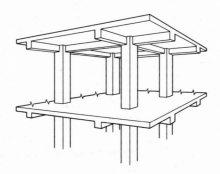

Fig. 7–1. Two-way slab construction.

The other type of construction, known as **flat slab,** is shown in Fig. 7–2. It consists of slabs reinforced in two or more directions, which are *supported only at their corners* by the columns, there being usually no beams or girders. When there are a number of such spans in both directions, this construction is quite economical.

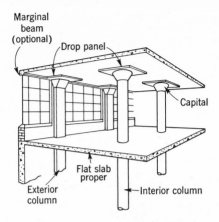

Fig. 7–2.   Flat slab construction.

A. Two-Way Slabs, USD

7–1. INTRODUCTION

All rectangular slabs supported on beams, girders, or walls along their edges bend in both directions.   In other words, they exhibit, to a greater or lesser degree, two-way action.   One-way slabs, discussed in Chapter 6, may therefore be considered as special cases of the general two-way slabs. It will be recalled that, in one-way slab design, although all the principal reinforcement is placed in the short direction (as if all bending took place in that direction), additional negative reinforcement is provided in the long direction over the supports, aimed to inhibit the formation of undesirable cracks induced thereat primarily by two-way action.

A slab may be treated as a plate, and analyzed by the elementary elastic plate theory, as was done by Westergaard [1] and others.   In general, a slab element is subject to bending moments and transverse shears in both directions, plus twisting moments on the faces of the slab element.   Normally, the twisting moments are small, and are therefore usually neglected in design.   The bending moments in each direction are not uniformly distributed.   For design purposes, the bending moments used are neither the maximum moments, nor the actual moments which vary from point to point.   Instead, most specifications consider that a slab panel to be designed consists of *strips*, within each of which the bending moments are assumed to be either uniformly or linearly distributed, as will be seen later in Arts. 7–4 and 7–10.   In building codes using such an empirical or semi-empirical approach, recommended bending moment coefficients are usually specified.   They are applied to the different strips of a slab panel to yield the design moments, provided certain limitations are satisfied. The transverse shears are treated in a similar manner.

7–2. ACI CODE DESIGN METHODS

The ACI Code requirements for two-way slab design may be found in Sec. 2002 and the subsequent Appendix A thereof. Three design methods are included and approved for use by the Code. The three methods yield slightly different results because their underlying assumptions differ somewhat. However, their use will result in satisfactory structures if they are applied with due regard to their respective limitations.

All three methods are based primarily on elastic analyses,[1] but they also contain certain modifications which are based on experimental and/or empirical results. Method 1 gives more detailed information than the other two, but is the most cumbersome of the three. Method 2 is the simplest for practical use, but is also the crudest. Method 3 is rather similar to Method 2, but it provides much more data, and is reasonably simple to use. In this book, only Methods 2 and 3 will be discussed at length.

7–3. GENERAL DESIGN LIMITATIONS[2]

The following limitations of the ACI Code are common to its three design methods.

Minimum Slab Thickness. Section 2002(e) stipulates a minimum slab thickness of $3\frac{1}{2}$ in. This limit will be found to control the slab thickness only for average span lengths less than about 13 ft. Another requirement is that the minimum slab thickness be equal to the perimeter of a slab panel divided by 180. This requirement is empirical and is aimed to limit slab deflection.

Minimum Reinforcement. Section 2002(e) provides that the minimum reinforcement in each direction be that specified in Sec. 807 for shrinkage and temperature reinforcement, namely: for deformed bars, $0.0020bt$ if $f_y < 60$ ksi, and $0.0018bt$ if $f_y = 60$ ksi, and for welded wire fabric, $0.0018bt$, where b and t are the width and total thickness of a slab strip. This requirement is therefore similar to that for a one-way slab.

---

[1] Method 1 is based on work done by DiStasio, van Buren, and Bertin [2, 3]. Method 2 came from the 1940 Joint Committee Report [4], which in turn was based on Westergaard's work [1]. Method 3 is an adaptation of a European method due to Marcus [5], and was introduced into the United States by Rogers [6].

[2] The ACI Code provisions for two-way slabs apply generally also to two-way joist construction. The discussion presented in this text will be restricted to *solid* two-way slabs. For detailed special provisions for joist construction, refer to Sec. 2001.

Maximum Spacing of Reinforcement. Section 2002(e) stipulates a maximum center to center spacing of reinforcement equal to three times the slab thickness. As explained in Art. 6–10, some such limit is necessary in order to insure slab action, prevent cracking, and provide for the possibility of local heavy concentration of loads.

Special Corner Reinforcement. Section 2002(b) provides that additional reinforcement be placed at exterior corners of slab panels. This matter will be given more detailed attention in Art. 7–13.

ACI Method 2 for Two-Way Slab Designing

7–4. DESIGN PROCEDURE

Here we undertake a general description of the design procedure for Method 2. A numerical design example is presented in Arts. 7–6 through 7–9.

1. Limitations. In addition to the general limitations described in Art. 7–3, Sec. A2002(a) stipulates that Method 2 be applied *only when the supporting beams or walls are built monolithically with the slabs.* This is to insure that, consistent with the basic assumptions of Method 2, some torsional restraints exist on all edges of a panel whether it is isolated or continuous with another panel. This requirement may therefore be interpreted to imply that Method 2 is also applicable to slabs securely tied to precast concrete beams or to completely encased steel beams, as long as such beams have adequate torsional rigidity and provision is made for effective transfer of moments between the slabs and beams.

2. Division of Panel into Strips. For designing, each panel is divided into strips in each direction: the **middle** and the **column strips.** The widths of such strips depend on the ratio of the sides of the panel. Let S = the short-span length and L = the long-span length, as in Fig. 7–3,

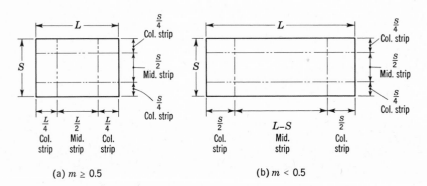

Fig. 7–3. Division of panel into strips—Method 2.

and $m = S/L$. The span length in each direction is the center-to-center distance between the supports or the clear span plus twice the slab thickness, whichever is the smaller.

In the long-span direction, the widths of the middle strip and the corresponding column strip are always $S/2$ and $S/4$, respectively, as shown in Fig. 7–3. In the short-span direction, the middle strip is $L/2$ wide and the corresponding column strips are each $L/4$ wide when $m \geq 0.5$ (that is, for more nearly square panels), as shown in Fig. 7–3a. When $m < 0.5$ (that is, for longer and narrower panels), the middle strip is $(L - S)$ wide, and the column strips are each $S/2$ wide, as shown in Fig. 7–3b. This is reasonable because, for the longer and narrower panels, the short-span moments are more nearly uniformly distributed over a central region wider than $L/2$. Hence for $m < 0.5$, the short-span middle-strip width is made equal to $(L - S)$ because, if $m = S/L < 0.5$, then $(1 - S/L) > (1 - 0.5)$, or $(L - S) > 0.5L$.

3. Bending Moments. Section A2002(b) recommends that design bending moments be determined as indicated below.

a. MIDDLE STRIPS. The bending moments per foot of width in the middle strips, M, *in both directions* are computed by

$$M = CwS^2 \qquad (7\text{–}1)$$

where w = the total uniform load on the slab per sq. ft. (service-level values for WSD, and load-factored values for USD)

C = a moment coefficient as given in Table 7–1.

Table 7–1 covers five types of support conditions: panels continuous with adjacent panels on all four sides (i.e., interior panels), and panels with one, two, three, or four discontinuous edges. The values of m considered range from 1.0 to 0.0. Slabs with m less than 0.5 (i.e., long, narrow panels), are to be designed as if their m values were 0.5; some designers prefer to design such slabs as one-way slabs. Table 7–1 also indicates that, regardless of the value of m, any slab supported on four sides must have adequate reinforcement in the long span to resist the moments shown in the last column of the table.

The reader should note that, in Eq. 7–1, the coefficient C from Table 7–1 is *always* multiplied by the quantity (wS^2) whether one is calculating the bending moment in the short or long direction.

The middle-strip bending moments are assumed to be uniformly distributed across the widths of the strips.

b. COLUMN STRIPS. The *average* bending moments in the column strips are taken to be equal to two-thirds of those in the corresponding middle strips. The Code permits the column-strip moments to be considered as varying from a maximum at the edge of the middle strip to a

Table 7–1. Bending Moment Coefficients, C, for Two-Way Slabs
Method 2, ACI Code Sec. A2002(b)

Moments	Short Span, Values of m						Long Span, All Values of m
	1.0	0.9	0.8	0.7	0.6	≤ 0.5	
Case 1—Interior panels							
Negative moment at—							
Continuous edge	0.033	0.040	0.048	0.055	0.063	0.083	0.033
Discontinuous edge	—	—	—	—	—	—	—
Positive moment at midspan	0.025	0.030	0.036	0.041	0.047	0.062	0.025
Case 2—One edge discontinuous							
Negative moment at—							
Continuous edge	0.041	0.048	0.055	0.062	0.069	0.085	0.041
Discontinuous edge	0.021	0.024	0.027	0.031	0.035	0.042	0.021
Positive moment at midspan	0.031	0.036	0.041	0.047	0.052	0.064	0.031
Case 3—Two edges discontinuous							
Negative moment at—							
Continuous edge	0.049	0.057	0.064	0.071	0.078	0.090	0.049
Discontinuous edge	0.025	0.028	0.032	0.036	0.039	0.045	0.025
Positive moment at midspan	0.037	0.043	0.048	0.054	0.059	0.068	0.037
Case 4—Three edges discontinuous							
Negative moment at—							
Continuous edge	0.058	0.066	0.074	0.082	0.090	0.098	0.058
Discontinuous edge	0.029	0.033	0.037	0.041	0.045	0.049	0.029
Positive moment at midspan	0.044	0.050	0.056	0.062	0.068	0.074	0.044
Case 5—Four edges discontinuous							
Negative moment at—							
Continuous edge	—	—	—	—	—	—	—
Discontinuous edge	0.033	0.038	0.043	0.047	0.053	0.055	0.033
Positive moment at midspan	0.050	0.057	0.064	0.072	0.080	0.083	0.050

minimum at the edge of the panel. As shown in Fig. 7–4, this amounts to assuming a linear variation of the column-strip moment from a maximum equal to the middle-strip moment M at the edge of the middle strip to a minimum equal to $M/3$ at the edge of the panel. However, a quite common practice is to assume that the design column-strip moment is

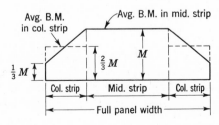

Fig. 7–4. Assumed variation of design bending moment.

uniformly equal to $2M/3$, the average column-strip moment. This is not at all unsafe or unrealistic if some inelastic redistribution of moments is taken into account.

c. DIFFERENCE IN NEGATIVE MOMENTS AT A COMMON SUPPORT. The Code provides that if the negative moment on one side of a support is less than 0.80 times that on the other side, two-thirds of the difference is to be distributed to the two sides in proportion to the relative stiffnesses of the slabs.

4. Slab Shears. Section A2002(c) and (d) provides that shear stresses in the slab be computed in accordance with the load distribution pattern as shown in Fig. 7–5, wherein each of the two long beams is assumed to carry the load in the tributary trapezoidal area formed by the 45° lines from the corners and the center line of the panel, and each of the short beams carries the load on the contiguous triangular area. This distribution is in accord with typical crack patterns found in slabs tested to failure.

5. Load on Beams. The loads carried by the supporting beams of a two-way slab panel are as indicated by the distribution pattern of Fig. 7–5. As this will result in a triangular loading on the short beams, and a trapezoidal loading on the long beams, the Code gives, in the interest of simplicity, for *the calculation of beam bending moments*, the following approximate formulas for the equivalent load per foot of the beams *for each panel supported:*

For short-span beams: Equivalent uniform load $= wS/3 = w'$ (7–2a)
For long-span beams: Equivalent uniform load $= (wS/3)(3 - m^2)/2$
(7–2b)

These formulas were derived by equating the simple-beam moments produced by the loading of Fig. 7–5 and the equivalent uniform loading. Thus, for a short-span beam, as shown in Fig. 7–6a, the triangular load

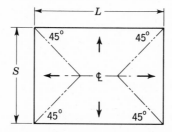

Fig. 7–5.   Load distribution in two-way slabs.

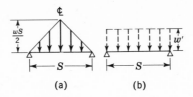

Fig. 7–6.   Equivalent uniform load on short-span beams.

has a peak intensity of $wS/2$ at midspan, and produces a maximum moment, for simply supported ends, of $(\frac{1}{6})(\frac{1}{2})(wS/2)(S)(S)$ or $(\frac{1}{24})wS^3$. If the equivalent uniform load, w' per ft., is placed on the beam, as shown in Fig. 7–6b, it produces the maximum moment of $w'S^2/8$. Hence, for the two moments to be equal, $wS^3/24 = w'S^2/8$, and w' is found to be $wS/3$, which is Eq. 7–2a. Equation 7–2b may be similarly derived. It is presumably further assumed that these formulas, derived on the basis of simply supported beam spans, are usable for continuous beams as well.

7–5. ARRANGEMENT OF SLAB REINFORCEMENT

The bending moments in a two-way slab panel are usually larger for the short span. Accordingly, it is reasonable to give the short-span reinforcement the preferential position (i.e., closer to the concrete surface in tension), so as to secure a slightly larger effective depth than for the long-span reinforcement thereat. For a square panel, some designers use the average d for designing in both directions; others use the actual d provided in each direction, or the smaller of the two d's.

It is rather common practice to use a uniform spacing of bars in any single strip, and to avoid several different bar sizes in any panel. When bending of the reinforcement is desired, one commonly bends up about two-thirds of the positive bars over the supports to provide for the usually larger negative moments thereat. The bend-up points of the truss bars, the distances they are to extend into the adjacent panels, and the lengths of any top negative bars over the supports, are governed by moment requirements as well as bond and anchorage considerations. For normal conditions of loading and spans, the standards given in the ACI "Manual of Standard Practice for Detailing" [7] are usually adequate.

7–6. TWO-WAY SLAB DESIGN EXAMPLE BY METHOD 2

To illustrate the ACI Method 2 design procedure, the following example is presented, which considers the same building floor that was designed as one-way slabs in Example 6–1.

EXAMPLE 7–1

(Calculation Sheets 1 Through 4)

Given the building of Example 6–1 to redesign for two-way slab framing. The column center lines form 22-by-26-ft. panels, the *service* live load is 300 psf, the concrete is 4000-lb., the reinforcing steel has a 40,000-psi yield point, and the rest of the data are as shown in Calculation Sheet 1. The ACI Code on USD, and Method 2 thereof are to be followed.

See the solution in the following articles and the Calculation Sheets.

7–7. PRELIMINARY DESIGN

To minimize extensive revision later, rough preliminary calculations will prove an effort well spent. The goal of such calculations is to establish a slab thickness which is adequate for flexure and diagonal tension, and results in satisfactory steel arrangement.

From Sec. 2002(e), the minimum slab thickness is $3\frac{1}{2}$ in. or the panel perimeter divided by 180, the latter amounting roughly to $2(22 + 26)(12)/180 = 6.5$ in. Taking a tentative $6\frac{1}{2}$-in. slab with $\frac{3}{4}$-in. cover and #6 bars, and giving preferential placement to the short-span bars, the effective d in the short and long directions would then be

$$d \text{ (short)} = 6.5 - 0.75 - 0.38 \qquad = 5.37 \text{ in.}$$
$$d \text{ (long)} = 6.5 - 0.75 - 0.75 - 0.38 = 4.62 \text{ in.}$$

To determine whether the $6\frac{1}{2}$-in. slab is satisfactory for flexure, one needs to spot the sections of maximum bending moments in the entire floor. The following considerations will be found helpful guides toward this end:

1. Middle-strip moments are usually larger than corresponding column-strip moments.
2. Short-span moments are larger than long-span moments in the same panel, but the effective depth in the short direction is also larger. So short-span moments do not necessarily control the slab thickness.
3. As in continuous beams of approximately equal spans and similarly loaded, maximum negative moments over supports are generally larger than positive midspan moments. Also, maximum negative moments over the first interior supports are usually larger than those at other supports.

It would then appear that the two regions marked A and B on the continuous edges of the corner panel (Fig. 7–7) are the most critical flexurally.

Region A is the short-span middle-strip negative moment section between panels 1 and 2, the former having two discontinuous edges and the latter having one. For $m = \frac{22}{26} = 0.85$, Table 7–1 shows, by interpolation, 0.061 and 0.052 as the moment coefficients in region A.

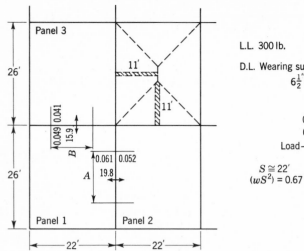

Fig. 7–7. Critical moments in preliminary design—Example 7–1.

As $0.052/0.061 = 0.85 > 0.80$, no adjustment is needed, and the controlling moment there is then $0.061(wS^2) = 0.061(325) = 19.8$ kip-ft. Region B is the long-span middle-strip negative moment section between panels 1 and 3. Similarly, the moment coefficients are found from Table 7–1 to be 0.049 and 0.041, which again require no adjustment. The controlling moment is therefore $0.049(325) = 15.9$ kip-ft.

At A:
$$M_{uf} = 19.8 \text{ kip-ft.}, \qquad d = 5.37 \text{ in.}$$
$$M_{uf}/\phi bd^2 = (19.8)(12)/(0.9)(12)(5.37)^2 = 0.76 \text{ ksi}$$

From USD Beam Chart A–1 (Appendix A),

Reqd. $p = 2.20\%$, and $A_s = 2.20\%(12)(5.37) = 1.42$ sq. in.

Similarly, at B:
$$M_{uf} = 15.9 \text{ kip-ft.}, \qquad d = 4.62 \text{ in.}$$
$$M_{uf}/\phi bd^2 = (15.9)(12)/(0.9)(12)(4.62)^2 = 0.83 \text{ ksi}$$
Reqd. $p = 2.44\%$, and $A_s = 2.44\%(12)(4.62) = 1.35$ sq. in.

The required 1.42 sq. in. per ft. of slab may be furnished by something like #6 at 3½-in. spacing. The designer will have to decide whether this reinforcement is too heavy. He will note also that the most critical sections are being investigated here, and that elsewhere the required reinforcement would be lighter. This also brings up the question whether the corner panels should be made thicker than the rest of the floor. For an industrial building, thickened corner panels may not be architecturally objectionable, and may result in some economy and better steel arrangement. However, the final decision must be also based on consideration of diagonal tension.

According to the load distribution pattern shown in Fig. 7–7, per Sec. A2002(c) and (d), the slab maximum shears in the long and short directions, at distance d from the faces of assumed 15-in.-wide girders, are:

Long span, $V_u = (0.67)[11.0 - (7.5 + 4.62)/12] = 6.69$ kips
Short span, $V_u = (0.67)[11.0 - (7.5 + 5.37)/12] = 6.65$ kips

Hence the shear stresses, $v_u = V_u/bd$, are

Long span, $v_u = 6.69/(12)(4.62) = 0.121$ ksi
Short span, $v_u = 6.65/(12)(5.37) = 0.103$ ksi

The allowable stress is $v_c = 2\phi \sqrt{f'_c} = 2(0.85) \sqrt{4000} = 0.108$ ksi [Sec. 1701(c)]. The long span is obviously overstressed, although the argument may be advanced that the overstress occurs locally within a 1-ft. strip only and therefore is not unduly crucial.

After similar calculations, it was finally decided to use a slab thickness of 8 in. for the corner panels and 7 in. for all others.

7–8. DETAILED DESIGNING

The preliminary calculations of Art. 7–7 having indicated tentative slab thicknesses of 8 in. for the corner panels and 7 in. for the others, the designing of Example 7–1 may now proceed with the more refined calculations shown in Calculation Sheets 1 through 3.

(a) Loads and Spans (Sheet 1). First, the total load per unit area was computed. The spans S and L were computed as the center-to-center distances of the supports, or the clear span plus twice the estimated slab thicknesses, whichever was the smaller. It was seen that the computed S and L did not differ appreciably from the center-to-center span lengths of 22 and 26 ft. Hence, the latter values were used in the interest of simplicity. The quantity (wS^2) was then computed for the corner and other panels.

(b) Check on Slab Thickness for Maximum Bending Moment and Calculated "Reqd. A_s" (Sheet 1). At this stage, Calculation Sheets 2 and 3 were first partially started. These two sheets show that, in preference to a tabular form of bookkeeping, a sketch of the floor plan was made separately for short-span (Sheet 2) and long-span (Sheet 3) designing, and all calculations were recorded directly thereon at the locations to which they pertained. The coefficients C for the middle-strip bending moments

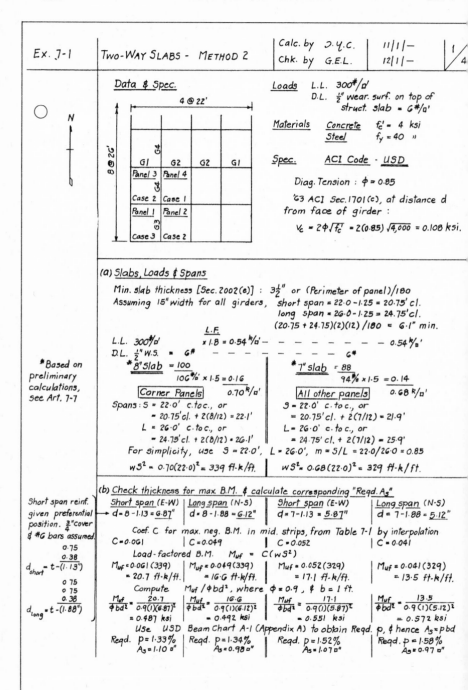

Ex. 7-1   **TWO-WAY SLABS - METHOD 2**

Calc. by J.Y.C.   11/1/—   1
Chk. by G.E.L.   12/1/—   /4

Data & Spec.

4 @ 22'

N

8 @ 26'

G4			
G1	G2	G2	G1
Panel 3	Panel 4		
G4			
Case 2	Case 1		
Panel 1	Panel 2		
G3			
Case 3	Case 2		

Loads L.L. 300#/□'
D.L. ½" wear. surf. on top of
struct. slab = 6#/□'

Materials Concrete f'_c = 4 ksi
Steel f_y = 40 ,,

Spec. ACI Code - USD

Diag. Tension : ϕ = 0.85
'63 ACI Sec.1701(c), at distance d
from face of girder :
$v_c = 2\phi\sqrt{f'_c} = 2(0.85)\sqrt{4,000} = 0.108$ ksi

(a) Slabs, Loads & Spans

Min. slab thickness [Sec. 2002(e)] : $3\frac{1}{2}$" or (Perimeter of panel)/180
Assuming 15" width for all girders,   short span = 22.0 - 1.25 = 20.75' cl.
        long span = 26.0 - 1.25 = 24.75' cl.
        (20.75 + 24.75)(2)(12) /180 = 6.1" min.

         L.F.
L.L. 300#/□'   x 1.8 = 0.54 k/□' — — — — — — — — 0.54 k/□'
D.L. ½" W.S. = 6# — — — — — — — — — 6#

Based on preliminary calculations, see Art. 7-7

8" Slab = 100
106%/□' x 1.5 = 0.16

| Corner Panels | 0.70 k/□' |

Spans : S = 22.0' c.to c., or
    = 20.75'cl. + 2(8/12) = 22.1'
   L = 26.0' c.to c., or
    = 24.75'cl. + 2(8/12) = 26.1'
For simplicity, use   S = 22.0', L = 26.0', m = S/L = 22.0/26.0 = 0.85
wS^2 = 0.70(22.0)² = 339 ft-k/ft.

7" Slab = 88
94%/□' x 1.5 = 0.14

| All other panels | 0.68 k/□' |

S = 22.0' c.to c., or
  = 20.75'cl. + 2(7/12) = 21.9'
L = 26.0' c.to c., or
  = 24.75'cl. + 2(7/12) = 25.9'
  m = S/L = 22.0/26.0 = 0.85
wS^2 = 0.68(22.0)² = 329 ft-k/ft.

(b) Check thickness for max. B.M. & calculate corresponding "Reqd. A_s"

Short span reinf. given preferential position. ¾"cover & #6 bars assumed.

$d_{short} = t - (1.13")$
  0.75
  0.38

$d_{long} = t - (1.88")$
  0.75
  0.75
  0.38

Short span (E-W)	Long span (N-S)	Short span (E-W)	Long span (N-S)
d = 8 - 1.13 = 6.87"	d = 8 - 1.88 = 6.12"	d = 7 - 1.13 = 5.87"	d = 7 - 1.88 = 5.12"

Coef. C for max. neg. B.M. in mid. strips, from Table 7-1 by interpolation

C = 0.061	C = 0.049	C = 0.052	C = 0.041

Load-factored B.M. M_{uf} = C(wS^2)

M_{uf} = 0.061(339)	M_{uf} = 0.049(339)	M_{uf} = 0.052(329)	M_{uf} = 0.041(329)
= 20.7 ft-k/ft.	= 16.6 ft-k/ft.	= 17.1 ft-k/ft.	= 13.5 ft-k/ft.

Compute $M_{uf}/\phi bd^2$, where ϕ = 0.9, & b = 1 ft.

$\dfrac{M_{uf}}{\phi bd^2} = \dfrac{20.7}{0.9(1)(6.87)^2}$	$\dfrac{M_{uf}}{\phi bd^2} = \dfrac{16.6}{0.9(1)(6.12)^2}$	$\dfrac{M_{uf}}{\phi bd^2} = \dfrac{17.1}{0.9(1)(5.87)^2}$	$\dfrac{M_{uf}}{\phi bd^2} = \dfrac{13.5}{0.9(1)(5.12)^2}$
= 0.487 ksi	= 0.492 ksi	= 0.551 ksi	= 0.572 ksi

Use   USD Beam Chart A-1 (Appendix A) to obtain Reqd. p, & hence A_s = pbd

Reqd. p = 1.33%	Reqd. p = 1.34%	Reqd. p = 1.52%	Reqd. p = 1.58%
A_s = 1.10 □"	A_s = 0.98 □"	A_s = 1.07 □"	A_s = 0.97 □"

at all locations in both directions were obtained from Table 7–1, and the middle-strip moments were then calculated by multiplying C by (wS^2). According to Sec. A2002(b), when the negative moment on one side of a support is less than 80 per cent of that on the other side, two-thirds of the difference is to be distributed in proportion to the relative stiffness of the abutting slabs. For this example, no such adjustment was needed at any support, although a space was provided thereat.

A scanning of the moments shown on Sheets 2 and 3 will reveal the critical moments which will flexurally control the slab thicknesses in the corner and other panels. At this point, return to Calculation Sheet 1 to determine whether the tentative concrete thicknesses chosen earlier will be adequate for the steel now contemplated.

(c) **Check on Slab Thickness for Diagonal Tension** (Sheet 2). Next, the shear force, V_u, for diagonal tension check was computed at distance d from the faces of the supporting beams in both directions, using the load distribution of Sec. A2002(c), as shown in Fig. 7–5 or Fig. 7–7. This shear was compared with the ACI allowable shear capacity $V_c = 2\phi \sqrt{f'_c} (bd)$.

(d) **Short-Span (E-W) Reinforcement** (Sheet 2). Having checked the slab thicknesses for flexure and diagonal tension, one now proceeds with designing the short-span reinforcement of Sheet 2.

MIDDLE-STRIP REINFORCEMENT. At each location, the effective depth d was entered, assuming $\frac{3}{4}$-in. cover, #6 bars, and giving the short-span bars the preferential position. $M_{uf}/\phi bd^2$ was then calculated. Using the USD Beam Chart A–1 of Appendix A, the required steel percentage, p, was obtained, from which the required A_s was determined.

The selection of bar spacings is best postponed until the steel required at all locations in the short-span middle strips has been determined. One then starts by selecting the positive-moment bar spacings. For instance, for the short-span middle strips through panels 3 and 4 shown on Sheet 2, #6 at $6\frac{1}{2}$-in. and #6 at $7\frac{1}{2}$-in. centers were chosen, furnishing areas of 0.81 and 0.70 sq. in. per ft. (given in parentheses), versus the required areas of 0.78 and 0.66 sq. in. per ft., respectively. Bending up two of every three bottom bars over the supports, the area furnished by the bentup bars between panels 3 and 4 would be equal to $(\frac{2}{3})(0.81 + 0.70) =$ 1.01 sq. in., versus the 1.07 sq. in. required thereat. Hence, additional top straight bars of #3 at 13-in. centers were placed over the support, bringing the total area of steel furnished up to 1.11 sq. in. Similar calculations were made for the negative-moment section in the middle strip over the support adjacent to the two identical panels 4. There, bending up two of every three of the positive steel (#6 bars at $7\frac{1}{2}$-in.) from each panel, the total area furnished by the bentup bars was $(\frac{2}{3})(0.70 + 0.70) =$ 0.93 sq. in. over the support, versus the 0.92 sq. in. required thereat. At the exterior edge of the short-span middle strip in panel 3, two-thirds of

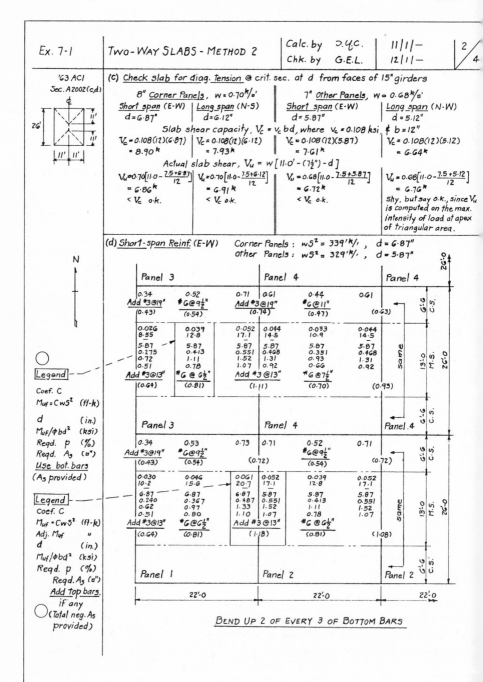

Ex. 7-1 | Two-WAY SLABS - METHOD 2 | Calc. by D.Y.C. | 11/1/— | 2/4
Chk. by G.E.L. | 12/11/—

'63 ACI
Sec. A2002(c,d)

(c) Check slab for diag. tension @ crit. sec. at d from faces of 15" girders

8" Corner Panels, w = 0.70^k/□'   7" Other Panels, w = 0.68^k/□'

Short span (E-W) | Long span (N-S) | Short span (E-W) | Long span (N-W)
d = 6.87" | d = 6.12" | d = 5.87" | d = 5.12"

Slab shear capacity, $V_c = v_c\,bd$, where $v_c = 0.108$ ksi, b = 12"

$V_c = 0.108(12)(6.87)$ | $V_c = 0.108(12)(6.12)$ | $V_c = 0.108(12)(5.87)$ | $V_c = 0.108(12)(5.12)$
= 8.90^k | = 7.93^k | = 7.61^k | = 6.64^k

Actual slab shear, $V_u = w\,[11.0' - (7\frac{1}{2}") - d]$

$V_u = 0.70[11.0 - \frac{7.5 + 6.87}{12}]$ | $V_u = 0.70[11.0 - \frac{7.5 + 6.12}{12}]$ | $V_u = 0.68[11.0 - \frac{7.5 + 5.87}{12}]$ | $V_u = 0.68[11.0 - \frac{7.5 + 5.12}{12}]$
= 6.86^k | = 6.91^k | = 6.72^k | = 6.76^k
< V_c o.k. | < V_c o.k. | < V_c o.k. | Shy, but say o.k., since V_u is computed on the max. intensity of load at apex of triangular area.

(d) Short-span Reinf. (E-W)   Corner Panels : $wS^2 = 339'^k$/',   d = 6.87"
     other Panels : $wS^2 = 329'^k$/',   d = 5.87"

N

Legend
Coef. C
$M_{uf} = C\,wS^2$ (ft-k)
d   (in.)
$M_{uf}/\phi bd^2$ (ksi)
Reqd. p (%)
Reqd. A_s (□")
Use bot. bars
(A_s provided)

Legend
Coef. C
$M_{uf} = C\,wS^2$ (ft-k)
Adj. M_{uf} »
d (in.)
$M_{uf}/\phi bd^2$ (ksi)
Reqd. p (%)
Reqd. A_s (□")
Add Top bars,
if any
(Total neg. A_s provided)

Panel 3 | Panel 4 | Panel 4

Panel 3 | Panel 4 | Panel 4

Panel 1 | Panel 2 | Panel 2

22'-0 | 22'-0 | 22'-0

BEND UP 2 OF EVERY 3 OF BOTTOM BARS

the bottom bars bent up furnished $(\frac{2}{3})(0.81) = 0.54$ sq. in., versus the 0.51 sq. in. required. The maximum spacing of the bentups at the exterior edge was 13 in., which was less than the ACI maximum allowable spacing of 18 in. or $3t = 3(7) = 21$ in., and would be satisfactory. However, a few top straight bars at the exterior end are always necessary to reinforce the slab between the upper bar bend point and the inflection point for the spandrel effect (see Art. 6–10). Accordingly, additional top bars of #3 at 13 in. were arbitrarily placed thereat.

The reinforcement in other middle strips was designed in a similar fashion. Note that, in accordance with common practice, no set of bars is called for more than once, even though a set may perform dual functions, such as the bentup bars doubling as positive steel near the center of a span and as negative steel near the supports. This practice results in less confusion, and makes it easier for the draftsman to "take off" information from the design calculation sheets and transfer it to the drawings.

COLUMN-STRIP REINFORCEMENT. According to the ACI Code, the average column-strip bending moments are two-thirds of those in the corresponding middle strips. The required A_s values were therefore computed accordingly.

(e) Long-Span (N-S) Reinforcement (Sheet 3). The designing of the long-span reinforcement was performed in precisely the same manner as for the short-span reinforcement.

(f) Slab Reinforcement Sketch (Sheet 4). The slab reinforcement is shown in a sketch drawn to scale on Sheet 4. The reinforcement was called out by "bands"; and, based on the bar spacings selected in Sheets 2 and 3, the total number of straight and bent bars in each band was indicated. All similarly located bands are to have the same reinforcement as the one shown.

The ends of all straight bottom bars are to be embedded 6 in. in the girders, or made continuous.

At the discontinuous ends of all strips, both the bentup bars and top straight bars should have full anchorage beyond the inside face of the girder, by bending them if necessary. This anchorage should be increased by 25 per cent if a flexural bond stress check is to be avoided [Sec. 1801(c)]. For *spandrel effect*, the top straight bars thereat should be carried beyond the inflection point for a partial anchorage equal to d, or $\frac{1}{16}$ of the clear span [Sec. 918(e)]. This inflection point may be estimated to be at about $\frac{1}{5}$ of the slab span from the exterior edge.

The negative reinforcement at the interior supports should extend beyond the assumed quarter-span inflection points for a partial anchorage equal to d or $\frac{1}{16}$ of the clear span.

The bendup points of truss bars may be assumed to be those shown in the ACI "Detailing Manual" [7]. Roughly, they are located at $\frac{1}{7}$ of the

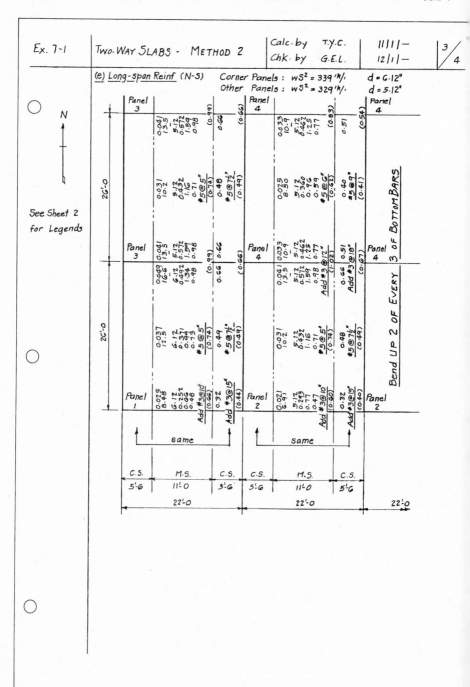

Ex. 7-1	Two-Way Slabs - Method 2	Calc. by T.Y.C.	11/11/—	3
		Chk. by G.E.L.	12/1/—	4

(e) Long-span Reinf. (N-S)   Corner Panels : wS^2 = 339 'k/,   d = 6.12"
                               Other Panels : wS^2 = 329 'k/,   d = 5.12"

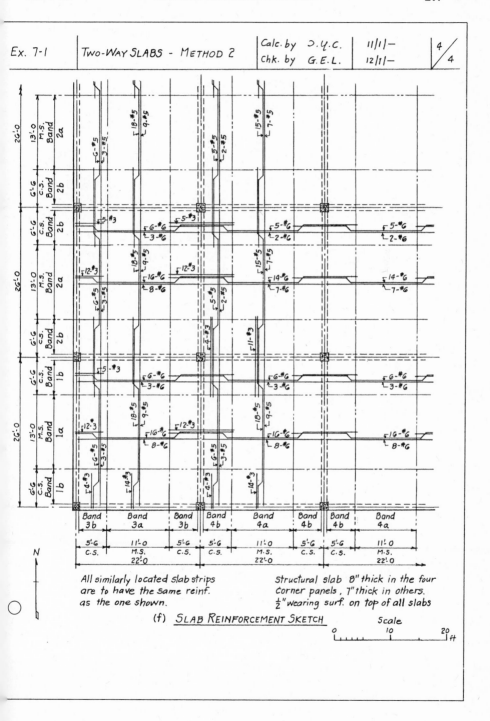

| Ex. 7-1 | Two-Way Slabs - Method 2 | Calc. by O.Y.C. | 11/11– | 4/4 |
| | | Chk. by G.E.L. | 12/11– | |

(f) *Slab Reinforcement Sketch*

All similarly located slab strips
are to have the same reinf.
as the one shown.

Structural slab 8" thick in the four
corner panels, 7" thick in others.
½" wearing surf. on top of all slabs

Scale
0 — 10 — 20 ft

clear span from the exterior support and at $\frac{1}{5}$ of the clear span from the interior supports.

7-9. SLAB LOADS ON SUPPORTING GIRDERS

The loads carried by the girders of Example 7–1 may be determined by using the load distribution pattern of Fig. 7–5. The equivalent uniform loads on the girders used to determine girder bending moments, may be calculated by using Eqs. 7–2. For instance, for the girders *G1*, *G2* and *G3*, *G4* shown in the framing plan of Calculation Sheet 1, the loads transmitted from the slab panels supported were calculated as shown in Fig. 7–8.

Note that the loads shown in Fig. 7–8 are only the slab loads on the girders. For designing the girders, the girder weight plus whatever loads bear directly on the girders would of course have to be added to those shown. The actual designing of the girders is not included in this example, since it involves no new principles.

ACI METHOD 2—TWO-WAY SLAB PROBLEMS

7–1. Design the two-way roof slabs for the building of Example 7–1. Take a service live load of 50 psf, and a dead load of 20 psf for roofing and finish. Use the same concrete and reinforcing steel strengths as in Example 7–1. Follow ACI USD and Method 2 thereof.

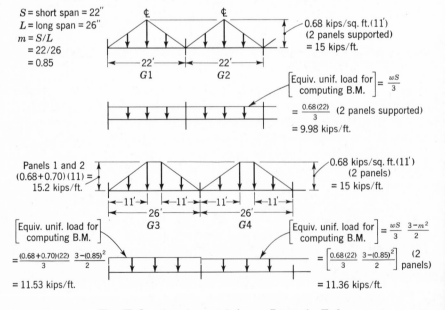

Fig. 7–8. Loads on girders—Example 7–1.

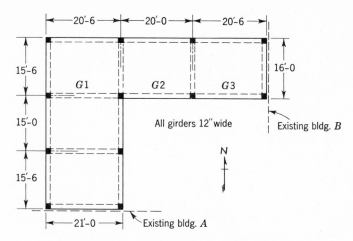

Fig. 7–9. Framing plan—Problem 7–2.

7–2. The framing plan of the typical floor of a footbridge linking two existing buildings is as shown in Fig. 7–9. The floor carries superimposed service loads of 120 psf live and 30 psf dead for ceiling and finish. Take 4000-lb. concrete and 40,000-psi-yield-point steel. It is required to design the floor as two-way slabs, and also to determine the loads transmitted from the slabs to the girders *G1*, *G2*, and *G3*. Use a uniform slab thickness throughout. The ACI Code, USD, and Method 2 thereof are to be followed.

ACI Method 3 for Two-Way Slab Designing

7–10. DESIGN PROCEDURE

This article contains a general description of ACI Method 3 for designing two-way slabs, as outlined in Sec. A2003 thereof. The differences between Methods 2 and 3 are enumerated in Art. 7–11. A numerical example using Method 3 will be found in Art. 7–12.

1. Limitations. The general requirements, described in Art. 7–3, regarding minimum slab thicknesses, minimum reinforcement, and maximum spacing of bars apply.

2. Notation. The following notation has been adopted in the Code:

A = clear short-span length.

B = clear long-span length.

$m = A/B$.

C = bending moment coefficients for Method 3, given in Tables 7–2, 7–3, and 7–4.

w = uniform load per unit area (service-level values for WSD, and load-factored values for USD).

Table 7–2. Coefficients for Negative Moments in Two-Way Slabs*
Method 3, ACI Code Sec. A2003(b)

$$\left.\begin{array}{l} M_{A,\text{neg}} = C_{A,\text{neg}} \times w \times A^2 \\ M_{B,\text{neg}} = C_{B,\text{neg}} \times w \times B^2 \end{array}\right\} \text{ where } w = \text{total uniform dead plus live load}$$

Ratio $m = \dfrac{A}{B}$		Case 1	Case 2	Case 3	Case 4	Case 5	Case 6	Case 7	Case 8	Case 9
1.00	$C_{A,\text{neg}}$	0.045		0.050	0.075	0.071			0.033	0.061
	$C_{B,\text{neg}}$	0.045	0.076	0.050			0.071	0.061	0.033	
0.95	$C_{A,\text{neg}}$	0.050		0.055	0.079	0.075			0.038	0.065
	$C_{B,\text{neg}}$	0.041	0.072	0.045			0.067	0.056	0.029	
0.90	$C_{A,\text{neg}}$	0.055		0.060	0.080	0.079			0.043	0.068
	$C_{B,\text{neg}}$	0.037	0.070	0.040			0.062	0.052	0.025	
0.85	$C_{A,\text{neg}}$	0.060		0.066	0.082	0.083			0.049	0.072
	$C_{B,\text{neg}}$	0.031	0.065	0.034			0.057	0.046	0.021	
0.80	$C_{A,\text{neg}}$	0.065		0.071	0.083	0.086			0.055	0.075
	$C_{B,\text{neg}}$	0.027	0.061	0.029			0.051	0.041	0.017	
0.75	$C_{A,\text{neg}}$	0.069		0.076	0.085	0.088			0.061	0.078
	$C_{B,\text{neg}}$	0.022	0.056	0.024			0.044	0.036	0.014	
0.70	$C_{A,\text{neg}}$	0.074		0.081	0.086	0.091			0.068	0.081
	$C_{B,\text{neg}}$	0.017	0.050	0.019			0.038	0.029	0.011	
0.65	$C_{A,\text{neg}}$	0.077		0.085	0.087	0.093			0.074	0.083
	$C_{B,\text{neg}}$	0.014	0.043	0.015			0.031	0.024	0.008	
0.60	$C_{A,\text{neg}}$	0.081		0.089	0.088	0.095			0.080	0.085
	$C_{B,\text{neg}}$	0.010	0.035	0.011			0.024	0.018	0.006	
0.55	$C_{A,\text{neg}}$	0.084		0.092	0.089	0.096			0.085	0.086
	$C_{B,\text{neg}}$	0.007	0.028	0.008			0.019	0.014	0.005	
0.50	$C_{A,\text{neg}}$	0.086		0.094	0.090	0.097			0.089	0.088
	$C_{B,\text{neg}}$	0.006	0.022	0.006			0.014	0.010	0.003	

* A cross-hatched edge indicates that the slab continues across or is fixed at the support; an unmarked edge indicates a support at which torsional resistance is negligible.

Table 7–3. Coefficients for Dead Load Positive Moments in Two-Way Slabs*
Method 3, ACI Code Sec. A2003(b)

$$\left. \begin{array}{l} M_{A,\text{pos},DL} = C_{A,DL} \times w \times A^2 \\ M_{B,\text{pos},DL} = C_{B,DL} \times w \times B^2 \end{array} \right\} \text{ where } w = \text{total uniform dead load}$$

Ratio $m = \dfrac{A}{B}$		Case 1	Case 2	Case 3	Case 4	Case 5	Case 6	Case 7	Case 8	Case 9
1.00	$C_{A,DL}$	0.036	0.018	0.018	0.027	0.027	0.033	0.027	0.020	0.023
	$C_{B,DL}$	0.036	0.018	0.027	0.027	0.018	0.027	0.033	0.023	0.020
0.95	$C_{A,DL}$	0.040	0.020	0.021	0.030	0.028	0.036	0.031	0.022	0.024
	$C_{B,DL}$	0.033	0.016	0.025	0.024	0.015	0.024	0.031	0.021	0.017
0.90	$C_{A,DL}$	0.045	0.022	0.025	0.033	0.029	0.039	0.035	0.025	0.026
	$C_{B,DL}$	0.029	0.014	0.024	0.022	0.013	0.021	0.028	0.019	0.015
0.85	$C_{A,DL}$	0.050	0.024	0.029	0.036	0.031	0.042	0.040	0.029	0.028
	$C_{B,DL}$	0.026	0.012	0.022	0.019	0.011	0.017	0.025	0.017	0.013
0.80	$C_{A,DL}$	0.056	0.026	0.034	0.039	0.032	0.045	0.045	0.032	0.029
	$C_{B,DL}$	0.023	0.011	0.020	0.016	0.009	0.015	0.022	0.015	0.010
0.75	$C_{A,DL}$	0.061	0.028	0.040	0.043	0.033	0.048	0.051	0.036	0.031
	$C_{B,DL}$	0.019	0.009	0.018	0.013	0.007	0.012	0.020	0.013	0.007
0.70	$C_{A,DL}$	0.068	0.030	0.046	0.046	0.035	0.051	0.058	0.040	0.033
	$C_{B,DL}$	0.016	0.007	0.016	0.011	0.005	0.009	0.017	0.011	0.006
0.65	$C_{A,DL}$	0.074	0.032	0.054	0.050	0.036	0.054	0.065	0.044	0.034
	$C_{B,DL}$	0.013	0.006	0.014	0.009	0.004	0.007	0.014	0.009	0.005
0.60	$C_{A,DL}$	0.081	0.034	0.062	0.053	0.037	0.056	0.073	0.048	0.036
	$C_{B,DL}$	0.010	0.004	0.011	0.007	0.003	0.006	0.012	0.007	0.004
0.55	$C_{A,DL}$	0.088	0.035	0.071	0.056	0.038	0.058	0.081	0.052	0.037
	$C_{B,DL}$	0.008	0.003	0.009	0.005	0.002	0.004	0.009	0.005	0.003
0.50	$C_{A,DL}$	0.095	0.037	0.080	0.059	0.039	0.061	0.089	0.056	0.038
	$C_{B,DL}$	0.006	0.002	0.007	0.004	0.001	0.003	0.007	0.004	0.002

* A cross-hatched edge indicates that the slab continues across or is fixed at the support; an unmarked edge indicates a support at which torsional resistance is negligible.

Table 7–4. Coefficients for Live Load Positive Moments in Two-Way Slabs*
Method 3, ACI Code Sec. A2003(b)

$$M_{A,\text{pos,LL}} = C_{A,\text{LL}} \times w \times A^2$$
$$M_{B,\text{pos,LL}} = C_{B,\text{LL}} \times w \times B^2$$

where w = total uniform live load

Ratio $m = \dfrac{A}{B}$		Case 1	Case 2	Case 3	Case 4	Case 5	Case 6	Case 7	Case 8	Case 9
1.00	$C_{A,\text{LL}}$	0.036	0.027	0.027	0.032	0.032	0.035	0.032	0.028	0.030
	$C_{B,\text{LL}}$	0.036	0.027	0.032	0.032	0.027	0.032	0.035	0.030	0.028
0.95	$C_{A,\text{LL}}$	0.040	0.030	0.031	0.035	0.034	0.038	0.036	0.031	0.032
	$C_{B,\text{LL}}$	0.033	0.025	0.029	0.029	0.024	0.029	0.032	0.027	0.025
0.90	$C_{A,\text{LL}}$	0.045	0.034	0.035	0.039	0.037	0.042	0.040	0.035	0.036
	$C_{B,\text{LL}}$	0.029	0.022	0.027	0.026	0.021	0.025	0.029	0.024	0.022
0.85	$C_{A,\text{LL}}$	0.050	0.037	0.040	0.043	0.041	0.046	0.045	0.040	0.039
	$C_{B,\text{LL}}$	0.026	0.019	0.024	0.023	0.019	0.022	0.026	0.022	0.020
0.80	$C_{A,\text{LL}}$	0.056	0.041	0.045	0.048	0.044	0.051	0.051	0.044	0.042
	$C_{B,\text{LL}}$	0.023	0.017	0.022	0.020	0.016	0.019	0.023	0.019	0.017
0.75	$C_{A,\text{LL}}$	0.061	0.045	0.051	0.052	0.047	0.055	0.056	0.049	0.046
	$C_{B,\text{LL}}$	0.019	0.014	0.019	0.016	0.013	0.016	0.020	0.016	0.013
0.70	$C_{A,\text{LL}}$	0.068	0.049	0.057	0.057	0.051	0.060	0.063	0.054	0.050
	$C_{B,\text{LL}}$	0.016	0.012	0.016	0.014	0.011	0.013	0.017	0.014	0.011
0.65	$C_{A,\text{LL}}$	0.074	0.053	0.064	0.062	0.055	0.064	0.070	0.059	0.054
	$C_{B,\text{LL}}$	0.013	0.010	0.014	0.011	0.009	0.010	0.014	0.011	0.009
0.60	$C_{A,\text{LL}}$	0.081	0.058	0.071	0.067	0.059	0.068	0.077	0.065	0.059
	$C_{B,\text{LL}}$	0.010	0.007	0.011	0.009	0.007	0.008	0.011	0.009	0.007
0.55	$C_{A,\text{LL}}$	0.088	0.062	0.080	0.072	0.063	0.073	0.085	0.070	0.063
	$C_{B,\text{LL}}$	0.008	0.006	0.009	0.007	0.005	0.006	0.009	0.007	0.006
0.50	$C_{A,\text{LL}}$	0.095	0.066	0.088	0.077	0.067	0.078	0.092	0.076	0.067
	$C_{B,\text{LL}}$	0.006	0.004	0.007	0.005	0.004	0.005	0.007	0.005	0.004

* A cross-hatched edge indicates that the slab continues across or is fixed at the support; an unmarked edge indicates a support at which torsional resistance is negligible.

In the foregoing notation, w is the total dead and live load when computing negative slab moments, or slab shears, or loads transmitted to the supports. When computing positive slab moments, w is separated into its dead and live load components. Accordingly, subscripts are attached to the moment coefficients C to identify their affiliation. The letters A and B indicate the directions of the spans being considered. The subscript "DL" or "LL" denotes that a dead or live load *positive* moment is being computed. The subscript "neg" denotes that a *negative* moment produced by the *total dead and live load* is being computed. For example, $C_{A,DL}$ represents the coefficient for a short-span positive bending moment produced by dead load, and $C_{B,neg}$ represents the coefficient for a long-span negative bending moment produced by live plus dead load.

3. **Division of Panel into Strips.** Analogous to Method 2, the division of a panel into the middle and column strips for $m \geq 0.5$ is as shown in Fig. 7–10.

In Method 3, panels with $m < 0.5$ are to be designed as one-way slabs, but negative reinforcement is required in the long direction, and it has the same area as would be required for panels with $m = 0.5$.

4. **Bending Moments.** Section A2003(b) provides that design bending moments in slabs be determined as described below.

a. MIDDLE STRIPS. The middle-strip moments per foot of width of slab are to be computed by:

$$\text{Short-span moments: } M_A = CwA^2 \qquad (7\text{--}3a)$$
$$\text{Long-span moments: } M_B = CwB^2 \qquad (7\text{--}3b)$$

In Eqs. 7–3, the value of w to be used and the C-values to be obtained from Tables 7–2, 7–3, and 7–4 are to be in accordance with the following:

Table 7–2: Negative moments, w = dead plus live load	⎱ Service-level values
Table 7–3: Positive moments, w = dead load	⎰ for WSD, and load-
Table 7–4: Positive moments, w = live load	factored values for USD

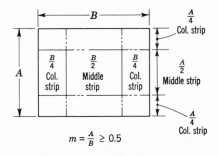

$$m = \frac{A}{B} \geq 0.5$$

Fig. 7–10. Division of panel into strips—Method 3.

Table 7–5. Ratio of Load w in A and B Directions for Shear in Two-Way Slab and Load on Supports*

Method 3, ACI Code Sec. A2003(c, d)

Ratio $m = \dfrac{A}{B}$		Case 1	Case 2	Case 3	Case 4	Case 5	Case 6	Case 7	Case 8	Case 9
1.00	W_A	0.50	0.50	0.17	0.50	0.83	0.71	0.29	0.33	0.67
	W_B	0.50	0.50	0.83	0.50	0.17	0.29	0.71	0.67	0.33
0.95	W_A	0.55	0.55	0.20	0.55	0.86	0.75	0.33	0.38	0.71
	W_B	0.45	0.45	0.80	0.45	0.14	0.25	0.67	0.62	0.29
0.90	W_A	0.60	0.60	0.23	0.60	0.88	0.79	0.38	0.43	0.75
	W_B	0.40	0.40	0.77	0.40	0.12	0.21	0.62	0.57	0.25
0.85	W_A	0.66	0.66	0.28	0.66	0.90	0.83	0.43	0.49	0.79
	W_B	0.34	0.34	0.72	0.34	0.10	0.17	0.57	0.51	0.21
0.80	W_A	0.71	0.71	0.33	0.71	0.92	0.86	0.49	0.55	0.83
	W_B	0.29	0.29	0.67	0.29	0.08	0.14	0.51	0.45	0.17
0.75	W_A	0.76	0.76	0.39	0.76	0.94	0.88	0.56	0.61	0.86
	W_B	0.24	0.24	0.61	0.24	0.06	0.12	0.44	0.39	0.14
0.70	W_A	0.81	0.81	0.45	0.81	0.95	0.91	0.62	0.68	0.89
	W_B	0.19	0.19	0.55	0.19	0.05	0.09	0.38	0.32	0.11
0.65	W_A	0.85	0.85	0.53	0.85	0.96	0.93	0.69	0.74	0.92
	W_B	0.15	0.15	0.47	0.15	0.04	0.07	0.31	0.26	0.08
0.60	W_A	0.89	0.89	0.61	0.89	0.97	0.95	0.76	0.80	0.94
	W_B	0.11	0.11	0.39	0.11	0.03	0.05	0.24	0.20	0.06
0.55	W_A	0.92	0.92	0.69	0.92	0.98	0.96	0.81	0.85	0.95
	W_B	0.08	0.08	0.31	0.08	0.02	0.04	0.19	0.15	0.05
0.50	W_A	0.94	0.94	0.76	0.94	0.99	0.97	0.86	0.89	0.97
	W_B	0.06	0.06	0.24	0.06	0.01	0.03	0.14	0.11	0.03

* A cross-hatched edge indicates that the slab continues across or is fixed at the support; an unmarked edge indicates a support at which torsional resistance is negligible.

In Tables 7–2 through 7–4, a cross-hatched edge indicates that the panel is either fixed at or continuous across the edge. An unmarked edge is one at which there exists negligible torsional restraint; it implies essentially a simply supported edge, or a spandrel beam of small torsional rigidity, but it is *not* intended to mean the free edge of a cantilever.

The tables do not show the moment coefficients for unmarked edges. The design negative moments thereat are to be taken as equal to one-third of the corresponding positive moments.

b. COLUMN STRIPS. The moments in column strips are to be taken as gradually varying from a full value of M_A or M_B at the edge of the middle strip to one-third of these values at the edge of the panel. If a linear variation of the moments is assumed, the average column-strip moments are equal to two-thirds of the corresponding middle-strip moments.

c. DIFFERENCE IN NEGATIVE MOMENTS AT A COMMON SUPPORT. If the negative moment on one side of a support common to two panels is less than 0.80 times that on the other side, the *full* difference (in contrast with two-thirds of the difference as in Method 2) is to be distributed to the two sides in proportion to their relative stiffnesses.

5. Slab Shears and Loads on Supporting Girders. ACI Code Sec. A2003(c) and (d) provides that the slab shears be computed in accordance with the load distribution as specified in Table 7–5, which gives the fraction of the total dead and live load carried in the A and B directions. Once the load in each direction is determined, it is divided equally between the two supporting beams, and is assumed to be uniformly distributed along each beam. The Code further specifies, however, that in no case may the load on a short edge beam be less than that contained in a tributary triangle bounded by the 45° lines drawn from the corners of a panel. This amounts to specifying a minimum equivalent uniform load on a short edge beam as $wA/3$ per lineal ft., similar to that in Method 2 shown in Figs. 7–5 and 7–6 of Art. 7–4.

7–11. METHOD 3 VERSUS METHOD 2

As stated in Art. 7–2, Method 3 is generally rather similar to Method 2, but provides more elaborate data. It is somewhat more rational than Method 2, and often results in a more economical design. So far as the details of the two methods are concerned, the following differences may be noted.

Method 3 considers as two-way slabs only those panels with $m \geq 0.5$ whereas Method 2 considers m-values ranging from 1.0 to 0.0 in the limiting case. Narrow panels in Method 3 are designed as one-way slabs, but with some negative reinforcement to be provided in the long direction over the supports.

Slab moments in middle strips are computed by formulas of the same form in both methods, that is, embracing the product of a coefficient, C, the uniform load, w, and a span length squared. In Method 2, however, the load w is the total dead and live load, and the span used is always the short-span length. In Method 3, the dead and live loads are considered separately in computing positive moments, and the short-span length is used for short-span moments, and the long-span length is used for long-span moments.

Method 3 provides an additional table for the calculation of slab shears and loads carried by the supporting beams. However, a minimum load is imposed on the short-span beams of Method 3, which, in effect, partially reverts to the load distribution of Method 2 as shown in Fig. 7–5.

There is also a slight difference in the determination of the effective span lengths used in the calculations of the two methods, as well as in the way in which adjustment is made for unequal negative moments at the two faces of a supporting beam common to two panels.

7–12. TWO-WAY SLAB EXAMPLE BY METHOD 3

The same building floor of Example 7–1 will now be reconsidered, using ACI Method 3. In order to effect a comparison of Methods 2 and 3 on a common basis, the same slab thicknesses as chosen in Example 7–1 are used, namely: 8 in. for the corner panels, and 7 in. for all other panels.

The floor is not to be redesigned, but to be *investigated* to determine what alternate design forces, arising from the same floor loads, will be involved if Method 3 is followed.

EXAMPLE 7–2

(Calculation Sheets 1 Through 4)

Given the building floor and data of Example 7–1 and the slab thicknesses finally adopted therein.

It is required to determine by ACI Method 3 the alternate design forces involved: the slab bending moments and shears, and the loads transmitted to the supporting girders.

See the **Solution** in Calculation Sheets 1 through 4 and the following brief comments.

(a) **Loads and spans** (Sheet 1). The floor loads were easily computed. Assuming 15-in.-wide girders, the clear short- and long-span lengths, A and B, and their ratio, $m = A/B$, were next determined. Anticipating the need for separating the dead and live loads for finding positive slab moments, and for combining them to find negative slab moments, the values of the repeatedly used quantity, [(load) (span length)^2], were next calculated. As shown in Sheet 1,

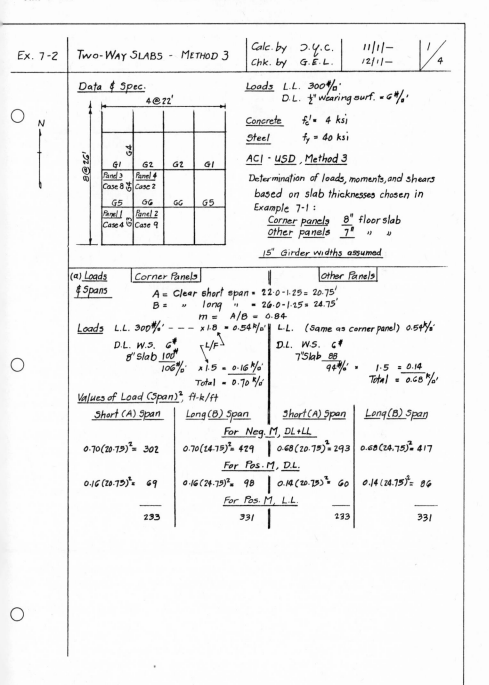

Ex. 7-2	Two-Way Slabs - Method 3	Calc. by D.Y.C. 11/11/—	1/4
		Chk. by G.E.L. 12/11/—	

Data & Spec.

4 @ 22'

8 @ 26'

G4			
G1	G2	G2	G1
Panel 3 Case 8	Panel 4 Case 2		
G5	GG	GG	G5
Panel 1 Case 4	Panel 2 Case 9		

Loads L.L. 300 #/☐'
D.L. ½" wearing surf. = 6 #/☐'

Concrete $f_c' = 4$ ksi

Steel $f_y = 40$ ksi

ACI - USD , Method 3

Determination of loads, moments, and shears
based on slab thicknesses chosen in
Example 7-1 :
Corner panels   8" floor slab
Other panels   7"   "   "

15" Girder widths assumed

(a) Loads & Spans

Corner Panels		Other Panels

A = Clear short span = 22.0 - 1.25 = 20.75'
B =   "   long   "   = 26.0 - 1.25 = 24.75'
m = A/B = 0.84

Loads L.L. 300 #/☐' - - - x 1.8 = 0.54 k/☐'   L.L. (Same as corner panel) 0.54 k/☐'

D.L. W.S. 6#   (L/F)   D.L. W.S. 6#
8" slab 100#   7" slab 88
          106 #/☐' x 1.5 = 0.16 k/☐'   94 #/☐' x 1.5 = 0.14
                    Total = 0.70 k/☐'   Total = 0.68 k/☐'

Values of Load (Span)², ft-k/ft

Short (A) Span	Long (B) Span	Short (A) Span	Long (B) Span
	For Neg. M, DL+LL		
0.70(20.75)² = 302	0.70(24.75)² = 429	0.68(20.75)² = 293	0.68(24.75)² = 417
	For Pos. M, D.L.		
0.16(20.75)² = 69	0.16(24.75)² = 98	0.14(20.75)² = 60	0.14(24.75)² = 86
	For Pos. M, L.L.		
233	331	233	331

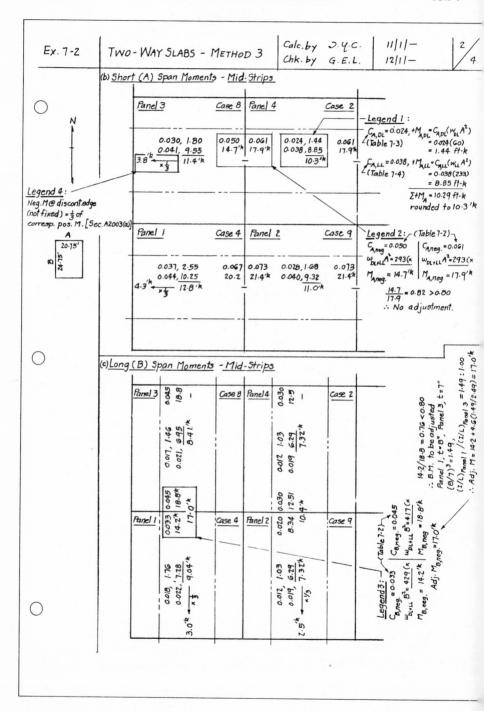

| Ex. 7-2 | Two-Way Slabs – Method 3 | Calc. by J.Y.C. | 11/1/– | 2 |
| | | Chk. by G.E.L. | 12/11/– | 4 |

(b) *Short (A) Span Moments - Mid-Strips*

Panel 3   Case 8   Panel 4   Case 2

0.030, 1.80
0.041, 9.55
3.8$^{'k}$ ×$\frac{1}{3}$ 11.4$^{'k}$

0.050   0.061
14.7$^{'k}$ 17.9$^{'k}$

0.024, 1.44   0.061
0.038, 8.85   17.9$^{'k}$
10.3$^{'k}$

Legend 1:
$C_{A,DL} = 0.024$, $+M_{A,DL} = C_{A,DL}(w_{DL}A^2)$
(Table 7-3) $= 0.024(60)$
   $= 1.44$ ft-k
$C_{A,LL} = 0.038$, $+M_{A,LL} = C_{A,LL}(w_{LL}A^2)$
(Table 7-4) $= 0.038(233)$
   $= 8.85$ ft-k
$\Sigma + M_A = 10.29$ ft-k
rounded to 10.3$^{'k}$

Legend 4:
Neg. M @ discont. edge
(not fixed) = $\frac{1}{3}$ of
corresp. pos. M. [Sec. A2003(a)]

A
20.75′
B
24.75′

Panel 1   Case 4   Panel 2   Case 9

0.037, 2.55
0.044, 10.25
4.3$^{'k}$ ×$\frac{1}{3}$ 12.8$^{'k}$

0.067   0.073
20.2   21.4$^{'k}$

0.028, 1.68   0.073
0.040, 9.32   21.4$^{'k}$
11.0$^{'k}$

Legend 2: (Table 7-2)
$C_{A,neg} = 0.050$ $C_{A,neg} = 0.061$
$w_{DL+LL}A^2 = 293(x$ $w_{DL+LL}A^2 = 293(x$
$M_{A,neg} = 14.7^{'k}$ $M_{A,neg} = 17.9^{'k}$

$\frac{14.7}{17.9} = 0.82 > 0.80$
∴ No adjustment.

(c) *Long (B) Span Moments - Mid-Strips*

Panel 3   Case 8   Panel 4   Case 2

0.045 18.8 —
0.017, 1.46
0.021, 6.95
8.41$^{'k}$

0.030 12.5 —
0.012 1.03
0.019 6.29
7.32$^{'k}$

Panel 1   Case 4   Panel 2   Case 9

0.045 18.8$^{'k}$
14.2$^{'k}$
17.0$^{'k}$

0.018, 1.76
0.022, 7.28
3.0$^{'k}$ ×$\frac{1}{3}$ 9.04$^{'k}$

0.030 12.51
8.34 10.4$^{'k}$

0.012, 1.03
0.019, 6.29
2.5$^{'k}$ ×$\frac{1}{3}$ 7.32$^{'k}$

Legend 3: (Table 7-2)
$C_{B,neg} = 0.033$
$w_{DL+LL}B^2 = 429(x$
$M_{B,neg} = 14.2^{'k}$

$C_{B,neg} = 0.045$
$w_{DL+LL}B^2 = 417(x$
$M_{B,neg} = 18.8^{'k}$
Adj: $M_{B,neg} = 17.0^{'k}$

$14.2/18.8 = 0.76 < 0.80$
∴ B.M. to be adjusted
Panel 1, t = 8″, Panel 3, t = 7″
$(8/7)^3 = 1.49$,
$(I/L)_{Panel 1} / (I/L)_{Panel 3} = 1.49 : 1.00$
∴ Adj. M = 14.2 + 4.6(1.49/2.49) = 17.0$^{'k}$

these values were determined for both directions in the 8-in.- and 7-in.-thick panels, and for dead load only, live load only, and total dead and live load.

(b, c) **Middle-strip slab moments** (Sheet 2). Since, in both Methods 2 and 3, the average column-strip moments are two-thirds of the corresponding middle-strip moments, only the latter values are needed for comparison, and were therefore the ones calculated on Sheet 2 for the short and long spans.

The four typical panels, marked 1 through 4, first had to be identified according to the classification of edge conditions as depicted in the tables of Method 3. For instance, panel 2 having one *short* edge discontinuous was classified as case 9, whereas panel 3 having one *long* edge discontinuous was classified as case 8. Similarly, panels 1 and 4 were identified as cases 4 and 2, respectively.

For positive moments in middle strips, the coefficients were obtained by interpolation from Table 7–3 for dead load, and Table 7–4 for live load. Multiplying these by values of [(load) (span length)^2] from Sheet 1, and adding the results, the required positive moments were obtained, as shown by the typical calculations given in legend 1, for the short-span middle strip in panel 4. Legend 2 shows typical calculations for the negative moments at continuous edges, the coefficients thereof being obtained from Table 7–2. When the negative moments on the two faces of a common supporting girder differ by more than 20 per cent of the larger, they are to be adjusted. Such a situation developed at the negative moment section in the long-span middle strip through panels 1 and 3, and it required calculations given in legend 3. At discontinuous edges that are not fixed, the negative moments are to be taken as $\frac{1}{3}$ of the corresponding positive moments, as indicated by legend 4.

(d, e) **Slab shears and girder loads** (Sheet 3). Table 7–5 gives the fraction of the total dead plus live load carried in each direction of a panel. Taking panel 4 of this example for illustration, the short direction took 0.67 times the total load of 0.68 ksf or 0.46 ksf, the remainder, 0.22 ksf, being carried in the long direction. Accordingly, the shear in a 1-ft.-wide slab strip spanning the short direction was $0.46(20.75)/2 = 4.73$ kips, at the face of each of the two supporting long-span girders, and that in the long direction was $0.22(24.75)/2 = 2.77$ kips at the face of each supporting short girder. The slab shears elsewhere were similarly calculated.

The load on long-span girders may be obtained easily from the short-span slab shears in the panels they support. For instance, girder $G4$ carries a load from panels 3 and 4 equal to $(3.53 + 4.73) = 8.26$ kpf. The load on short-span girders was calculated similarly, except that here this load should be checked against the value of $(wA/3)$ for each panel supported, the larger of the two being the controlling value [Sec. A2003(d)]. For example, taking girder $G1$, which supports two identical panels 3, the load based on previously determined long-span slab shears was $2(4.21)$ or 8.42 kpf, whereas $(wA/3)$ was $0.68(20.75)/3 = 4.70$ kpf per panel, or 9.40 kpf for the two panels. Hence, $G1$ carried 9.40 kpf.

(f, g, h) **Comparison of design forces for Methods 2 and 3** (Sheet 4). The design forces obtained in this example were summarized on Sheet 4 for comparison with those obtained in Example 7–1 by Method 2.

The reader should note that any general conclusions he might wish to draw from such a limited comparison would be unwarranted, and might very well be misleading. Differences are expected to exist in the results of the two methods because of the differences in some of their underlying assumptions, and it would be quite pointless to attempt to reconcile them, or to justify one method, condemning the other. The important thing to bear in mind is that the ultimate

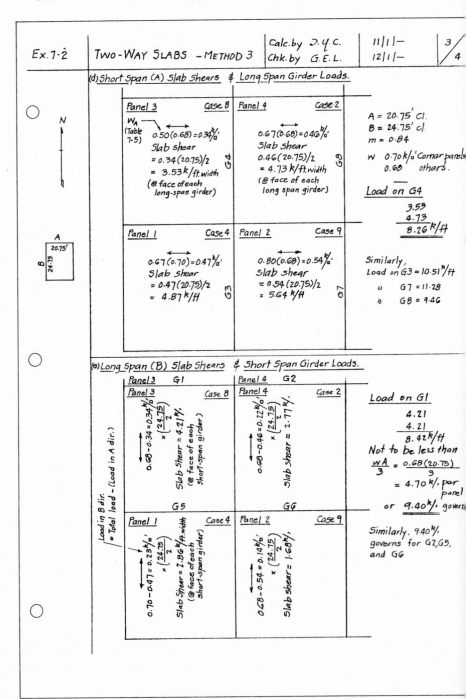

| *Ex. 7-2* | TWO-WAY SLABS — METHOD 3 | Calc. by Ə. Y. C. | 11/11/— | 3 |
| | | Chk. by G. E. L. | 12/11/— | /4 |

(d) <u>Short Span (A) Slab Shears</u> & <u>Long Span Girder Loads.</u>

N

Panel 3   *Case 8*

W_A (Table 7-5)

0.50 (0.68) = 0.34 $^k/_o'$

Slab shear

= 0.34 (20.75)/2

= 3.53 $^k/$ft. width

(@ face of each long-span girder)

G4

Panel 4   *Case 2*

0.67 (0.68) = 0.46 $^k/_o'$

Slab shear

0.46 (20.75)/2

= 4.73 $^k/$ft. width

(@ face of each long span girder)

G8

A = 20.75' Cl.
B = 24.75' cl.
m = 0.84
w   0.70 k/o' Corner panels
    0.68   others.

<u>Load on G4</u>

   3.53
   4.73
   8.26 $^k/$ft

Panel 1   *Case 4*

0.67 (0.70) = 0.47 $^k/_o'$

Slab shear

= 0.47 (20.75)/2

= 4.87 $^k/$ft

G3

Panel 2   *Case 9*

0.80 (0.68) = 0.54 $^k/_o'$

Slab shear

= 0.54 (20.75)/2

= 5.64 $^k/$ft

G7

Similarly,
Load on G3 = 10.51 $^k/$ft
   "   G7 = 11.28
   "   G8 = 9.46

A
20.75'
B
24.75

(e) <u>Long Span (B) Slab Shears</u> & <u>Short Span Girder Loads.</u>

Panel 3   G1   Panel 4   G2

Load in B dir.
(= Total load − (Load in A dir.)

Panel 3   *Case 8*

0.68 − 0.34 = 0.34 $^k/_o$

x $\left(\frac{24.75}{2}\right)$

Slab Shear = 4.21 $^k/$
(@ face of each short-span girder)

G5

Panel 4   *Case 2*

0.68 − 0.46 = 0.22 $^k/$

x $\left(\frac{24.75}{2}\right)$

Slab shear = 2.77 $^k/$

G6

<u>Load on G1</u>

   4.21
   4.21
   8.42 $^k/$ft

Not to be less than

$\frac{wA}{3} = \frac{0.68(20.75)}{3}$

= 4.70 k/. per panel

or   9.40 $^k/$. governs

Panel 1   *Case 4*

0.70 − 0.47 = 0.23 $^k/_o$

x $\left(\frac{24.75}{2}\right)$

Slab Shear = 2.86 $^k/$ft. width
(@ face of each short-span girder)

Panel 2   *Case 9*

0.68 − 0.54 = 0.14 $^k/$

x $\left(\frac{24.75}{2}\right)$

Slab Shear = 1.68 $^k/$.

Similarly, 9.40 $^k/$.
governs for G2, G5,
and G6

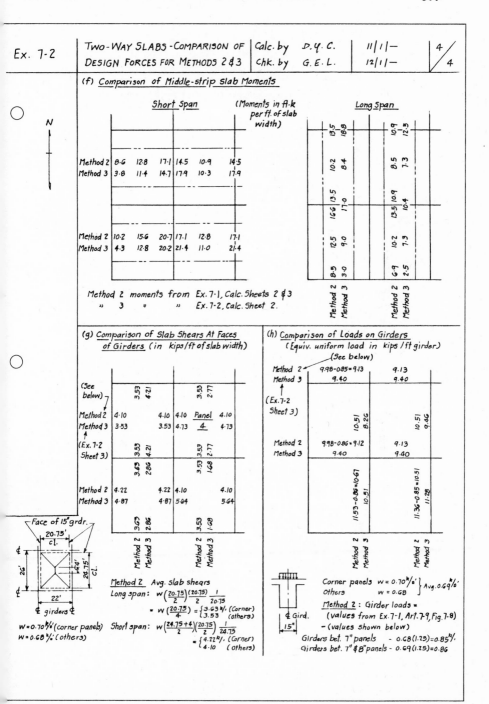

Ex. 7-2

Two-Way Slabs - Comparison of Design Forces for Methods 2 & 3 | Calc. by D.Y.C. | 11/1/— | 4/4
Chk. by G.E.L. | 12/1/— |

(f) Comparison of Middle-strip Slab Moments

Short Span   (Moments in ft-k per ft. of slab width)   Long Span

Method 2 8·6 12·8 17·1 14·5 10·9 14·5
Method 3 3·8 11·4 14·7 17·9 10·3 17·9

Method 2 10·2 15·6 20·7 17·1 12·8 17·1
Method 3 4·3 12·8 20·2 21·4 11·0 21·4

Method 2 moments from Ex. 7-1, Calc. Sheets 2 & 3
  "   3   "   "   Ex. 7-2, Calc. Sheet 2.

Short span values (long-edge labels): 13·5 / 18·8, 10·2 / 8·4, 16·6 / 17·0, 12·5 / 9·0, 8·5 / 3·0
Long span values: 10·9 / 12·5, 8·5 / 7·3, 13·5 / 10·4, 10·2 / 7·3, 6·9 / 2·5
(Method 2 / Method 3)

(g) Comparison of Slab Shears At Faces of Girders (in kips/ft of slab width)

(See below)
Method 2 4·10   4·10 4·10 Panel 4·10
Method 3 3·53   3·53 4·73   4   4·73
(Ex. 7-2 Sheet 3)

Method 2 4·22   4·22 4·10   4·10
Method 3 4·87   4·87 5·64   5·64

(edge values: 3·53/4·21, 3·53/2·77, 3·53/4·21, 3·53/2·77, 3·63/2·86, 3·53/1·68, 3·63/2·86, 3·53/1·68)

Face of 15" grdr.
20·75' cl.
24·75' cl.
26'
22'
℄ girders ℄

w = 0.70 k/□'(corner panels)
w = 0.68 k/□'(others)

Method 2 Avg. slab shears
Long span: $w\left(\frac{20.75}{2}\right)\left(\frac{20.75}{2}\right)\frac{1}{20.75}$
= $w\left(\frac{20.75}{4}\right) = \begin{cases} 3.63\ k/.\ (Corner) \\ 3.53\ (others) \end{cases}$
Short span: $w\left(\frac{24.75+4}{2}\right)\left(\frac{20.75}{2}\right)\frac{1}{24.75}$
= $\begin{cases} 4.22\ k/.\ (Corner) \\ 4.10\ (others) \end{cases}$

(h) Comparison of Loads on Girders
(Equiv. uniform load in kips/ft girder)
(See below)
Method 2   9.98-0.85=9.13   9.13
Method 3   9.40   9.40
(Ex. 7-2 Sheet 3)

Method 2   9.98-0.86=9.12   9.13
Method 3   9.40   9.40

(edge values: 10·51/8·26, 10·51/9·46, 11·53-0·86=10·67 /10·51, 11·36-0·85=10·51 /11·28)

℄ Gird.
15"

Corner panels w = 0.70 k/□' } Avg. 0.69 k/□'
Others   w = 0.68
Method 2 : Girder loads =
  (values from Ex. 7-1, Art. 7-9, Fig. 7-8)
  - (values shown below)
Girders bet. 7" panels - 0.68(1.25)=0.85 k/.
Girders bet. 7"&8" panels - 0.69(1.25)=0.86

load-bearing capacity of a structure must be based, in the final analysis, on a consideration of inelastic redistribution of forces in the structure as a whole, rather than on elastically determined forces at any particular section. The designer's concern should be, whether Method 2 or 3 is used, that its limitations be satisfied and its design procedure be followed consistently throughout.

(f) *Middle-strip slab moments.* These moments were taken directly from the pertinent calculation sheets of the two examples. Method 3 is seen to give smaller positive moments throughout than Method 2, whereas negative moments over interior supports are of comparable order of magnitude for the two methods. The most pronounced difference between the two methods occurs at the discontinuous edges. This is understandable since, at such edges, Method 2 demands "adequate torsional rigidity of the beams," whereas Method 3 allows such supports to have negligible torsional rigidity unless they are specified to be fixed. Accordingly, treating these edges as "unmarked" edges in Table 7–2, Method 3 gives much smaller negative moments thereat than Method 2.

(g) *Slab shears at faces of girders.* The slab shears at the faces of the girders in Method 3 were taken directly from Sheet 3 of Example 7–2. The slab shears used in Example 7–1 to determine the slab thicknesses were the *maximum* shears at the critical sections, and therefore had to be recomputed as shown to result in average values at the faces of the girders, in order to be compared with Method 3 values on the same basis.

These shears are seen to differ for the two methods. Taking the interior panel 4 for example, Method 2 gives 4.10 kpf along each of the long girders, and 3.53 kpf along each of the short girders, whereas Method 3 gives 4.73 kpf and 2.77 kpf, respectively. However, it should be noted that these local differences are of secondary importance, as long as the total slab shears of the entire panel at the faces of the four girders are essentially the same for both methods, as shown by the following calculations.

Taking panel 4 as 20.75 by 24.75 ft. along the faces of the girders, the total panel shears are:

$$\text{Method 2: } 4.10(24.75)(2) + 3.53(20.75)(2) = 349.4 \text{ kips}$$
$$\text{Method 3: } 4.73(24.75)(2) + 2.77(20.75)(2) = 349.1 \text{ kips}$$

Similarly close agreement in the total panel shears for the two methods may be found for other panels. In fact, if this were not so, the designer would have genuine reason for concern.

(h) *Loads on girders.* The load values shown for comparison are the equivalent uniform loads on the girders, and for Method 3, they were taken directly from Example 7–2, Sheet 3, wherein they had been computed on the basis of *clear* span lengths. The loads on the girders for Method 2 were calculated in Example 7–1, Art. 7–9, on the basis of the center-to-center distances of the supports, and hence for comparison with Method 3, they had to be modified by deducting the load on the assumed 15-in. girder width, as shown on Sheet 4 of this example.

ACI METHOD 3—TWO-WAY SLAB PROBLEMS

7-3. Following the design of Problem 7–1, recalculate the design forces based on the same loads but using ACI Method 3.

7-4. Following the design of Problem 7–2, recalculate the design forces based on the same loads but using ACI Method 3.

7–13. SPECIAL CORNER REINFORCEMENT

When a rectangular panel simply supported along all four edges is loaded, the four corners tend to rise. The elementary theory of bending of elastic plates, on which the ACI design methods are based, implicitly assumes that the rising of the corners is prevented, either by the presence of concentrated corner reactions or by equivalent twisting moments on the edges [8]. Hence, the presence of localized corner moments is implicit in such slab analysis. As a matter of fact, no published solution exists, as far as known, for simply supported rectangular slabs whose corners are free to rise during loading.

The potential crack pattern near the corners of such a slab panel is as shown in Fig. 7–11. Recognizing this behavior, Sec. 2002(b) recommends special reinforcement at the exterior corners of slab panels not securely tied to supports as follows:

(1) Special corner reinforcement should extend in each direction for a distance equal to $\frac{1}{5}$ of the long-span length; (2) the top corner reinforcement is to be parallel to the diagonal from the corner, and the bottom corner reinforcement is to be normal to the diagonal; and (3) such corner reinforcement in each band should be equivalent to the reinforcement required for the maximum positive moment in the slab panel.

Requirement (2) above may be substantially met by having bars placed parallel to the panel edges, and having their areas such that their components in the diagonal direction and in the direction normal thereto satisfy requirement (3).

For example, consider the corner panel, panel 1 of Example 7–2, and suppose that it is supported on, but not securely attached to, a masonry wall along its exterior edges. Calculation Sheet 2 shows the maximum positive moment in the panel to be 12.8 kip-ft. Using an average d of 6.50 in., $M_{uf}/\phi b d^2 = 12.8/(0.9)(1.0)(6.50)^2 = 0.337$ ksi. From USD Beam Chart A–1 (Appendix A), the required p is 0.89 per cent, and the required A_s is $0.89\%(12)(6.50) = 0.69$ sq. in. per ft. of slab width in each of the top and bottom bands of corner reinforcement, as shown in Fig. 7–12a and b.

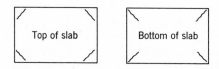

Fig. 7–11. Corner crack pattern of simply supported panels.

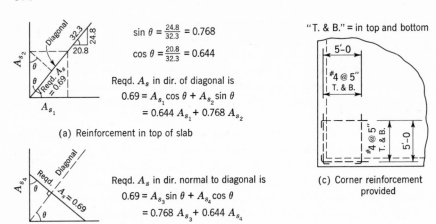

$\sin \theta = \frac{24.8}{32.3} = 0.768$

$\cos \theta = \frac{20.8}{32.3} = 0.644$

Reqd. A_s in dir. of diagonal is

$0.69 = A_{s_1}\cos \theta + A_{s_2}\sin \theta$

$= 0.644\, A_{s_1} + 0.768\, A_{s_2}$

(a) Reinforcement in top of slab

"T. & B." = in top and bottom

Reqd. A_s in dir. normal to diagonal is

$0.69 = A_{s_3}\sin \theta + A_{s_4}\cos \theta$

$= 0.768\, A_{s_3} + 0.644\, A_{s_4}$

(b) Reinforcement in bottom of slab

(c) Corner reinforcement provided

Fig. 7–12.   Special reinforcement at exterior corners.

If the steel areas parallel to the edges at the corner are A_{s1} and A_{s2} in the top of the slab, and A_{s3} and A_{s4} in the bottom, they must be such as to satisfy the expressions shown in Fig. 7–12a and b. If the four steel areas are made equal, as is convenient, then each is equal to $0.69/(0.644 + 0.768)$, or 0.49 sq. in. per ft. of slab width per band in top and bottom. This may be furnished by #4 at 5 in. in top and bottom in each direction, as shown in Fig. 7–12c. Each band has a width of $(\frac{1}{5})(24.8)$, or about 5 ft., and the bars therein extend for a length of about 5 ft. plus adequate end anchorage.

In general, it can be easily shown from geometry that, if the four steel areas A_{s1} through A_{s4} are made equal, each is equal to the required corner reinforcement area in the top or bottom multiplied by the ratio of the panel diagonal length to the sum of the short and long panel lengths. For instance, $(0.69)(32.3)/(20.8 + 24.8) = 0.49$ sq. in. per ft. per band, as before.

7–14. SUMMARY OF TWO-WAY SLAB DESIGNING

If slab panels are square, or have lengths less than twice their widths, they should be designed as two-way slabs. In two-way slabs, the bending moments are larger in the short direction; hence the short-span reinforcement is usually given the preferential position. In arranging reinforcement, part of the bottom bars may be bent up and extended over the supports to resist negative moments. The bend points and cut-off points of such truss bars as shown in the ACI "Detailing Manual" [7] are normally satisfactory. Alternately, an all-straight bar arrangement may be used.

The bending moment coefficients tabulated under ACI Method 2 presuppose that the slab will be placed monolithically with the supporting girders or walls so that adequate torsional rigidity is provided thereat, whereas Method 3 permits such supports to have only negligible torsional rigidity.

When slabs are not placed monolithically with the supports, nor tied securely thereto, additional reinforcement must be provided in the exterior corners of the slab, according to Sec. 2002(b).

The beam shears for computing diagonal tension in two-way slabs are calculated at distance d from the face of a girder. In Method 2, these shears are calculated on the assumption of a 45° division of tributary slab areas carrying uniformly distributed load. In Method 3, the calculation of the shears is based on the ratio of the total load carried in each direction as specified in Table 7–5. The loads transmitted to the girders are calculated in a manner similar to that of the shears.

Flexural bond stress in two-way slab reinforcement tends to be high in the top steel at the face of the end supports. Smaller bars are recommended at such points. On the other hand, flexural bond stress calculations may be omitted if the actual end anchorage of the bars is over 25 per cent in excess of that required.

TWO-WAY SLAB CONTINUATION PROBLEMS

7–5. Redesign the typical interior floor panel of Example 7–1 as a one-way metal-pan joist system spanning the 22-ft. direction, using the same class of concrete and reinforcing steel. Be sure to consider diagonal tension, and if tapered pans are needed, the instructor will indicate the increase joist stem width attainable therewith.

Make a tabular comparison of the required quantities of material with the results of Example 7–1, the two-way slab design, and comment. Also secure data on form costs in the two cases.

7–6. Rework Problem 7–5, using a two-way metal-pan joist system. Make a tabular comparison of the required quantities and costs of material with the results of Example 7–1, the two-way slab design, and of Problem 7–5, the one-way joist system.

B. Flat Slabs, USD

7–15. INTRODUCTION

When reinforced concrete slabs are supported by columns only, the construction is known as **flat slab.** As shown in Fig. 7–13, the columns are usually round, and conically enlarged at their tops to form a **capital.** The effective spans are shortened thereby, thus preventing high diagonal tension and bending stresses. Flat slabs are distinguished from two-way slabs by being *supported only at their corners*, along the quarter-circle boundary of each capital.

Plate 7–1. Long-span ribbed-type flat slab construction. The columns are on 50-by-51½-ft. centers. Note that, instead of using drop panels, the recesses near the columns were simply filled in, thus providing diagonal tension resistance.

Continuity is all-important to economical use of flat slab construction, a minimum of three spans being required. Furthermore, the column spacing should be approximately uniform in each direction. The presence of several large openings in a floor tends to destroy the continuity. If unavoidable, such openings demand great care in framing them.

Flat slab formwork is relatively simpler and cheaper than if beams and girders are used. The absence of girders also means that for the same clear story heights the structure will be only about 90 per cent as high, which reduces wall, column, and footing costs. The unbroken ceiling expanse not only presents a better appearance, but also facilitates better lighting, simplifies the installation of piped services, and improves ventilation. The decreased number of edges increases the fire resistance.

7–16. DROP PANELS AND CAPITALS

As shown in Fig. 7–13, the slab may be thickened in the vicinity of a column to form what is called a **drop panel,** or simply a **drop.** A drop panel serves to enhance the diagonal tension and bending resistance of the

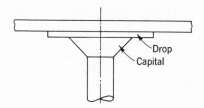

Fig. 7–13.　Drop panels and capitals.

slab by increasing its effective thickness. Most columns supporting flat slabs are enlarged at their tops to form a **capital,** in the form of a truncated cone for round columns, or a truncated pyramid for polygonal columns. (When a floor is not cantilevered out beyond the faces of exterior rectangular columns, *brackets* are substituted for capitals, such as those shown in Fig. 7–2.) Column capitals, although sometimes considered unsightly and expensive, do provide a wider support for the slabs, thereby reducing considerably the diagonal tension and bending stresses around the columns, and resulting in a more rigid structure.

A variation of flat slab construction is the **flat plate,** wherein the drop and the capital are omitted. Flat plate floors have been quite advantageously used for relatively light loads, as in apartment buildings.

In flat slabs, the slab proper may be a solid slab, or the ribbed type in the form of a waffle (see Plate 7–1), in which, instead of drop panels, the recesses near the columns are filled in to provide additional diagonal tension resistance.

A drop panel is usually rectangular or square. An effective drop panel, according to Sec. 2102(c)4, should have a minimum length in each direction equal to $\frac{1}{3}$ of the parallel span length, and a minimum projection below the slab proper equal to $\frac{1}{4}$ of the slab thickness. However, in designing the reinforcement, the *effective* projection of the drop below the slab, as stipulated by Sec. 2102(c)5, should not be taken to be more than $\frac{1}{4}$ of the distance between the edge of the drop and that of the capital. The practical total thickness (slab plus drop) of a drop panel usually ranges from 1.25 to 1.50 times the slab thickness.

The diameter of the column capital just below the slab is usually about $\frac{1}{5}$ to $\frac{1}{4}$ of the span length. The part of the capital that may be considered structurally effective, according to Sec. 2101(b), is that which lies entirely within the largest right circular cone with a 90° vertex angle that can be included within the outlines of the capital.

7–17. REINFORCEMENT OF FLAT SLABS

In flat slabs of an early vintage, a four-way reinforcement system was used in which, in addition to bars parallel to the column lines, there were bars running diagonally across the panels and over the columns. This created such a congestion of bars at the columns that the system is not currently used and has been replaced by the more convenient two-way system. On the other hand, a three-way system may be quite efficient for triangular panels, often used for garage floors. Still another system was the circumferential system, in which radial steel bars emanated from the columns, and circumferential bars surrounded the columns in concentric rings, in addition to concentric rings of bars placed about the middle of each panel and the midpoints of its edges. Today, for rectangular panels, by and large, the two-way system is by far the more common.

7–18. METHODS OF ANALYSIS

According to Sec. 2102(a), whether a design is based on USD or WSD, one may elect to use the **method of elastic analysis,** or the **empirical method** (provided certain limitations set forth in the Code are satisfied).

In the *elastic analysis method*, the bending moments are obtained by analyzing a complete frame centered about each column line in each direction. This method will be briefly outlined later on.

In the *empirical method*, the design bending moments are obtained by multiplying a quantity, M_o, by the coefficients given in the Code. This M_o represents the total panel bending moment in each direction. The establishment of its value has undergone an interesting evolution, which will now be described.

7–19. TOTAL PANEL BENDING MOMENT, M_o—A HISTORICAL NOTE

The first flat slab construction[3] was built in 1906 by C. A. P. Turner, who originated and obtained patents for the new floor system. Between 1906 and 1913, over 1000 flat slab buildings were built all over the world, but there had been no generally accepted theory of design, despite a number of loading tests and various proposed design methods.

Nichols' Analysis. The first rational attempt at flat slab analysis was made in 1914 by Nichols [9], who considered a square interior panel (Fig. 7–14a), amongst an array of individual panels, all uniformly loaded. The edges of such a panel, being lines of symmetry, are free from vertical shear and torsional moments; so is the section along the center line *1-2* of the panel. Nichols then assumed that (1) the panel is supported by vertical reactive forces uniformly distributed around the perimeter of the capital, and (2) no twisting moments exist along these edges. He next considered the static equilibrium of one-half of the panel under a uniform load of w per unit area.

[3] C. A. Bovey Building, Minneapolis, Minnesota.

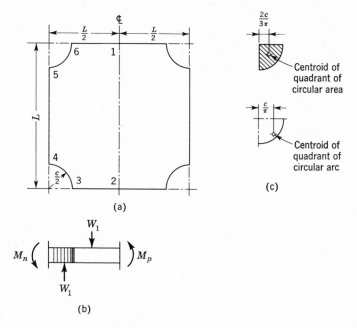

Fig. 7–14. Nichols' statical analysis.

Referring to Fig. 7–14, let L be the panel length; c be the diameter of the column capital; W_1 be the total downward load on the half-panel (which, to satisfy equilibrium, must equal the sum of the vertical reactive forces on the edges 3-4 and 5-6); M_p be the total positive bending moment along the centerline 1-2; and M_n be the total negative bending moment along edge 3-4-5-6.

The total downward load on the half-panel is

$$W_1 = \frac{wL^2}{2} - \frac{w\pi c^2}{8}$$

which produces a moment about 4-5 equal to

$$\frac{wL^2}{2}\left(\frac{L}{4}\right) - \frac{w\pi c^2}{8}\left(\frac{2c}{3\pi}\right) = w\left(\frac{L^3}{8} - \frac{c^3}{12}\right)$$

This load is equal to the resultant of the reactive forces on 3-4 and 5-6, which acts through the centroid of the quarterly arc, i.e., at c/π from 4-5. Hence the resultant of the reactive forces creates a moment about 4-5 equal to

$$\left(\frac{wL^2}{2} - \frac{w\pi c^2}{8}\right)\frac{c}{\pi} = w\left(\frac{cL^2}{2\pi} - \frac{c^3}{8}\right)$$

Therefore the downward load W_1 and the resultant reaction W_1 form a couple whose moment is

$$w\left(\frac{L^3}{8} - \frac{c^3}{12}\right) - w\left(\frac{cL^2}{2\pi} - \frac{c^3}{8}\right) = \frac{wL^3}{8}\left(1 - \frac{4c}{\pi L} + \frac{1}{3}\frac{c^3}{L^3}\right)$$

For equilibrium, this couple must be balanced by the sum of M_p and M_n. Therefore,

$$M_o = M_p + M_n = \frac{wL^3}{8}\left(1 - \frac{4c}{\pi L} + \frac{1}{3}\frac{c^3}{L^3}\right)$$

$$= \frac{WL}{8}\left(1 - \frac{4c}{\pi L} + \frac{1}{3}\frac{c^3}{L^3}\right)$$

where M_o = sum of the numerical values of the total positive and negative bending moments, and

W = total panel load = wL^2.

The above formula may be approximated by

$$M_o = 0.125WL\left(1 - \frac{2}{3}\frac{c}{L}\right)^2 \tag{7-4}$$

with a resultant error ranging from about $\frac{1}{2}$ per cent for c/L of 0.10 to 2 per cent for c/L of 0.30.

While Eq. 7-4 does not reveal the distribution of M_o between M_p and M_n, its validity is irrefutable, since it is neither more nor less than a statement of equilibrium, as long as the assumptions about the reactive forces along the edges of the capital are valid or approximately so. However, a great controversy[4] ensued immediately upon the publication of Nichols' paper because of the impossibility of reconciling Nichols' analysis with the interpretation of test results available at that time. Tests seemed to show much smaller steel stresses than indicated by Nichols' formula, and skepticism was heaped on it. Among Nichols' critics, the originator of flat slabs, Turner, was surprisingly enough, one of the most vituperative.

Westergaard and Slater's Work. Nichols' critics did not realize that the steel stresses, and hence the bending moment based thereon, which they calculated from the measured steel strains, had been calculated on the assumption of a linear moment-strain relationship. Therefore, such erroneously computed moments came out to be smaller than given by Nichols' static analysis, and the critics' aspersions on his work were unwarranted.

In 1921, Westergaard and Slater pointed out [10] that previous load tests had been misinterpreted, and that the correct steel stresses and bending moments were larger than claimed by Nichols' critics. However, as a compromise (which was unfortunate since, in essence, it condoned the violation of equilibrium conditions), the following formula for working

---

[4] For a succinct account of the evolution of flat slab analysis, the paper by Sozen and Siess (Reference 10) is highly recommended.

stress design of flat slabs was suggested:

$$M_o = 0.09WL\left(1 - \frac{2}{3}\frac{c}{L}\right)^2 \qquad (7\text{--}5)$$

which represented a 28 per cent reduction from Nichols' formula.

Westergaard and Slater, using the M_o of Eq. 7–5, presented a solution to the problem of its distribution. First, a panel was divided into a middle strip having a width equal to one-half of the panel width, and two half-column strips each having a width equal to one-quarter of the panel width. For a square interior panel with capitals but without drop panels, the distribution of moments expressed as percentages of the total panel moment, M_o, as recommended by Westergaard and Slater, was to be as follows:

$$\text{Panel } M_o \begin{cases} \text{Negative moment } 65\% \begin{cases} \text{In column strip } 48\% \\ \text{In middle strip } 17\% \end{cases} \\ \text{Positive moment } 35\% \begin{cases} \text{In column strip } 21\% \\ \text{In middle strip } 14\% \end{cases} \end{cases} \quad (7\text{--}6)$$

For panels with drops, the negative moment in the column strips was somewhat larger, with a correspondingly smaller positive moment than given by Eq. 7–6.

DiStasio's Work. With the introduction of flat plate construction in 1941, capitals came to be omitted from such floors, resulting in greater concentration of stresses at the relatively small column heads. The old tests had been on flat slabs having c/L ratios of the order of 0.2, and might not apply to flat plates having lower c/L ratios. In order to provide for more conservative values of moments for designing flat plates, without disturbing the form of Eq. 7–5 for standard flat slabs, a proposal was made by DiStasio (who originated flat plates), and eventually adopted in the 1956 ACI Code, to introduce a new factor, F, into Eq. 7–5, which then became:

$$\left. \begin{array}{l} M_o = 0.09WLF\left(1 - \dfrac{2c}{3L}\right)^2 \\[2mm] \text{where} \quad F = 1.15 - \dfrac{c}{L} \text{ but } \geq 1.00 \end{array} \right\} \quad \text{[ACI WSD Formula 21–6]} \quad (7\text{--}7)$$

In Eq. 7–7, c is the diameter or the side dimension of a column when applied to flat plates; when applied to flat slabs, c is the diameter of the capital.

The Present Formula for USD. Before 1963, flat slabs had been proportioned in accordance with working stress design concepts. The 1963 ACI Code permits, for the first time, the proportioning of flat slabs by ultimate strength methods. While the determination of M_o as given by

Eq. 7–7 is retained for use with WSD, it has been modified for USD as:

$$M_o = 0.10WLF\left(1 - \frac{2c}{3L}\right)^2 \left.\rule{0pt}{40pt}\right\} \quad \begin{array}{l}\text{[ACI USD} \\ \text{Sec. 2101(e)1]}\end{array} \quad (7\text{--}8)$$

where $\quad F = 1.15 - \dfrac{c}{L} \geq 1.00$, as formerly

In Eq. 7–7 or 7–8, W is equal to wLB for a rectangular panel L by B, and in calculating M_o in the direction of L or B, the corresponding span length, L or B, should of course be used.

The coefficient 0.09 of our Eq. 7–7 was changed[5] to 0.10 for Eq. 7–8 for USD, in view of the fact that "the original method of flat slab design based on working stress concepts already contains implicit allowance for many features which anticipate the benefits of ultimate strength theory" [12].

To prevent the larger deflections likely to result from the higher steel stresses used in USD, the 1963 ACI Code stipulates minimum slab thicknesses for USD, as given in Table 2101(e) thereof, to which the reader is referred.

7–20. DIAGONAL TENSION

According to Sec. 1707, the shear stress in flat slabs, as a measure of diagonal tension, must be checked in two ways:

1. **Check of shear in a slab considered as a one-way reinforced wide beam,** with a potential diagonal crack extending in a plane across the entire width of a panel. As for beams, the critical section is assumed to be at distance d from the face of support, which is either the edge of the capital or, in the absence of a capital, the face of the column. Where a column (which is usually round) is present, the face of support may be taken to be the side of a fictitious square having the same area as the capital, as shown in Fig. 7–15; a round column in the absence of a capital is treated in the same fashion.

The nominal shear stress on this critical section is then calculated in the same way as for beams, that is, by

$$v_u = V_u/bd \quad (7\text{--}9a)$$

in which b is the entire width of the panel. Unless diagonal tension rein-

---

[5] This drift in the right direction toward the original coefficient of 0.125 is most welcome to the authors. In this connection, the statement quoted above is reasonable because in the past the coefficient 0.125 was modified to 0.09 in defiance of statics, in order that, together with 0.09 as the coefficient for M_o, the erroneous assumption of a linear moment-strain relation in WSD would still result in a nearly correct steel content. Now that this assumption has been discarded in USD, the coefficient 0.09 is properly no longer applicable, and should be increased; otherwise the resulting steel content would not be adequate.

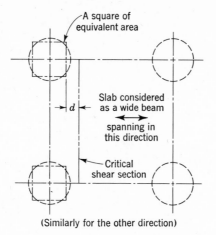

A square of
equivalent area

Slab considered
as a wide beam
◄─►
spanning in
this direction

Critical
shear section

→ d ←

(Similarly for the other direction)

Fig. 7–15. Critical sections for shear in flat slabs acting as one-way reinforced wide beams.

forcement is anticipated (see Art. 7–21), this shear stress is not to exceed the permissible shear strength of an unreinforced beam web as given by

$$v_c = 2\phi \sqrt{f'_c} \qquad \text{[Sec. 1701(c)]} \qquad (7\text{-}9b)$$

2. **Check of shear in a two-way reinforced slab, at concentrated loads or reactions,** referred to as *"two-way action"* in Sec. 1707(a)2. In flat slabs with both capitals and drop panels, and supporting uniform loads only, this action tends to produce diagonal tensile cracking along the surface of the truncated cone surrounding the capital as shown in Fig. 7–16a, or along the surface of the truncated pyramid surrounding the drop panel as shown in Fig. 7–16b. The *concentrated reaction area*, over which the heavy reaction W shown in Fig. 7–16 is considered to be distributed, is the area of the capital just below the drop in (a), or the area of the drop panel in (b).

Based on test results, ACI Committee 326 found [13] that the shear strength of the slab near the concentrated reaction area was a function of several factors, including the concrete strength f'_c, the shape of this area, and its dimensions relative to the effective depth of the slab. However, it was also found that, by taking a *pseudo-critical section* at a distance equal to half of the effective depth from the periphery of the concentrated reaction area, the *laboratory-determined* shear strength of the slab was approximately equal to $4 \sqrt{f'_c}$. Therefore, in the interest of simplicity, Sec. 1707(b) and (c) provide that the two-way action shear be checked at a pseudo-critical section "at a distance $d/2$ out from the periphery of the concentrated load or reaction area," and that the nominal shear

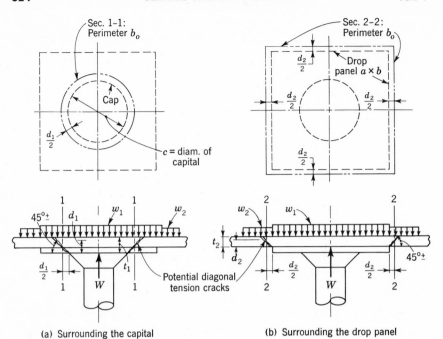

(a) Surrounding the capital   (b) Surrounding the drop panel

Fig. 7–16. Pseudo-critical sections for "two-way action" shear in uniformly loaded flat slabs with capitals and drop panels.

stress be computed by

$$v_u = V_u/b_o d \qquad (7\text{--}10a)$$

in which V_u is the total shear along the perimeter b_o of this section. This stress, representing diagonal tension, is not to exceed

$$v_c = 4\phi \sqrt{f'_c} \qquad (7\text{--}10b)$$

unless diagonal tension reinforcement is provided (see Art. 7–21).

Accordingly, for the flat slab of Fig. 7–16, there are two such critical sections:

Section 1–1, as shown in (a), is a circle concentric with the capital and at $d_1/2$ outside the edge of the capital, d_1 being the effective depth of the slab plus drop thickness, t_1. The shear stress is then calculated by $v_u = V_u/b_o d_1$, in which b_o is the circumference of the circle at section 1–1, and V_u is equal to the total panel load W less the total downward load within section 1–1. If w_1 is the uniform load intensity on the slab within section 1–1, V_u is given by

$$V_u = W - (w_1)[(\pi/4)(c + d_1)^2]$$

Section 2–2, as shown in (b), is a rectangle whose sides are at $d_2/2$

outside the drop panel a by b, d_2 being the effective depth of the slab proper of thickness t_2. The shear stress at section 2–2 is calculated by $v_u = V_u/b_o d_2$, in which b_o is equal to $(2)[(a + d_2) + (b + d_2)]$. The total shear V_u may be calculated by deducting the total downward load within the rectangle at section 2–2 from the total panel load W; or, if w_1 is the uniform load intensity on the slab proper beyond the drop panel, and the length and width of all panels adjacent to the column in question are identically L by B, V_u may be more conveniently calculated as

$$V_u = (w_1)[(\text{Area of a panel}) - (\text{area within section 2–2})]$$
$$= (w_1)[(LB) - (a + d_2)(b + d_2)]$$

Heavy concentrated loads on slabs other than reactions may be similarly treated.

Comment. In the past, it was thought that a heavy concentration of flexural reinforcement through the critical shear area increased the shear resistance of slabs. Accordingly, the 1956 ACI Code specified different WSD shear stresses varying with the percentage of negative steel over the columns. The results of a study made by ACI Committee 326 led to its elimination.

There are, however, certain advantages to be gained by concentrating flexural steel in the column area; it increases the slab stiffness and decreases the midspan deflections; it reduces the violence of shear failures; and it increases the load at which the first yielding of the flexural steel occurs. Therefore, while disassociating the matter of concentration of flexural steel in the column area from the shear behavior of slabs, the 1963 ACI Code nevertheless encourages this practice for *flexural* reasons, as indicated in Sec. 2102(d)5 thereof, to which the reader is referred.

7–21. DIAGONAL TENSION REINFORCEMENT OF SLABS

The results of tests on slabs having *diagonal tension* reinforcement[6] indicated that it increased the load capacity of the slabs [13]. The ultimate capacity was found to be greater than either that of the concrete alone or that of the diagonal tension reinforcement alone, but smaller than the sum of the individual capacities of the concrete and the diagonal tension reinforcement. Although not firmly supported by test data, the explanation might be that diagonal tension reinforcement (hereafter abbreviated to **D.T. reinforcement**) in slabs is not fully effective. There are other difficulties with slab D.T. reinforcement: in thin slabs, it is difficult to secure adequate anchorage for the D.T. reinforcement; and

---

[6] The term "diagonal tension reinforcement," although awkward, is more accurately descriptive than the much-used but misleading "shear reinforcement," and more appropriate for slabs than "web reinforcement."

heavy D.T. reinforcement may cause shear-compression failures before it becomes fully effective.

Therefore, in many cases, it may be more advantageous to use a thicker slab and/or a higher-strength concrete instead of D.T. reinforcement. However, if D.T. reinforcement must be used, as sometimes occurs in flat plate construction, Sec. 1707(c) and (d) provide the following recommendations as a guide to its design:

1. D.T. reinforcement is not to be used in slabs thinner than 10 in.
2. When the slab is 10 in. or thicker, and when D.T. reinforcement is used, the computed v_u at critical sections should not exceed $6\phi \sqrt{f'_c}$.
3. D.T. reinforcement of slabs that is used to take care of the shear that is in excess of that permitted without it should be proportioned on the basis that it is only 50 per cent effective.

7–22. ANCHORAGE OF FLAT SLAB REINFORCEMENT

Flexural bond stress in flat slabs is not very easy to calculate because of the two-way action. However, compared to anchorage bond, this stress is of secondary importance. The best safeguard against failure is obtained by providing adequate anchorage. If the *empirical method* of design is used, the minimum bar lengths and locations of bend points of truss bars as set forth in Sec. 2104(g) should be followed. When the *elastic analysis method* is used, anchorage lengths should be provided as described for beam reinforcement in Chapter 3 for USD or Chapter 10 for WSD.

Empirical Method of Flat Slab Design

7–23. LIMITATIONS OF THE EMPIRICAL METHOD

The empirical method of design of flat slabs may be applied if the following limitations, stated in Sec. 2104(a), are satisfied:

1. There must be at least three continuous panels in each direction.
2. When two successive span lengths differ, the shorter of the two must be at least 80 per cent of the longer.
3. The ratio of the length to width of each panel must not exceed 1.33.
4. The grid pattern of the columns must be approximately rectangular, although columns may be offset for a maximum distance equal to 10 per cent of the span, in the direction of the offset, from either axis between the lines of successive columns.

It is further required that the superimposed loading on the slabs be

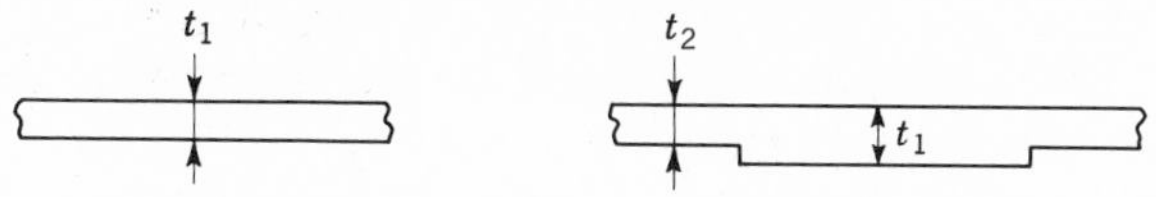

(a) Slabs without drops   (b) Slabs with drops

$$t_1 = 0.028L \ (1 - \tfrac{2}{3}\tfrac{c}{L}) \ \sqrt{\frac{w'}{f_c'/2000}} + 1\tfrac{1}{2}, \ \text{ACI formula 21-4}$$

$$t_2 = 0.024L \ (1 - \tfrac{2}{3}\tfrac{c}{L}) \ \sqrt{\frac{w}{f_c'/2000}} + 1, \ \text{ACI formula 21-5}$$

Increase the above values by 15% for exterior panels if the exterior
supports provide only negligible restraint to the slab

Fig. 7–17. Minimum flat slab thicknesses.

primarily uniformly distributed. When heavy concentrated loads are
present, the elastic analysis method of Sec. 2103 should be used.

Minimum Slab Thickness. In addition to the minimum values specified
in ACI Table 2101(e), Sec. 2104(d) further provides minimum slab thickness, as shown in Fig. 7–17.

In the empirical formulas of Fig. 7–17, c and L are in feet, f_c' is in psi,
w' is the total uniform load in psf (interpreted to be that at the *service
level*), and t_1 and t_2 will be in inches.

Size of Drop Panel. According to Sec. 2104(e), each side dimension
of an effective drop panel should be at least $\tfrac{1}{3}$ of the panel span length.

Also, in view of Secs. 2102(c)5 and 2104(e)1, both of which place maximum limits on the thickness of the drop panel which may be considered
effective when determining the negative reinforcement thereat, it would
be structurally wasteful to have a t_1 larger than $1.5t_2$, or larger than t_2
plus $\tfrac{1}{4}$ of the distance between the edges of the capital and the drop panel.

Maximum Reinforcement Spacing. The maximum spacing of bars at
critical sections of flat slabs is twice the slab thickness [Sec. 2102(d)1].

7–24. BENDING MOMENTS

The bending moments in each direction of a flat slab panel are expressed
as percentages of M_o which is computed according to Eq. 7–8 for USD.
These percentages or coefficients are given in ACI Table 2104(f) or
Figs. 2104(f)a and b.

The distribution of moments in interior panels is based on, though
slightly modified from, the solution presented by Westergaard and Slater,
as shown in Eq. 7–6. For moments in exterior panels, the end and side
support conditions must be known or assumed. Reference to ACI Table
2104(f) shows that the moment coefficients are established for three types
of *end* supports, labeled as A, B, and C, and for three types of *side* sup-

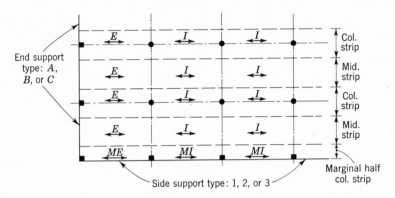

Fig. 7–18. Identification of flat slab strips.

ports, labeled as *1*, *2*, and *3*. To clarify, consider the strips, and bending moments therein, in the direction indicated by the arrows in Fig. 7–18.

For all strips marked *I* in Fig. 7–18, the moment coefficients are those under the heading "Interior Panel" in ACI Table 2104(f), and they are not affected by the end or side support conditions. For all strips marked *E*, the moment coefficients to be used are those given in Table 2104(f) under the heading "Exterior Panel," and they vary with the end support types only. For the marginal half-column strips marked *MI*, the moment coefficients are those under the heading "Interior Panel" and in the block labeled "Half column strip adjacent to marginal beam or wall," and they are affected by the side support conditions only. For the marginal half-column strip in the corner panel marked *ME*, the moment coefficients are affected by both the end and side support conditions, and they are given in Table 2104(f) under the heading "Exterior Panel" and in the block labeled "Half column strip adjacent to marginal beam or wall."

7–25. EFFECTIVE WIDTH OF STRIPS

In the *empirical method* of ACI Code, Sec. 2102(c)1 provides that the effective width of any strip used in computing flexural compression be taken to be $\frac{3}{4}$ of the actual width, except that on a section through the drop panel, $\frac{3}{4}$ of only the drop panel width should be used. This is an attempt to adjust for the possibility that the actual compressive stresses might be excessive due to the use of the arbitrarily reduced total panel moment M_o (see Art. 7–18), and for the variation in bending moment across the width of the strips.

7–26. FLAT SLAB DESIGN EXAMPLE BY THE EMPIRICAL METHOD

The same industrial building floor used to illustrate one-way slab and two-way slab constructions (Chapter 6 and Section A of Chapter 7) will now be designed using flat slabs.

EXAMPLE 7–3

(Calculation Sheets 1 Through 6)

Given the building floor, data, and specifications of Calculation Sheet 1.

It is required to design the floor as flat slabs with capitals and drop panels, by the empirical method, and USD of ACI Code.

Solution. The design calculations given in Sheets 1 through 6 are almost self-explanatory.

Sheets 1 through 4 show the determination of the concrete dimensions: the size of the capital, the plan dimensions of the drop panel, and the thicknesses of the slabs through the drop and beyond.

Sheets 5 and 6 show the design of the slab reinforcement in the long (N–S) and short (E–W) directions respectively. The bookkeeping system used in recording the calculations is similar to that in the two-way slab design example of Section A of this chapter. The insets labeled "Legend" show typically what the computed results represent.

The reader should note that, in contrast to two-way slabs, the long-span bending moments in flat slabs are larger than short-span slab moments, and hence the long-span reinforcement is given the preferential position. Furthermore, column-strip moments in flat slabs are always much larger than the corresponding middle-strip moments. Also, if positive steel bars are to be bent up, one usually bends about ½ of the middle-strip bars, and about ⅔ of the column-strip bars.

In Sheets 5 and 6, the reinforcement content is given by the total number of bars in each strip, which are assumed to be spaced approximately uniformly across the width of the strip. One may of course elect to give the reinforcement used by specifying a bar size and spacings. In either case, according to ACI Sec. 2102(d)1, the spacing of bars at critical sections should not exceed twice the slab thickness.

It is assumed that the reinforcement is to be bent and anchored according to ACI Table 2104(g)1 and 2 or Fig. 2104(g)a. In unusual situations, the designer should compute exactly how much of the reinforcement can be bent up, and where, and how much anchorage is to be provided, similar to the treatment in the one-way slab floor design examples of Chapter 6.

FLAT SLAB DESIGN PROBLEMS

7–7. A flat slab floor consisting of six bays in each direction with panels of 20 by 26 ft. between column center lines is to be designed without drop panels, but with capitals, and with spandrel beams which may be assumed to be of Type *B3*. At service load level, the loads on the floor are 100 psf live, and 10 psf for floor finish plus weight of the slab. Take f'_c of 3000 psi, and f_y of 40,000 psi. Use the ACI empirical method and USD. Design the floor slab and the slab reinforcement in both directions at all typical sections.

7–8. Assuming that diagonal tension governs, find the thickness of the floor slab of Problem 7-7 if both drop panels and capitals are to be omitted, and no slab diagonal tension reinforcement is to be used.

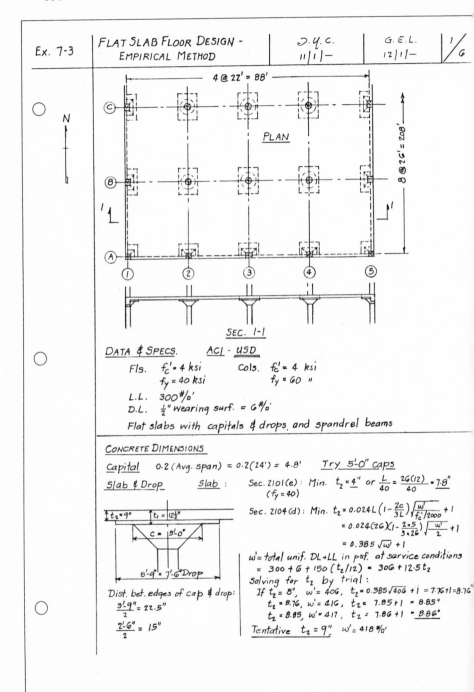

| Ex. 7-3 | _FLAT SLAB FLOOR DESIGN -_
EMPIRICAL METHOD | _D. Y. C._
11/1/- | _G. E. L._
12/1/- | 1/
6 |

PLAN

N

4 @ 22' = 88'

8 @ 26' = 208'

SEC. 1-1

DATA & SPECS.   ACI - USD

Fls. $f'_c = 4$ ksi   Cols. $f'_c = 4$ ksi
     $f_y = 40$ ksi $f_y = 60$ "

L.L. 300 #/□'
D.L. $\frac{1}{2}$" wearing surf. = 6 #/□'

Flat slabs with capitals & drops, and spandrel beams

CONCRETE DIMENSIONS

Capital   0.2 (Avg. span) = 0.2(24') = 4.8'   Try 5'-0" caps

Slab & Drop   Slab :   Sec. 2101(e) : Min. $t_2 = \underline{4}$" or $\frac{L}{40} = \frac{26(12)}{40} = \underline{7.8}$"
                              ($f_y = 40$)

$t_2 = 9$" $t_1 = 12\frac{1}{2}$"

c = 5'-0"

8'-9" x 7'-6" Drop

Dist. bet. edges of cap & drop:
$\frac{3'-9"}{2} = 22.5$"
$\frac{7'-6"}{2} = 15$"

Sec. 2104(d) : Min. $t_2 = 0.024 L \left(1 - \frac{2c}{3L}\right) \sqrt{\frac{w'}{f'_c /2000}} + 1$

$= 0.024(26)\left(1 - \frac{2 \cdot 5}{3 \times 26}\right) \sqrt{\frac{w'}{2}} + 1$

$= 0.385 \sqrt{w'} + 1$

w' = total unif. DL+LL in psf. at service conditions
$= 300 + 6 + 150 (t_2/12) = 306 + 12.5 t_2$

Solving for t_2 by trial :
If $t_2 = 8$", w' = 406, $t_2 = 0.385\sqrt{406} + 1 = 7.76 + 1 = 8.76$"
     $t_2 = 8.76$, w' = 416, $t_2 = 7.85 + 1 = 8.85$"
     $t_2 = 8.85$, w' = 417, $t_2 = 7.86 + 1 = \underline{8.86}$"

Tentative $t_2 = 9$"   w' = 418 #/□'

Ex. 7-3	FLAT SLAB FLOOR DESIGN – EMPIRICAL METHOD (cont.)	D. Y.C. 11/11–	G. E.L. 12/1/–	2/6

Drop: Side dimensions, Sec. 2104(e)2 : $26'/3 = 8.67'$ $22'/3 = 7.33'$
Use $8'-9'' \times 7'-6''$

t_1 = thickness thru drop   Sec. 2102(c)4 : $1.25 t_2 = 1.25(9) = 11.25$
(slab + drop)   Sec. 2104(d)2 : Min. $t_1 = 0.028 L \left(1 - \dfrac{2c}{3L}\right)\sqrt{\dfrac{\omega'}{f_c'/2000}} + 1\tfrac{1}{2}$

$\left\{ \begin{array}{l} \text{See calc.} \\ \text{for min } t_2 \\ \text{on Sheet 1.} \end{array} \right\}$ $\dfrac{0.028}{0.024}(0.385)\sqrt{418} + 1\tfrac{1}{2}$
$= 10.7''$

If not req'd for D.T. , it would be wasteful to use
$t_1 > 1.5 t_2$ or $1.5(9) = 13.5''$ [Sec. 2104(e)1]
or $t_1 > t_2 + \tfrac{1}{4}(\text{dist. betw. edges of cap & drop}), [\text{Sec. 2102(e)5}]$
$\left. \begin{array}{l} 9 + \tfrac{1}{4}(22.5) = 14.6 \\ 9 + \tfrac{1}{4}(15) = 12.75 \end{array} \right\}$ (See sketch, Sheet 1)

∴ Choose t_1 betw. $11.25''$ & 12.75 Say $t_1 = 9'' + 3\tfrac{1}{2}'' = 12\tfrac{1}{2}''$

Trial Dimensions : $9''$ Slab, $8'-9'' \times 7'-6'' \times 12\tfrac{1}{2}''$ thru drop, $5'-0''$ Cap.

Load : L.L. $300^{\#}/\text{o}'$ $\times 1.8 = 0.54^k/\text{o}'$
D.L. Slab $\dfrac{9}{12}(150) = 112$ $\left. \right\}$ $118^{\#}/\text{o}'$ ——— ACI L/F
$\tfrac{1}{2}''$ W.S. $= 6$ $\times 1.5 = 0.18$
Total, on slab : $\overline{0.72^k/\text{o}'} \times (26' \times 22') = 412^k$
Drop below slab $\dfrac{3.5}{12}(150) = 44^{\#}/\text{o}'$ $\times 1.5 = 0.07^k/\text{o}' \times (8.75 \times 7.5) = 4^k$
Total, over drop : $\overline{0.79^k/\text{o}'}$ $\overline{416^k} = W$
Load-factored Panel load

Check of diag. Tension based [Secs. 1707(a)1 & 1701]
on one-way beam action Crit. sec. @ d from face of supp. (capital)

$d_{avg.} = 9'' - 0.75''(\text{Cover}) - 0.75''(\#6 \text{ assumed})$
$= 7.5'' = 0.62'$
Convert $5'-0$ capital circle to equivalent square
$\pi(2.5)^2 = a^2$, ∴ $a = 2.5\sqrt{\pi} = 4.43'$
∴ Crit. sec. @ $2.21 + 0.62 = 2.83'$ from ₵ col

Long span more critical since therein b = 22',
which is < 26' for short span

Ignoring part of drop @ crit. sec.,
$V_u = \dfrac{416}{2} \dfrac{10.17}{13} = 163^k$
$v_u = V_u/bd = 163/(22 \times 12)(7.5) = 0.083$ ksi
Allowed $2\phi \sqrt{f_c'} = 2(0.85)\sqrt{4000} = 0.107$ ksi o.k.

Ex. 7-3	FLAT SLAB FLOOR DESIGN- EMPIRICAL METHOD (cont.)	J. Y. C. 11/1/–	G. E. L. 12/1/–	3/6

Refer to '63 ACI Secs. 2102(c)2, 1707(a)2, 1707(b), 1707(c).

Check of diag. tension based on two-way slab action

Sec. 1 @ $\frac{1}{2}(d_{1avg.})$ from edge of cap

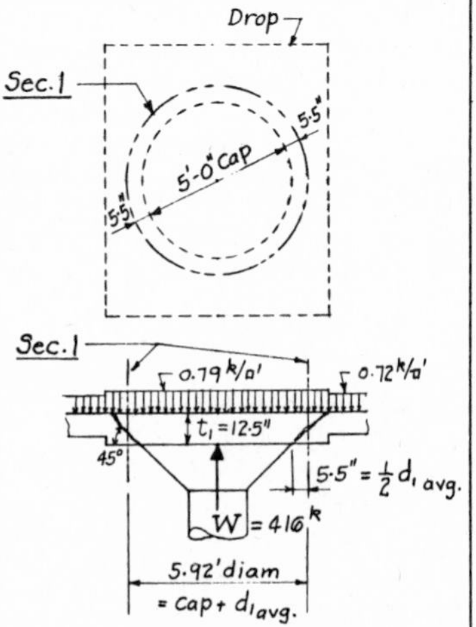

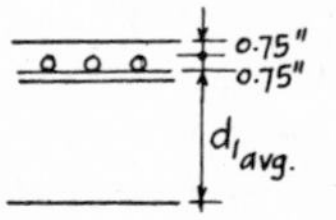

t_1 = 12.5"
Cover = − 0.75"
#6 bar = − 0.75"
$d_{1avg.}$ = 11.0"

Sec. 1 is a concentric circle having diam. = cap + $d_{1avg.}$ = $5' + \frac{11}{12} = 5.92'$

V_u = (Total panel load W) − (This circular area times the unif. load over the drop)

$= 416^k - \frac{\pi(5.92)^2}{4}(0.79^k/\square')$

$= 394^k$

$v_u = \frac{V_u}{b_o d} = \frac{394}{\pi(5.92)(12)(11.0)} = 0.161$ ksi

Allowed $v_c = 4\phi\sqrt{f'_c}$ = 0.214 ksi, so o.k.

Sec. 2 @ $\frac{1}{2}(d_{2avg.})$ from edge of drop

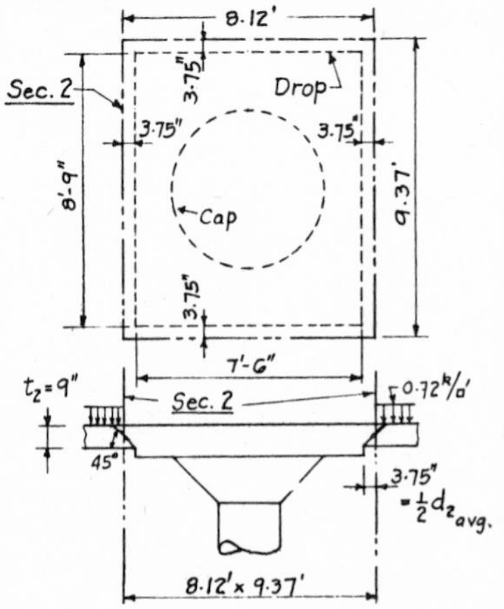

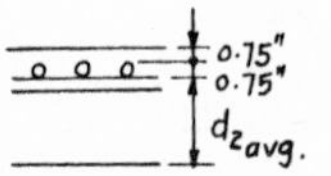

t_2 = 9.0"
Cover = −0.75"
#6 bar = −0.75"
$d_{2avg.}$ = 7.50"

Sec. 2 is a rectangle having sides of $(8.75 + \frac{7.50}{12})$ by $(7.50 + \frac{7.50}{12})$, or 9.37' by 8.12'

V_u = (Total panel area − this rectangular area) times (the unif. load over slab proper beyond the drop)

$= (22' \times 26' - 9.37' \times 8.12')(0.72^k/\square')$

$= 357^k$

$v_u = \frac{V_u}{b_o d} = \frac{357}{2(9.37+8.12)(12)(7.50)} = 0.113$ ksi, < 0.214 ksi, o.k.

Ex. 7-3	$F_{LAT} S_{LAB} F_{LOOR} D_{ESIGN-}$ $E_{MPIRICAL} M_{ETHOD}$ (cont.)	$\supset.\mathcal{Y}.c.$ $11/1/-$	$G.E.L.$ $12/1/-$	$4\!\!\Big/\!6$

Check of flexure at crucial locations

The trial concrete dimensions chosen on Sheet 2 should also be checked to determine whether they will be adequate flexurally for the steel now contemplated.

Assume long-span reinforcement given preferential placement, and #6 bars. (In the long span, M_o is larger, and widths of strips are smaller, but the eff. depth d is larger. In panels wherein the length and width do not differ as much as 26' versus 22', the difference in d in the two directions may require checking of flexure in both directions. However, for the present example, it can be verified that the long span is more critical. Furthermore, in the long span, the column strips are usually more critical than the middle strips.)

$\underline{Long\ span}$ $L = 26'$, $c = 5'$, $W = 416^k$

$\qquad F = 1.15 - c/L = 1.15 - 5/26 = 0.96.$ Use min. $F = 1.0$

$\qquad M_o = $ total panel moment $= 0.10\,WLF\left(1 - \frac{2}{3}\frac{c}{L}\right)^2$

$\qquad\qquad = 0.10(416)(26)(1.0)\left(1 - \frac{2\times 5}{3\times 26}\right)^2 = 822\,'k$

Moment coefs. are from '63 ACI, Sec. 2104. End supp. Type B and side supp. Type 3 are assumed.

$\underline{Col.\ strip}$ thereof :   Max. $-M$ @ 1st int. support $= 0.56\,M_o = 460\,'k$

$\qquad d$ thru drop $= 12.5" - 0.75" - 0.38" = 11.37"$

$\qquad$ Eff. width $= \frac{3}{4}$(drop width) $= \frac{3}{4}(7.50') = 5.625'$

$\qquad \dfrac{M_u}{\phi bd^2} = \dfrac{460\,'k}{0.9(5.625')(11.37")^2} = 0.703$ ksi

$\qquad$ From Chart A-1 of Appendix A, p(reqd.) $= 2.00\%$

$\qquad$ Max. $+M$ in exterior panel $= 0.24\,M_o = 197\,'k$

$\qquad d = 9" - 0.75" - 0.38" = 7.87"$

$\qquad$ Eff. width $= \frac{3}{4}$(strip width) $= \frac{3}{4}(11.0') = 8.25'$

$\qquad \dfrac{M_u}{\phi bd^2} = \dfrac{197\,'k}{0.9(8.25')(7.87")^2} = 0.428$ ksi

$\qquad$ From Chart A-1, p(reqd.) $= 1.15\%$

$\underline{C_{ONCRETE} D_{IMENSIONS}}$ Use: $5'-0"$ diam. Capital

$\qquad\qquad\underline{Drop = 8'-9" \times 7'-6"}$

$\qquad\qquad\underline{Slab + Drop\ thickness = 9" + 3\frac{1}{2}"}$

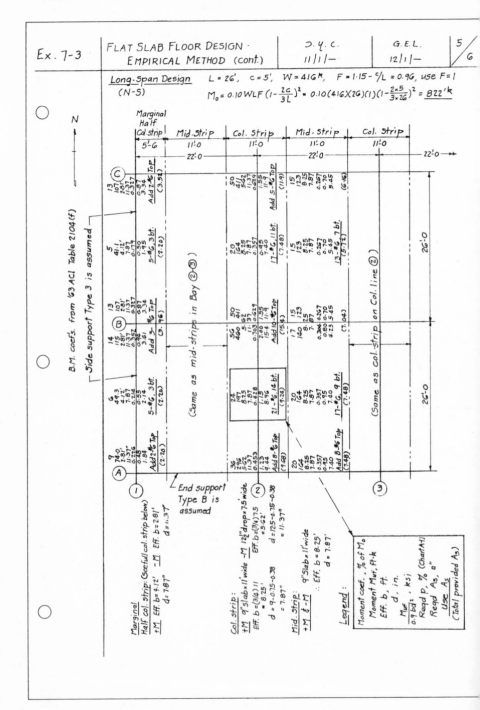

Ex. 7-3 FLAT SLAB FLOOR DESIGN ·   ⊃. 𝑌. 𝐶.   G.E.L.   5/6
         EMPIRICAL METHOD (cont.)   11/1/—   12/1/—

Long-Span Design   L = 26',   c = 5',   W = 416ᴷ,   F = 1·15 – ᶜ/L = 0.96, use F = 1
(N-5) $M_o = 0.10 \, WLF \, (1 - \frac{2c}{3L})^2 = 0.10(416)(26)(1)(1 - \frac{2 \times 5}{3 \times 26})^2 = \underline{822'^k}$

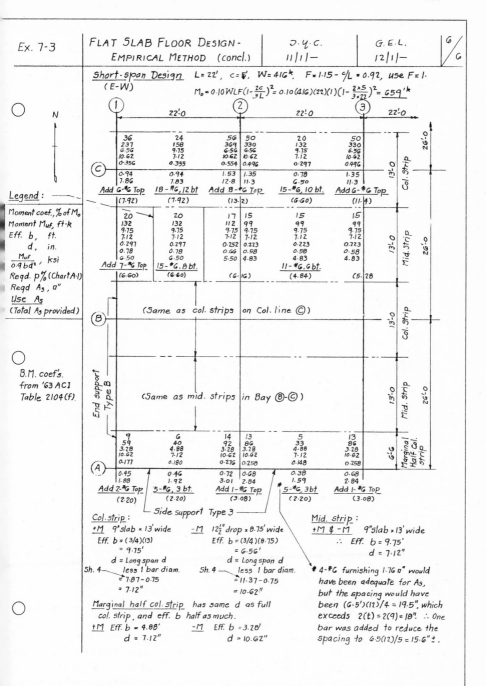

Empirical Method of Flat Slab Column Design

7–27. LIMITATIONS ON COLUMN SIZE

ACI Sec. 2104(b)1 stipulates the minimum sizes of columns supporting flat slabs designed by the empirical method. The following essentials have been excerpted therefrom.

Minimum dimension: 10 in. in diameter or size dimension.

When there are columns above and below a slab in question:

$$\text{Min. average gross } I_c = 1000 \text{ in.}^4$$

or

$$= \frac{t^3 H}{(0.5 + W_D/W_L)} \quad \text{[ACI Formula 21–1]}$$

of which the larger value governs. In the above formula, t is the thick-

Plate 7–2. Flat slab reinforcing steel in place, ready for the concreting operation. Note the spiral column reinforcement and the form for the column capital. Small plain-rod *high chairs* support the steel in the top of the slab. Deformed bars were used throughout. (Courtesy of Inland Steel Co.)

ness of the slab proper in inches; H is the average story height from center to center of slab in feet; W_D is the total panel dead load; and W_L is the larger of the total live loads in any two panels adjacent to the column in question.

When there is no column above the slab in question:

Min. gross I_c of the column below the slab $= 1000$ in.[4]

or the value given by ACI Formula 21–1 multiplied by

$$2 - 2.3h/H$$

where $h =$ the distance from the top of the slab to the bottom of the capital, in feet.

Columns smaller than required by Formula 21–1 may be used if the slab moments are modified according to Sec. 2104(b)1b, to which the reader is referred.

7–28. COLUMN DESIGN MOMENTS—EMPIRICAL METHOD

According to ACI Sec. 914, all columns (including those supporting flat slabs) are to be designed for:

Case 1—the *maximum axial loads* with the accompanying bending moments, and

Case 2—the axial loads that accompany the *maximum bending moments* produced by unequally loaded panels and/or unevenly spaced columns.

To produce Case 1 for practical design purposes, one usually assumes that all floors and all panels are fully loaded. For Case 2, one may assume that all the floors above the one in question are fully loaded, and alternate panels in the floor being considered are loaded with full live load.

In the empirical method of flat slab design, Sec. 2104(b)2 provides that the sum of the total column moments at any floor be the *maximum derivable* from

$$(WL_1 - W_DL_2)/f \qquad (7\text{–}11)$$

in which L_1 and L_2 are adjacent span lengths; W is the total dead and live panel load in L_1; W_D is the total dead panel load in L_2; and f is 30 for exterior columns and 40 for interior columns. This sum of column moments is then to be distributed between the columns above and below the floor in question in proportion to their relative stiffnesses and used for design without further reduction.

In order to use Eq. 7–11 intelligently, an understanding of its development is essential. It is assumed therein that the column moments are due to the column-strip moments at the columns in question. For an exterior panel L_1 to be subjected to the full panel load W as shown in

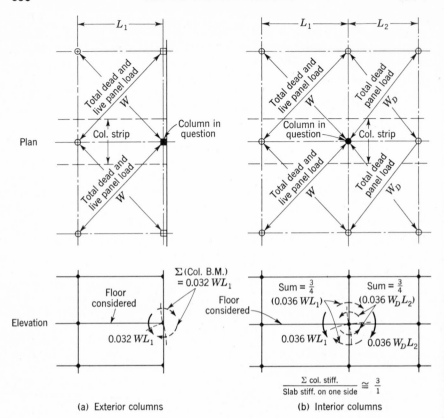

Fig. 7–19. Flat slab column bending moments, empirical method.

Fig. 7–19a, the exterior negative moment in its column strip is $0.44M_o$ for slabs with drop panels and Type A end support. For an average c/L value of 0.225, M_o is $0.10WL_1[1 - (\frac{2}{3})(0.225)]^2 = 0.072WL_1$. Hence the exterior negative moment in the column strip is $0.44(0.072WL_1) = 0.032WL_1$, or roughly $(\frac{1}{30})(WL_1)$. This moment is to be resisted by the columns above and below the floor in question. Therefore, the sum of column moments is $(\frac{1}{30})(WL_1)$, which is what Eq. 7–11 would give for the exterior columns, for which L_2 is taken as zero and f is taken as 30.

For an interior column strip, with panel L_1 subjected to the full panel load W and panel L_2 subjected to its panel dead load W_D as shown in Fig. 7–19b, the negative moment on each side of the columns is 0.50 times the respective values of M_o, for slabs with drop panels. For an average c/L value of 0.225, the M_o values may be found to be, respectively, $0.072WL_1$ and $0.072W_DL_2$. Therefore, the negative column-strip moments are respectively $0.036WL_1$ and $0.036W_DL_2$. Each of the two moments is to be distributed between the slab on the other side of the columns, and the columns above and below the floor considered, in proportion to their relative stiffnesses. If the ratio of the stiffness of the slab on one side of the columns to the sum of the column stiffnesses is taken to be 1 to 3, then the sum of the column moments is $0.036WL_1(\frac{3}{4})$ due to panel L_1, and $0.036W_DL_2(\frac{3}{4})$ due to panel L_2. Since these moments oppose each other, the resultant sum of column moments then becomes $(WL_1 - W_DL_2)(0.036)(\frac{3}{4}) = (0.027)(WL_1 - W_DL_2)$. The coefficient 0.027 is roughly $\frac{1}{40}$, which explains why f is taken as 40 in Eq. 7–11 for interior columns.

It is noted that, in the above derivation, the column moments are based on moments in *full* column strips. Accordingly, for exterior columns, when the column moments arising from the marginal half-column strips are considered, their values should be *half* of those given by Eq. 7–11.

7–29. FLAT SLAB COLUMN DESIGN EXAMPLES—EMPIRICAL METHOD

In the following examples, one typical interior column and one typical exterior column for the flat slab building designed in Example 7–3 will be considered. Design principles for these columns have been described in Chapters 4 and 5.

EXAMPLE 7–4

(Calculation Sheets 1 Through 3)

Given the building of Example 7–3.

It is required to design a typical interior column, *C3*, from the roof level down to the top of the footing, the other data being as shown in Calculation Sheet 1.

Solution. The interior columns were designed as round spiral columns, and the building was assumed to be laterally unbraced. First, the roof and floor loads were estimated; also the loads on spandrel beams were computed for later use, in the designing of exterior columns. Next, the minimum column sizes were computed on Sheet 1 according to Sec. 2104(b)1.

On Sheet 2, the full panel dead and live loads, including the weight of the capital and estimated column weights, were first computed for each story. Note that the column loads were computed at two levels in each story: just below the capital, and at the lower end of a column. Guided by the minimum size calculations, column sizes for the three stories were assumed and their properties computed.

Two loading conditions were considered: **Case 1,** in which all floors and all bays were fully loaded; and **Case 2,** in which all floors above the one in question were fully loaded, but for the floor considered, the two bays on one side of column line *C* were loaded. As will be seen later, Case 1 usually controls the design of interior columns. (The reader may note that the design of the column supporting the second floor herein constituted the Practice Problem 5–12.)

For Case 1, there were no computed bending moments in the columns. Hence using the column charts of Appendix C, the required p_tm may be easily obtained

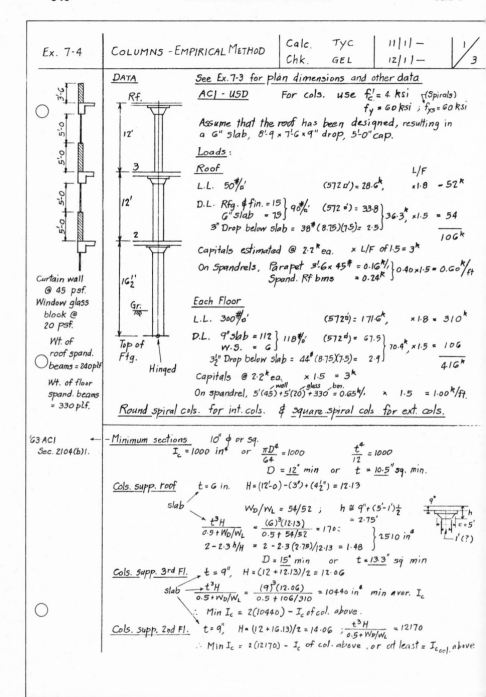

| Ex. 7-4 | COLUMNS - EMPIRICAL METHOD | Calc.   TYC   11/11 — | 1 |
| | | Chk.   GEL   12/11 — | 3 |

DATA   See Ex.7-3 for plan dimensions and other data

ACI - USD   For cols. use $f_c' = 4$ ksi   (Spirals)
$f_y = 60$ ksi ; $f_{ys} = 60$ ksi

Assume that the roof has been designed, resulting in
a 6" slab, 8'-9 x 7'-6 x 9" drop, 5'-0" cap.

Loads:

Roof   L/F

L.L. 50#/☐' $(572 \,☐') = 28.6^k$,   x1.8   = 52^k

D.L. Rfg. & fin. = 15 ⎫
      6" slab = 75 ⎬ 90#/☐ $(572 \,☐') = 33.8$ ⎫
3" Drop below slab = 38# (8.75)(7.5)= 2.5 ⎭   36.3^k, x1.5 = 54
                                                   $\overline{106^k}$

Capitals estimated @ 2.2^k ea.   x L/F of 1.5 = 3^k

On Spandrels, Parapet 3'-6 x 45# = 0.16$^{k/'}$⎫
               Spand. Rf bms   = 0.24^k ⎬ 0.40x1.5 = 0.60^{k}/ft

Each Floor

L.L. 300#/☐' $(572☐) = 171.6^k$,   x1.8 = 310^k

D.L. 9" slab = 112 ⎫ 118#/☐ $(572^d) = 67.5$ ⎫
      W.S. = 6 ⎬   ⎬ 70.4^k x1.5 = 106
3½" Drop below slab = 44# (8.75)(7.5) = 2.9 ⎭ $\overline{416^k}$

Capitals @ 2.2^k ea.   x 1.5 = 3^k
On spandrel, 5'(45) + 5'(20) + 330 = 0.65$^{k/'}$ x   1.5 = 1.00^k/ft
                     ↑wall   ↑glass ↑bm.

Round spiral cols. for int. cols. & square spiral cols for ext. cols.

'63 ACI ←
Sec. 2104(b)1.   — **Minimum sections**   10" ⌀ or sq.
              $I_c = 1000$ in^4 or $\dfrac{\pi D^4}{64} = 1000$ $\dfrac{t^4}{12} = 1000$
                              $D = 12^-$ min   or $t = 10.5"$ sq. min.

Cols. supp. roof $t = 6$ in. $H = (12'-0) - (3') + (4\frac{1}{2}") = 12.13$

       slab $W_D / W_L = 54/52$; $h \cong 9" + (5'-1")\frac{1}{2}$
          ↱$\dfrac{t^3 H}{0.5 + W_D/W_L}$ = $\dfrac{(6)^3 (12.13)}{0.5 + 54/52}$ = 170=   = 2.75'
                  $2 - 2.3 \,h/H$ = $2 - 2.3(2.75)/12.13 = 1.48$ ⎬ 2510 in^4
                          $D = 15^-$ min   or $t = 13.3"$ sq min

Cols. supp. 3rd Fl. $t = 9"$, $H = (12 + 12.13)/2 = 12.06$
       slab ↱$\dfrac{t^3 H}{0.5 + W_D/W_L}$ = $\dfrac{(9)^3 (12.06)}{0.5 + 106/310}$ = 10440 in^4 min aver. I_c
          ∴ Min I_c = 2(10440) − I_c of col. above.

Cols. supp. 2nd Fl. $t = 9"$, $H = (12 + 16.13)/2 = 14.06$; $\dfrac{t^3 H}{0.5 + W_D/W_L}$ = 12170
          ∴ Min I_c = 2(12170) − I_c of col. above, or at least = $I_{c_{col}}$ above

Ex. 7- 4	Typ. Int. Col. C3 –	Empirical Method	Calc. O. Y. C.	11/1/ —	2/
			Chk. G.E.L.	12/1/ —	/3

$f_c'=4$　$f_y=60$	Loads		Assumed col. size & properties			Case 1				Case 2		
Round Spiral Col. 5'-0 Caps.						$P_{u,sl.}$ P_u	e/D	Reqd K $= P_u/f_c'D^2$	Reqd. $P_t m$	$P_{u,sl.}$ P_u	$M_{u,sl.}$	e/D
	DL	LL										

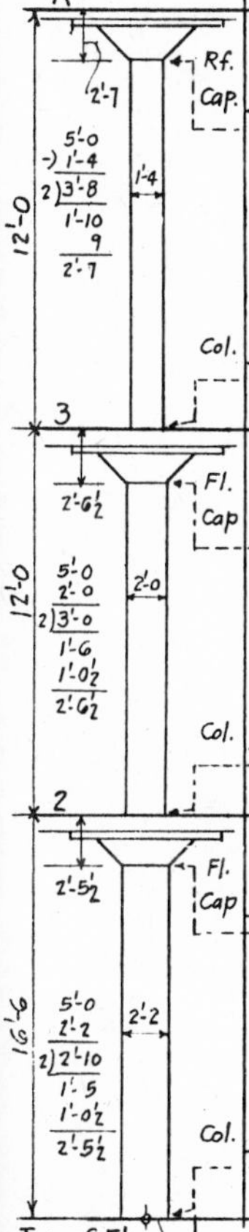

Top of Ftg.
Cols. assumed hinged.

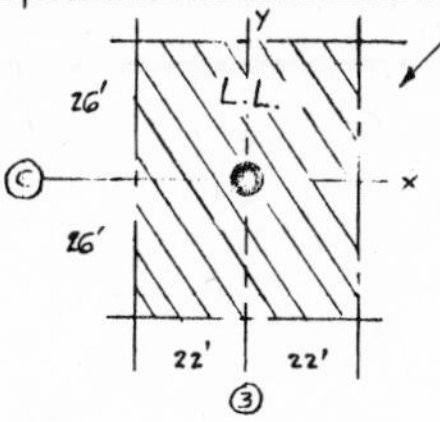

Case 1 — All floors, all bays fully loaded.

Case 2 — For floor considered, load bays as shown, with all floors above fully loaded.

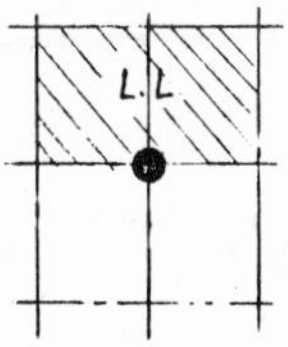

$m = \dfrac{f_y}{0.85 f_c'}$
$= 17.6$
Min. $P_t = 1\%$
Min. $P_t m$
$= 0.176$

Ex. 7-4	TYP. INT. COL. - C3 (concl.)	Calc.	D.Y.C.	11/11-	3/
		chk.	G.E.L.	12/11-	/3

R	Case 2 (cont.)		Final reqd.			Final used	Notes
	Reqd.K $\dfrac{P_u}{f_c' D^2}$	Reqd. $p_t m$	$p_t m$	$p_t \%$	A_{st}	Column size & Reinf.	1. All columns here controlled by compression failure.
	0.098	< min.	Min. 0.176	Min. 1.00	2.01	16"φ 6-#6 (2.34) 3/8"φ spiral @ 2" pitch	2. All columns are designed using Charts C-1, Appendix C
3	0.132	< min.					3. For details of column design, see Chaps. 4 & 5.
	0.189	< min.	Min. 0.176	Min. 1.00	4.52	24"φ 6-#8 (4.66) 3/8"φ spiral @2 1/4" pitch	
2	0.269	< min.					
	0.593	0.41	0.69	3.92	20.8	26"φ 14-#11 (21.8) 3/8"φ spiral @2 1/4" pitch	The design of this column constitutes the solution to Prob. 5-12.
Ftg.							

for the axial load combined with the ACI minimum eccentricity of $0.05D$ at each location. The use of the column charts was explained in Arts. 5–24 and 5–25.

For Case 2, the sum of column moments at each floor level was first computed by Eq. 7–11 according to Sec. 2104(b)2, as explained in Art. 7–28, and then distributed to the columns above and below the floor in question. The corresponding direct loads were easily calculated, and the values of e/D determined. The required $p_t m$ values were then obtained from the charts in Appendix C.

From the results of designing for the two loading conditions, the final column sizes and reinforcement were chosen. It will be noted that all the columns herein were controlled by compression failure; hence the design was fairly straightforward.

EXAMPLE 7–5

(Calculation Sheets 1 Through 3)

Given the building of Example 7–3.

It is required to design a typical exterior column, *A3*. Also refer to Example 7–*4* Calculation Sheet 1, for loads on the roof and floors and on the spandrels thereof.

Solution. The exterior columns were designed as square spiral columns with reinforcing bars arranged uniformly on the circumference of the core circle. As shown on Sheet 1, the properties of the columns for the assumed dimensions were first calculated. Since biaxial bending was expected, the column properties were evaluated with respect to both the x- and y-axes.

Two loading conditions were considered, as shown by the sketches at the bottom of Sheet 1.

Case 1 involved all floors being fully loaded. This produced uniaxial bending about the x-axis only. The sum of column bending moments at any floor level was computed by Eq. 7–11, in which W = total panel dead and live load, $L_1 = 26$ ft., $L_2 = 0$, and $f = 30$.

Case 2 involved all floors above the one in question being fully loaded whereas, for the floor in question, only the bay to one side of the y-axis was loaded with live load. This produced biaxial bending of the columns. The sum of column moments at each floor level with respect to either axis was calculated according to Eq. 7–11, as shown on Sheets 2 and 3. The reader is urged to review Art. 7–28 at this time to be sure that he understands how Eq. 7–11 should be correctly used.

So far as bending of the columns about the x-axis is concerned, the columns acted as exterior columns, and therefore, $f = 30$ in Eq. 7–11. Furthermore, the column strip which delivered the bending moments to the columns at the floor in question was fully loaded with dead load, but only half-loaded with live load. Hence, in Eq. 7–11, W = full panel dead load plus half of panel live load, $L_1 = 26$ ft., $L_2 = 0$, and $f = 30$.

With respect to the y-axis, the columns were treated as if they were *interior* columns, and hence $f = 40$ in Eq. 7–11. Also, the marginal *half*-column strip in one bay was fully loaded with live and dead load, whereas that in the other bay was loaded with dead load only. This, combined with the fact that Eq. 7–11 was developed for the *full* column strip, required the following values to be assigned to the quantities of Eq. 7–11: W = *half* of total panel dead and live load, W_D = *half* of panel dead load, $L_1 = L_2 = 22$ ft., and $f = 40$.

Having computed the design forces involved in both loading conditions, the columns were first designed for Case 1, arriving at the tentative reinforcement as shown on Sheet 2. Then the columns were investigated for biaxial bending of

Ex. 7-5	Typ. Ext. Col. - A3 -	Empirical Method	Calc. Chk.	Tyc GEL	11/11 — 12/11 —	1 3

$f_c' = 4$ $f_y = 60$

Sq. spiral col.

R |←—— 5'-0 ——→|

Loads   **Assumed column dimensions**   and properties   **Case 1**

	D.L.	L.L.			Abt. x-axis	Abt. y-axis	$P_{u,sl}$	$M_{x,sl}$	e/t	Failure controlled by compression
					Slab $\frac{l}{h}$= 13·2	Slab $\frac{l}{h} = \frac{13(6)^3}{12(22)} = 10.6$				
			t	14	$r' = \frac{28.6}{15.2} = 1.88$	$r' = \frac{28.6}{21.2} = 1.35$		$\frac{106(26)}{30}$		R
RF	27	26	gt	9				=92		P_u
Brkt.	3		g	0.64	Avg. r'= 2.90	Avg. r' = 2.08				Reqd. K
Spand.	13		A_g	196	$h'= h(.78+.22r')$	$h' = 1.24h$				" $P_t m$
	— 43	26	I	3,200	=1.42h		69	92	1.14	e_b/t
			h	9'-4 =112	R= 1.07- .008$\frac{h'}{r}$	R = 0.80				
			I/h	28.6	= 0.76					
			r	4.05						
			$f_c' t^2$	784						R
Col.	3									P_u
	— 46	26			Slab $\frac{l}{h}$= 51·4	Slab $\frac{l}{h} = \frac{13(9)^3}{12(22)} = 359$	72	51	0.607	Reqd. K " $P_t m$ e_b/t
			t	22	$r' = \frac{203}{51.4} = 3.92$	$r' = \frac{203}{71.8} = 2.81$		$\frac{416(26)}{30}$ = 361		R
Fl.	53	155	gt	17						P_u
Brkt.	3		g	0.77	Avg. r'= 5.25	Avg. r'= 3.76				Reqd K
Spand.	22		A_g	484	$h'=1.94h$	$h' = 1.61h$				" $P_t m$
	—124	181	I	19,520	R= 0.80	R = 0.84	305	310	0.554	e_b/t
			h	9'-4½ =113						R 0.80
			I/h	173						P_u 390
			r	6.36						Reqd K 0.201
Col.	7		$f_c' t^2$	1936						" $P_t m$ *0.176
	—131	181			Slab $\frac{l}{h}$= 51·4	Slab $\frac{l}{h}$= 35·9	312	185	0.323	e_b/t 0.35
			t	24	$r' = \frac{340}{51.4} = 6.58$	$r' = \frac{340}{71.8} = 4.71$		361		
Fl.	53	155	gt	19						
Brkt.	3		g	0.79	$h' = 2h(.78 + .22r')$	$h' = 2h(1.82)$				
Spand.	22		A_g	576	= 2h(2.23)					
	—209	336	I	27,650	R= 1.07-0.008$\frac{h'}{r}$	R = 0.37	545	176	0.161	(And so on)
			h	13'-11½ =168	= 0.21					
			I/h	165						
			r	6.93						
Col.	17		$f_c' t^2$	2304						
	—226	336					562		0.05	

R

$\frac{2'-8}$ RF

5'-0
-) 1'-2   16"
2)3'-10
1'-11
+) 9
2'-8

Top of Ftg.
Col. assumed hinged.

Elev. of Col.
(viewed toward
south)

Case 1. All fls., all bays fully loaded

Case 2 Bays of floor considered loaded as shown; all floors above fully loaded.

* Min. $P_t m$ = 0.176.
Reqd. $P_t m$ <
min. $P_t m$, which
is therefore used.

Note: For typical calculations, refer to Ex. 5-12 of Chap. 5, for the column supp. 3rd Fl.

Ex. 7-5	TYP. EXT. COL.-A3 (cont.)	Calc. TYC	11/11–	2/3
		Chk. GEL	12/11–	

	Case 1 (cont.)				Case 2

	Failure controlled by tension		Check Sec.1901(c)	Trial Reinf.	Axial load	Bend. Abt. x-axis

R

			$K\frac{e}{t}(\frac{.75}{.9})$	Reqd	$P_{u,sl.}=69-13=56$	$(54+26)\frac{(26)}{30}=69$
Assume R'	0.88		=0.094			$M_{x,sl.}=69$ $e_x/t=1.06$
P_u	78		For K=0,	$P_t m$ 0.45	If $e_x=e_y=0$:	If $e_y=0$:
Reqd.K	0.099		$P_t m=0.45$	P_t 2.56%	$K_0=0.92$	$K_x=0.107$, $R'=1-(1-0.76)\frac{0.52}{1.06}=0.88$
" $P_t m$	0.48		$e_b/t=0.50$	A_{st} 5.02.	$R=0.76$	$K_x(\frac{e_x}{t})=0.118,(\frac{0.9}{0.75})(0.097)=0.116,<0.118$
e_b/t	0.52		R'=0.89	Try 3-#8+3-#9		∴ $K_x=0.107$
Check R'	0.89					
Assume R'	0.85			A_{st} 5.37	$P_{u,sl.}=72$	$M_{x,sl.}=32$ $e_x/t=0.393$
P_u	.85			$P_t m$ 0.48	$K_0=0.92$	$K_x=0.3$, $R=0.76$
Reqd.K	0.108			e_b/t 0.52	$R=0.76$	
" $P_t m$	*0.176					
e_b/t	0.36					
Check R'	0.86					

3

			$K\frac{e}{t}(\frac{.75}{.9})$	Reqd.	$P_{u,sl}=305-77=228$	$(106+155)\frac{26}{30}=226$
Assume R'	0.85	0.87	=0.084			$M_{x,sl.}=184$ $e_x/t=0.440$
P_u	359	351	For K=0,	$P_t m$ 0.22	If $e_x=e_y=0$:	If $e_y=0$:
Reqd.K	0.185	0.181	$P_t m=0.34$	P_t 1.25%	$K_0=0.78$	$K_x=0.24$, $R'=1-(1-0.80)\frac{0.37}{0.44}=0.83$
" $P_t m$	0.24	0.22	∴ not	A_{st} 6.05	$R=0.80$	$K_x(e_x/t)=0.106$, $(\frac{0.9}{0.75})(0.06)=0.07,<0.106$
e_b/t	0.37	0.37	used.	Try 6-#9		∴ $K_x=0.24$
Check R'	0.87	0.87				
Assume R'				A_{st} 6.00	$P_{u,sl.}=312$	$M_{x,sl.}=116$, $e_x/t=0.203$
P_u				$P_t m$ 0.22		$K_x=0.46$, $R=0.80$
Reqd.K				e_b/t 0.37		
" $P_t m$						
e_b/t						
Check R'						

2

					$P_{u,sl.}=515-71=468$	226
						$M_{x,sl.}=110$

(And so on)

* $P_t m$ reqd. < min. $P_t m$; the latter is used here.

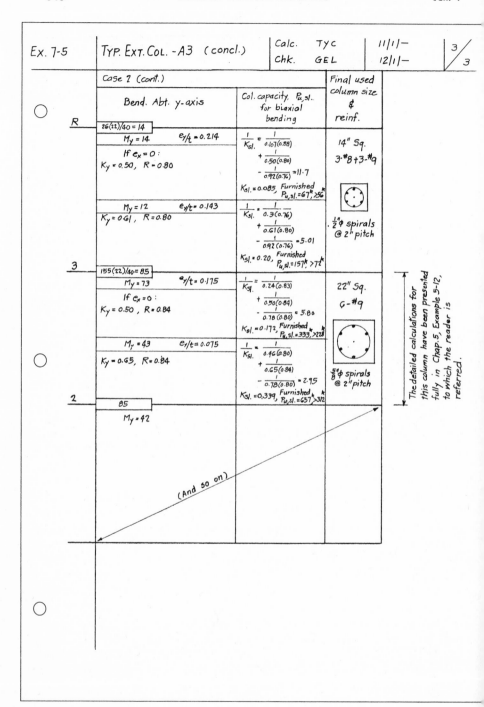

| Ex. 7-5 | TYP. EXT. COL. -A3 (concl.) | Calc.   TYC | 11/1/— | 3 |
| | | Chk.   GEL | 12/1/— | 3 |

Case 2 (cont.)

Bend. Abt. y-axis | **Col. capacity, $P_{u,sl}$. for biaxial bending** | **Final used column size & reinf.**

R

$26(22)/40 = 14$

$M_y = 14$ $e_y/t = 0.214$

If $e_x = 0$:
$K_y = 0.50$, $R = 0.80$

$\frac{1}{K_{sl}} = \frac{1}{0.107(0.88)} + \frac{1}{0.50(0.80)} - \frac{1}{0.92(0.76)} = 11.7$

$K_{sl} = 0.085$, Furnished $P_{u,sl} = 67^k, 56^k$

14" Sq.
3-#8 + 3-#9

$\frac{1}{2}^{"}\phi$ spirals @ 2" pitch

$M_y = 12$ $e_y/t = 0.143$
$K_y = 0.61$, $R = 0.80$

$\frac{1}{K_{sl}} = \frac{1}{0.3(0.76)} + \frac{1}{0.61(0.80)} - \frac{1}{0.92(0.76)} = 5.01$

$K_{sl} = 0.20$, Furnished $P_{u,sl} = 157^k, > 71^k$

3

$155(22)/40 = 85$

$M_y = 73$ $e_y/t = 0.175$

If $e_x = 0$:
$K_y = 0.50$, $R = 0.84$

$\frac{1}{K_{sl}} = \frac{1}{0.24(0.83)} + \frac{1}{0.50(0.84)} - \frac{1}{0.78(0.80)} = 5.80$

$K_{sl} = 0.172$, Furnished $P_{u,sl} = 333^k, > 228^k$

22" Sq.
6 - #9

$\frac{5}{8}^{"}\phi$ spirals @ 2" pitch

$M_y = 43$ $e_y/t = 0.075$
$K_y = 0.65$, $R = 0.84$

$\frac{1}{K_{sl}} = \frac{1}{0.46(0.80)} + \frac{1}{0.65(0.84)} - \frac{1}{0.78(0.80)} = 2.95$

$K_{sl} = 0.339$, Furnished $P_{u,sl} = 657^k, > 312^k$

2

85

$M_y = 42$

(And so on)

The detailed calculations for this column have been presented fully in Chap. 5, Example 5-12, to which the reader is referred.

Case 2, using Bresler's approximate formula presented in Chapter 4, as shown on Sheets 2 and 3.

The reader will note that when biaxial bending is present, the calculations become necessarily quite involved as in the present example, which does not contain full explanations of all details. However, the reader is referred to Example 5–12, wherein typical calculations are presented in full detail for the column supporting the third floor in the present example.

FLAT SLAB COLUMN DESIGN PROBLEMS

7–9. Following up Problem 7–7, design a typical interior column from the roof level through the third and second floors down to the top of the footing. The building is laterally unbraced, and the column is assumed to be hinged at the top of the footing. The roof service loads are 40 psf live, 10 psf for roofing, plus the weight of 6-in. flat slabs with 7-ft. square drop panels projecting 3 in. below the slabs, and 4 ft. 6 in. capitals. Take f'_c of 4000 psi and f_y of 60,000 psi for column designing, and ACI Code, USD.

7–10. Following up Examples 7–4 and 7–5, find the design forces for the typical corner column, $A1$, from the roof down to the footing.

7–30. FLAT SLAB DESIGN BY THE ELASTIC METHOD

When the span lengths of flat slabs are irregular, and/or the panels are far from square, and/or heavy concentrated loads are present, the elastic method *must* be used. This method is broadly outlined in the ACI Code. It requires essentially that the structure be designed as a rigid frame continuous from story to story, as well as horizontally in both directions. Each frame or bent so taken consists of a row of columns plus half of the adjacent panel on either side of the column center line.

In analyzing such a frame, infinite rigidity (infinite moment of inertia) may be assumed to extend in the slabs from the column center line to the edge of the capital, and in the column from the top of the slab to the bottom of the capital. To simplify the frame analysis, the columns at any floor may be assumed to be fixed at their remote ends. The necessary elastic constants for performing moment distribution on such frames with members having infinite moment of inertia at one or both ends, that is, the values of stiffnesses, carry-over factors, and fixed-end moments, may be found in Reference 14.

The frame is then subjected to checkerboard loading, and the maximum positive and negative moments are determined. The maximum negative moments are then reduced to those at the critical sections, whose location with respect to the column center line is specified in the ACI Code. The maximum moments for the entire frame are then distributed to the column and middle strips according to ACI Table 2103(c). The designing for flexure and diagonal tension following such an analysis is similar to that in the empirical method.

7–31. SUMMARY OF FLAT SLAB DESIGNING

Flat slab construction consists of continuous slabs supported on columns with enlarged heads called capitals, or caps. The slab is often thickened at the column to form a drop panel, or drop.

The empirical method of the ACI Code may be used in designing if the limitations specified therein are satisfied. Otherwise, the more general elastic method must be used.

The slab must be thick enough to meet flexural strength requirements at all sections. Furthermore, it should be strong enough to safely resist diagonal tension, which may be checked by investigating the vertical shears in the slab acting as a wide beam, and the two-way shears in the neighborhood of the columns and/or heavy concentrated loads.

The variation in concrete compressive stress across the width of a strip is allowed for by using only $\frac{3}{4}$ of the actual width as the effective width in the beam formula, or $\frac{3}{4}$ of the width of the drop in the case of negative column strip moments.

In flat slabs, the long-span moments are usually larger than the short-span moments in the same panel. Therefore, the long-span reinforcement is usually given the preferential position. Bentup bars may be advantageously used with straight bars. Their bend-up points and lengths must be such as to satisfy flexural and anchorage requirements.

The possible unbalanced bending moments in columns should always be provided for. In particular, if the empirical method is used in designing, the column dimensions must not be less than the minimum values set forth in the ACI Code.

FLAT SLAB CONTINUATION PROBLEMS

7–11. Given a flat slab floor with 3 panels in the E–W direction and 6 panels in the N–S direction. The columns are spaced as follows: 22 ft., 18 ft., and 22 ft. in the E–W direction, and uniform spacings of 23 ft. each in the N–S direction. The service floor loads are 100 psf live, 30 psf for floor finish and ceiling, plus weight of the slab. Take f'_c of 3000 psi and f_y of 40,000 psi, and ACI Code, USD, and the empirical method thereof. Design the floor with drop panels but without capitals or slab diagonal tension reinforcement.

7–12. Following up Problem 7–10, finish the design of the corner column.

TWO-WAY SLAB QUESTIONS

1. Distinguish between one-way, two-way, and flat slab floors.

2. What factors influence the choice of slab thickness?

3. What practical limitations, if any, affect the choice of a two-way slab when the lengths of the two sides are quite unequal?

4. Why do ACI Methods 2 and 3 give appreciably different negative bending moments at discontinuous edges?

5. What is the function of special reinforcement in the exterior corners of slabs not securely tied to the supports?

FLAT SLAB QUESTIONS

1. What several limitations are there upon the use of the empirical method of the ACI Code?
2. Do flat slabs or two-way slabs carry a greater bending moment in the shorter direction?
3. Tell in detail how to examine a flat slab design for diagonal tension.
4. Explain the ACI Code requirement, Sec. 2102(d)5, in regard to the distribution of the bars in the column strip in the vicinity of the column or column capital.
5. If the girders in a two-way slab floor are extremely shallow or no deeper than the slab itself, should the floor be designed as two-way slabs or flat plates? Take an interior panel of such a floor with assumed dimensions, and find the design moments treating the panel as a two-way slab and as a flat plate. Are the moments different? If so, comment on whether or not inconsistencies exist in the present ACI Code.

REFERENCES

1. WESTERGAARD, H. M. "Formulas for the Design of Rectangular Floor Slabs and the Supporting Girders," *Proc. ACI*, 1926, Vol. 22, pp. 26–43.
2. DiSTASIO, J., and VAN BUREN, M. P. "Slabs Supported on Four Sides," *Proc. ACI*, 1936, Vol. 32, pp. 350–364.
3. BERTIN, R. L., DiSTASIO, J., and VAN BUREN, M. P. "Slabs Supported on Four Sides," *Proc. ACI*, 1945, Vol. 41, pp. 537–556.
4. JOINT COMMITTEE. "Recommended Practice and Standard Specifications for Concrete and Reinforced Concrete," *Proc. ASCE*, 1940, Vol. 66.
5. MARCUS, H. *Die vereinfachte Berechnung biegsamer Platten.* Berlin: Julius Springer, 1929.
6. ROGERS, P. "Two-Way Reinforced Concrete Slabs," *Proc. ACI*, 1944, Vol. 41, pp. 21–36.
7. AMERICAN CONCRETE INSTITUTE. "Manual of Standard Practice for Detailing Reinforced Concrete Structures," *ACI Standard 315-65*, 1965.
8. TIMOSHENKO, S. P., and WOINOWSKY-KRIEGER, W. *Theory of Plates and Shells* (2d ed.). New York: McGraw-Hill Book Co., Inc., 1961.
9. NICHOLS, J. R. "Statical Limitations upon the Steel Requirements in Reinforced Concrete Flat Slab Floors," *Trans. ASCE*, 1914, Vol. 77, pp. 1670–1736.
10. SOZEN, M. A., and SIESS, C. P. "Investigation of Multiple-Panel Reinforced Concrete Floor Slabs," *Proc. ACI*, 1963, Vol. 60, pp. 999–1028.
11. WESTERGAARD, H. M., and SLATER, W. A. "Moments and Stresses in Slabs," *Proc. ACI*, 1921, Vol. 17, pp. 415–538.
12. AMERICAN CONCRETE INSTITUTE. "Commentary on Building Code Requirements for Reinforced Concrete (ACI 318-63)," *ACI Publication SP-10*, 1965, p. 63.
13. "Shear and Diagonal Tension (Part 3, Report of ACI-ASCE Committee 326)," *Proc. ACI*, 1962, Vol. 59, pp. 355–405.
14. PORTLAND CEMENT ASSOCIATION. *Frame Analysis Applied to Flat Slab Bridges.* Chicago: The Association.

8

FOOTINGS

A. Ultimate Strength Method

8-1. INTRODUCTION

From an engineering standpoint, a structure consists of the *super-structure* and the substructure or *foundation*. The former is the portion which is entirely above the ground surface, while the latter is partly below ground. The function of the foundation is to transmit the superstructure loads safely to the ground without causing undue settlement thereof.

Since foundations must not be subject to destruction by rot, insects, or borers, concrete is now almost universally used. The upper part consists of a foundation wall or a column-like *pedestal;* the flat lower portion, resting directly on earth, is called the **footing**. The function of the latter is **to distribute a concentrated load** to the ground at a safe unit pressure called the **bearing value** or *"bearing power."*

When a structure is to be built upon sound rock, no footing or excavation is necessary. The great majority of structures rest upon earth, which varies greatly in bearing value. In the northern United States proper, the bases of footings must be located from 3 to 5 ft. below the exposed ground surface to prevent their dislocation by frost action. Additional excavation is often necessary in order to get down to firm bearing. Other factors being equal, the deeper a stratum, the greater its safe bearing value, since all strata have been naturally compacted by the weight of the overburden.

Figure 8-1 illustrates the five most common types of footings. They are shown in the order of their suitability to progressively poorer ground

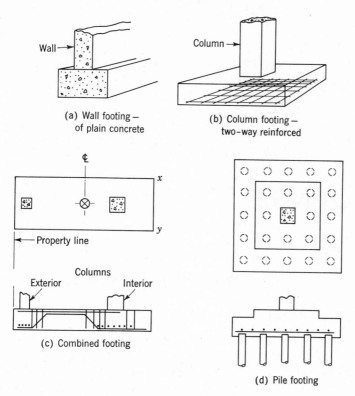

Fig. 8—1. Types of footings.

conditions.   For light loads and good soil bearing values, a plain concrete **wall footing** (Fig. 8–1a) serves very well.   The reinforced concrete two-way, or **column footing** (b) is common for supporting interior columns of either steel or concrete.   A *pedestal* (Fig. 8–1b) serves to spread the load coming upon the footing and to take up the variation in footing elevation over the building site.   **Combined footings** (c) become necessary adjacent to property lines, or whenever footings tend to overlap.   If the position of end xy is restricted also, or if the exterior column carries the heavier load, a trapezoidal shape becomes necessary.   A **pile footing** (d) is a footing whose load is transferred to firm earth or rock at a lower level by means of piles.   A **rigid frame foundation** (Fig. 8–2) is a large, well-braced, boxlike structure of reinforced concrete designed to support a whole building on soil of low bearing value and also to resist earth and water pressure.   The removal of enough earth to offset the weight of the structure is a feature of such designs.   It is fundamentally a boat.

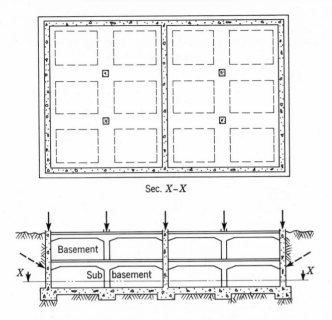

Fig. 8–2.   Rigid frame foundation.

8–2. THE ACTION OF EARTH UNDER LOAD

Since all ground settles more or less when load is applied, it should be considered as a spongelike mass which compresses as the load squeezes the water out. At one end of the scale of soil classification we find **clay,** which consists of very small soil particles with correspondingly small diameter void channels between them. Such a soil usually has a large percentage of water-filled voids from which the water cannot readily escape because of the constricted channels. Consequently, clay soils settle slowly, but for a very long time, and therefore a great deal. A low **bearing value** is assigned to soft clay, as shown in Table 8–1.

Sand, which consists of comparatively large (rock) particles, is at the other end of the scale. (Most common soils fall between the above mentioned extremes.) Large particles mean large-diameter void channels, or pipes, from which water escapes easily under the pressure of the load. Therefore a sandy soil settles very quickly. Unless it is very loose at the outset, the total settlement to be expected is very small compared to that of clay.

Gravel, which may be thought of as an extremely coarse sand, makes an excellent foundation. It must, however, be confined, just like sand. It is literally a rock pile.

Shale is a clay which has been compressed by nature to the state of a

Table 8–1. Safe Service-Load Soil Bearing Values of the Boston Building Code

Material	Tons per sq. ft.
Rock (variable)	100 to 35
Shale or hardpan	10
Gravel or sand-gravel mixture	
Compact	5
Loose	4
Sand	
Coarse and loose, or fine and compact	3
Fine and loose	1
Clay	
Hard	6
Medium	4
Soft	1

weak rock. Some shales disintegrate rather quickly upon exposure to the air.

In the absence of data from *borings* taken at the building site, and comprehensive *soil tests,* including particle size analysis, load tests, consolidation and shear tests on undisturbed samples, the conservative safe bearing values of Table 8–1 may be used.

Each footing should be proportioned for a uniform distribution of soil pressure if possible. Furthermore, the whole group of footings for a given structure should have relative bearing areas conducive to uniform settlement throughout. Unequal settlements cause cracking and even failure of structures.

8–3. FOOTING CALCULATIONS

It is customary to consider a footing rigid and the supporting earth elastic. This means that the centrally loaded footing of Fig. 8–3 is assumed to be supported by a uniform soil pressure even though, due to bending, the pressure may actually be smaller at the edges. If the load is applied eccentrically, but within the middle third of the footing width, a straight-line variation of earth pressure is considered to exist across the width of the footing. If the load, or **resultant force,** is outside the middle third, the pressure will be greatest along the side nearest the force and will decrease to zero at some undetermined point within the footing width. Obviously, tension cannot exist unless the footing is a pile footing.

Since a plastic mass of concrete conforms perfectly to the irregularities of the ground, **the weight of the footing itself is considered to be non-existent** so far as forces tending to shear or bend the footing are concerned. The decreased value of earth pressure obtained by deducting the footing dead load pressure from the total pressure is called the **net footing pressure.** It is used in computing footing strength, but the total pressure is taken when referring to that which bears upon the earth itself.

Although the weight of a normal backfill over a footing would appear further to decrease the shear and bending in the cantilevers of a footing, and increase the total pressure upon the ground, its effects are usually disregarded because of the probable **arching** of the backfill as the footing settles.

8–4. THE DESIGN OF REINFORCED CONCRETE FOOTINGS

For the heavier loads, massive plain concrete footings are avoided by reinforcing the concrete. Such a footing is illustrated in Fig. 8–3 to the same scale as that of Fig. 8–17 which was designed for the same loading, but by a different method.

Diagonal tension largely governs the thickness of reinforced concrete footings. Formerly they were proportioned by the "punching shear" concept, involving a vertical shearing, as in punching holes in structural steel plate. Normally, current practice for one-way reinforced footings conforms with the results of Talbot's tests at the University of Illinois [1], which showed that reinforced concrete footings tend to fail in diagonal tension across the 45° lines shown in Fig. 8–3, and that the maximum value thereof is to be computed at his section $Y\text{-}Y$, at a distance d from the face of the wall, column, or pedestal. Stirrups in wall footings are usually avoided by designing to a safe low value of diagonal tension, v, which is related to concrete's shear strength.

The **flexure** of footings under (rigid) concrete walls was found in Talbot's tests to be such that the bending moment may be computed at the face of the wall, rather than at the center thereof.

Bond stress is quite important. It is computed at the face of the concrete wall, column, or pedestal, as is flexure. The ACI Code formerly required that all footing steel be hooked, since the bond stresses tended to be high. With the advent of the high-bond type of bar (ASTM A305), hooks were shown by test to be superfluous, so they are ordinarily no longer demanded, except on plain (obsolete) bars.

A good design procedure, illustrated in Example 8–1, is first to establish the outside dimensions of the footing by (a) using the safe soil bearing value to get the required area, and (b) using the allowable diagonal tension stress to find the required thickness. Next (c) calculate the thickness required for flexure, and the necessary steel content, A_s. Finally, (d) select *bar size* from a systematic study of bar perimeter required for safe bond stress.

In USD reinforced concrete footing design, the precise value of j should be used in bond calculations since, in Fig. 2–4c, it differs appreciably from the common flat value of $\frac{7}{8}$ taken for WSD beams. Refer to the upper portion of the beam chart L–2 of Appendix L.

EXAMPLE 8–1

U-S Design of a Reinforced Concrete Wall Footing

Given the one-way wall footing of Fig. 8–3 and the service-level loading delivered as shown. The safe value for the sandy soil (Table 8–1) is 3 tons psf. Take ACI 3000-lb. concrete and 40,000-psi-yield-point steel. The USD-allowed footing diagonal tension is $v_c = 2\phi\sqrt{f'_c} = 93$ psi, from Sec. 1701(a) and (c), and at distance d from the wall. The ultimate flexural bond stress is $u_u = V_u/\phi\Sigma ojd$, with limiting values in Sec. 1801(c)(1) for the A305 bars. Provide 3-in. cover for these bars.

Required to proportion the width, thickness, and steel content, by the USD method.

Solution. (Refer to Fig. 8–3.)

(a) *Footing width.* From Table 2–1, the load-factored superimposed loading, $P_{uf} = 1.5(20) + 1.8(20) = 66$ kips per ft. of wall. Estimating the footing weight at 4% of the superimposed (service) load:

$$\text{Reqd. width } B = 40(1.04)/3(2) = 6.94 \text{ ft.} \qquad \underline{\text{Try 7 ft. 0 in.}}$$

(b) *Calculation of USD net footing pressure.*

$$\text{Ult. on the soil} = 3 \text{ tsf}(2)(\text{Avg. L.F. } 1.65) = 9.90 \text{ ksf}$$
$$\text{Less D.L. of est. } 1\frac{1}{2}\text{-ft. base} = 1.5(0.15 \text{ kips})(\text{L.F. } 1.5) = \underline{0.34}$$
$$\text{USD net pressure} = \overline{9.56} \text{ ksf}$$

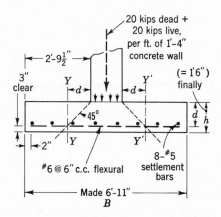

Fig. 8–3. U-S wall footing design.

Improved $B = 66.0/9.56 = 6.90$ ft.   Make $B = $ 6 ft. 11 in.

Corresp. final USD net pressure $= 66.0/6.92 = $ 9.53 ksf, used

Note that for the above calculation of *pressure* only the *load* factors were applied. The ϕ factor will now enter the computing of the thickness of the footing, and the other dimensions.

(c) *Thickness required at sections Y-Y for one-way diagonal tension,* using no stirrups. Refer to Sec. 1701(a) and (c):

Permissible USD $v_c = 2\phi \sqrt{f'_c} = 2(0.85) \sqrt{3000} = 93$ psi

Corresp. reqd. $d_v = \dfrac{V_u}{bv_c} = \dfrac{9530(33.5 - d_v)}{12(12)(93)} = 13.94$ in.

Est. max. bar rad. $=$ 0.38
Cover $=$ 3.00
Reqd. $h = $ 17.32 in.

Expecting final thickness of 1 ft. 6 in.

(d) *Thickness required for flexure.* The load-factored $M_u = 9530(33.5)(16.75)/12 = 446{,}000$ lb.-in. From Appendix A, Chart A–1, at top of 40–3 stress curve, find $M_u/\phi bd^2 = 870$. So reqd. $d^2 = M_u/870\phi b = 446{,}000/870(0.9)(12) = 47.5$.

Reqd. $d_f = 6.89$ in., < 13.94 in.

So diagonal tension rules thickness. Have 1 ft. 6 in. ftg.,

actual $d = 14.62$ in.

(e) *Flexural steel* (for a d of 14.62 in.). $M_u/\phi bd^2 = 446{,}000/0.9(12)(14.62)^2 = 193$. From Appendix Chart A–1 find reqd. $p = 0.0049$.

Reqd. $A_s = pbd = 0.0049(12)(14.62) = $ 0.86 sq. in./ft. of wall.

(f) *Bar perimeter required for flexural bond.*

$\Sigma o = \dfrac{V_u}{\phi u_u jd} = \dfrac{9530(33.5)}{0.85(12)(694)(0.96)(14.62)} = $ 3.22 in. min./ft. of wall.
$\qquad\qquad\qquad\qquad\qquad$ #6

(Reqd. min. perimeter/area) ratio $= 3.22/0.86 = 3.75$

From Table 1–3, this permits consideration of sizes through #8.   Use #6.

(g) *Bar spacing.*   12(bar A_s)/Reqd. $A_s = 12(0.44)/0.86 = 6.13$ in.

Use #6 deformed bars at 6 in. c.c.

(h) *Maximum aggregate size.* By Sec. 804(a),

Max. $= (S - D)/1.33 = (6 - 0.75)/1.33 = 3.95$ in.

Say may use 2 in. max. aggregate.

(i) *(Closure).* Compare these resulting dimensions of concrete and steel with those of Example 8–5, designed by WSD for the same initial conditions.

Settlement reinforcement. Some reinforcement should usually be placed in the footing longitudinally of the wall to enable the structure to bridge soft spots in the foundation soil. A minimum of 0.3 per cent thereof called for 8–#5 bars, or the equivalent, as shown in Fig. 8–3.

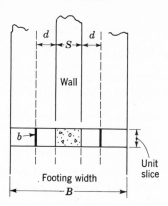

Fig. 8–4

Final comments. The concrete in the frustum between sections Y-Y and Y'-Y' acts mainly in compression, as distinguished from the diagonal tension action outside thereof. Between Y and Y' the horizontal frictional forces developed between the swelling concrete and the soil appear to be large enough to prevent the formation of tensile cracks.

A 3-in. minimum of protection is required between the ground of the footing bed and the flexure steel. For *formed* surfaces, such as at the sides of the footing, the minimum is 2 in. Refer to Sec. 808(a) and to Fig. 8–3 of this text.

To arrive at the proper bar size, form the habit of computing the required amount of bar perimeter per square inch of bar area, and refer to the Perimeter/Area column of Table 1–3.

The occasional tendency for bond requirements to demand a number of small bars means that they must sometimes be arranged in two layers to ensure proper placing of the concrete.

The application of Sec. 1707 to computing the diagonal tension in one-way reinforced wall footings has been considered to be as shown in Fig. 8–4. No appurtenant truncated pyramid is possible.

CONCENTRIC R/C WALL FOOTING PROBLEMS

8–1. Thoroughly investigate the footing design of Example 8–1, assuming that the soil pressure varies parabolically to zero at the edges, as for loose sandy soil.

8–2. Redesign the reinforced concrete wall footing of Example 8–1 for a wall thickness of 24 in. Make a tabular comparison of the quantities of steel and concrete required in the two cases, and comment.

8–3. Redesign the reinforced concrete wall footing of Example 8–1 for soil bearing values of 6 and $1\frac{1}{2}$ tons per sq. ft. Study in each case the d's required for diagonal tension and flexure, and plot a curve of d_v/d_f versus soil bearing value to determine at what soil value the required depths are equal.

8–4 (Individual). Given a 20-in. wall thickness, a 20-kip dead, plus a 20-kip live service-level loading per ft. of wall, and the $f'_c = 3000$, $f_y = 40,000$ materials. Take the same USD ACI-allowed stresses and other Code values as in Example 8–1.   Individually design to an assigned safe soil value (comparable to the 3-tsf value of Example 8–1) as follows: 4, 5, 6, 7, 8, 9, 10, 11, or 12 tsf.   Assume 1-in. aggregate size.

It is required to design the wall footing to the nearest safe whole inch of outside dimensions.   The bars are to be spaced by half-inches, observing the minimum spacing of Sec. 804.   See also Sec. 808(a).   The minimum bar size is #4.   Take the weight of reinforced concrete at 150 pcf.

8–5. THE DESIGN OF ECCENTRIC FOOTINGS

Even when there is a moment at the base of the wall in addition to the direct vertical load, as in retaining walls and fixed-ended rigid frames, it is often possible to design a practical footing that bears uniformly upon the ground by offsetting it with respect to the wall or column.   As shown in Fig. 8–5, let B be the required footing width as set by the uniform allowed ultimate soil bearing pressure, p, when loading w only is acting, as at (a). If a moment, m, is added, compute $e = m/w$, **the position of the resultant force,** and center the footing upon it as shown by the solid vertical lines in (b) for the limiting case.   If the moment is smaller, the footing will be less eccentric, as shown dotted.   If the moment is greater than m, the footing will partially pass from under the wall unless B is arbitrarily increased.

In rigid frame buildings the bending moment at the base of exterior columns is likely to be in the direction which demands that the footing project outward considerably, as in Fig. 8–6a.   If the column abuts the

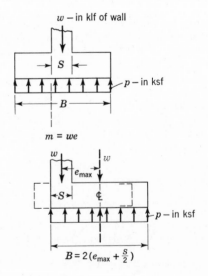

Fig. 8–5.   Locating a footing eccentrically.

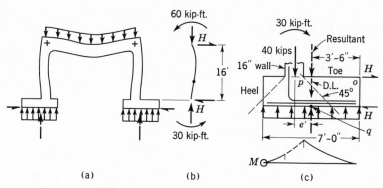

Fig. 8–6. Rigid frame footing designing.

property line, the footing cannot project, so a *combined footing* such as that shown in Fig. 8–12 must be designed.

Example 8–2 illustrates how a uniform soil pressure can be achieved at the base of a fixed-ended rigid frame by designing an outwardly projecting eccentric footing.

EXAMPLE 8–2

U-S Design of an Eccentric Reinforced Concrete (Wall-Type) Footing for a Rigid Frame

Given the same 40-kip dead plus live service wall load of Example 8–1, but combined with a bending moment of 30 kip-ft. from the rigid frame action shown in Fig. 8–6a and b.

Required to U-S design the footing for a service uniform soil pressure of 3 tons per sq. ft., if uniformity is possible. Specification: use 3000-lb. concrete and 40,000-psi-yield-point steel. Use USD allowed *footing* diagonal tension, $v_c = 2\phi \sqrt{f'_c} = 93$ psi, from Sec. 1701(c) on one-way footings. Use $u_u = V_u/\phi\Sigma ojd$ with the limiting values of Sec. 1801(c)(1) for the particular size of A305 deformed bars to be used, with 3-in. cover.

Solution. (Refer to Fig. 8–6.)

(a) *Trial footing width.* Estimating the footing weight at 4% of the superimposed load, as in Example 8–1, the required width B would be $40.0(1.04)/3(2) = 6.94$ ft.   Try 7 ft. 0 in.

(b) *Loading.* The load-factored loading is

$$W_{uf} = 1.5(20) + 1.8(20) = \qquad\qquad 66 \text{ kips}$$

(c) *Calculation of available net footing pressure* (U-S basis).

Ultimate pressure on soil = (3 tsf)(2)(avg. L.F. 1.65) = 9.90 ksf
Less est. D.L. of footing = (1.83 ft.)(0.15)(L.F. 1.5) = 0.41
                                                                9.49 ksf

Reqd. width = 66.0 kips/9.49 ksf = 6.96 ft.   Make B = 7 ft. 0 in.

Corresp. USD net pressure = 66 kips/7 ft. =   9.42 ksf

(d) *Offsetting of footing.* Try for a uniform soil pressure. From Fig. 8–6b the service loading shear force H at the top of the footing will be $(60 + 30)/16 =$ 5.63 kips, which produces additional moment upon the base plane of the footing.

Let e' be the required offsetting of the centroid of the footing at the ground level with respect to the position of the 40-kip load. Then make a summation of the moments of all forces about the base point q at the centroid of the footing, estimating the footing thickness at 20 in.:

$$40e' + \text{D.L.}[0] - 5.63[\overset{23}{\cancel{20}}] - 30(12) \equiv 0$$

$$\overset{12.24}{e' = \cancel{11.82}} \text{ in.}$$

Now $$42 + \overset{12.24}{\cancel{11.82}} - 8 = \qquad \overset{46.24}{\cancel{45.82}} \text{ in. for } op, \text{ the toe.}$$

TOE SIDE

(e) **Diagonal tension.** USD net footing pressure (from above) = 9.42 ksf.

$$\text{Reqd. } d_v = \frac{V_u}{bv_c} = \frac{9420[46.24 - d_v]}{12(12)(93)} = 19.10 \text{ in.}$$

$h = 23.00$
$\quad -3.00$
$\quad -0.44$
$\overline{}$
$d = 19.56$

Est. max. bar radius = 0.44
Cover = 3.00
$\overline{}$
Reqd. h = 22.54 in.
Make thickness 1 ft. 11 in.

(f) **U-S designing of flexure steel,** toe side. Taking a 1-ft. strip of the 46.24/12 = 3.86-ft. cantilever:

$$M_u = 9420(46.24)[23.12]/12 = 840,000 \text{ lb.-in.}$$

From Appendix Chart A–1, $d^2 = M_u/870\phi b = 840,000/870(0.9)(12) = 89.4$, so required $d = 9.46$ in. But from (e), $23.00 - 3.44 = \qquad$ 19.56 in. rules.

Now $M_u/\phi bd^2 = 840,000/0.9(12)(19.56)^2 = 203$. From Chart A–1, find reqd. $p = 0.0052$. And reqd. $A_s = pbd = 0.0052(12)(19.56) =$
1.22 sq. in. per ft. of wall.

(g) **Perimeter required for bond** at point p, the face of wall.

$$\Sigma o = \frac{V_u}{\phi u_u jd} = \frac{9420(46.24)}{0.85(12)(520)(0.91)(19.56)} = \qquad 4.37 \text{ in. min. per ft. of wall.}$$
#8 trial

Perimeter reqd. per sq. in. of bar area = 4.37/1.22 = 3.58

From Table 1–3, bars #3 through #8 may be considered.

(h) *Possible bar spacings.* If #6 bars are taken, the average spacing in the toe is

$$s = 12(\text{bar } A_s)/\text{reqd. } A_s \text{ per ft.} = 12(0.44)/1.22 = \qquad 4.33 \text{ in. c.c.}$$

HEEL SIDE

(i) **Proportioning the heel steel for bending and bond.** In item (f) above, the cantilever bending moment per foot of wall, at the face thereof, was found to be 840,000 lb.-in., for which 1.22 sq. in. was required (at 0.0052 steel ratio). But since the 21.75-in. heel is less than half as long, and its bending moment correspondingly less than one fourth as much, one would expect that not over one fifth of the toe steel need be extended to reinforce the heel cantilever also.

However, one fifth of the 0.0052 toe steel ratio would be only about 0.0010, which, by Sec. 911, is entirely too small to forestall sudden failure via the concrete. Instead, the minimum S. & T. steel content of Sec. 807 is used; but note that it calls for $0.0025bh$, which in this case is $0.0025(12)(23) = 0.69$ sq. in. This says that more than half of the toe bars are also needed in the heel. *The left ends of the remaining bars, 0.53 sq. in. per ft. of wall, were bent up into the wall as dowels.*

RECONCILIATION

(j) **Closure.** The size and spacing of any bar chosen to provide the required 0.69 sq. in. of heel steel, and have an acceptable perimeter, will be different from what is required on the toe side.

Time was saved by selecting a single size of bar, and arranging two overlapping *bar mats* differing basically only in bar spacings (see Fig. 8–7).[1]

(k) **Trial of #6 bars for heel.**

$$\text{Spacing } s = \frac{12(\text{bar } A_s)}{A_s \text{ reqd. per ft.}} = \frac{12(0.44)}{0.69} = 7.65 \text{ in.}$$

Take #6 at $7\frac{1}{2}$ in. c.c.

Corresp. check on bond stress to see whether $u_u = V_u/\phi\Sigma o jd \leq 800$ psi:

$$u_u = \frac{(7.50/12)(9420)(21.75)}{0.85(12)(\frac{3}{4})(\pi)(0.97)(19.62)} = \underline{280 \text{ psi, } {<}800 \quad \text{O.K.}}$$

(l) **Trial of same #6 bars at $7\frac{1}{2}$ in. c.c. for toe.**

$$u_u = \frac{(7.50/12)(9420)(46.25)}{0.85(12)(\frac{3}{4})(\pi)(0.95)(19.62)} = \underline{608 \text{ psi, } {<}800 \quad \text{O.K.}}$$

Reqd. area of additional #6 bars in toe $= 1.22 - 0.70 = 0.52$ sq. in.

$$\text{Corresp. spacing} = \frac{12(0.44)}{0.52} = 10.2 \text{ in.}$$

<u>Use #6 at 10 in. c.c.</u>

(m) *Schematic of bar arrangement.* See Fig. 8–7.

8–6. COMMENTS UPON ECCENTRIC FOOTING DESIGNING

The horizontal thrust, H in Fig. 8–6, of 5.63 kips is assumed to be safely resisted by the ground friction developed by the 42.02-kip vertical pres-

---

[1] By placing the lower mat with its transverse tie rods underneath, all the #6 bars can rest upon the 3-in. bolsters.

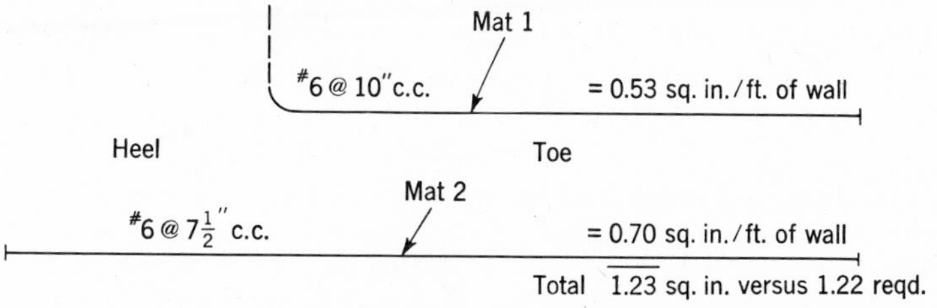

Fig. 8–7. The two mats (both lying upon the same 3-in. bolsters).

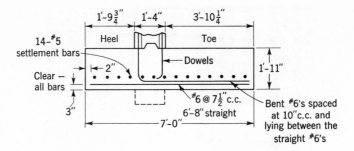

Fig. 8–8. Final design sketch (Example 8–2).

sure. In case there is doubt, a trench may be cleanly excavated in the footing bed, and a *shear lug* of concrete placed, as shown dashed in Fig. 8–8. It is also possible to lay tie rods in a trench between the two footings and do the first backfilling with concrete to protect the steel. In no case should the backfill along the side of the footing be relied upon to resist the horizontal thrust.

The design sketch also shows the endings of the steel from the wall above. This steel was calculated as for a column-like member subject to heavy bending.

ECCENTRIC WALL FOOTING DESIGN PROBLEM

8–5. Redesign the eccentric wall footing of Example 8–2 for 75 kip-ft. of bending moment instead of 30 kip-ft.

What different situation is approached thereby? How should it be handled?

8–7. THE DESIGN OF TWO-WAY REINFORCED CONCRETE FOOTINGS
(Professor Richart's Tests: Report of ACI–ASCE Committee 326 on Shear and Diagonal Tension)

A footing supporting a concentrated load, such as a column, should be square (or round), or substantially so. Such footings are ordinarily reinforced in both directions for two-way strength, and are known as **two-way footings, column footings,** or **isolated footings.**

During the fifty-five years since the early footing tests [1] were made, concrete strengths had increased greatly, stronger steels had been used, and new patterns of deformed bars with greater bond strength had appeared. Consequently in 1944 Professor Frank E. Richart, of the University of Illinois, undertook a new series of footing tests in cooperation with the American Iron and Steel Institute. The results, reported [2] in 1949, include:

1. Data indicating that the 45° design practice with respect to diagonal tension is too optimistic; that the critical section should be set closer to the column or wall. (Not evident from Plate 8–1.)
2. Data showing that the anchorage bond value of certain high bond types of deformed bars is not appreciably increased by hooking the ends.

Plate 8–1. Typical Richart series two-way test footing after failure. The bars were cut to permit separation of the two parts. The square block is a stub column placed integrally with the footing.

Items 1 and 2 are reflected in certain clauses of the ACI Code which (a) investigate footing diagonal tension closer to a column or wall, and (b) omit former demands for hooking bars. These clauses are to be found in the 40-page 1962 "Report of ACI Committee 326 on Shear and Diagonal Tension" [3], which culminated about ten years of research work in cooperation with ASCE. A good many changes have already been made, and several more are included in the closing "Recommendations." These latter are largely devoted to *slab-column* situations, which include two-way footings.

Example 8–3 and Fig. 8–9 illustrate the designing of a two-way-reinforced footing for a 400-kip service load. The work proceeds through the same four basic items of study, as for one-way footings. A pyramidal frustum of concrete, with a base $d/2$ inches outside the limits of the column [Sec. 1707(a)(2) and (b)], defines a compression region outside of which the soil pressure is considered to produce *diagonal tension*, which is assumed to be a maximum all around the base of the frustum. Bending and bond stresses are computed over a full-width right section at the face of the column [Secs. 2304(b)1 and 2305(c)].

The effective depth, d, has conservatively been measured to the center of the bars of the upper mat.

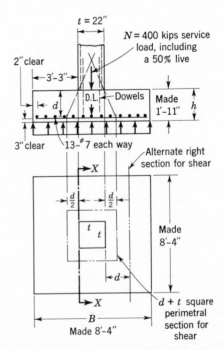

Fig. 8–9. Two-way footing designing.

EXAMPLE 8–3

U-S Design of a Square Two-Way R/C Column Footing

Given a 22-by-22-in. tied column with 12-#9 high bond deformed bars of 50,000-psi-yield-point, carrying a total of 400 kips service loading, equally dead and live.

Required to U-S design the corresponding Code two-way footing for a 3-ton-per-sq.-ft. safe soil value, taking 3000-lb. concrete, 40,000-psi-yield-point steel. Take USD allowed footing diagonal tension $v_c = 4\phi \sqrt{f'_c}$ at $d/2$ distance from the column faces, per Code Sec. 1707(b) and (c). For bond, use $u_u = V_u/\phi \Sigma ojd$, but governed by the limiting values of Sec. 1801(c)(1) for the particular size of A305 deformed bars to be used, with 3-in. cover.

Solution. Refer to Fig. 8–9.

(a) *Development of footing width*, based on estimated d and Fig. 8–11. From trial:

$$\text{Est. } d = 18.50 \text{ in.}$$
$$\text{Est. bar radius} = 0.44$$
$$\text{Lower mat} = \underline{0.88}$$
$$\text{Cover} = \underline{3.00} \text{ in.}$$
$$\text{Total} = \overline{22.82} \text{ in.}$$

From Fig. 8–10:

$$\text{Est. ftg. wt.} = 0.0525(400 \text{ kips}) = 21 \text{ kips}$$
$$\text{Corresp. volume} = 21/0.15 = 140 \text{ cu. ft.}$$
$$\text{Trial ftg. width, } B = \sqrt{140/1.92} = 8.52 \text{ ft.}$$

(b) *U-S design net pressure.*

$$\text{Ultimate to soil} = (3 \text{ tsf})(2)(\text{avg. L.F. } 1.65) = 9.90 \text{ ksf}$$
$$\text{Less 23 in. est. ftg. wt.: } (1.92 \text{ ft.})(0.15)(\text{L.F. } 1.5) = \underline{0.43}$$
$$9.47 \text{ ksf}$$

$$\text{Improved width } B = \sqrt{1.65(400)/9.47} = 8.35 \text{ ft.}$$

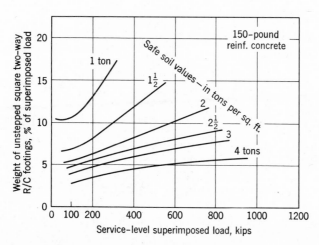

Fig. 8–10. Chart for estimating weights of ACI two-way footings.

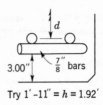

Try $1'-11'' = h = 1.92'$

Fig. 8–11

Make $B = 8$ ft. 4 in.

Use $400(\text{L.F. } 1.65)/(8.33)^2 =$ 9.50 ksf $\overline{\text{USD}}$ net ftg. pressure.

(c) *Footing thickness required for diagonal tension.* Perimetral study at $d/2$ from face of the column. Refer to Sec. 1707(b) and (c): U-S allowed $v_u = V_u/b_o d$, reqd. $d_v = V_u/v_u b_o$ with $v_u \leq 4\phi \sqrt{f'_c}$, and $b_o = 4(d + t)$ in Fig. 8–9. Then $V_u = p_u[B^2 - (d + t)^2]$. So

$$\text{Reqd. } d_v = \frac{p_u[B^2 - (d + t)^2]}{4v_u(d_v + t)} \qquad \text{(quadratic)} \qquad (8\text{--}1)$$

In this case, with $B = 100$ in., $p_u = 9500$ psf, $t = 22$ in., and $v_u = 186$ psi:

$$d_v{}^2 - 23.76 d_v = 774.5 \qquad \text{Reqd. } d_v = 18.38 \text{ in.}$$

(d) *Required alternate diagonal tension study for thickness* (Fig. 8–9). Right section study at d distance, per Sec. 1707(a)(1). From Problem 8–6, the required d became 16.18 in.   So the 18.38 in. of the $d/2$ study governs.

(e) *Thickness required for flexure.* Refer to Sec. 2304(b). From Fig. 8–9, the bending moment at section X-X is:

$$\text{B.M.} = \frac{wL^2}{2} = \frac{(9.5)(100)(39)(39)}{(12)(12)(2)(12)} = 418 \text{ kip-ft.}$$

From $R_u = M_u/\phi b d^2$, and Appendix Chart A–1, the required $d = \sqrt{M_u/R_u \phi b} = \sqrt{418,000/(870)(0.9)(100)} = 8.0$ in. From (c), the diagonal tension demand for an 18.38-in. d rules. From (a), d may henceforth be taken at 18.50 in. or more.

(f) *Required flexural A_s.* With $d = 18.50$ in.,

$$R_u = \frac{M_u}{\phi b d^2} = \frac{418(12,000)}{0.9(100)(18.50)^2} = 162$$

From Appendix Chart A–1, corresp. reqd. $p = 0.0041$, which is larger than the minimum S. & T. steel percentage of 0.002.

A_s reqd. over 8 ft. 4 in. width $= 0.0041(100)(18.5) =$ 7.59 sq. in.

(g) *Choice of bars* involves bond stress at face of column. Since maximum $V_u = 9.5(100/12)(39/12) = 257$ kips,

$$\text{Reqd. } \Sigma o = \frac{V_u}{\phi u_u j d} = \frac{257,000 \text{ lb.}}{0.85(594)(0.97)(18.50)} = 28.4 \text{ in. over 8 ft.4 in. width.}$$
$$\#7$$

Ratio: Reqd. perimeter/reqd. bar area $= 28.4/7.59 = 3.24$. From Table 1–3, #7 bars can be used.

Need $7.59/0.60 =$ 12.7 bars each way.

(h) **Summary.** Make footing **8 ft. 4 in.** square by **1 ft. 11 in.** thick, and distribute **13-#7 A305** deformed bars of **40,000-psi** minimum yield point in each direction. **Use 3-in. bolsters.**

TWO-WAY FOOTING PROBLEMS

8-6. Regarding item (d) of Example 8–3, compute the d required for diagonal tension at the "alternate right section for shear" shown in Fig. 8–9, and as required by ACI Sec. 1707(a)(1), to determine which section will call for the greater depth.

Ans. $d_v = 16.18$ in.

8-7 (Individual). U-S Design of Square Two-Way Column Footings. Given the cases tabulated below and deformed bars. Take 3000-lb. concrete, 50,000-psi-yield-point steel and the ACI Code. Examine Secs. 1707 and 2304 entire.

Allow 3-in. clear dampproofing. Select the thinnest footing meeting all requirements. Utilize Fig. 8–10.

Required to design the footing:

Case	Safe Soil Bearing Value (tsf)	Superimposed Concentric Load[2] (kips)	Square Column Size t (in.)
a	1.50	110	12
b		50	10
c		330	16
d		190	15
e		380	16
f		270	16
g	2.50	210	14
h		490	17
i		90	10
j		330	16
k		560	18
l		610	18
m	2.00	50	10
n		250	16
o		470	16
p		130	12
q		525	18
r		370	16
s	4.00	350	14
t		130	12
u		790	21
v		900	22
w		570	18
x		1060	26
y	3.00	430	16
z		250	14
a′		80	10
b′		610	20
c′		800	22
d′		760	20

[2] Includes a live loading equal to the dead loading.

8–8. COMBINED FOOTINGS

A footing which carries two or more columns is called a *combined footing*. Such an arrangement should be considered whenever the load from a single column cannot be spread uniformly over the footing soil. A common case is that of an exterior building column which abuts the property line. Refer to Figs. 8–1c and 8–12.

When the adjacent interior column has been embraced, the position of the resultant of the two column loads is computed and the combined footing is centered upon it. Usually the exterior column carries the smaller load, so the footing can be rectangular. (Why?) However, if there is any restriction upon the length of the footing, it cannot be made rectangular. (Again, why?)

After the center of the footing has been located, the required area is easily found by dividing the total load by the safe soil value, from which the required rectangular footing width follows.

Figure 8–12 illustrates the concept of combined footings which is directly applicable to the designing to be performed in Example 8–4. By turning the book upside down one sees that the structure consists of a uniformly loaded simple span slab with an overhang. The column forces are distributed across the slab by *transverse beams*, which are shown in phantom because they often do not exist in reality except for the **transverse reinforcement** finally provided. The work consists principally in computing and arranging the *longitudinal reinforcement*, as may be seen from Fig. 8–14.

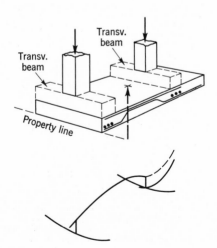

Fig. 8–12. Concept of combined footing forces and deformations.

EXAMPLE 8–4

U-S Design of a Combined Footing

Given an 18-by-18-in. exterior column abutting a property line and carrying 265 kips, and the 22-by-22-in. 530-kip interior column of Example 8–3 centered 15 ft. away, as shown in Fig. 8–13. The above U-S column loads include equal dead and live service-level loads. The footing length is to be 21 ft. 6 in.

Required to U-S design the necessary combined footing for a 1½-ton-per-sq.-ft. safe soil value, taking A305 deformed bars, 3000-lb. concrete, and 40,000-psi-yield-point steel.

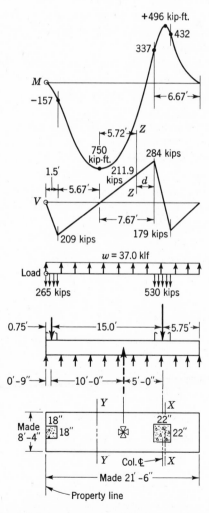

Fig. 8–13. Combined footing U-S loads, shears, and moments.

Follow Sec. 1707(a)(1) on shear, also Sec. 1801(a) and (c)(1) for lowered bond allowables for top bars. Provide 3-in. min. bar cover.

Solution. (See Fig. 8–13 and Art. 8–9.)

(a) *Calculation of USD net footing pressure.*

On soil at (1.5 tsf)(2)(avg. L.F. 1.65) = 4.95 ksf
Less D.L. of est. 2¼-ft. ftg.: 2.25(0.15)(L.F. 1.5) = 0.50
U-S design net pressure = 4.45 ksf

(b) *Footing width and forces from diagonal tension requirements.* Repeated trials[3] for a footing width adequate for *diagonal tension* without using stirrups led to a *b* of 8 ft. 4 in. Then 4.45(8.33) gave the 37-klf loading, from which the *Load*, *V*, and *M* diagrams of Fig. 8–13 followed.

(c) *Flexural steel designing at section Y-Y.* Since #9 bars of 1.13-in. diameter will likely be required, and with 3-in. cover, the actual *d* will be 27 in. minus 3.57 in. = 23.43 in.

Calculating therewith:

$$R_u = \frac{M_u}{\phi b d^2} = \frac{750(12,000)}{0.9(100)(23.43)^2} = 182$$

Corresp. *p* from Chart A–1 = 0.00464
Reqd. $A_s = pbd = 0.00464(100)(23.43) = 10.9$ sq. in. Use 11-#9 in the top.

8–9. COMBINED FOOTING DESIGNING

In Example 8–4, (a) and (b), the net footing pressure and the dimensions of the base of the footing were evolved from trials, and load, shear, and moment diagrams were drawn in Fig. 8–13.

The structural concept. From the very beginning one must visualize the deformed shape of the structure, and the localities where flexural steel will be needed. The solid curved lines of the lower view in Fig. 8–12 show the behavior of typical top and bottom reinforcing bars. Note the two-way action underneath the distant column.

The *required footing width*, *b*, and the effective depth, *d*, were evolved using *b/d* trials in the diagonal tension formula $v = V_u/\phi bd$, and working to get the product *bd* large enough to avoid the necessity for using stirrups.

Flexure reinforcement was designed in item (c) at the principal section *Y-Y*, and proportioned elsewhere by reference to the bending moment diagram, all of which is shown to large scale in Fig. 8–14.

EXAMPLE 8–4 (*Continued*)

(d) **Investigation of shear and diagonal tension.** Refer to Code Secs. 1707 and 1701. At section *Z-Z* at *d* = 23.43 in. = 1.95 ft. from the face of the 22-by-22-in. column,

$$V_u = 284 \text{ kips} - 1.95(37) = 211.9 \text{ kips} \quad (\text{Figs. 8–13 and 8–14})$$

---

[3] The desired diagonal tension unit stress can be approached by trials of varying combinations of *b* and *d*.

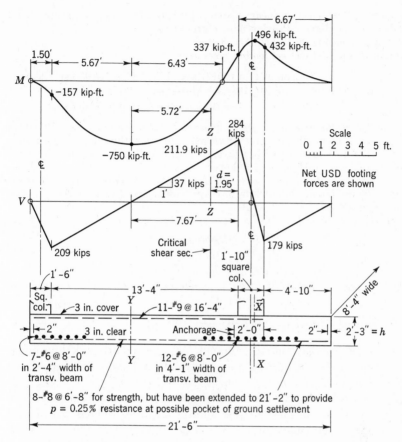

Fig. 8–14. Final design sketch of combined footing.

From Secs. 1707(a)(1) and 1701(a):

$$\text{Nominally } v_u = \frac{V_u}{bd} = \frac{211{,}900}{100(23.43)} = 90.3 \text{ psi}$$

$$< 2\phi \sqrt{f'_c} = 93 \text{ psi}, \qquad \underline{\text{O.K.}}$$

Had v_u turned out greater than 93 psi, as when the width of the footing is less than the above, the Code permits reliance upon a somewhat higher allowable v_c if it is computed by the more precise formula:

Allowed $v_c = \phi[1.9 \sqrt{f'_c} + 2500 p_w(Vd/M)]$ when $M \geq Vd$ [ACI Formula 17–2]

In this case, if $Vd = M$:

$$\text{Allowed } v_c = 0.85[1.9(54.8) + 2500(0.00464)] = 98 \text{ psi}   \text{ [Sec. 1701(d)]}$$

If the actual v_c-value exceeds the allowed v_c of Formula 17–2, provide some stirrups to "cover" the excess *beam shear area* involved, as in Fig. 3–8b and Art. 3–6.

8–10. SHEAR IN COMBINED FOOTINGS

Since combined footings are usually of an elongated shape, and from Fig. 8–14 can hardly be said to be two-way reinforced, the *right section* method of computation of Sec. 1707(a)(1) and 1701 is being followed. It locates the critical section for maximum shear (and diagonal tension) at d distance from the left face of the larger column, where the USD beam shear is shown to be 211.9 kips.

The latter half of the preceding item (d) illustrates how Code Formula 17–2 can permit an increased allowable v_c, except when M at the critical section turns out numerically less than Vd. In the present case, from Fig. 8–14, Vd equals 211.9(1.95) = 414 kip-ft. From the shear diagram areas, M of the formula is *numerically* the 248-kip average, times 1.95 ft., minus 337, or 147 kip-ft., which is roughly ⅓ of Vd, so the whole Vd/M item must be dropped, to prevent a tripling boosting of v_c.

8–11. THE CONTRAFLEXURE LOCALITIES

These have been found to be *hazards* for reinforced concrete. In continuous members, relatively large beam shears often are present. Thereat the shear-related diagonal tensile cracks can "open up" far into the compression portion of a beam because there is little or *no mass of concrete flexural compressive stress* to oppose their advance to the extreme compression fiber. The result can be a fracture failure in the *flexurally* safe locality. Within the past fifteen years a group of very disastrous and expensive failures [4, 5] have been traced largely to such fracturing. The watchword is "Provide additional stirrups, and *extend* any flexure bars being discontinued."

The Vd/M portion of Code Formula 17–2 provides some safeguard, by limiting the increase in allowed v_c when V times d is greater than M.

CONTINUATION PROBLEM

8–8. Undertake a complete redesigning of the footing of Example 8–4 to utilize stirrups in the two or three localities of high beam shear, and so have considerably less *width*, with probably also a different thickness.

For the allowed v_c value, follow Sec. 1701(c) or (d), as dictated by the instructor.

Make a large-scale complete redesign sketch similar to Fig. 8–14.

EXAMPLE 8–4 *(Continued)*

(e) **Bond stress in #9 top bars.** The *anchorage*[4] bond stress, u_{ua}, in the 13 ft.

---

[4] Refer to Figs. 8–14 and 8–15, and Art. 3–3. When part of the anchorage for a bar, or bar end, must be achieved within a locality wherein the concrete is actually or potentially cracked in flexural tension, Code Sec. 1801(c) requires that the permissible average u_u value must be decreased to 0.8 of the formula value; presumably to allow for the impairment of part of the resisting concrete. Such an anchorage, or bond stress, may be said to be *developmental* partly because it is somewhat problematical as to how great a unit bond resistance can safely be relied upon.

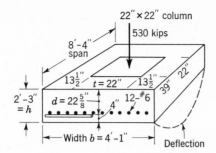

Fig. 8–15.   Transverse "beam."[5]

4 in. span will now be calculated from the "*development length*" [7], a_u, and compared with the permissible bond stress of Code Sec. 1801(b) and (c).   See Fig. 8–14.

From the basic expression for *cantilevers*, $a\Sigma ou = T = A_s f_s / jd$, there is also, for *simple spans*, $u_{ua} = M_u/\phi jd\Sigma oa_u$, wherein a_u is the shorter distance from the section in question to the end of the member.   In the case at hand, due to the reversal of moment at the right end of the span, we will conservatively use only the 6.43 ft. to the contraflexure point.   So:

$$u_{ua} = \frac{750(12,000)}{0.85(0.96)(23.43)(11 \times 3.54)[6.43 \times 12]} = 157 \text{ psi}$$

From ACI Sec. 1801(c) the permissible $u_u = 6.7 \sqrt{3000}/1.13 = 325$ psi, and
$$0.8(325) = 260 \text{ psi}$$

Conclusion: Since $157 < 260$, the Code accepts the member, even though the flexural bond stress (Code Formula 18–1) is greater, 381 psi in this case.

(f) **Flexure steel required in the bottom of the 4 ft. 10 in. cantilever.**   This calculation is the same as that of (c) except that the moment is now 432 kip-ft., and d is now 23.50 in. due to the use of #8 bars.   The reqd. p was 0.00263, and
8-#8 bars were used.

(g) **Required end anchorage, a', of the cantilever steel.**   This is simply a matter of equating the tension, T_u, in a single bar to the sliding resistance between the steel and the surrounding concrete.   Refer to Chapter 3.

$$0.85u_u\Sigma oa' \equiv T_u = 0.9A_s f_y, \qquad \text{so reqd. } a' = 0.9A_s f_y/0.85u_u\Sigma o$$

Since these #8's are bottom bars, the permissible $u_u = 520$ psi.

Reqd. anchorage, $a' = \dfrac{0.9(0.79)(40,000)}{0.85(520)(3.14)} = 20.5$ in.

Conservatively, make 2 ft. 0 in.

(h) **Transverse designing.**   Refer to Fig. 8–12.

---

[5] The effective width b of this member was taken as $t + h$ in Fig. 8–15, i.e., 22 in. + 27 in. = 49 in.

(1) Transverse "beam" flexure under the 530-kip interior column.

$$w = 530/8.33 = 63.6 \text{ klf of 8 ft. 4 in. beam}$$
$$M_u = 63.6(3\%_{12})[3\%_{24}] = 336 \text{ kip-ft.}$$

$$\text{Reqd. } d = \sqrt{\frac{M_u}{R_u \phi b}} = \sqrt{\frac{336(12,000)}{870(0.9)(49)}} = \sqrt{105} = 10.2 \text{ in.}$$

The d used $= 22.63$ in.

$$\text{So } R_u = \frac{M_u}{\phi b d^2} = \frac{336(12,000)}{0.9(49)(22.63)^2} = 178, \text{ corresponding } p = 0.0045. \quad \text{Reqd.}$$

$A_s = 0.0045(49)(22.63) = 5.00 \text{ sq. in.}$ <u>Use 12–#6.</u>

(2) Calculation of both the *flexural* and the *developmental* maximum bond stresses in the "beam" under the 530-kip column. Refer to Code Sec. 1801 entire.

Solution for flexural bond:

$$u_u = \frac{V_{u \text{ max}}}{\phi \Sigma ojd} = \frac{(3.25 \text{ in.})(63.6)(1000)}{0.85(12)(3\!/\!4)(\pi)(0.96)(22.63)}$$
$$= 396 \text{ psi, } < \text{ the permissible } 9.5 \sqrt{f'_c}/D = 694 \text{ psi, so O.K.}$$

Solution for developmental bond [7]:

$$u_{ud} = \frac{M_u}{\phi jd \Sigma oa_u} = \frac{63.6(3\%_{12})(3\%_{24})(12,000)}{0.85(0.96)(22.63)(12)(3\!/\!4)(\pi)(39)} = 198 \text{ psi}$$

Section 1801(c): Since the 198-psi development bond was less than 0.8 of the permissible value of 694 psi, the flexural bond calculation of 396 psi need not have been performed.

(3) **Transverse "beam" under the 265-kip 18-by-18-in. exterior column.** This "beam" was designed in the same manner as the preceding one, except that its $18 + 13\frac{1}{2}$ in. width extends beyond the column on one side only. Refer to lower corner of Fig. 8–14.

Solution:
$$w = 265/8.33 = 31.8 \text{ klf of 8.33-ft. beam}$$
$$M_u = 31.8(4\frac{1}{12})(4\frac{1}{24}) = 186 \text{ kip-ft.}$$
$$R_u = \frac{M_u}{\phi b d^2} = \frac{186(12,000)}{0.9(31.5)(22.63)^2} = 154$$

From Appendix Chart A–1,

$$p = 0.0039$$
Reqd. $A_s = 0.0039(31.5)(22.63) = 2.77$ sq. in.   <u>Use 7–#6 bars.</u>

8–12. GROUND SLOPE AND PEDESTALS

On a building site, the bases of the footings often cannot all be set a uniform distance below the ground surface, as set by northern climates, because to do so would mean that lateral earth pressure from an upper footing might act to dislodge a lower one. Such a situation arose in Fig.

8–16 wherein the footing for Column B had to be set deeply to keep within the 1 on 4 safe slope (tan⁻¹ 0.25) as set by the *angle of repose*[6] of the soil. A column-like member called a **pedestal,** or pier, was used to reach above the ground surface.

Pedestals are used to take up the difference in the elevations of footings over a site and to distribute the column load over an area advantageous for the design of the footing, especially when steel columns are used.

The cross-sectional areas of pedestals are governed by the allowable compressive stress of $0.25f'_c$ [Code Sec. 2307(a), for plain concrete pedestals], or arbitrarily by the size of the column base plate, or by the desirability of distributing the footing load more widely.

If the ratio of height to least lateral dimension exceeds three, the member is technically not a pedestal [Code Sec. 301]. It must be reinforced as a column, such as that for Column A of the figure.

If a pedestal has very little height, such as that for Column C, it is more like a block, and has been called a **block pedestal.** Such a member may be more a footing than a column and should be so computed. The enlarged view at Column C shows the section Z-Z specified for a study of bending in Code Secs. 2307(b) and 2304(b)(3), and the assumed uniform pressures involved. Of course, if the block concrete is placed integrally

[6] As mentioned by Krynine [6], the angle of repose is smaller than the soil mechanics *angle of internal friction, ϕ,* whose tangent varies from about 0.58 to 0.70 for sands in the loose and dense states, respectively. The angle of repose of sand may be taken the same as ϕ for the loose state.

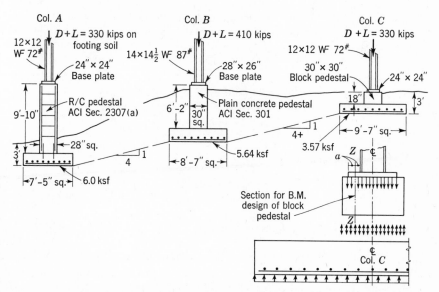

Fig. 8–16. A site plan using three types of pedestals.

with the footing slab, then the block is part of a stepped footing and should be so computed.

8–13. PILE AND MAT FOOTINGS

These types of footings are needed when the soil bearing values are poor to very poor. Their design is beyond the present scope of this text, but will be found in a number of standard works on reinforced concrete design, including *Substructure Analysis and Design*, by Paul Andersen (2d ed.; New York: The Ronald Press Company, 1956).

8–14. SUMMARY OF FOOTING DESIGN

Structurally, footings are inverted double-cantilever beams loaded with the distributed upward pressure of the ground, less the dead load pressure of the footing itself.

Because a footing is placed in a plastic condition, it is unstressed under its own dead load.

The common assumption that the ground pressure is uniformly distributed is a safe one for footing design except for unusual cases wherein the pressure may be greatest toward the edges of the footing. Normally, the deformation of the footing and the ground tends to decrease the pressure in the outer portions.

The outside dimensions of footings are dictated by the allowable bearing pressure upon the ground and the necessity for having enough depth, or thickness, safely to resist bending, and the diagonal tension resulting from shear.

To design a concentric reinforced concrete footing (a) use the safe soil value to get the required area, (b) calculate the thickness, d_v, required to resist diagonal tension safely, (c) compute the thickness, d, required for flexure, and (d) choose the bar size to suit the bond requirement.

Eccentric footings should be designed to deliver a uniformly distributed

---

Plate 8–2. Lift slab construction. Typically, a ground floor slab is placed which becomes the casting bed for the successive upper floors; these are separated by a membrane to prevent adhesion. Hydraulic jacks on the top of each column are connected to threaded vertical rods at the faces of the columns. They engage the cast-in lifting collars of the upper slab, or slabs, of the *flat-plate*-designed slabs surrounding the columns. Finally, each slab is slowly lifted into place, and the collars are welded to the columns. The concrete of about 90 per cent of such projects is being precompressed by post-tensioning the steel. This prevents tensile cracking of the concrete, and controls deflections. (Refer to Art. 14–24.) (Courtesy of Lift Slab Company of Ohio)

pressure to the soil whenever possible by offsetting the footing with respect to the column or wall.

The soil pressure under eccentrically loaded footings may be *investigated* by employing the $N/A + Mc/I$ column expression, using the whole width of the footing as the *depth* in the expression for moment of inertia. If uplift develops on one side, the method must be abandoned.

In designing eccentric footings, first draw the position of the resultant vertical force, then build the footing around it.

The use of the $d/2$ truncated pyramid for footing shear calculations presupposes two-way reinforcement.

Bond stresses in footings are kept low by using the smaller bars, which have much greater perimeter per square inch of cross-sectional area. But unfortunately, each *size* of bar now has a different allowable bond *unit* stress.

Plain concrete footings serve well when loads are light and ground conditions excellent, but for the reverse conditions they must be very thick, requiring too much concrete and sometimes an excessive amount of excavation.

The vertical (punching) shear method of reinforced concrete footing design has long since been abandoned in favor of the recognition of a limiting frustum observed in Talbot's tests and others. On the other hand, *bending* and *bond* stresses must be calculated at, or near, the face of the column or pedestal.

Combined footings supporting two or more columns are often necessary at property lines in order to maintain a uniform soil pressure in cases where there is no room for the spread of a single footing.

CONTINUATION PROBLEMS

8-9. Redesign the square two-way footing of Example 8–3 or Problem 8–7 (as assigned by the instructor) to be of rectangular shape, two and one-half times as long as wide. Refer to ACI Sec. 2304(g).

8-10. Proportion the base dimensions of the footing of Fig. 8–13, Example 8–4, if the 22-in. column and its load abuts the property line and the 18-in. column is the interior one.

8-11. Redesign an assigned square two-way footing of Problem 8–7 if the resultant superimposed column load is made eccentric an amount $t/2$, the half-dimension of the column.

What new situations arose, and how were they met?

B. Working Stress Method

The remainder of the chapter is a supplementary discussion, with examples, of the calculation of footings by the working stress method. Therefore, it is suggested that the reader postpone studying this until he has finished Chapters 9 and 10.

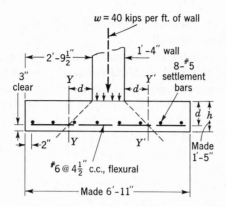

Fig 8–17. W-S designing a wall footing.

EXAMPLE 8–5

W-S Redesign of a Reinforced Concrete Wall Footing

Given the same service wall load, safe soil value, and class of concrete as in Example 8–1, namely, $w = 40$ kips per ft., a safe soil bearing value of 3 tons per sq. ft., ACI 3000-lb. concrete and specification: 20,000–1350–9, $v = 60$ at section Y-Y below, and $u = 350$ psi for #6 deformed bars in one-way footings. Secure 3-in. cover for the bars. (Check the above stress values with the Code, using its "Index.")

It is required to design the footing by the W-S method, taking a 1-ft. length of wall.

Solution. (Refer to Fig. 8–17.)

(a) *Footing width.* Estimating the footing weight at a conservative 4% of the superimposed load:

$$\text{Reqd. width } B = 40(1.04)/6 = 6.92 \text{ ft.}$$

Take a trial width of 6 ft. 11 in.

(b) *Diagonal tension.* Referring to Talbot's tests [1] and Code Table 1002(a) and Sec. 1201, design at section Y-Y:

$$\text{Tentative net footing pressure} = 40/6.92 = 5.78 \text{ ksf}$$

$$\text{Reqd. } d = \frac{V}{vb} = \frac{5780(33.5 - d)}{12(60)(12)} = \underline{13.42 \text{ in.}}$$

Trying #6 bars:

$$h = 13.42 + 0.38 + 3.00 = 16.80 \text{ in.}$$

See Code Sec. 808(a).   Try 1 ft. 5 in. total thickness.

(c) *Flexure designing.*
$$(\tfrac{1}{2})f_c b(kd)[jd] = \text{B.M.}$$
$$675(12)(0.378)(0.874)d^2 = 5780(33.5/12)(16.75) = 270,000 \text{ lb.-in.}$$
$$= 22.5 \text{ kip-ft.}$$

Reqd. flexural $d = 10.05$ in., < 13.42 in. demanded by diagonal tension

Therefore, diagonal tension governs the thickness.

Make thickness 1 ft. 5 in.

Assuming #6 bars, actual $d = 17.0 - 3.38 = 13.62$ in.

(a') *Width recalculation.* A 1 ft. 5 in. thickness makes a dead load of 0.21 ksf. Since

$$B = \frac{40 + 0.21B}{6}$$

therefore, Reqd. $B = 6.91$ ft.

Make width 6 ft. 11 in., as earlier tried.

Net footing pressure stands at 5.78 ksf.

(c') *Flexure steel.* M stands at 270,000 lb.-in. from (a).

$$R = \frac{M}{bd^2} = \frac{270,000}{12(13.62)^2} = 121$$

Refer to Appendix Chart L-2: Find $p = 0.68\%$.

Reqd. $A_s = pbd = 0.0068(12)(13.62) = 1.11$ sq. in. per ft. of wall

(d) *Perimeter required for bond.* From ACI Sec. 1301(c)(1),

Allowed $u = 4.8 \sqrt{3000}/0.75 = 350$, limit 500 psi

$$\text{Reqd. } \Sigma o = \frac{V}{ujd} = \frac{5780(33.5/12)}{350(\tfrac{7}{8})(13.62)} = 3.86 \text{ in. per ft. of wall}$$

For proper bar size refer to Chapter 1, Table 1-3:

Perimeter reqd. per sq. in. of area $= 3.86/1.11 = 3.48$ in.

Found all bars #3 through #9 acceptable. Use #6 bars.

$$\text{Bar spacing} = \frac{0.44(12)}{1.11} = 4.75 \text{ in.}$$

Use #6 deformed bars at $4\tfrac{1}{2}$ in. c. to c.

By Code Sec. 804(a):

Max. aggregate size $= (4.50 - 0.75)/1.33 = 2.82$ in.

Say use $1\tfrac{1}{2}$ in. aggregate.

Compare this W-S design with the corresponding U-S design (Fig. 8–3) of Example 8–1, with respect to material required.

EXAMPLE 8–6

W-S Investigation of the Wall Footing Designed in Example 8–5 for a 22.5-kip-ft. B.M. of Item (c) Thereof

Solution. Refer to the $n = 9$ WSD Beam Chart L–2 of Appendix L. Taking a 1-ft. length of wall:

$$R = \frac{M}{bd^2} = \frac{22.5(12,000)}{12(13.62)^2} = 121$$

$$\text{Corresp. } p = \frac{A_s}{bd} = \frac{0.44(12/4.5)}{12(13.62)} = 0.717\%$$

Find answer:

$$f_c = 893 \text{ psi}, f_s = 18,600 \text{ psi}, <1350 \text{ and } 20,000 \text{ allowed, O.K.}$$

8–15. NONUNIFORM SOIL BEARING (W-S)

Frequently, in designing, there is more than one loading situation to be considered, in which case the footing design becomes a compromise resulting from *designing* for one situation and *investigating* it for other loading conditions. These latter situations generally cause nonuniform pressures upon the soil which must be evaluated and mitigated as much as possible. In all such cases the maximum pressure should be kept well below the uniformly loaded allowable soil pressure. Example 8–7 illustrates the two most common cases of base investigation.

EXAMPLE 8–7

W-S Investigations of Soil Pressures Under an Eccentrically Loaded Footing

Given the 7-ft. wall footing pictured in Fig. 8–18.
Required to find the maximum soil pressure if the *superimposed* loading is:

(A) Wall load 20 kips, wall moment 35 kip-ft. clockwise.

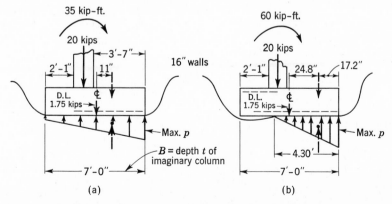

Fig. 8–18. W-S soil pressure investigations.

(B) Wall load 20 kips, wall moment 60 kip-ft. clockwise.

Solution (A) (Fig. 8–18a). ΣM about the centerline of the footing, at the ground level, to find the position of the resultant force:

$$
\begin{array}{rl}
1.75 \times & 0 = \quad\ \ 0 \\
20.00 \times (-9) = & -180 \\
12(35) = & +420 \\
\hline
21.75 \text{ kips} & 240 \text{ kip-in.}
\end{array}
$$

$$\frac{240}{21.75} = 11 \text{ in. from the center}$$

$$< {}^{84}\!/_6 \text{ or } 14 \text{ in.,} \qquad \text{therefore no uplift.}$$

As for columns:

$$\frac{w}{A} = \frac{21.75}{7} \qquad\qquad = 3.11$$

$$I = \frac{bt^3}{12} = \frac{(1)(7)^3}{12} = 28.6 \text{ ft.}^4$$

$$\frac{Mc}{I} = \frac{20(3.5)}{28.6} \qquad\qquad = 2.45$$

$$\text{Max. } p = 5.56 \text{ ksf} = 2.78 \text{ tsf.}$$

Method.

1. Working at the ground level, locate the position of the resultant downward vertical force with reference to the kern limit (i.e., the middle third) of the footing width. If it falls within the kern, proceed as follows:

   a. Find the direct pressure by dividing the total vertical load by the area of the footing.
   b. Find the pressure distribution due to the moment of all the applied forces about the center of gravity of the base, using Mc/I as in columns, taking the width of the footing, B, as t, the depth of the imaginary column.
   c. Add the (a) and (b) results to get the combined soil pressure.

2. *If the resultant vertical force lies outside the kern limit of the footing*, there will be uplift. The combined soil pressure diagram will then be triangular, with its centroid directly beneath the resultant vertical force.

Solution (B). ΣM about the centerline of the footing to find the position of the resultant force:

$$
\begin{array}{rl}
1.75 \times & 0 = \quad\ \ 0 \\
20.00 \times (-9) = & -180 \\
12(60) = & +720 \\
\hline
21.75 \text{ kips} & 540 \text{ kip-in.}
\end{array}
$$

$$\frac{540}{21.75} = 24.8 \text{ in. from center}$$

$$24.8 > {}^{84}\!/_6, \text{ therefore, there is uplift along the left side.}$$

Referring to Fig. 8–18b, the resultant ground reaction must be 17.2 in. from the right side.

Assuming the customary straight-line variation of pressure, and knowing that the centroid of a triangle is at one-third the distance from its base, the pressure must vary from a maximum to zero at $(3)(17.2)/(12) = 4.30$ ft. from the right side.

$$\text{Max. } p = \frac{21.75}{0.5(4.30)} = 10.1 \text{ ksf} = \qquad \underline{5.05 \text{ tsf}} \quad \underline{\text{Ans.}}$$

8–16. DESIGN OF PLAIN CONCRETE FOOTINGS

Figure 8–16 illustrates at the extreme right a shallow *block pedestal* which serves as a plain concrete footing. They tend to be roughly three times as thick as the corresponding *reinforced* one, and often require a great deal more excavation, but serve well when steel is scarce.

In Sec. 2307 of the Code, the allowable stresses for compression, plain concrete bending and average shear stress are given.

Also, it is well to call for at least two additional inches of thickness to allow for ground and drainage irregularities.

QUESTIONS

1. Define the terms *superstructure, pedestal, footing,* and *foundation.*
2. Classify footing types and state the field of each.
3. Discuss the physical properties of four common earth materials, especially their action under load. Assign safe bearing values to each.
4. Discuss the four essential items of procedure in designing a reinforced concrete footing.
5. Is there one correct size of reinforcing bar for every footing, or several? Explain.
6. In designing an eccentric footing for direct load and bending moment, what force relationship should be computed at the outset?
7. What is meant by *moment of inertia of a footing?* How is it used, and why?
8. If a column or wall has bending therein, must the footing necessarily bear non-uniformly upon the ground? Explain.
9. Tell how to investigate the pressure variation under an eccentrically loaded footing.
10. It has been asserted that if plain bars were used in footings, instead of deformed ones, "there would have to be more of them, which increases the steel tonnage." Explain thoroughly.
11. Demonstrate a general method for finding the correct size and shape of combined footings. In which cases are trapezoidal shapes needed?

REFERENCES

1. TALBOT, ARTHUR N. "Reinforced Concrete Wall Footings and Column Footings," *Bulletin No. 67,* University of Illinois Engineering Experiment Station, 1913.
2. RICHART, FRANK E. "Reinforced Concrete Wall and Column Footings," Parts I and II, *Proc. ACI,* 1949, Vol. 45, pp. 97 and 237.
3. "Shear and Diagonal Tension" (Report of Joint ASCE-ACI Committee 326), *Proc. ACI,* 1962, Vol. 59 (January, "General Principles"; February, "Beams and Frames"; March, "Slabs and Footings").
4. ANDERSON, BOYD G. "Rigid Frame Failures," *Proc. ACI,* 1957, Vol. 53, p. 625.
5. ELSTNER, R. C., and HOGNESTAD, EIVIND. "Laboratory Investigation of Rigid Frame Failure," *Proc. ACI,* 1957, Vol. 53, p. 637.
6. KRYNINE, DIMITRI P. *Soil Mechanics* (2d ed.). New York: McGraw-Hill Book Co., Inc., 1947, p. 307.
7. FERGUSON, PHIL M., and THOMPSON, J. NEILS. "Development Length of High Strength Reinforcing Bars in Bond," *Proc. ACI,* 1962, Vol. 59, p. 887.

Part **II**

Working
Stress
Designing

BENDING OF BEAMS

9-1. INTRODUCTION

This chapter presents, in somewhat condensed form, the alternate method of designing beams for bending.

As indicated in Chapters 1 and 2, concrete in compression performs substantially elastically up through the service load range to about halfway to failure. Thus in the *working stress method*[1] of design (WSD), concrete and steel stresses are considered to vary linearly with the strain, as revealed in the test data in Fig. 1-3.

9-2. REINFORCED CONCRETE BEAMS

When steel is embedded in concrete in a manner which assists it in carrying imposed loads, the combination is known as *reinforced concrete.* Since the tensile strength of concrete is far less than the compressive, hairline tensile cracking tends to occur around the design service load level. *Reinforced concrete designing consists principally in predicting the position and direction of **potential tension cracks** in concrete, and in forestalling the cracking by locating sufficient steel across them.*

In the *transformed section method* of calculation used throughout this chapter, the flexure steel is conceived to be replaced by a larger area of imaginary concrete which can take tension. This creates a homogeneous **transformed section** of concrete to which ordinary beam mechanics may be applied.

The basis for the transformation is an elastic one, maintaining the original bending strain, and recognizing that concrete is several times as soft as steel. Taking E_c as the modulus of elasticity, suppose $E_c =$

---

[1] A review of the calculation of the working stress in a (*homogeneous*) timber beam will be found in the first few pages of Chapter 2.

3,000,000, and $E_s = 30,000,000$ psi. A 1-in. cube of steel will deform axially 0.001 in. under a load of 30,000 lb., but if we substitute concrete for steel there will have to be $E_s/E_c = 10$ one-inch cubes, each carrying 3000 lb., if we are to have the same 0.001 in. deformation or strain.

In WSD, the ratio of the moduli of elasticity, E_s/E_c, equals n. It is much used to define the concrete areas being relied upon for strength, and to compute f_s/f_c at certain points.

EXAMPLE 9–1

Figure 9–1a shows the cross section of a reinforced concrete beam. It carries a bending moment of 50.4 kip-ft. What are the maximum unit stresses in steel and concrete? Take 3000-lb. concrete, $E_c = 3,150,000$ psi, $E_s = 29,000,000$ psi, use $n = 9$. Refer to Code Secs. 1002 and 1102.

Solution. Draw the transformed section, (b), by first discarding all tensile concrete (considered of no value in bending). Next, conceive the steel[2] to be replaced by an elastically equivalent area of ideal concrete which can take tension, equal to $E_s/E_c = n$ times the steel area. From mechanics, **the neutral axis for bending will be at the centroid of this equivalent homogeneous section.**

To find the neutral axis, *take the sum of the moments, ΣM, of the transformed areas,* **about the unknown neutral axis,** distant kd inches from the top of the beam:

$$8(kd)\,\frac{kd}{2} = 9(2)(17 - kd)$$

$$(kd)^2 + 4.5(kd) = 76.5$$

Solving the above quadratic equation, one gets $kd = 6.78$ in., and $kd/3 = 2.26$ in. Then the lever arm of the internal couple is $jd = d - kd/3 = 14.74$ in. Now, $T = C = M/jd = 50.4(12,000)/14.74 = 41,000$ lb.
Also, C is the volume of the wedge of compressive stress:

$$C = b(kd)(f_c/2) = 8(6.78)(f_c/2) = 41,000 \text{ lb.}$$

So $f_c = 41,000/27.1 =$ \hfill 1,510 psi.

And $f_s = T/A_s = 41,000/2.00 =$ \hfill 20,500 psi. \quad **Ans.**

[2] Refer to Table 1–3 for bar sizes and areas.

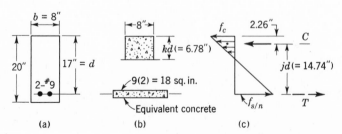

Fig. 9–1. Beam investigation by the transformed section method.

EXAMPLE 9–2

What is the maximum bending moment that the beam of Example 9–1 can carry if the allowable unit stresses in steel and concrete are 20,000 and 1350 psi, respectively? $E_s/E_c = 9$, as before.

Solution. Since the cross section of the beam is unchanged, jd, the arm of the internal couple, will be 14.74 in., as before.

Determine which side of the beam is the weaker, by calculating:

Max. safe $T = (2)(20,000) = 40,000$ lb.
Max. safe $C = (^{1350}\!/_{2})(6.78)(8) = 36,600$ lb.

Therefore the strength of this beam is limited by the concrete. The safe internal **resisting moment** of the section $= 36,600(14.74)/12,000 =$

$$45.0 \text{ kip-ft.} \quad \underline{\text{Ans.}}$$

which equals the maximum safe bending moment.

9–3. STUDENT PROBLEM WORK

This textbook is based upon the idea that one learns principally from personal attempts made after having watched another's performance. The **Examples** are followed by lists of **Problems,** the solution of which will develop the thorough understanding of the subject which comes with practice.

The importance of being systematic about such calculations is very great. Poorly arranged, slovenly, and unclear figures lead to arithmetical errors which obscure the learning process. A well-organized sheet, similar to Fig. 2–7, is familiar to students of engineering problems courses and should be emulated by all. In engineering offices, lasting first impressions often are formed after noting the degree to which the novice organizes his first calculations.

PRACTICE PROBLEMS

Always take the weight of reinforced[3] concrete at 150 lb. per cubic ft.

9–1. A timber beam, of the built-up section shown in Fig. 9–2, has a simple span of 14 ft. It carries a uniform dead plus live load of 0.8 kip per lin. ft., and a concentrated load of 4 kips at 4 ft. from the right end.

[3] For dense natural stone *reinforced* concrete members. Refer to Art. 1–10.

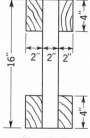

Fig. 9–2

(a) Find the maximum bending unit stress, using the internal couple idea. Recognize the variation in beam width.

(b) Check (a) by the $s = Mc/I$ formula.

(c) Evaluate C, the total compressive force.

✶

9–2. (a) A rectangular reinforced concrete beam is 10 in. wide by 22 in. deep to the center of its two #11 bars. The total bending moment to be carried is 90 kip-ft. $E_s/E_c = n = 10$. Find the unit stresses f_s and f_c.

Ans.   N.A. at 9.00 in., $f_s = 18,200$, $f_c = 1260$ psi.

(b) How much bending moment can the beam carry safely if the allowable steel and concrete stresses are 20,000 and 1000 psi, respectively?

(c) Suppose the allowable stresses are 16,000 and 1050 psi. Find the maximum safe bending moment.

✶

9–3. A cantilever rectangular beam 8 ft. long carries a concentrated load of 19 kips at its outer end. It is 14 in. wide by 30 in. total depth, and has four #9 bars centered 3 in. from the top. Report upon its safety, taking the Code specification 20,000–1125–10 (f_s, f_c, and n), from Table 1002(a) thereof.

9–4. INVESTIGATION VERSUS DESIGN

All reinforced concrete beam problems are of two types, namely, *investigational*, or *designing* problems. It is very important that the student early learn to distinguish between them, since the methods of attack are quite different in the two cases.

Investigation problems. These problems call for a strength *investigation*, or analysis, of an existing (or proposed) beam, all the dimensions of the concrete and steel being given, together with the class of the concrete.

Required:

A. With the applied bending moment given, to find the unit stresses, or

B. With the allowable unit stresses given, to find the maximum safe bending moment, or load that the beam can carry.

Design problems. *Designing is deciding upon dimensions.* In these problems the applied bending moment, the allowable stresses, and the class of the concrete are given.

Required:

To find all or some of the dimensions of the beam cross section, including that of the steel reinforcement.

There are several cases of these problems, the most important of which follow.

In attacking any beam problem, first determine whether it is a *design* or an *investigation*, since in the two types of problems the neutral axis is located by entirely different methods. Its correct position is of critical importance in the succeeding work. The preceding Examples 9–1 and

9–2, and Problems 9–2 and 9–3 are *investigations*. The following examples are *design* problems.   Notice how the neutral axis is found, and that
there are always some dimensions to be decided upon.

EXAMPLE 9–3

Balanced[4] Beam Design

Given a total bending moment of 50.4 kip-ft. and the specification 20,000–
1350–9.

It is required to design a beam to suit. (Note that the cross section taken in
the preceding examples was not strong enough.)   Refer to ACI Table 1002(a).

Solution.   The work consists of (1) predetermining a neutral axis location such
that both steel and concrete will work economically at their allowable stresses
(balanced); and (2) providing adequate steel and concrete areas consistent
therewith:

Considering the similar right triangles of Fig. 9–3 cornering at q and r:

$$\frac{kd}{d} = \frac{1350}{1350 + 2222}, \quad kd = 0.378d, \quad jd = 0.874d$$

Next, take the very useful fundamental expression: $Cjd = M$.

$$(^{135}\!\%_{2})(b)(0.378d)[0.874d] = 50.4(12,000)$$
$$bd^2 = 2710$$

Obviously there are many combinations of b and d that will yield a correct
design.   To make a convenient comparison with other examples, suppose we
choose $b = 8$ in., corresponding $d = 18.40$ in.

b	d	$C = T$	A_s
8 in.	18.40 in.	37,600 lb.	1.88 sq. in.
( )	( )	( )	( )

To get the correct steel area, A_s, substitute back, evaluating C:

$$C = 675(8)(0.378)(18.40) = 37,600 \text{ lb.}$$

---

[4] *Stress*-balanced, as distinguished from the *strain*-balanced approach of USD
Chapter 2.

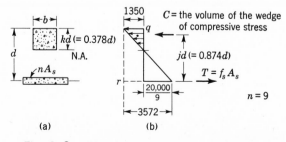

Fig. 9–3.   The design of a balanced beam.

or, evaluating T for a check:

$$T = M/jd = \frac{50.4(12,000)}{0.874(18.40)} = 37,600 \text{ lb.}$$

$$\text{Reqd. } A_s = (37,600/20,000) = 1.88 \text{ sq. in.}$$

EXAMPLE 9–4

The Beam Made Arbitrarily Deeper

Suppose that architectural considerations dictate that d of Example 9–3 be made 20 in., with b still 8 in.

How much steel will be required?

Solution. First consider in a *qualitative* manner what change takes place in the internal couple if the beam in Figs. 9–3 and 9–4a is replaced by a deeper one, as at (b). The greater depth means a longer arm, called $jd+$, but since the bending moment is unchanged, the internal forces become $C-$ and $T-$, both less than in the balanced beam. We can still work the steel to 20,000 psi by using less of it. However, the beam is now an unbalanced one, since bd^2 no longer equals 2710 as in the preceding (balanced design) Example 9–3. Therefore the concrete must be the material which is stressed to less than its 1350 psi allowable, the steel being at 20,000 psi. Knowing this, it is possible to write $Cjd = M$, utilizing the known steel stress at its allowable value, similar stress triangles, and the volume of the wedge of compressive stress, all in terms of the unknown kd. (The student should be prepared to do this.) Unfortunately, the equation proves to be a cubic, and is not readily solved by all.

Ans. $kd = 7.06$ in., $jd = 17.65$ in., $f_c = 1210$ psi, $A_s = 1.72$ sq. in.

Approximate method (use). Noting that the value of kd just found differs little from the 6.96 in. one of the ideal *balanced beam*, the following statement will be found helpful:

The neutral axis distance, kd, is not appreciably affected by small percentage-wise changes in depth, d, accompanied by corresponding inverse changes in steel area, A_s.

This is tantamount to saying that the levels of C and $C-$ are about the same, and suggests that we may get the steel area from the 1.88 sq. in. balanced beam

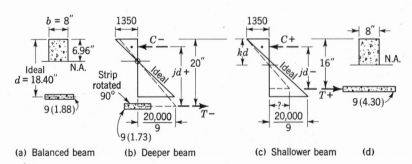

(a) Balanced beam   (b) Deeper beam   (c) Shallower beam   (d)

Fig. 9–4. The geometry of unbalanced design.

steel area by taking a proportion upon the arms of the couples.   Instead, designers conveniently use the ratio of the beam depths:

$$\text{Reqd. } A_s = \frac{18.40}{20.0} (1.88) = 1.73 \text{ sq. in.}$$

Query.   Why are such beams said to be "under-reinforced"?

EXAMPLE 9–5

The Beam Made Arbitrarily Shallower

What steel area will be required if d is made 16 in., with b still 8 in.?   B.M. = 50.4 kip-ft.   Specification: 20,000–1350–9.

Solution.   The situation is shown qualitatively by Fig. 9–4c and d which has been drawn with the top of the beam in projection with that of the *balanced beam* at (a).   In this case the lesser depth means a shorter arm, $jd-$, and a correspondingly greater internal compressive force, $C+$.   Therefore the concrete area resisting the compression must be increased somehow, in order to keep f_c down to 1350 psi.   Referring to the indented statement in the preceding example, one sees that the necessary increase in kd, cannot be obtained by using more steel in inverse proportion to the depths.   A much greater amount of steel will be needed to pull the neutral axis down.   Again writing $Cjd = M$:

$$\frac{1350}{2} (8)(kd) \left[16 - \frac{kd}{3} \right] = 50.4(12,000)$$

$$kd = 8.51 \text{ in., } jd = 13.16 \text{ in., } C = T = 46,000 \text{ lb.}$$

From the figure, by similar triangles **this steel does not work at the allowable stress** but at:

$$\frac{16.0 - 8.51}{8.51} (1350)(9) = 10,690 \text{ psi}$$

$$\text{Reqd. } A_s = T/f_s = 46,000/10,690 = 4.30 \text{ sq. in.}   \text{ Ans.}$$

Check.   By ΣM of transformed areas about the neutral axis:

$$A_s(9)[7.49] = 8(8.51)[4.26]   \qquad A_s = 4.30 \text{ sq. in.}   \text{ Ans.}$$

Such beams are elastically over-reinforced, uneconomical of steel, and to be avoided.   When the available depth is less than about 90 per cent of the ideal depth, steel should be provided in both the upper and lower portions of beams, as in the following Example 9–6.   Such beams are said to be *doubly reinforced.*

BEAM DESIGN PROBLEMS

Unless otherwise noted, take 2500-lb. concrete, ACI Sec. 1002(a) Specification 20,000–1125–10.

9–4. (a) Find the theoretical d and A_s for a singly reinforced beam 14 in. wide. The total bending moment is 300 kip-ft.

$$\text{Ans.}   d = 37.92 \text{ in., } A_s = 5.43 \text{ sq. in.}$$

(b) Find b and A_s for a singly reinforced beam 30 in. deep to center of steel.   The total B.M. is 240 kip-ft.

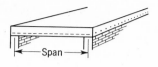

Fig. 9–5

9–5. (a) Find the theoretical A_s for Problem 9–4(a) if d is arbitrarily made 40 in.

Ans. $A_s = 5.11$ sq. in.

(b) Find the theoretical A_s for Problem 9–4(a) if d is arbitrarily made 33 in.

Ans. N.A. $= 16.70$ in., $A_s = 12.0$ sq. in.

9–6. Calculate the required steel area for a singly reinforced beam 20 in. wide by 50 in. deep to center of steel, to resist a total bending moment of 900 kip-ft.

HINT. Make a preliminary study to find whether the given space is larger or smaller than it should be.

9–7. The total bending moment is 60 kip-ft. Compute b and d for a singly reinforced beam to use 2–#9 bars from stock.

9–8. Formulate a rule governing the use of the allowable stresses to find the neutral axis in design problems.

9–9 (Individual). It is desired to completely design a reinforced concrete slab for the loading platform shown in Fig. 9–5. Assume a 1-ft. strip of slab for study, estimate the dead load at 150 lb. per cu. ft., and adjust as found necessary.

Method. Do not initially assume a value of d. Let it work out algebraically.

Design total slab thickness to *nearest* half-inch and use only standard reinforcing bars, all one size, spaced from 3 to 6 in. center to center, by half-inches. Provide exactly 1 in. of fireproofing concrete. As always, make a final design sketch (Art. 9–6).

Use the thinnest slab consistent with the above instructions.

Cases	f'_c	Specification	Live Load in psf	Span in ft.
Series A		18,000–1000–8	300	10
29 assignable		[5] 18,000–1200–10	250	11
combinations		18,000–1000–10		12
				13
				14
Series B		ACI Specs.		
30 combinations	2500	20,000–1125–10	300	10
	4000	20,000–1800–8	250	11
	3000	20,000–1350–9		12
				13
				14

[5] For this specification, load, and span, the answer is: Make slab 6 in. thick, and use #5 bars spaced $3\frac{1}{2}$ in. c. to c.

EXAMPLE 9–6

The Design of Double Reinforcement

Given a bending moment of 50.4 kip-ft., a specification of 20,000–1350–9, and a space $b = 8$ in., by $d = 16$ in.

Calculate double reinforcement, the upper steel to be centered $2\frac{1}{2}$ in. from the top, as in Fig. 9–6.

Method. Determine to have the neutral axis in the *balanced beam* location, and provide both bottom and top reinforcement consistent therewith.

Solution. (1) First find how much of the given bending moment can be resisted by designing *balanced single reinforcement* for the section:

$$\frac{kd}{16} = \frac{1350}{3572}, \quad kd = 6.05 \text{ in.}, \quad jd = 13.98 \text{ in.}$$

$$\text{Balanced } C_1 = T_1 = 675(8)(6.05) = 32{,}660 \text{ lb.}$$

$$A_{s_1} = \frac{32{,}680}{20{,}000} = 1.63 \text{ sq. in.}$$

$$\text{Corresponding safe B.M.} = \frac{32{,}660(13.98)}{12{,}000} = 38.1 \text{ kip-ft.} = M_1$$

(2) Allocate the remaining moment, M_2, to a supplementary steel couple, $T_2(d - d')$, and calculate the additional tensile steel needed:

$$M_2 = 50.4 - 38.1 = 12.3 \text{ kip-ft.}$$

$$\text{Reqd. } A_{s_2} = \frac{M_2}{f_s(d - d')} = \frac{12.3(12{,}000)}{20{,}000(13.5)} = 0.55 \text{ sq. in.}$$

$$\text{From Step 1, } A_{s_1} = \underline{1.63}$$

$$\text{Reqd. } A_s, \text{ total bottom steel area} = \underline{2.18} \text{ sq. in.}$$

(3) Calculate the compression steel area by taking moments of the steel couple transformed areas[6] about the neutral axis:

$$(9 - 1)(A'_s)[6.05 - 2.5] \equiv 9(0.55)[9.95]$$

Top steel, $\text{Reqd. } \underline{A'_s = 1.73 \text{ sq. in.}}$

---

[6] The multiplier $n - 1$, equal to 8 in this case, is used on the compression side of beams to allow for the area of compression concrete displaced by the steel.

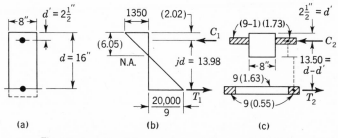

Fig. 9–6. Doubly reinforced beam designing.

Query. In what other manner can the upper steel area be obtained? It should check perfectly.

BEAM DESIGN PROBLEMS

9–10. Calculate the required areas of double reinforcement for a beam 14 in. wide by 2 ft. 6 in. total depth, if the DL + LL bending moment is 250 kip-ft. Conveniently assume that all steel can be centered $2\frac{1}{2}$ in. from the top or bottom surfaces. Specification: 20,000–1125–12.   Ans.   Bottom steel = 6.21, top steel = 3.85 sq. in.

9–11 (Individual). Design double reinforcement for the case assigned. Specification: 20,000–1200–10. Fireproof the steel 2 in. all around. Observe a minimum clear horizontal spacing of one bar diameter but not less than one and one-third times the 1-in. aggregate maximum size. Use two layers in the bottom, all one size, spaced at one inch clear, vertically. Use one layer in the top, all one size, not necessarily the same as the bottom bar size.

Investigate your design, working from your final design sketch, after studying Example 9–7. The maximum safe bending moment of an economical design should not be over 3% greater than the design bending moment. Show results clearly and completely.

Student's Name	Case	Width b, in.	Total Depth h, in.	B.M. (DL + LL), kip-ft.
	a	12	38	297
	b	15	40	414
	c	14	34	287
	d	14	38	344
	e	14	33	266
	f	16	43	530
	g	19	40	550
	h	18	34	368
	i	13	43	430
	j	16	47	613
	k	17	58	977
	l	20	37	476
	m	14	49	560
	n	14	36	330
	o	18	41	555
	p	21	46	805
	q	16	45	571
	r	18	38	461
	s	21	44	770
	t	14	35	308
	u	20	36	450
	v	15	38	370
	w	18	32	330
	x	22	46	870
	y	20	40	575
	z	15	36	340

9–5. PRACTICAL DESIGN CONSIDERATIONS

The designer's choice of steel must be limited to the upper ten concrete reinforcing bar sizes shown in Table 1–3, unless otherwise directed.

Code Secs. 804(a) and (b), and 808(b) govern the spacing and covering of bars. *Horizontally*, the minimum clear distance is the nominal diameter of the bar, but must never be less than 1 in., nor less than one and one-third times the maximum size of the coarse aggregate. The outer surface of all beam steel must be covered with a minimum of $1\frac{1}{2}$ in. of concrete all around to serve as fireproofing (f'p'f'g).

It is customary to round off the beam width, b, and the total depth, h, to a whole number of inches. The standardized heights of the reinforcing bar supports, called *bolsters*, are also an influence.[7] See Fig. 9–7.

In Table 9–1, bar sizes and total beam depths have been selected for the beams of the preceding examples. Note that the "shallow beam" did not prove so in the end, after the bar arrangement had been worked out. Sometimes there is more steel but less depth, d, than desired, so the safety of a design can be proven only by a final *investigation*.

Table 9–1. Summary of Rectangular Beam Designs

Design safe B.M. = 50.4 kip-ft.; spec., 20,000–1350–9; $1\frac{1}{2}$ in. f'p'f'g
All concrete dimensions shown below are in inches

Example	Case	b	d	Reqd. A_s	Selection Bars	h	Remarks
9–3	Balanced beam	8	18.40	1.88	2–#9	$20\frac{1}{2}$	Means 21-in. h?
9–4	Deep beam	8	20	1.73	$\begin{cases} 1\text{–}\#9 \\ 1\text{–}\#8 \end{cases}$	22	Enough head room?
9–5	Shallow beam	8	16	4.30	$\begin{cases} 1\text{–}\#10 \\ 2\text{–}\#11 \end{cases}$	$18\frac{1}{2}$	Must change to two layers of steel
9–6	Doubly reinf. shallow beam	8	16	Top 1.73	3–#7	18	Best
				Bot. 2.18	$\begin{cases} 2\text{–}\#8 \\ 1\text{–}\#7 \end{cases}$		
				Tot. 3.91			

Query. Do all the beams of Table 9–1 have the same live-load carrying capacity? Explain.

---

[7] Refer to the ACI "Manual of Standard Practice for Detailing Reinforced Concrete Structures" for illustrations and standard heights of bolsters and chairs.

Plate 9–1. Scioto Downs, Columbus, Ohio. The grandstand roof is hyperbolic-paraboloid thin-shell construction. At the upper left, the roof over the clubhouse is folded plate design, 100 ft. in length, 40 ft. of which is a cantilever. Designed by R. M. Gensert and Associates, Cleveland, Ohio. (Courtesy of Portland Cement Association)

9–6. THE DESIGN SKETCH

The designer's decisions are summarized in final *design sketches* of the member, such as Fig. 9–7a. They are made principally to save the time of supervisors and draftsmen who must read "the answer" at a glance. They must always be made to scale (same scale vertically as horizontally), with the scale stated. The outside dimensions of the concrete are clearly shown. The number of bars, their location, spacing, the bar size number and the concrete coverage thereof must be included. The dimensions most useful to the construction man are presented, e.g., the total beam depth, and the bolster height, not d. No decimal measurements are to appear.

A *complete* design sketch shows all the dimensions necessary for planning the forms and detailing the steel, without straining the eyes or exercising mental arithmetic. Incomplete ones are not tolerated. Design sketches are required of students at the completion of all design problems.

Finally, make sure that the *calculations* submitted are up to date with the *dimensions* appearing on the final design sketch.

EXAMPLE 9–7

Investigation of a Doubly Reinforced Beam

Draw the final design sketch of the cross section of the doubly reinforced beam designed in Example 9–6 **and investigate it** to find the stresses under the design bending moment of 50.4 kip-ft. Specification: 20,000–1350–9.

Solution. Referring to the design sketch (Fig. 9–7a), the centroid of the bottom bar group, has conservatively been taken at 2.0 in. from the bottom:

ΣM of areas to find the neutral axis of the transformed section at (b):

$$4(kd)^2 + 8(1.8)[kd - 2.50] = 9(2.18)[16.0 - kd]$$
$$kd = 6.02 \text{ in.}$$

Due to the presence of compression steel, C *does not act at kd/3 in. from the top,* but must be located by taking **moments of compressive stress volumes,** preferably about the top of the beam.

Always use the tabular form:

Piece No.	Stress Volume	Arm to Top, in.	Moment
1	$(f_c/2)(8)(6.02) = 24.08f_c$	2.01	$48.40f_c$
2	$0.584f_c(9 - 1)(1.8) = 8.41f_c$	2.50	$21.03f_c$
	$C = 32.49f_c$		$69.43f_c$

$$z = \frac{69.43}{32.49} = 2.14 \text{ in.}$$

$$jd = 13.86 \text{ in.}$$

$$C = T = \frac{M}{jd} = \frac{50.4(12,000)}{13.86} = 43,600 \text{ lb.}$$

$$f_c = \frac{43,600}{32.49} = 1340$$

$$\text{Top } f_s = n(0.584f_c) = 9(0.584)(1340) = 7040$$

$$\text{Bot. } f_s = \frac{43,600}{2.18} = 20,000$$

<u>Ans. in psi.</u> The <u>design is</u> <u>satisfactory.</u>

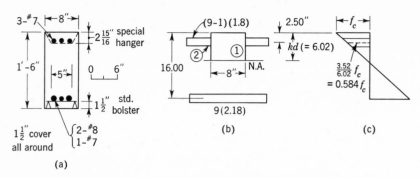

Fig. 9–7. Doubly reinforced beam investigation.

PRACTICE PROBLEM

9–12. A doubly reinforced rectangular beam is 16 in. wide by 3 ft. 4 in. deep to the centroid of the tensile steel bar group consisting of 8–#11 bars. There are also 4–#11 bars centered $2\frac{1}{2}$ in. from the top.

Find the maximum safe bending moment for the beam. Specification: 20,000–1500–8.   Ans. $kd = 15.37$ in., safe B.M. = 709 kip-ft.

9–7. T-BEAMS

Wide beams with concrete missing from the tension side are called *T-beams*. The undercut portion of Fig. 9–8b shows how a great deal of concrete may be saved thereby. Furthermore, the resulting T-beam can then carry more superimposed load, equal to the weight of the concrete removed. Thus the removal of *this* material from the section makes it stronger!

Technically, a T-beam is one consisting of a horizontal compression **flange**, or **slab**, and a vertical web, or **stem**, so proportioned that the neutral axis falls below the slab, as at Fig. 9–8a. If the recess extends upward some lesser distance, as shown dotted in (b) and (c), the neutral

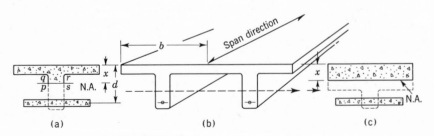

Fig. 9–8. T-beams and otherwise.

axis may fall within the slab, in which case rectangular beam calculations apply in spite of appearances to the contrary.

T-beam problems are also of two types, *investigation* and *design*, depending respectively upon whether the dimensions of the beam cross section are known or to be found, as in rectangular beams. Three examples of T-beams will be taken up, one investigation and two design. The student should note the parallelism of the T-beam cases with those of rectangular beams.

In T-beam calculations it is customary to omit the stem concrete areas, *pqrs*, of Fig. 9–8a, which makes a negligible error in most cases.

EXAMPLE 9–8

(a) **Given** the T-shaped section of Fig. 9–9a, with a slab thickness of $t = 6$ in., a bending moment of 70 kip-ft., and $n = 9$.

It is **required** to find f_c and f_s.

Solution. First, take a summation of moments of transformed areas about the bottom of the slab to find if it is really a T-beam:

$$40(6)[3] > 9(3)[12]$$

Therefore the neutral axis is within the slab, making it a rectangular beam calculation similar to Example 9–1.

(b) **Same** as (a) above, except that the slab thickness, t, has been decreased to 4 in.

Solution. A quick mental recalculation having indicated that the neutral axis is below the slab, the transformed section, Fig. 9–9b, was drawn and the neutral axis evaluated:

$$40(4)[kd - 2] = 9(3)[18 - kd]$$
$$kd = 4.31 \text{ in.}$$

The centroid distance, z, at (c) may be found conveniently by dividing the trapezoidal stress prism into two triangular ones, and **taking moments of stress volumes** about the top of the beam, using a 1-in. width of slab, as shown on the following page.

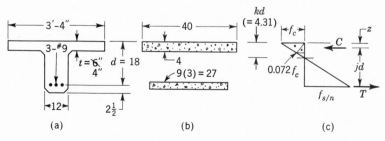

Fig. 9–9. T-beam investigation.

Piece	Compressive Stress Volume per Inch of Slab Width	Arm to Top, in.	Moment/40
Upper	$\dfrac{f_c}{2}(4) = 2.000 f_c$	1.33	$2.670 f_c$
Lower	$\dfrac{0.072}{2} f_c(4) = 0.144 f_c$	2.67	$0.385 f_c$
	$C/40 = \overline{2.144 f_c}$		$\overline{3.055 f_c}$

$$z = 3.055 \div 2.144 = 1.42 \text{ in.,} \quad jd = 16.58 \text{ in.}$$

$$T = C = \frac{\text{B.M.}}{jd} = \frac{70(12{,}000)}{16.58} = 50{,}700 \text{ lb.}$$

$$f_s = \frac{50{,}700}{3} \qquad\qquad = \underline{16{,}900 \text{ psi}}$$

$$f_c = \frac{50{,}700}{40(2.144)} \qquad = \underline{590 \text{ psi.}} \quad \underline{\text{Ans.}}$$

Due to the relatively great width of T-beam compression flanges, the concrete stress is usually well below the allowable.

(c) **Find** the maximum safe bending moment for the section, **if the allowable stresses are 20,000 and 1350 psi.**

Solution. From the preceding, since

Short-cut: $\dfrac{20{,}000}{16{,}900} < \dfrac{1350}{590}$

so the strength is limited by the steel.

$$\text{Max. safe B.M.} = \frac{20{,}000}{16{,}900}(70) = \underline{82.8 \text{ kip-ft.}} \quad \underline{\text{Ans.}}$$

T-BEAM INVESTIGATION PROBLEMS

Unless otherwise noted, take 2500-lb. concrete, specification 20,000–1125–10, and make all investigations by the internal couple method.

9–13. A T-beam has a slab portion 30 in. wide by 3 in. thick. Its depth to the center of 2–#10 bars is 16 in. Is it safe under a total bending moment of 60 kip-ft.?
    Ans.   Yes, N.A. = 4.67 in., $jd = 14.71$ in., $f_s = 19{,}300$, $f_c = 760$ psi.

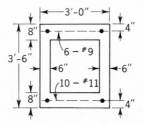

Fig. 9–10

*
9–14. Find the maximum safe bending moment for a T-beam having a slab portion 30 in. wide by 3 in. thick, and a depth of 18 in. to the center of 2–#11 bars.

9–15. Find the maximum safe total bending moment that the box girder section of Fig. 9–10 can carry.

9–8. T-BEAM DESIGN

T-beam design theory involves one more variable than in rectangular beams, namely the slab thickness, t. Nevertheless, by conveniently assuming a slab thickness as some fraction of d, *balanced* T-beams can be evolved by a straightforward procedure, as in the following example.

EXAMPLE 9–9

Given a total bending moment of 30.2 kip-ft. and the specification 20,000–1350–9.

It is required to design a balanced T-beam.

Solution. Since no dimensions are initially set, the neutral axis can be put in the ideal balanced location of $0.378d$ defined by the allowable stresses, as shown in Fig. 9–11.

Conveniently assuming a slab thickness divisible by 3, take $0.21d$, and a unit width of slab. Take moments of stress volumes to find the centroid for C:

Piece	Compressive Stress Volume per Inch of Slab Width	Arm to Top	Moment/b
Upper	$675(0.21d) = 141.8d$	$0.07d$	$9.93d^2$
Lower	$300(0.21d) = \underline{\;\;63.0d}$	$0.14d$	$\underline{8.82d^2}$
	$C/b = 204.8d$		$18.75d^2$

$$z = \frac{18.75d^2}{204.8d} = 0.0916d, \quad \text{so } jd = 0.908d$$

Now

$$C = T = 204.8bd$$

and

Therefore

$$Cjd = \text{B.M., so } 204.8bd[0.908d] = 30.2(12,000)$$

$$bd^2 = 1947$$

from which to prepare a table of values.

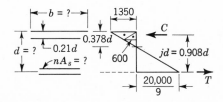

Fig. 9–11. T-beam design, t/d assumed.

The corresponding

$$A_s = \frac{T}{20,000} = \frac{204.8bd}{20,000} = 0.01024bd$$

b	d	$t\,(= 0.21d)$	Reqd. A_s	Remarks
12.0	12.72	2.67	1.56	2–#8
( )	( )	( )	( )	

The table of values shows the resulting dimensions if a b of 12 in. is initially tried. Obviously, other combinations exist.

Balanced T-beams are seldom achieved in practice because they are usually units of a repeating construction having the stems so widely spaced to save dead load that the slab width, b, is much greater than necessary for concrete strength. However, tests have shown that there is a limit to the width of slab that may be relied upon to *act with the stem* as a beam. The Code, Sec. 906(b), wisely limits b to (1) one-fourth of the span, (2) the center-to-center distance between stems, or (3) the stem thickness plus 16 times the slab thickness, whichever is the smaller.

Stem and slab must be placed monolithically, for integral action.

The required stem thickness, b', is dictated by the beam shear, and is taken up in Chapter 10.

A continuing floor slab with stems only a very few feet apart, as in Fig. 9–8b, is called *concrete joist* construction.

9–9. "PAN SYSTEM" T-BEAM FORMS

Figure 9–13 illustrates how T-beam construction is facilitated by employing removable metal forms, called "pans," which are used repeatedly on a rental basis. The most common pan width is 20 in., the soffit plank being 5 in., making the b of the slab 25 in. The standardized depths of pans available are 6, 8, 10, 12, and 14 in. The pans of some systems are devised for early removal and reuse, while the soffit and shoring remain until the concrete has attained full strength. A conservative minimum slab thickness is $2\frac{1}{2}$ in.

In pan T-beam *designing*, the dimensions of the slab are predetermined, leaving only the pan depth and steel area to be found.[8] One procedure is to try two or three pans, computing the necessary steel, and then to decide which is the most suitable and economical. The deeper pans require less steel but more concrete, having greater dead weight, and sometimes interfere with head room.

---

[8] Sometimes the slab thickness and slab width also are to be chosen.

In *designing* any singly reinforced WSD beam, the allowable stresses define k if not more than one of the following has already been set: namely, b, d, and A_s.

EXAMPLE 9–10

Given the specification 20,000–1350–9, a 2½-in. slab thickness, and a live load of 200 psf. over a 19 ft. 8 in. simple span.

It is required to design a pan T-beam section.   Provide one inch of fireproofing. Assume, for a start, that the bars will be of 1-in. diameter.

Solution.   (Trial of a 10-in. pan illustrated in Fig. 9–12.)

Loads:

$$\text{L.L.} = 200(^{25}\!\!/_{12}) \qquad\qquad = 417$$

$$\text{D.L.} = \frac{[25(2.5) + 6(10)]150}{144} = 128$$

$$\text{Total} = \overline{545} \text{ plf}$$

$$\text{Bending moment} = \frac{wL^2}{8} = \frac{545(19.67)^2}{8} = 26,300 \text{ lb.-ft.}$$

The neutral axis can neither be gotten by moments of transformed areas nor from a diagram of allowable stresses.   (Why not?)

It is permissible in this one case (1) to assume a trial value of jd, usually $0.9d$, from which an approximate steel content can be quickly calculated; then (2) to *investigate* the section to find an improved value of jd for use in correcting the steel area:

Trial.

$$jd = 0.9d = 9.90 \text{ in.}$$

$$\text{Approx. } A_s = \frac{M}{f_s jd} = \frac{26,300(12)}{20,000(9.90)} = 1.59 \text{ sq. in.}$$

Investigation. ΣM of transformed areas:

$$25(2.5)[kd - 1.25] = 9(1.59)[11 - kd]$$
$$kd = 3.06 \text{ in.}$$

Referring to Fig. 9–12c, it is possible *in T-beams* to circumvent the summation of moments of stress volumes to find the distance z to the centroid for C.   The desired centroid will be on a straight line between those pictured for the individual triangular prisms.   Upon examining the moment-taking of the table of Example 9–8, it was evident[9] that the desired elevation of C was nearer to the centroid

---

[9] If this shortcut is not fully understood, avoid it by taking moments of stress volumes, as formerly, such as in Example 9–8.

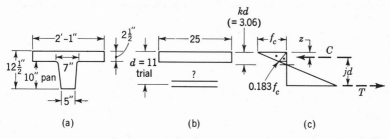

Fig. 9–12.   Design of pan T-beam steel.

of the larger triangle in inverse proportion to the areas, or the *horizontal dimensions* of the triangles.

In **Example 9-10:** Have at bottom of slab

$$\frac{0.56 \text{ in.}}{3.06 \text{ in.}} (f_c) = 0.183 f_c$$

$$\text{Measurement } z = \frac{2.50}{3} + \left(\frac{0.183}{1.0 + 0.183}\right)(0.83) = 0.96 \text{ in.}$$

Corresp. improved $jd = 10.04$ in., > 9.90 in.

Redesign.

$$\text{Corrected } A_s = \frac{9.90}{10.04}(1.59) = 1.57 \text{ sq. in. reqd.} \qquad \underline{\text{Use 2–\#8.}}$$

$$f_s = 20,000, \qquad f_c = \frac{3.06}{7.94}\left(\frac{20,000}{9}\right) = \qquad \underline{855 \text{ psi., O.K.}}$$

Comment. When a true T-beam is being made either deeper or *shallower*, the required bottom steel area may be calculated by an inverse proportion upon the depths, d, involved, subject only to a later check upon the actual f_c value.

This procedure is possible when such beams are being made shallower because the compression concrete area does not abut the neutral axis, as it does in rectangular beams; and because T-beam f_c values are *usually* well below the allowable anyway.

NOTE TO THE INSTRUCTOR: Since Example 9–10 is the last of the basic examples of flexural computation by the transformed section method, the corresponding examples of Appendix L, illustrating the time-saving use of the *beam charts*, may well be taken up at this point.

T-BEAM DESIGN PROBLEMS

Take 2500-lb. concrete, specification 20,000–1125–10, unless otherwise noted.

✴
9–16. Calculate the steel area and slab width required for a T-beam having a slab thickness of 5 in. and a depth to center of steel of 20 in. The beam is to carry 5 kips D.L. + L.L. per lin. ft. over a 20-ft. simple span. The beam stem is 14 in. wide. Refer to Code Sec. 906(b).

Can the design be managed so that the neutral axis will be in the ideal location? Explain.

✴
9–17. The total bending moment is 61 kip-ft. Calculate the exact amount of steel required for a T-beam 17 in. deep to center of steel if the slab is 30 by 3½ in.

Ans. $A_s = 2.35$ sq. in.

★
9–18. Design of a Pan-Construction T-Beam Floor (Concrete Joist). Refer to Fig. 9–13 for dimensions of available forms. The minimum slab thickness, t, is 2 in. Provide exactly 1-in. fireproofing, vertically and laterally. Allow a minimum clear distance of one diam. between bars, but never less than 1 in. Refer to Art. 9–5. Use 2 bars of one size in your design. The (simple) span is 20 ft. center to center of supports.

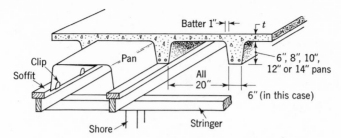

Fig. 9–13.   Pan system forms for a concrete joist floor.

Indiv. Case	Live Load (lb. per sq. ft. of floor)	Specification f_s f_c n	Class of Concrete f'_c
a	200	20,000–1000–10	2500
b	125	20,000–1200–10	2500
c	100	20,000–1688– 8	4000
d	150	20,000–1200– 9	3000
e	150	20,000–1450– 9	3000
f	150	20,000–1750– 8	4000
g	75	20,000–1100–10	2500
h	100	24,000–1350– 9	3000
i	80	24,000–1125–10	2500
j	125	24,000–1800– 8	4000
k	175	20,000– 900–10	2500
l			
m			
n			
o			

Required (for the case assigned):

(a) To evolve the first design by assuming only t/d and the dead load at one-third to one-half of the live load.   Solve algebraically for the required balanced d and A_s, choose the corresponding pan and slab thickness having meantime corrected the dead load and retraced all.

(b) Make a second design, assuming a different pan depth at the outset and striving for better *steel economy.*

(c) Study *over-all economy* by taking the steel at 15 cents per lb. in place, and concrete (including form costs) at $65 per cu. yd.   Report which of your two designs is best.   Steel weighs 490 lb. per cu. ft.

If uncertainties develop, *investigate* designs after choosing standard bars but before making the two final design sketches.   Refer to Art. 9–6.

9–10. BEAM INVESTIGATION BY THE Mc/I METHOD

It is also possible to *investigate* any reinforced concrete beam by computing the moment of inertia of the transformed section and using the traditional Mc/I expression to find the stresses.   *Irregular sections,* especially, are most easily handled by this method, since it sidesteps the necessity for the determination of the location of the centroid of the compressive force, C.

EXAMPLE 9–11

Reinvestigate the doubly reinforced beam of Example 9–7 by the Mc/I method. Refer to Fig. 9–7.

Solution. The neutral axis was found by the usual method to be at 6.02 in. down (Example 9–7).

Moment of inertia of the transformed section about the neutral axis:

$$\text{Concrete, } b(kd)^3/3 = 8(6.02)^3/3 = \quad 583$$
$$\text{Transf. steel, } (n - 1)Ay^2 = 8(1.8)[3.52]^2 = \quad 179$$
$$n(Ay^2) = 9(2.18)[9.98]^2 = \overline{1958}$$
$$I = 2720 \text{ in.}^4$$

$$f_c = \frac{Mc}{I} = \frac{50.4(12,000)(6.02)}{2720} = 1,340 \text{ psi}$$

$$f_{sc} = \frac{nMc}{I} = \frac{9(50.4)(12,000)(3.52)}{2720} = 7,040 \text{ psi}$$

$$f_{st} = \frac{nMc}{I} = \frac{9(50.4)(12,000)(9.98)}{2720} = 19,960 \text{ psi}$$

Satisfactory checks.

Obviously this method would be cumbersome for *designing* beams. The *internal couple method*, $Cjd = Tjd = M$, illustrated repeatedly throughout this chapter, is useful both in investigating and designing.

9–11. DOUBLY REINFORCED BEAM INVESTIGATION BY THE CODE $2n$ APPROXIMATION TO CREEP EFFECT

As mentioned in Art. 1–13 of Chapter 1, concrete is not truly elastic. It **creeps** with lapse of time even under small loads. This phenomenon, formerly called *plastic flow*, practically ceases after a few years. In the meantime a redistribution of stress takes place in members such as columns and doubly reinforced beams wherein concrete and steel *share* a compressive stress. The creeping concrete gradually relieves itself of part of its stress by unloading it upon the unyielded compression steel. The **2n creep method** of beam stress investigation recognizes that such steel may be stressed to fully twice the corresponding elastically calculated value by applying a factor of 2 in neutral axis, moment of inertia, and steel stress calculations. [See Code Sec. 1102(c).]

EXAMPLE 9–12

Reinvestigate the doubly reinforced beam of Example 9–7 by the $2n$ creep method and compare the stress results with those of Example 9–7.

Solution. Referring to Fig. 9–7, the neutral axis will be given by:

$$4(kd)^2 + [2(9) - 1](1.8)[kd - 2.50] \equiv 9(2.18)[16 - kd]$$
$$kd = 5.43 \text{ in.}$$

The moment of inertia of the transformed section will be:

$$\text{Concrete, } \frac{b(kd)^3}{3} = \frac{8(5.43)^3}{3} \qquad = \quad 428$$

$$\begin{array}{llr}
\text{Comp. steel, } 2Ay^2 = [2(9) - 1](1.8)[2.93]^2 = & 263 \\
\text{Tens. steel, } Ay^2 = 9(2.18)[10.57]^2 & = & 2191 \\
\hline
& & 2882 \text{ in.}^4
\end{array}$$

Now $\qquad\qquad M/I = 50.4(12,000)/2882 = 209.6$

So, **stresses are:**

	ELASTIC
Ex. 9–12 (Comp. steel at $2n$)	Ex. 9–7 (n through-out)

$$f_c = \frac{Mc}{I} = 209.6(5.43) \qquad = \qquad 1{,}140 \text{ psi} \qquad 1{,}340 \text{ psi}$$

$$f_{sc} = 2n\frac{Mc}{I} = 18(209.6)2.93 = \qquad 11{,}060 \text{ psi} \qquad 7{,}040 \text{ psi}$$

$$f_{st} = n\frac{Mc}{I} = 9(209.6)10.57 = \quad 19{,}900 \text{ psi} \qquad 20{,}000 \text{ psi}$$

Answer

Note the much greater stress in the compression reinforcement when creep is recognized.

Alternate procedure: A simpler and better method having general application is first to evolve your particular increased n-value using a decreased E_c value, as from a Fig. 1–3 lightweight aggregate concrete, and then use it to transform *both* the compressive and tensile steel areas.

Mc/I METHOD AND CREEP PROBLEMS

Take 2500-lb. concrete, ACI Specification: 20,000–1125–10.

9–19. Find the maximum safe resisting moment for the precast reinforced concrete joist of Fig. 9–14a by the Mc/I method.

9–20. Find the maximum safe resisting moment for the irregular doubly-reinforced beam section of Fig. 9–14b by the Mc/I method, (a) considering concrete elastic, and (b) considering concrete creep, following the Code.

9–21. Recalculate the stresses in the beam of Example 9–12 recognizing creep, following a $\frac{1}{3}E_c$ Alternate Procedure, as outlined therein, taking the Spec. 20,000–1350–27. Also tabulate a comparison of the stresses found by all three methods, and comment upon the trends thereof.

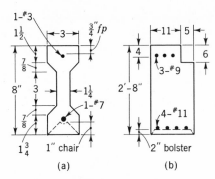

Fig. 9–14

9–12. DEFLECTION OF WORKING-STRESS-DESIGNED BEAMS

This topic is taken up from the WSD viewpoint beginning with Art. 2–22 and Example 2–13 (following Code Secs. 909 and 1507), to which the reader is referred.

9–13. SUMMARY OF WORKING STRESS DESIGNING FOR FLEXURE

In calculating the bending strength of reinforced concrete beams, the relatively small tensile strength of the concrete is ignored and the steel is relied upon to take all the tensile stress.

By conceiving the steel to be transformed into an elastically equivalent amount of imaginary concrete, a homogeneous section is created, to which ordinary mechanics principles may be applied.

It is quite necessary to distinguish clearly between situations involving the *investigation* of a section of known dimensions and those of a *design* nature wherein dimensions must be solved for, since the methods of attack in the two cases differ widely.

To design intelligently it is necessary to visualize the internal couple, equate it to the applied external bending moment, and provide enough concrete and steel to safely resist the compressive and tensile forces, respectively.

In working stress design, beams are said to be "balanced" when both the steel and concrete allowable bending stresses are realized simultaneously.

For any given bending moment and allowable stresses, there are many combinations of beam breadth and depth which will produce balanced designs.

In *designing* singly reinforced beams by the working stress method, determine the neutral axis from the diagram of allowable stresses when not more than one of the following dimensions is already set, namely:

b, d, and A_s. *Less freedom makes a balanced beam an impossibility.*

To save (total) steel, beams that are decidedly shallower than required for balance should be doubly reinforced.

To design a doubly reinforced beam, first find how much of the applied bending moment can be safely resisted if only balanced single reinforcement is provided. Then take care of the remaining bending moment with additional steel in the bottom, and some in the top.

Due to the time-dependent creep property of concrete, the compressive reinforcement of a beam becomes more highly stressed than the common elastic theory indicates. Such steel must be well tied in place.

The effect of loading and creep upon beam stresses may be approximated by taking an n value of two times the common figure (at early ages, four times after one year) and calculating steel and concrete stresses in the usual manner.

REVIEW PROBLEMS

Take ACI 2500-lb. concrete and specification 20,000–1125–10, unless otherwise noted.

9–22. Calculate the maximum safe D.L. + L.L. bending moment for the column section of Fig. 9–15 if used as a beam.

NOTE. Treat the two layers of tension steel separately.

9–23. Calculate the required amount of single reinforcement for a rectangular-section cantilever beam 14 in. wide by 30 in. total depth which carries a uniformly distributed live load of 6.1 kips per ft. over its 8-ft. length. The required cover for steel is 2 in.

9–24. Same as Problem 9–17, except that the slab is 15 in. by 3½ in.

Ans. $A_s = 3.50$ sq. in.

What new situation was encountered?

9–25. A 16-by-32-in. rectangular beam has 3–#9 bars centered 3 in. from the top. The bottom reinforcement consists of 5–#9 bars centered 3 in. from the bottom, plus 2–#9 in a second layer centered 2½ in. higher up. Find the maximum safe resisting moment of the section.

9–26. Conservatively compute balanced single reinforcement for this beam (Fig. 9–16), and report the corresponding maximum safe resisting moment.

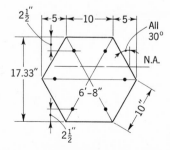

Fig. 9–15

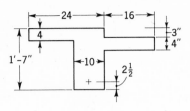

Fig. 9–16

9-27. Accurately calculate the maximum safe resisting moment, for this flexicore-type of section (Fig. 9–17) by the Mc/I method.   Refer to Shank's Chart C–5 of Appendix C.

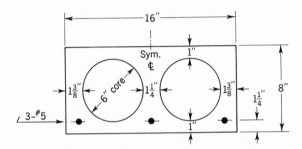

Fig. 9–17

Take ACI $n = 8$ concrete and specification.

QUESTIONS

1. Distinguish clearly between the *design* and *investigation* types of beam problems.
2. Why not use the ratio of the two allowable stresses to transform the steel of a beam? Explain.
3. In singly reinforced rectangular beam design, give, qualitatively, the reasoning behind the method of designing (a) a beam deeper than necessary, and (b) a beam shallower than it should be.   What is an "over-reinforced" beam?
4. Are all doubly reinforced beams balanced beams?   Explain.
5. Are all T-shaped beams truly T-beams?   Explain.
6. Tell in detail how to design a doubly reinforced beam.
7. Tell in detail how to find the centroid of compressive forces for a doubly reinforced T-beam.
8. In what single designing situation may the arm of the internal couple be assumed? How is the value later corrected?
9. What are the advantages of the Mc/I method (a) for investigating? (b) for designing?
10. Tell how to design an economical pan-construction T-beam floor.
11. Formulate a general rule governing the use of the allowable stresses to find the neutral axis in the design of rectangular beams, T-beams, and doubly reinforced beams.

BOND, SHEAR, AND DIAGONAL TENSION IN BEAMS

A. Flexural Bond Stress Versus Anchorage Bond Stress

10–1. INTRODUCTION[1]

Although the concrete in the tension side of a reinforced concrete beam is considered of no value in bending, its *bond* strength is indispensable for preventing bar slippage. In addition, such concrete is relied upon to help resist certain *diagonal tension* forces that result from beam shear. This chapter is devoted entirely to problems illustrating these two functions.

EXAMPLE 10–1

Given the beam in (a) and (g) of Fig. 10–1. Consider it to be weightless, and carrying only the 18-kip load.

It is required to compute the bond, shear and diagonal tension unit stresses in the concrete at a section 24½ in. from the left reaction, and to report upon safety. Take the Code 3000-lb. concrete and specification.

10–2. CALCULATION OF THE FLEXURAL BOND STRESS RELATED TO BEAM SHEAR BY THE UNIT SLICE METHOD

The shear and moment diagrams for the beam were drawn at (b) and (c), and a 1-in. unit slice taken out at the section in question, for study as a *free body* as at (d). The values of C and T on each side of the slice were obtained from the bending moments, using $\frac{7}{8}d$ as the arm of the internal couples, as has been customary in bond and shear calculations.[2] A check

---

[1] Preferably, the use of the WSD beam flexure formulas and charts of Appendix L should be mastered before taking up this chapter.

[2] For WSD T-beams use $0.9d$. In most bond and shear-related calculations the rounded values give sufficient precision.

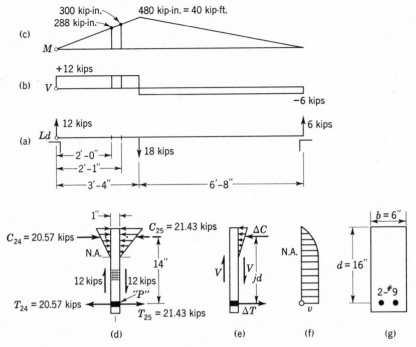

Fig. 10–1. Flexural bond and shear forces.

was made by a summation of moments about the point p:

$$(12)(1) - (21.43 - 20.57)(14) = 0$$

Flexural bond unit stress. At the bottom of the beam, the inequality of the two tensile forces, T_{24} and T_{25}, on each side of the unit slice, is made up by a horizontal force of adhesion between the steel and the concrete which is called *flexural bond*. The *flexural bond unit stress*, u, is the unit shear in an imaginary glue between the two materials and is an indication of the tendency for the bars to slip through the concrete.

In the case at hand, dividing the difference of the T's by the contact area:

$$u = \frac{(21.43 - 20.57)1000}{2(1.13)(\pi)} = 121 \text{ psi}$$

For 3000-lb. concrete, the WSD Code, Sec. 1301(c)(1), allows u to be 233 psi, assuming deformed bars. Therefore the beam is safe in flexural bond at the section taken.

Generalization. From the preceding development

$$M_{n+1} - M_n = V \qquad \text{(from fundamental mechanics)}$$

Therefore:

$$(T_{n+1} - T_n)jd = V$$
$$T_{\text{diff}} = \Delta T = V/jd \tag{10-1}$$

From which:

$$Flexural \text{ bond stress, } u = \frac{V}{\Sigma ojd} \tag{10-2}$$

wherein Σo is total tensile bar perimeter at the section studied.

Comment. From Eq. 10–2 and Fig. 10–1, $\Sigma ou = V/jd$ is the rate, ΔT, of 857 lb. per inch of span, at which *flexural* stress gets into the left portion of the beam.

Also, Σou is the shear, *per inch of span*, in the imaginary glue between steel and concrete, namely, $121(2)(1.13)(\pi) = 857$ lb.

Flexural bond stress is computed over the clear span of a beam or slab at sections of high beam shear, or zero bending moment (inflection points), or wherever some bars are terminating.

10–3. ANCHORAGE BOND STRESS [1]

Anchorage is the **extension,** a', of a reinforcing bar beyond its theoretical end point in order to prevent structural failure by bar slippage. The resulting longitudinal stress between the bar and the concrete is called *anchorage bond stress, u_a*. It differs fundamentally from the *flexural* bond stress explained earlier, because it is independent of the beam shear V, and ΔT.

For every stressed point along a bar there must be enough bar length on *each* side thereof to resist by bond at a safe value of u_a the direct force, T, existing therein.

The most dependable anchorage is achieved within a region of *compressed concrete*, because it will seize the bars more tightly as tensile stress is increased by the loading.

Code Sec. 1301(c) recognizes also that the adhesion of the concrete will be poor along the under side of a horizontal bar below which more than a 12-in. depth of concrete has been placed, because it settles from underneath thereof. The corresponding specified safe u_a value thereat (top bars) is only about 70 per cent of the normal one.

Since the occasional failure of a concrete structure has usually been traced to inadequate anchorage, the importance of the topic can hardly be overemphasized. Refer to Code Sec. 918 entire.

EXAMPLE 10–2

Anchorage of Top Flexural Steel

Given $f'_c = 3000$, $f_s = 20,000$, and allowable $u_a = 3.4 \sqrt{f'_c}/D$ from Code Sec. 1301.

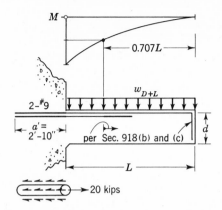

Fig. 10–2.   Full and partial anchorage.

Required to determine the endings of both bars of Fig. 10–2.

Solution. At the support, where the bending moment is greatest, each #9 bar is presumed to be stressed to the allowed 20 kips. Taking one bar, and a' as the required length of embedment for anchorage, equate the required safe bond resistance, in pounds, to the tension in the bar, using the decreased allowable bond of 165 psi for a top bar:

$$1.13(\pi)(165)(a') = 20(1000) = T$$
$$\text{Reqd. } a' = 34.0 \text{ in.} = \text{full anchorage}$$

Algebraically, using D for the bar diameter:

$$u_a(\pi D)(a') \equiv f_s \frac{\pi}{4}(D)^2$$

$$a' = \frac{f_s}{4u_a}(D), \quad \text{the anchorage formula} \qquad (10\text{–}3)$$

Thus for deformed bars in 3000-lb. concrete, the Code requires about 30 bar diameters of embedment for *full anchorage* of top bars.

In Fig. 10–2, obviously both bars must also extend from the face of the wall *into the beam* at least 30 diameters, or 2 ft. 10 in.[3]

Partial anchorage. Furthermore, Sec. 918(b) of the Code states that *within* any beam span every (flexural) reinforcing bar shall be extended at

---

[3] As press time approached, it appeared that the calculation of *flexural* bond stress may be displaced by a Code-required calculation of *developmental* bond stress within clear-span regions where the concrete is already subject to varying flexural tension, and some light cracking.

End anchorage bond stress would continue to be calculated as for the 2 ft. 10 in. anchorage of Fig. 10–2.

See Code Sec. 1301 or 1801. Also see Fig. 3–2, Example 8–4, Fig. 8–15, and appurtenant calculations (this textbook).

least 12 diameters[4] beyond the theoretical cut-off point.   Therefore both bars have been so extended.   Such extensions serve as insurance against a lack of uniformity in the loading distribution and in the quality of the concrete.   They also provide anchorage for the bit of tension in the last few inches of the bar, and are referred to as *partial anchorage*.

Flexural bond stress versus anchorage bond stress.   It is necessary to distinguish clearly between these stresses.   Fundamentally, flexural bond stress per inch, $\Sigma ou = V/jd$, is the *rate*, ΔT, in pounds per inch of span at which beam flexural stress gets into the reinforcement at points *along the clear span*.   Refer to Fig. 10–1d and e.

Anchorage bond stress exists in bar-end localities, and is caused by the adjacent *whole* value of T.   Typically, it develops *outside* the clear span, either in top or bottom bars.   In Fig. 10–2 the anchorage distance a' was made long enough to safely resist the summation of all the ΔT's over the full length of the cantilever, namely T.

End zones.   For calculating the required anchorages for both bottom and top steel at the ends of a continuous floor system, see USD Example 3–2 and Fig. 3–2.

BOND AND ANCHORAGE PRACTICE PROBLEMS

Take from Code Sec. 1002(a) and Chapter 13 thereof, $f'_c = 4000$, and A305 deformed bars.

10–1. (a) Calculate the maximum flexural bond stress at each end of the beam of Fig. 10–3.

(b) Calculate the permissible flexural bond stress, and comment upon the (a) results.

10–2. For the same beam, loading, and specification as in Problem 10–1:

(a) Calculate the anchorage bond stress at each end of the beam, and compare with the permissible.

(b) Comment upon the propriety of this bar arrangement.

[4] Or d distance, whichever is greater.

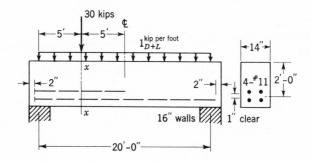

Fig. 10–3.   Bond stresses.

B. Shear, Diagonal Tension, and Web Reinforcement

10–4. HORIZONTAL SHEAR UNIT STRESS

Referring to the unit slice of Fig. 10–1d, the forces on the slice may be simplified as indicated at (e), from which one sees that **all horizontal planes below the neutral axis are subject to a horizontal shearing force equal to ΔT, the difference of the T's over the span distance taken.** Furthermore $\Delta T = V/jd$.

Let v be the horizontal shear unit stress in the concrete below the neutral axis. Then in the example:

$$v = \frac{(21.43 - 20.57)1000}{6} = 143 \text{ psi}$$

See Fig. 10–1f.

Vertical shear unit stress. In the accompanying Fig. 10–1 continuation, consider at (h) the forces on a 1-in. cube of concrete taken from the tension side of the slice at (d). The horizontal shearing forces, v, 1 in. apart, form a counterclockwise couple which is balanced by a clockwise couple consisting of corresponding *vertical* forces, v. Therefore **the unit vertical shear equals the unit horizontal shear,** and is 143 psi in this case.

Algebraically. From Eq. 10–1, $T_{\text{diff}} = V/jd$. So unit shear stress is

$$v = V/bjd \qquad \text{[the \textit{former} practice]} \qquad (10\text{–}4)$$

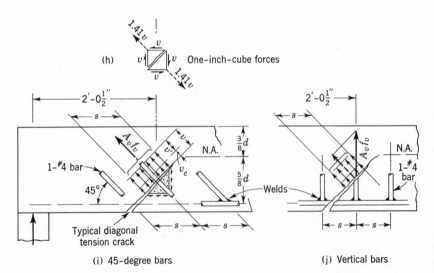

(h) One-inch-cube forces

(i) 45-degree bars

1-#4 bar

45°

Typical diagonal tension crack

Welds

(j) Vertical bars

1-#4 bar

Continuation Fig. 10–1 (h), (i), (j). Diagonal tension reinforcement.

Diagonal[5] tension unit stress.   Materials finally fail via normal (direct) stress or shear, whichever is the weaker.   Concrete's unconfined shear strength is approximately one fourth of its compressive; but the tensile strength is less than half of this shear strength.   If the unit cube's four shear forces, v, are progressively increased, they combine into opposing resultant diagonal forces acting in the particular diagonal direction indicated, producing *diagonal tension* in the cube, and early failure by tensile cracking perpendicular to the resultant forces, long before the shear failure strength of the cube is reached.   Refer to Table 1–1.

Returning to (h) of the figure, the resultant diagonal tensile force of $1.41v$ lb. acts on a fracture area of 1.41 sq. in., so the *diagonal tension unit stress* turns out to be *the same as the shear unit stress*.   Both are designated by v.

Query.   Show the forces upon a unit cube from the *compression* side of the beam.   Will diagonal tension cracks develop there?   Explain.

However, recent research has indicated that the *diagonal tension* stress intensity has not yet been closely enough determined to justify the precision suggested by retaining the j in Eq. 10–4.   Consequently, the Code, in Sec. 1201(a), states:

The *nominal* shear stress, *as a measure of diagonal tension*, . . . shall be computed by:

$$v = V/bd$$

or
$$= (t_d) \qquad \text{[Code Formula 12–1]}$$

In diagonal tension[6] stress calculations, the nominal unit vertical and horizontal shears and diagonal tension are considered equal in magnitude.

SHEAR, BOND, AND DIAGONAL TENSION PRACTICE PROBLEM

10–3. A singly reinforced beam carries a uniform dead load plus live load of 2.3 kips per lin. ft. over a simple span of 16 ft., center to center of 12-in. walls, and two concentrated loads of 12 kips each symmetrically located 3 ft. each side of the center line of span.   The beam is 16 in. by 25 in. ($b \times d$), and has four #9 plain bars.

For this problem, take 2500-lb. concrete, specification: 20,000–1125–10, $f_v = 20,000$, $v = 55$, and $u = 106$ psi (plain bars).

(a) Investigate the beam for both horizontal shear and bond unit stresses at the following three sections:

2 ft. 6 in. from center of span
5 ft. from center of span
at the inside face of wall.

(a') Alternately work individually at three sections s, $s + 28$ in., and $s + 56$ in. from the center of span, as assigned by the instructor.
Work from fundamental principles, taking unit slices.

[5] Throughout this discussion, 45° diagonal directions are meant.
[6] It is unfortunate that the important term *diagonal tension* is mentioned only twice in Code Chapter 12.   The *direction* of this tension (also obtained easily from Mohr's circle) is often highly important for locating reinforcement, or in analyzing a failure, and is *never the same* as that of the shear.

Make for each section a free-body sketch of the slice taken, showing *all* forces (there are more than five of them) exactly as applied, with their *values* as computed. The summations $\Sigma H \equiv 0$, $\Sigma V \equiv 0$, and $\Sigma M \equiv 0$ must be satisfied on each sketch.

(b) Check by the formulas.

(c) Make a large half-span graph (on 8½-by-11-in. good graph paper) from the findings, plotting V, v, and u vertically against span distance horizontally. Plot also the allowable values of v and u and *report* upon the safety of the beam in these respects.

10–5. DIAGONAL TENSION REINFORCEMENT

Numerous tests [2] have shown that the type of ultimate failure pictured in Fig. 10–4a may be expected if the diagonal tension unit stress in the concrete at the design service load is appreciably greater than $1.1 \sqrt{f'_c}$, or 60 psi for 3000-lb. concrete. In the central part of the span, where the bending moment was large, the vertical cracks attest to the weakness of the concrete in bending tension; but since the beam as a whole failed elsewhere, the bottom steel obviously was adequate for the bending imposed. In the outer portions of the span, where the beam shear was great, the cracks took the general 45° direction shown; and since additional steel was not placed across the direction of these diagonal tension cracks, two opened widely and caused sudden failure of the beam.

In the beam of Fig. 10–4b, 45° reinforcement was added in the outer portions, in the direction of the diagonal tension. Instead of long open diagonal cracks, numerous short ones developed but remained closed.

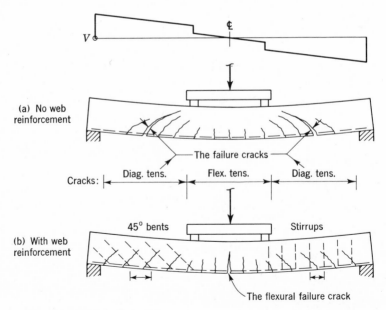

Fig. 10–4. Typical R/C beam cracking at overload.

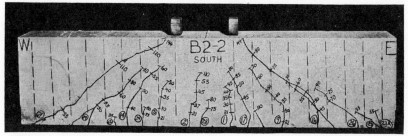

American Iron and Steel Institute

Plate 10–1. Typical cracking of stirruped beams which failed in diagonal tension. From a series of tests reported by Arthur P. Clark. (Courtesy of American Iron and Steel Institute)

This beam proved appreciably stronger than the beam at (a), and finally failed, due to the gradual yielding of the flexure steel, as indicated by the open crack at midspan. The closed cracks pictured are invisible at service loads.

Diagonal tension reinforcement is often called *web reinforcement* to distinguish it from the flange, or flexural, reinforcement used in the tension side.

To be effective, the 45° diagonal reinforcement should be firmly attached to the flexural steel, as by the welding pictured in Continuation Fig. 10–1i; or be integral with it, as when bottom bars are quite commonly *bent up* for this purpose.

Allowable diagonal tension unit stress. For 3000-lb. concrete, the Code allows a beam diagonal tension stress, v_c, upon the concrete of only 60 psi.[7] Since our Example 10–1 beam section of Fig. 10–1g has a b of 6 in. and a d of 16 in., then $v = V/bd$ at the section previously studied = $12,000/6(16) = 125$ psi, so the beam is unsafe without the addition of enough diagonal tension reinforcement to safely resist the 65-psi excess, known as v'. Note in Continuation Fig. 10–1i and j that v, v_c, and v' always act in the 45° diagonal tension direction, *regardless of the direction of the reinforcement.*

EXAMPLE 10–3

Forty-Five-Degree Web Reinforcement

Taking the beam of Continuation Fig. 10–1, **find** the unit stress in the 45° diagonal tension reinforcement at the section shown if, in (i), the spacing s is 8 in. and the bars are #4 size.

Solution. In studying diagonal tension reinforcement, the key thought is that the tension in a 45° diagonal bar, in pounds, equals the excess diagonal tension tributary to it which the concrete cannot safely assume.

[7] For all WSD beam allowables refer to Table 1002(a) of Code Sec. 1002.

Considering the middle 45° bar of Fig. 10–1i, and the region tributary to it, the tension therein will be, in pounds:

$$0.20(f_v) = 65(6)(0.707)(8)$$

from which

$$f_v = 11{,}050 \text{ psi}; <20{,}000, \text{ safe but very wasteful.}$$

The spacing *should be* $(20/11.05)(8) = 14.5$ in.

Algebraically,

$$T_v = A_v f_v = v'b(0.707)s$$

But $v' = V'/bd$, where V' is the portion of the whole beam shear at the section which is taken care of by the diagonal tension steel.

Therefore:

$$s = \frac{A_v f_v d}{0.707 V'} \qquad \textit{for 45° diagonal tension reinforcement}[8] \qquad (10\text{--}5)$$

10–6. STIRRUPS

Although the ideal arrangement of diagonal tension reinforcement is in the direction of that tension, namely at 45°, practical considerations often dictate that vertical steel be used instead, as in Continuation Fig. 10–1j. Fig. 10–4b also illustrates the widely used U-shaped *stirrups*. To be effective, stirrups[9] must extend around the flexural reinforcement. Refer to Code Sec. 919(c).

EXAMPLE 10–4

Vertical Web Reinforcement

Again taking the beam of Fig. 10–1, **find the unit stress** in the #4 bar welded vertical reinforcement, as at Continuation Fig. 10–1j, if the spacing, s, is again 8 in.

Solution. Referring to Example 10–3, equate *the component* of bar tension in *the diagonal tension direction*, in pounds, to the *excess diagonal tension* in the concrete:

$$0.707 A_v f_v = 0.707(0.20)f_v = 65(6)(0.707)(8)$$

Canceling coefficients and solving:

$$f_v = 15{,}600 \text{ psi}, \qquad \text{wasteful.}$$

Ans.   The spacing *should be* $(20/15.6)(8) = 10.25$ in.

Remarks. Upon comparing the two improved permissible spacings, Example 10–3 versus 10–4, note that vertical steel is only 0.707 as efficient as 45° steel, since the vertical bars *should be* spaced correspondingly closer together.[10]

[8] The reason for eliminating v' in favor of V' will become apparent in a succeeding example.   This applies to Eq. 10–6 as well.

[9] Throughout this textbook the stirrups discussed are vertical and are unwelded to the flexure reinforcement.

[10] But since (in Fig. 3–9) Code Sec. 1206(a) limits our web reinforcement spacings to 12 in. and 8 in., respectively, *they must stand.*

Algebraically:
$$0.707(A_v f_v) = v'b(0.707)s$$

But
$$v' = \frac{V'}{bd}$$

Therefore:
$$s = \frac{A_v f_v d}{V'} \quad \textit{for vertical stirrups} \quad (10\text{–}6)$$

DIAGONAL TENSION STEEL DRILL PROBLEMS

10–4. Given the beam and loading of Fig. 10–5.   Take ACI 2500-lb. concrete and specification: 20,000–1125–10, $f_v = 20,000$, $v_c = 55$ psi (without diagonal tension steel), and maximum $v = 250$ psi (with diagonal tension steel).
Required:

(a) If flexure steel is bent up at 45° as shown, compute f_v in the middle bar at x, and also at y, and comment.
(b) If no bar is bent up, but #5 bar vertical stirrups (having almost exactly the same useful cross section) are used at the same 18-in. spacing, find f_v at the same section at x, 2 ft. 1 in. inward.
(c) Same as (b), except that the stirrups are spaced 13 in. center to center.
(d) Compare and discuss the three results.

10–5. Given the cantilever beam and loading of Fig. 10–6, and the previous specification of Problem 10–4.   Additionally, take A305 (deformed) bars, and the permissible bond stress u from Code Sec. 1301.   Also study and apply Sec. 1202(a).

(a) Calculate the maximum flexural bond stress in Fig. 10–6 and show the comparison with the permissible.
(b) Calculate the required length of anchorage, a'.
(c) Sketch a typical diagonal tension crack (1) in direction and (2) in location.
(d) Dimension the span-wise locality theoretically needing diagonal tension reinforcement.
(e) Calculate the theoretically required number of #3 stirrups needed.   Refer to Example 10–5 below.
(f) Calculate the stirrup spacing at section Y-Y only.
(g) Find the maximum unit diagonal tension stress.
(h) Calculate the theoretical point along the span where one flexure bar may be discontinued.

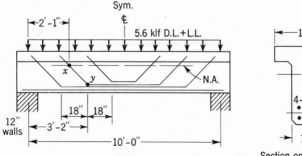
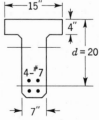

Fig. 10–5

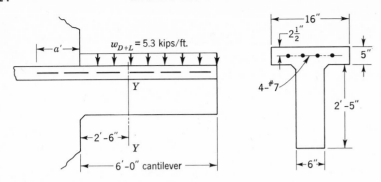

Fig. 10–6. Cantilever bond, anchorage, and diagonal tension.

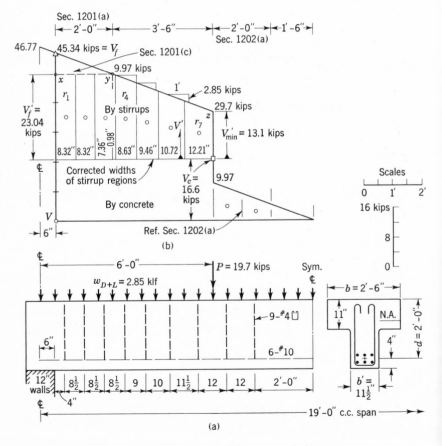

Fig. 10–7. W-S design of stirrup reinforcement.

EXAMPLE 10–5

The Design of Stirrup Reinforcement

Given the beam, loading, and specification of Fig. 10–7a.
Follow the corresponding items of the Solution below.

Required procedure

(a) To check the given concrete dimensions and flexural steel for adequacy in bending.[11]   Take $f'_c = 3000$, the $n = 9$ chart of Appendix L, and the Code's WSD Specification.   <u>Ans. Safe.</u>

(b) To demonstrate that the maximum diagonal tension is not <u>too high, but</u> that stirrups[12] are needed [Code Secs. 1205(b) and 1201(c) and Table 1002(a)].

(c) Clearly draw to scale, and dimension, the beam shear area requiring stirrups [Sec. 1201(c), and Fig. 10–7b].

(d) Determine the suitable maximum stirrup size. Also, incidentally, the minimum [Secs. 1203(a), 1206(a) and (b)].

(e) Calculate the *theoretically* required number of stirrups needed ($= \Sigma s V'/s V'$). Round off to the safe number, N.

(f) Compute the widths of the N stirrup *regions*, and therefrom the spacings of all the stirrups [Table 10–1 and Fig. 10–7a].

(g) Calculate the empirically required additional stirrups, and space them [Secs. 1202(a) and 1206(b)].

Solution

Code's WSD Specifications: $f'_c = 3000$, $f_s = f_v = 20{,}000$, $f_c = 1350$, $n = 9$.

$$v_c = 1.1 \sqrt{f'_c} = 60, \quad v_{max} = 5 \sqrt{f'_c} = 274 \text{ psi}$$

Refer to Fig. 10–7 and to items of the Required procedure. For a commentary in detail, refer to Art. 10–7.

(a) *Flexure check.* $p = 6(1.27)/30(24) = 1.06\%$. From the $n = 9$ beam chart of Appendix L, safe $R = 188$. Therefore,

$$M_R = Rbd^2 = 188(30)(24)^2/12{,}000 = 271 \text{ kip-ft.}$$

$$\text{Design } M = \frac{wL^2}{8} + 6P = \frac{2.85(19)^2}{8} + 6(19.7) = 247 \text{ kip-ft.} \qquad \text{O.K.}$$

(b) *Diagonal tension values.* $V_f = (2.85 \text{ klf})(9 \text{ ft.}) + 19.7 \text{ kips} = 45.34 \text{ kips.}$

$$\text{Max. } v = \frac{V_f}{b'd} = \frac{45{,}340}{11.5(24)} = 163, \; < 274 \text{ or } 5 \sqrt{f'_c}, \qquad \text{so O.K.}$$

$$> 60 \text{ or } 1.1 \sqrt{f'_c}, \qquad \text{so must use stirrups.}$$

Provide stirrups over 5 ft. 6 in. locale, at $\leq d/2$ spacing, since maximum $v < 3 \sqrt{f'_c}$ of Fig. 3–9.

(c) *Beam shear taken by concrete* is:

$$V_c = v_c b'd = 60(11.5)(24) = 16.6 \text{ kips}$$

---

[11] Item (a) should be done as preparatory home work.

[12] Unless otherwise noted, vertical stirrups are always meant herein.

CHOICE OF STIRRUPS

(d) *Suitable maximum stirrup size.* Dictated by minimum V' from Sec. 1203(a) A_v formula, and Sec. 1206(a) maximum s of $d/2$ from Fig. 3–9a.

$$\text{Max. } A_v = \frac{sV'_{\min}}{f_v d} = \frac{(12 \text{ in.})(13,100)}{20,000(24)} = 0.33 \text{ sq. in.}$$

Since #3's have only 0.22 sq. in., *try #4 stirrups* at 2(0.20) = 0.40 sq. in., but at not over $s = 12$ in. spacing.

(d′) *Minimum A_v*, from Sec. 1206(b), is $0.0015(s_{\max}b) = 0.0015(12)$ (11.5) = 0.207 sq. in. Since, in item (d), no stress-computed spacing of #4 stirrups exceeded 12 in.,   the #4 stirrups were used.

(e) *How many stirrups theoretically required?* A matter of V' shear areas and Code Sec. 1203(a). Since sV' for one stirrup $= A_v f_v d = 0.4(20)(24) = 192$ kip-in., the theoretically required number of stirrups is:

$$N = \frac{\Sigma sV'}{sV' \text{ for one stirrup}} = \frac{24(23.04) + 42(23.04 + 13.10)(0.5)}{192} = 6.84$$

This means 7 stirrups between x and z.

(f) *Determination of stirrup regions and spacings.* See Table 10–1.

(g) *Additional stirrups* are empirically required beyond the V_c point, for a distance d, per Code Sec. 1202(a), to guard against variations in the distribution of the loads. Two additional #4 stirrups at $d/2$ spacing have been provided. Section 1206(b) controls the minimum size of such stirrups. See item (d′) above.

The margin notes at left read:
2.85
× 3.5
———
9.98^k

19.70
———
29.68

29.7
16.6
———
13.1^k

10–7. COMMENTARY ON THE ITEMS OF STIRRUP DESIGNING PROCEDURE OF EXAMPLE 10–5 AND THE CORRESPONDING SOLUTION

(b) First, examine the beam shear diagram of Fig. 10–7b and the pertinent diagonal tension portions of the Specification. V_c of item (c) of the Solution limits the portion of the whole beam shear at a section which may be assigned to be taken care of by relying upon the small (diagonal) tensile strength of the concrete alone; the remainder of the beam shear at any section, designated V' in Fig. 10–7b, is to be taken care of by the stirrup steel to be designed. Note the horizontal line at the V_c level which separates these two portions of each beam shear ordinate. For its level refer to the 16.6-kip value in item (c) calculations of the Solution.

The Code also limits, in Sec. 1205(b), the *total* unit shear (or diagonal tension) at any section. In this case it is well below the 274-psi limit of (b) of the Solution.

Theoretically, the locality needing stirrups is only 5 ft. 6 in. long because the end reaction (Fig. 10–7a) gets distributed over the 12-in. wall thickness (and more), and effectively prevents the opening of diagonal tension cracks thereover.

(c) Furthermore, in the above connection, Sec. 1201(a) permits the beam shear at d distance from the face of the support to be the greatest that web reinforcement (e.g., stirrups) need be designed for.   Note the cut-off line xy on Fig. 10–7b.

(d) To select intelligently the proper *size* of stirrup, one must visualize the *beam shear area geometry* of ACI Formula 12–5 of Sec. 1203(a).   It says that each stirrup[13] of area A_v takes care of a *shear diagram area* defined by a vertical measurement V' and a horizontal distance s, which is the stirrup spacing.   Once the suitable stirrup size has been determined, the corresponding sV' beam *shear areas* should all be equal.[14] Near the support they will be tall and slender, but become shorter and wider as the V_c point is approached, as in Fig. 10–7b.

To insure that every possible 45° diagonal tension crack is prevented from developing, Fig. 3–9 and Sec. 1206(a) require that stirrup spacings, s, must not exceed $d/2$ inches.   In item (d) of the Solution this demand was used, in conjunction with the *minimum* V' to calculate the *maximum* stirrup size.   Note that "all stirrups are twins" with respect to A_v.

(d') The *minimum* size of stirrup for a given beam is governed by the Sec. 1206(b) demand that the stirrup area must not be less than 0.0015 times the corresponding tributary concrete area normal to it.

(e) The calculation of the *theoretically* required number, N, of stirrups of a chosen size for a given beam is often an important matter in connection with shear and diagonal tension.   Many graduates may seldom need to compute stirrup *spacings*, but may be confronted repeatedly with predicting the *tonnage* of stirrup steel when making bids or firm estimates on jobs.

For N, simply divide the whole sV' area by the sV' for one stirrup.

(f) To verify the stirrup *spacings* which appear across the bottom of Fig. 10–7a, first work out the widths, r, of the *stirrup "regions,"* into the middle of each of which a stirrup is to be located.   Starting at the face of the support, compute r_1, the width of the *first region*, working in tabular form as in Table 10–1.   Since the xy boundary is horizontal, we first have three equal-width regions, r_1, r_2, and r_3, which extend to a point about an inch to right of point y.

Continuing from point y are the rest of the region widths of the wide first column of Table 10–1.   These were obtained using the (conservative) Step Approximation, but later corrected in the last column of the table.

Region r_4, the first whole one on the sloping portion of the shear diagram, started out to be 8.41 in. wide, but was subject to later *increase* or *decrease*, depending upon whether r_7 extended beyond or short of point z. In this case the corrective coefficient proved to be 1.026, which was finally applied to all the region widths along the slope yz.   Then all seven stirrup regions fit the 5 ft. 6 in. distance.

---

[13] Ordinarily the same size of stirrup is used throughout a given beam.

[14] See previous footnote.

Table 10-1. Determination of WSD Stirrup Regions for Beam of Example 10-5

Principally by the step approximation method

Regions r, and Their Widths*	Corresponding Decrease in V' $= wr/12 = 0.2375r$	V' for Next Region	Corrected Region Widths, r
$r_1 = \dfrac{sV'}{V} = \dfrac{192 \text{ kip-in.}}{23.04 \text{ kips}} = 8.32 \text{ in.}$	—	—	
$r_2 = \text{same} = 8.32$	—	—	
From pt. x 16.64 in.			$\Sigma = 24.00$ in.
pt. y 7.36 in.			
$\Big\{$ 0.884r_3 = (yet uncorrected) = 9.00 in.	—	—	0.98 in.
$\Big\{$ 0.116r_3 = 9.85 (0.96)/12 = 0.2375r = 0.23 kips		22.81 kips	8.63
$r_4 = 192/22.81 = 8.41$	$\times 0.2375 = 2.00$	20.81	9.46
$r_5 = 192/20.81 = 9.22$	$\times 0.2375 = 2.18$	18.63	10.72
$r_6 = 192/18.63 = 10.46$	$\times 0.2375 = 2.48$	16.15	12.21†
$r_7 = 192/16.15 = 11.90$			42.00 in.
Sum = 40.95 in., <42 in. needed to reach pt. z.			

Apply (42.0/40.95) = 1.026 stretch factor to get "Corrected Region Widths," into the middle of each of which a stirrup is to be located.

* Beginning at face of left support.

† Refer to Fig. 10-7a: By locating the seventh stirrup at 6 in. to the left of pt. z, the distance from it to the sixth stirrup is less than 12 in. Therefore, the earlier tentative choice of #4 stirrup size has proven satisfactory.

The midpoints of the corrected stirrup regions of Fig. 10–7b were located, projected down to (a) as stirrup locations, and dimensioned to the nearest inch.[15]

(g) For the explanation of why two additional stirrups were used, see item (g) of the Solution.

Final comment. Since the beam design loads, shears, bending moments, and permissible stresses used in WSD are all approximately half those of a corresponding U-S designed beam, the resulting beam section *can* have about the same content of concrete and steer when not over $1\frac{1}{2}$ per cent of flexure steel is used, as may be seen by referring to Fig. 2–21.   This means that one can often "jump" from WSD to USD, or vice versa, using the approximate conversion factor of 2, and thereby uncover a possible error in the initial calculation, or perform a check.

10–8. CONTINUATION ON WEB REINFORCEMENT

As already mentioned in Art. 3–7, on USD, greater economy in stirrup designing can be achieved by using the more complicated formula for v_c, which results in a higher value of V_c for the beam shear diagram.   In WSD, consult Formula 12–2 of Code Sec. 1201(d).

For the designing of web reinforcement consisting of bars bent to the 45° direction, together with the use of (vertical) stirrups, refer to Example 3–4, which involves a cantilever beam.

10–9. SUMMARY OF BOND, ANCHORAGE, SHEAR, AND DIAGONAL TENSION

In a reinforced concrete beam, the difference of the bending moments at any two chosen sections causes a corresponding difference in the flexural steel tensions, which results in a tendency for bar slippage, through the concrete due to *flexural bond stress.*   Unit flexural bond stress, u, varies directly with the beam shear, but inversely as the jd depth of the beam and the perimeter of the bars.   Shallow beams subject to heavy shear, and having only a few large bars, tend to have prohibitively high flexural bond stresses.

Every tensile-stressed point on a reinforcing bar must also be correspondingly *end-anchored* (by bar extension when needed) within a region of zero or compressive concrete stress by enough anchorage length, a', on both sides thereof to develop the computed tensile stress therein.   The corresponding bond stress upon the bar surface must not exceed the per-

---

[15] In this case, in order to better demonstrate the method, some stirrups were located by half-inches.

missible value of Code Sec. 1301 for bars of such diameter, surface, condition, and elevation within the member.

Such *anchorage bond stress*, u_a, is proportional to the *whole* value of T at the point in question, and is permitted to be considered uniformly distributed over the whole length of the end anchorage, whether the bar is straight, or curved to a radius no less than that of the "standard hooks" of Code Sec. 801.   When this *anchorage* bond stress proves to be less than 0.8 of the permissible, the adjacent *flexural* bond stress need not be computed.

Due to the tendency for plastic concrete to settle from underneath horizontal bars that are more than 12 in. above the bottom of a "pour," only about 70 per cent of their perimeters are considered effective in flexural bond or anchorage.   Therefore, Code Sec. 1301 recommends that bond stresses in such "top" bars be computed using *100 per cent* of their perimeters, but must not exceed the allowable values of Sec. 1301(c)(1) and (2), set at *70 per cent* of those for other bars.

The difference of the flexural tensions, ΔT, at any two chosen sections produces *horizontal shear* in the concrete, which is presently considered to have a uniform psi value over the whole d depth of the beam.

Spanwise, the unit horizontal (and vertical) shears, v, vary directly with the beam shear, but inversely with the beam width and d depth. Beams of small cross-sectional area that are subject to heavy external shear can have destructively high unit shearing stresses.

The distinct relative *tensile* weakness of concrete invites the particular combination of unit vertical and horizontal shearing stresses which results in a unit *diagonal tension* at 45° to the horizontal, also of an intensity, v, over sections normal thereto.

Reinforced concrete beams are prevented from failing prematurely in diagonal tension [3] by providing *web reinforcement*, which is preferably aligned normal to the direction of the potential diagonal cracking.

In a well-designed simple span beam, *diagonal tensile cracking* near the supports does not develop in test until considerably more than the design service load has been applied, so the concrete is relied upon to resist a portion of the diagonal tension [4].   On the other hand, some *minute flexural tensile cracking* usually occurs in the central region of large bending moment *before* all of the design service load has been applied, so the tensile strength of *that* bottom concrete is prematurely destroyed.

The total unit diagonal tension, v, is controlled in designing by providing sufficient beam depth, d, and width, b', on the tensile side.   Diagonal tension ("web") reinforcement is usually needed near the supports of short beams, but is often unnecessary in longer spans.

To allow for unanticipated variations in the *distribution* of the loading throughout spans, the Code now requires that all flexural members contain an empirically determined amount of web reinforcement *additional to*

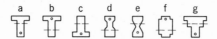

Fig. 10–8

that demanded by the accepted theory.   Typically, it calls for providing two additional stirrups inside the V_c point.   A specified *minimum percentage* for the web reinforcement also has been established.

CONTINUATION PROBLEM

10–6. In the sections pictured in Fig. 10–8, the steel indicates the tension side and the neutral axes are at the levels shown.

(a) Show clearly for each case what width to use in calculations for maximum diagonal tension unit stress.

(b) Formulate a rule defining the width to take in computing unit diagonal tension for any section.

(c) Show clearly, for each case pictured, the width to take in calculating p, the steel ratio, for use with the WSD flexure charts, where applicable (Appendix L).

QUESTIONS

1. Is bond stress entirely a form of shear?   Sketch thoroughly concrete's distribution of stress upon the surface of a modern deformed bar.

2. Distinguish *algebraically* between unit flexural bond stress and unit anchorage stress, with respect to the flexural tensile force T.

3. Evolve a formula for required anchorage length a', in terms of bar diameter, f'_c and allowable f_s; taking (a) bottom bars, and (b) top bars.   Follow the Code.

4. It has been stated that the flexural bond stress in flexural reinforcement is calculated at points along the *clear span*, while anchorage stress is calculated outside it. Now sketch how and where to provide the anchorage for the ends of (a) stirrups and (b) bent bars.

5. Sketch (a) the location and (b) the direction of the expected diagonal tension cracking at each end of a R/C beam that is fixed at the left end and hinged at the other.

6. Comparing bent bars and stirrups: Which is the more efficient?   Convenient? Expensive?

7. Should stirrups be placed inverted (a) in cantilever beams, or (b) near the (restrained) ends of continuous spans?   Why?   Is there a solution to the stirrup-setting difficulty involved?

8. Is there any Code flexural or shear regulation which, in effect, sets a minimum cross-sectional area for R/C beams?   Explain.

9. Can a horizontal flexure bar in the bottom near the end of a simple span resist diagonal tension as efficiently as a (vertical) stirrup of the same cross-sectional area? Explain.

REFERENCES

1. FERGUSON, PHIL M., and THOMPSON, J. NEILS, "Development [anchorage] Length of High Strength Reinforcing Bars in Bond," *Proc. ACI*, 1962, Vol. 59, pp. 887–922.

2. "Shear and Diagonal Tension (Part 2, Report of ACI–ASCE Committee 326)," *Proc. ACI*, 1962, Vol. 59, p. 353.

3. GURALNICK, SIDNEY A.   "Shear Strength of Reinforced Concrete Beams," *Trans. ASCE*, 1960, Vol. 125, p. 603.

4. "Warehouse Failures Pinpointed," *Engineering News-Record*, January 12, 1956, p. 21.

11

RETAINING WALLS

11-1. INTRODUCTION

The function of a retaining wall is to confine a mass of earth or other bulk materials.

Retaining walls are of two general types, *gravity* and *cantilever*. A gravity wall, illustrated in Fig. 11-1a, is usually built of plain concrete, though sometimes of stone masonry. It depends principally upon its weight for stability. Cantilever walls, shown throughout the rest of the illustration, achieve stability largely by having their rear portions tucked underneath the adjacent backfill. Thus the weight of a portion of the soil mass is used to help confine the whole in place. Cantilever walls consist of relatively slender elements well reinforced with steel. When such a wall is relatively high, the vertical *stem* and horizontal *base* portions are connected by ribs, making a *counterforted wall* when the ribs are hidden within the backfill, as at (c), or a *buttressed wall* if exposed in front of it, as shown at (d). *Bridge abutments* at (e) not only support the structure but also confine the approach fills and serve as a form of retaining wall.

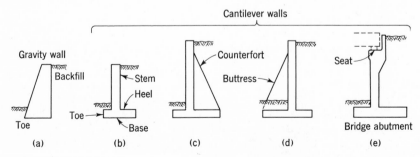

Fig. 11-1. Types of retaining walls.

11–2. FORCES UPON RETAINING WALLS

The designing of a retaining wall involves the determining of the earth pressure upon the back thereof and proportioning the wall for strength as well as for stability against overturning and sliding, while guarding against excessive settlement.

The pressure upon walls varies widely depending upon a number of factors, including the type of backfill soil, its seasonal condition, the drainage thereof, the possibility of an overloading of the surface of the backfill, and others. However, if the drainage facilities constructed are adequate, and if the backfill is a sandy or gravelly one of sufficient permeability and its grading is such that frost action will be negligible, the method of computing earth pressure illustrated in this chapter is applicable and conservative.[1]

The effects of some of the above-mentioned variable factors have been taken up briefly and evaluated in Appendix J. Others are beyond the scope of this text. A young engineer who encounters soil conditions appreciably different from those discussed in this chapter should, if he has had the benefit of formal training in *soil mechanics*, refer to the recent literature [1, 2, 3] of the field before proceeding with his designing. Otherwise, he should consult a specialist. Great strides have been made in this relatively new science, but the *maximum* pressure of a clay backfill still is unpredictable. Meanwhile its use should never be allowed. Granular (sandy) soils are assumed throughout this chapter.

11–3. THE COULOMB THEORY OF EARTH PRESSURE[2]

This well-established theory, developed over 190 years ago by C. A. Coulomb, a French army engineer, asserts that a dry sandy backfill tends to fail by the incipient slippage of a wedge thereof down a steeply inclined plane, called the *failure plane*, as the wall moves outward slightly and perhaps tilts a bit, as pictured in Fig. 11–2. The wedge comes into equilibrium under three forces W, P_A, and R—namely, the weight of the wedge,

---

[1] In this chapter the authors have undertaken to apply the findings of the science of *soil mechanics* to modernized designing of retaining walls without placing an undue burden upon those who have never studied the subject. A few soil mechanics terms and topics are used in connection with the illustrative Examples, and others less pertinent will be found in Appendix J.

[2] Modern developments suggest the use of the Coulomb method, and its graphic counterpart the Culmann method, for determining earth pressures generally.

The Terzaghi and Peck semiempirical chart method [1] may be used for relatively low walls and for quick preliminary earth pressure calculations for walls of any height.

The well-known simple and rapid Rankine method may well be used, instead of the semiempirical method, by those who still prefer it. Refer to Art. J–1 of Appendix J.

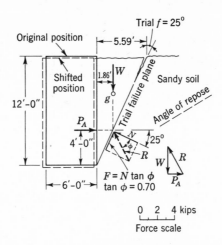

Fig. 11–2. Forces on a sliding wedge of sandy soil behind a gravity-type of retaining wall, after Coulomb (wall friction disregarded).

the resistance of the wall, and the resultant upward earth force, respectively —all of which must intersect in a point.

The incipient movement along the failure plane mobilizes a frictional force, $F = N \tan \phi$, where N is the intergranular pressure normal to the plane, and ϕ is the angle of friction, as in physics and mechanics. This friction between grains is called the *internal friction*. The resultant of forces N and F defines the resultant R. In Fig. 11–2, the third-point position of the point of intersection of the three forces is consistent with an assumed hydrostatic pressure variation along the failure plane and the back of the wall.

In the following example illustrating the Coulomb theory, the variable friction between the fill and the wall has conservatively been disregarded.

EXAMPLE 11–1

Gravity Retaining Wall Forces According to Coulomb

Given a rectangular plain concrete gravity-type retaining wall supporting a level backfill, as shown in Fig. 11–2.

It is desired to find the forces upon the sliding wedge of earth and upon the wall by the Coulomb theory of earth pressure.

The fill material is dry sand weighing 100 pcf; angle of internal friction, $\phi = 35°$; angle of repose, 30°. Take the weight of (plain) concrete at 145 pcf.

Required. Assuming that sliding is about to take place along the 25° trial failure plane, find by fundamental mechanics the magnitude, position, and direction of the earth force P_A per foot of wall. Disregard possible wall friction.

Solution. (All forces are per lineal foot of wall.)

The earth load, W, will act vertically downward at g, the centroid of the wedge, which is located at one-third of the distance from each side to the opposite vertex:[3]

$$W = 1\tfrac{2}{3}(5.59)(0.10) = 3.35 \text{ kips}$$

Making the customary assumption of hydrostatic variation of the pressure against the wall, the wall force, P_A, will act horizontally at one-third the distance up the wall.

From mechanics, the equilibrant earth force, R, must pass through the point of intersection of the forces W and P_A, as shown.   It is the resultant of the total normal force, N, over the whole failure plane *and* the internal frictional force, $F = 0.70N$, acting parallel thereto:

$$\tan 35° = 0.700, \quad \sin 35° = 0.574, \quad \cos 35° = 0.819$$
$$\sin 25° = 0.423, \quad \cos 25° = 0.906$$

Writing P_A, W, and R force components along the 25° trial failure plane:

$$P_A \sin 25° + R \sin \phi - W \cos 25° = 0 \tag{1}$$

While perpendicular to the plane we have:

$$P_A \cos 25° - R \cos \phi + W \sin 25° = 0 \tag{2}$$

Solving Eqs. 1 and 2 simultaneously:

$$P_A = 1.94 \text{ kips}$$

Also

$$R = 3.87, \quad N = 0.819R = 3.17, \quad \text{and} \quad F = 0.7N = 2.22 \text{ kips}$$

Earth Pressure Variations.   Obviously, the backfill which lies below the **angle of repose** shown in the figure does not contribute to the pressure upon a wall.   This fact should always be kept in mind no matter what method of earth pressure calculation is used.

The angle of repose for loose dry sand is approximately equal to ϕ. For uniformly graded round-grain sands, ϕ will vary from about 28°, determined from a loose-state heap, to about 35° for the dense state.

When the friction between the wall and the sand is considered, the force P_A pictured in Fig. 11–2 will be inclined upward, making an angle ϕ' with a normal to the wall surface, as defined by the frictional coefficient between sand and concrete.   In such cases it is probably best to reconcile the point of intersection of the three forces by moving the earth force R upward along the failure plane.

For the wall pressure P_A to have the low value computed above, it is necessary that the retaining wall be free to move (act) outward slightly under the pressure of the sand [2].   This situation is known as the (wall) **active case.**

If the wall is immovable, due to being connected to some larger structure, there can be no downward slipping of the sand, and because there is no motion, the helpful frictional force F cannot develop.   The wall

---

[3] The point is also at the intersection of *median* lines, drawn to each vertex from the midpoint of each side.

force P_A then has to be much larger in order to support the wedge of sand. This situation is known as the (wall) **at-rest case**, evaluated in Appendix J (Art. J–3).

Except by chance, the 25° failure plane assumed in Example 11–1 will not result in the maximum value of P_A for the active case. Other planes should also be studied, as outlined in the accompanying problems.

EARTH PRESSURE PRACTICE PROBLEMS

Assume sandy or gravelly soil.

11–1. Referring to Example 11–1 and Fig. 11–2, take an assumed sliding wedge failure angle of $f = 32°$ and recompute the Coulomb wall pressure, P_A. Then check independently by graphics, taking the scale 1 in. = 4 ft.

Partial Ans. $P_A = 1.91$ kips.

11–2. Same as Problem 11–1 except that $f = 20°$. Also plot all three of the values of P that have been found and deduce the maximum P by drawing a smooth curve through the points.

Ans. $P_A = 1.83$ kips. Maximum $P_A = 1.95$ kips, when f makes 27° 30′ with the vertical.

11–3. (a) Taking a coefficient of friction between the sand and the concrete of the wall of 0.45, recompute P_A of Example 11–1 considering wall friction.

(b) Recompute P_A for another assumed failure plane, and finally deduce the maximum P_A from a graph.

(c) Compare this maximum value of P_A with that found in Problem 11–2 and discuss.

11–4. THE STABILITY REQUIREMENTS

A good retaining wall must first of all be *stable;* that is, it must stay put. In this respect it should be proportioned to resist safely three possible destructive movements. This work is called the *stability designing.* There must be:

1. Adequate *resisting moment* about the toe to resist the *overturning moment* of the lateral pressure of the backfill,
2. Enough base width to distribute the load to the foundation soil without causing *excessive pressure concentration and settlement,* and
3. Sufficient frictional resistance along the plane of the base safely to resist the *sliding* tendency.

Resistance to overturning may be studied readily by constructing the *resultant force line* and extending it to the horizontal plane of the base, as shown in Fig. 11–3. The resultant of the lateral pressure P_A and the vertical gravity force W_c, representing the weight of the wall, is kj. From mechanics, its extension must fall within the middle third of the base if there is to be no uplift at the heel, and on the center of the base for the base pressure to be uniformly distributed, i.e., no tendency for unequal settlement. The ratio of the *resisting moment* of the weight of the retaining wall about the toe of the wall, t, together with that of any (inert) soil that may be resting thereon, to the overturning moment of the resultant

Plate 11–1. This roof system consists of repeating panels of 42-ft. square hyperbolic-paraboloid shells designed to a 3-in. thickness. All 88 shells were cast utilizing only 6 sets of movable forms, which were stripped and reset within an hour's time. (Courtesy of Portland Cement Association)

lateral pressure of the fill is termed the *factor of safety against overturning*. Its value should not be less than about 2.0, depending upon the specifications or the engineer's judgment.

Settlement is usually guarded against by ensuring that the vertical pressure at the base, particularly the toe, does not exceed an allowed value, such as the common safe footing values shown in Table 8–1. If the foundation soil is clayey, this practice is hardly satisfactory, since the clay consolidates as its entrapped moisture is very slowly squeezed out by the pressure of the wall, causing unsightly settlement and/or tilting.

Resistance to sliding is computed by multiplying the total vertical pressure upon the base by the appropriate coefficient of friction between the concrete and the foundation soil. The ratio of this sliding resistance to the horizontal component of the earth pressure against the wall is called the *factor of safety against sliding*. It should not be less than 1.5.

EXAMPLE 11–2

Stability of a Retaining Wall

Given the gravity wall studied in Example 11–1 and reproduced as Fig. 11–3.

Required. (a) To show graphically the forces acting upon the wall and to construct the path of the resultant force through the plane of the base.

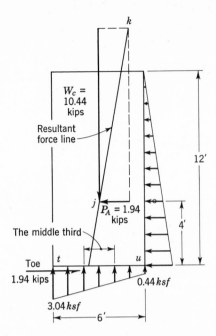

Fig. 11–3. Stability study.

Solution. The gravity force,

$$W_c = 6(12)(0.145) = 10.44 \text{ kips}$$

The resultant of W_c and P_A is the force kj which strikes the base at about three-fourths of the distance outward to the *edge of the middle third* of the base, so there will be no uplift.

(b) **Calculate** the factors of safety against (1) overturning, (2) sliding, and (3) the vertical soil pressures at both edges of the base. Take 0.4 as the coefficient of friction at the base.

Solution.

(1) The factor of safety against overturning is the ratio, about the toe point, t, of the moment of the gravity forces to the moment of the earth pressure forces:

$$\text{F.O.S.} = \frac{10.44[3]}{1.94[4]} = 4.04 \qquad \underline{\text{Against overturning.}}$$

(2) The factor of safety against sliding is the ratio of the potential resistance to sliding to the (earth) force tending to produce sliding:

$$\text{F.O.S.} = \frac{0.4(10.44)}{1.94} = 2.16 \qquad \underline{\text{Against sliding.}}$$

(3) The vertical soil pressure at both edges of the base may be computed as for footings subject to small overturning moment:

$$\text{Direct} = \frac{W_c}{A} = \frac{10.44}{6} \qquad = 1.74 \text{ ksf}$$

$$\text{Overturning: } I = \frac{bt^3}{12} = \frac{1(6)^3}{6} = 18 \text{ ft.}^4$$

$$\frac{Mc}{I} = \frac{1.94[4]3}{18} \qquad = 1.30$$

$$\text{Max.} = \overline{3.04} \text{ ksf} = 1.52 \text{ tsf}$$

$$\text{Min.} = 0.44 \text{ ksf} = 0.22 \text{ tsf}$$

Comments. If a downward wall friction force is developed upon the wall as the backfill moves downward, additional resistance to overturning will be created. On the other hand, if the wall also settles, such friction can be nullified, or even reversed in direction.

11–5. THE STRENGTH REQUIREMENTS

Although retaining walls of all types must meet the stability requirements, only the slender-membered cantilever ones require attention to strength: namely, the designing of three reinforced concrete cantilevers, the *stem*, *heel*, and *toe*. They must be proportioned for bending and diagonal tension, and the reinforcement checked for bond stress and anchorage as in other structures. This work will be illustrated in the succeeding Example 11–3.

11–6. CHOICE OF EARTH PRESSURE METHODS

In addition to the four variables mentioned in Art. 11–2, at least five more factors affect the pressure upon retaining walls; namely, the degree of care exercised in backfilling, the possible fixity of the wall, vibration (of sandy soil), the type of foundation soil, and the level of the water table. Some of these are taken up briefly in Appendix J. Nevertheless, Terzaghi and Peck [1] have summarized their masterly discussion as follows:

In connection with the design of retaining walls the planning of adequate drainage provisions and a careful consideration of the foundation conditions are more important than a correct evaluation of the earth pressure. The pressure exerted by the backfill can be estimated either on the basis of semiempirical rules or else by means of earth-pressure theory. The first method has the same drawbacks as the evaluation of the safe load on piles by means of pile formulas. Some walls designed according to this method are excessively safe, others are barely stable, and occasionally a wall fails. Nevertheless, for routine jobs the first method is cheaper and preferable. The second method requires that the backfill and the drainage system be constructed in strict compliance with the conditions imposed by the theory. The time and labor involved in this process are not justified, unless the retaining wall constitutes a prominent part of an individual job or has a height exceeding about 20 feet.[4]

The American Railway Engineering Association's 1953 *Specifications for Design of Retaining Walls and Abutments*, Section C, Article 2, third paragraph thereof, suggests the use of Rankine- or Coulomb-type earth pressure calculations (Art. J–1, Appendix J), but for walls not over 20 ft. high, these specifications permit the use of semiempirical charts,[5] such as the accompanying Fig. 11–4.

Since the AREA specification referred to was formulated relatively recently, and since it encourages practical usage of the findings of soil mechanics, we will follow it in designing a 16-ft. cantilever retaining wall, using the Terzaghi and Peck chart for the earth pressure.

EXAMPLE 11–3

The Design of a Cantilever Retaining Wall

It is desired to design a cantilever retaining wall of 16-ft. total height for Cooper's E-72 railway loading [4]. The 1953 AREA specification for retaining-wall design will be followed, taking AREA Type No. 1 backfill and foundation soil properties.

For concrete and steel, the ACI WSD Code, 3000-lb. concrete, specification 20,000–1350–9, and 50,000-psi-yield-point deformed reinforcing bars will be taken.

See accompanying Calculation Sheet 1 for additional starting information.

Solution. Refer to the several succeeding calculation sheets.

Retaining Wall Designing

11–7. THE PROPORTIONING OF A CANTILEVER RETAINING WALL (LARGE'S METHOD)

In Calculation Sheets 1 and 2, the earth pressure forces shown were gotten from the empirical charts previously mentioned. The railway equipment load was converted to an equivalent additional height of backfill, and the additional lateral pressure of this *surcharge* found. (If unfamiliar, refer to Appendix J.)

The design rule stated in Sheet 2 was utilized to get a trial base width, B, by taking moments of all forces to the rear of the front edge of the base of the stem. To do this, the desired position of the vertical component of the upward resultant reaction was set at e, just inside the edge of the

---

[4] Reprinted with permission from Terzaghi and Peck's *Soil Mechanics in Engineering Practice* (New York: John Wiley & Sons, Inc., 1948).

[5] Reprinted by permission from Peck, Hanson, and Thornburn's *Foundation Engineering* (New York: John Wiley & Sons, Inc., 1953).

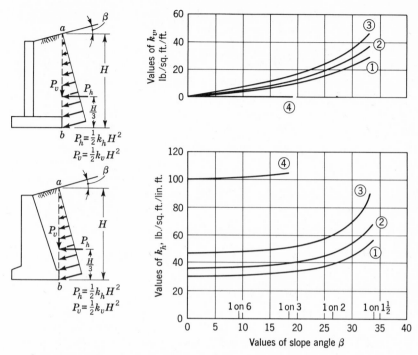

(1) Backfill of coarse-grained soil without admixture of fine particles, very permeable, as clean sand or gravel.

(2) Backfill of coarse-grained soil of low permeability due to admixture of particles of silt size.

(3) Backfill of fine silty sand, granular materials with conspicuous clay content, and residual soil with stones.

(4) Backfill of very soft or soft clay, organic silt, or silty clay.

Fig. 11–4. Chart[6] for estimating pressure of backfill against retaining walls supporting backfills with a plane surface. Use of chart limited to walls not over about 20 ft. high.

middle third[7] of the base, $0.66B$ from the rear edge in this case. The thickness of the base of the stem was then estimated at $0.14B$ and *centered* over the resultant force. The thickness of the base slab was taken the same as the base of the stem. Moments of the overturning and approximate[8] resisting forces *about e*, the resultant force point, yielded a trial base

[6] Included in Appendix K, which excerpts the specifications of the American Railway Engineering Association (AREA).

[7] For the poorer foundation soils, set the desired location of the reaction close to the center of the base, thus predetermining a substantially uniform pressure.

[8] In this approximate method, the moment of the disregarded toe portion is substantially offset by conveniently considering the concrete of the stem and heel portions no heavier than the soil.

Ex. 11-3	Design of a Cantilever Retaining Wall	$\mathscr{H.E.L.}$	11/9/-	1/8

DATA & SPECS — See Reference 4.

Rail Loading: Take 72,000 lb. axles at 5 ft. c-c on track and cross-section sketched on Calc. Sheet 2.

See Appendix K for '53 A.R.E.A. Specification

Backfill and Base Soil: The earth pressure will not be increased for impact or vibration per A.R.E.A., Secs. C1 & 2, third paragraph of each.
Consider water table at 15 ft. below foundation bed.

Sec.C2 —— Take A.R.E.A. *Type I soil:* $\gamma = 105$ pcf, $\phi = 33°42'$, tan. $= 0.667$.

Sec.D2 —— Coeff. of base-to-ground friction = 0.55,
Take sliding F. of S. = 1.5, O.T.M. F. of S. = 2.00 (added)

Sec.D3 —— Safe bearing capacity = 1.7 tsf (at F of S. of 2.0)

and its Fig. 2   Get foundation bed 4 ft. below final grade (frost).

$f'_c = 3,000$
$f_y = 50,000$
20,000-1350-9

Concrete & Steel: Per '63 ACI Sec. 808(a), provide 3 in. cover for steel if concrete is deposited against the ground.
    For concrete surfaces, after removal of the forms, and exposed to weather, or ground, a minimum of 2 in.
Assume $1\frac{1}{2}$ in. max. aggregate size.

Sec. F1 —— Heel stresses must not exceed $1\frac{1}{2}$ times allowable when foundation reaction is considered absent.

Sec. F1 —— Not less than 0.25 sq. in. temperature reinforcement in stem per foot of height.

"OLD RULES" - for proportions:

Sec.D1 —— "Get resultant force within the middle third of the base.
"Center the stem over the resultant force.
"Ten-inch min. stem top thickness (concrete placing)
"Try a base-of-stem thickness of $\frac{1}{6}$ to $\frac{1}{8}$ of the width of the base.
"Try a base thickness the same as the base-of-stem.

EARTH PRESSURE CALCULATIONS.

Use Terzaghi & Peck's empirical chart data for Type I soil: Refer to textbook Fig. 11-4.
For horizontal backfill, $k_v = 0$ and $P_v = 0$, $k_h = 31$.

$$P_h = \frac{1}{2} k_h H^2 = \frac{31}{2} \times \frac{(17)^2}{1000} = 4.48 \text{ kips}$$

Sec.C1 —— Equivalent soil head = $\dfrac{72000}{5(14)(105)} = 9.8$ ft.

Surcharge lateral pressure = 31(9.8) = 304 psf.

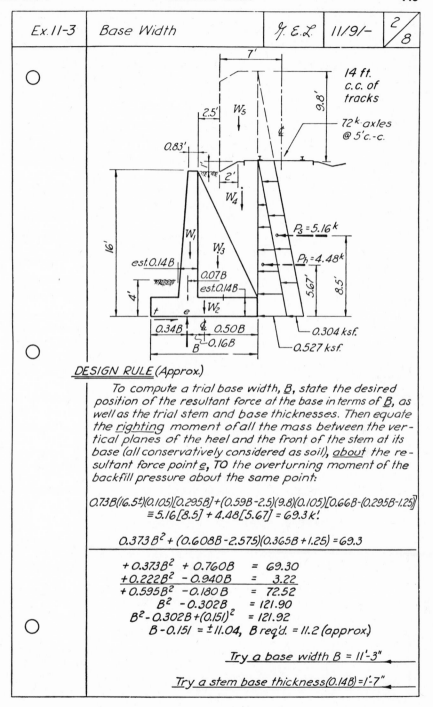

| Ex. 11-3 | Base Width | | 𝓎. E. L. | 11/9/– | 2/8 |

DESIGN RULE (Approx.)

    To compute a trial base width, B, state the desired position of the resultant force at the base in terms of B, as well as the trial stem and base thicknesses. Then equate the <u>righting</u> moment of all the mass between the vertical planes of the heel and the front of the stem at its base (all conservatively considered as soil), <u>about</u> the resultant force point e, TO the overturning moment of the backfill pressure about the same point:

$$0.73B(16.5±)(0.105)[0.295B] + (0.59B-2.5)(9.8)(0.105)[0.66B-(0.295B-1.25)]$$
$$\equiv 5.16[8.5] + 4.48[5.67] = 69.3k!$$

$$0.373B^2 + (0.608B-2.575)(0.365B+1.25) = 69.3$$

$$
\begin{aligned}
+0.373B^2 + 0.760B &= 69.30\\
\underline{+0.222B^2 - 0.940B} &= \underline{3.22}\\
+0.595B^2 - 0.180B &= 72.52\\
B^2 - 0.302B &= 121.90\\
B^2 - 0.302B + (0.151)^2 &= 121.92\\
B - 0.151 = \pm11.04, \quad B\,req'd. &= 11.2\ (approx.)
\end{aligned}
$$

<u>Try a base width B = 11'-3"</u>

<u>Try a stem base thickness (0.14B) = 1'-7"</u>

width of 11 ft. 3 in., which did not require revision later, in this instance.

The required base-of-stem thickness was next calculated in Sheet 3 because it is often the critical one.   The resulting 18.2-in. demand proved consistent with the 0.14B early assumed.   The thickness of the base of the wall was then tentatively taken at 19 in. also, awaiting calculation thereof.[9]

Throughout this portion of the work one undertakes to settle *only* the *concrete* dimensions, namely, the *outline* of the structure, leaving spaces on his sheets for the later computation of the reinforcement needed, as was done in this case.

11–8. THE CHECKS UPON STABILITY

In the lower half of Sheet 3 and the upper half of Sheet 4 the very important matter of *stability* could be accurately studied because the dimensions of the retaining wall had become established.

Overturning must always be studied in tabular form, keeping the vertical *resisting* forces separate from the horizontal *overturning* forces. It is also a good plan to isolate and identify the surcharge forces because they are transient ones and are sometimes excluded, as was done at the top of Sheet 4.

Of course, there are other combinations of loadings and manners of application, as well as different methods of getting the forces, but the two possibilities considered usually "bracket" the common cases.

Sliding of the wall upon the foundation soil is a possibility involving only the horizontal and vertical forces, not moments of forces.   In this case, the structure would probably prove safe without a base shear key if more vertical load were on the structure, increasing the sliding resistance. Such a condition would exist if the surcharge extended to the rear face of the stem, or if the heel portion were lengthened to "gather" more earth (gravity) load.

Toe pressure is some measure of the tendency of a retaining wall to settle at the toe and is almost independent of whatever the overturning moment factor of safety, computed earlier, may be.   In the present case the calculated maximum unit toe pressure was slightly less than the allowable of 1.7 tons per sq. ft. for our granular soil.   Oftentimes, with poorer foundation soils, this is the critical point in the stability calculations. When the toe stress turns out excessive, it can be brought under control rather easily by lengthening the toe portion, which decreases the eccentricity of the resultant ground reaction with respect to the centerline of the base, and incidentally, widens the base.   The overturning calcula-

---

[9] If the front face of the stem has batter, any slight tilting of the wall will never be noticed.

Ex. 11-3	Stability etc.	$\mathcal{G.E.L.}$ 11/9/-	3/8

STEM STRENGTH – 1'-7" stem & base being tried

○

17.00
1.58
15.42

$$Shear\ Force = \left(\frac{15.42}{17.0}\right)^2 (4.48) + \frac{15.42}{17.0}(5.16) = 8.38^k\ max.$$

$$D.T.\ \underline{d}\ req'd. = \frac{V}{bv} = \frac{8380}{12(60)} = 11.63"\ Per\ A.C.I.\ Table\ 1002(a)$$

3.69
4.69 3 [15.42'
8.38   5.14

Conservatively calculating diagonal tension at face of supporting member.

$$\underline{B.M.}_{max.} = 3.69\ [5.14] + 4.69\ [7.71] = 55.2^{k'}$$

19.0
36.2
55.2

$$Flex.d\ req'd. = \sqrt{\frac{M}{Rb}} = \sqrt{\frac{55.2\,(12000)}{224\,(12)}} = 15.70"$$

0.50 bar rad.
2.00 cover

Make base of stem 1'-7," trying #8 bars   18.20"

—————————//————————————————————//——————

See Calc. Sh.6
for arrange-
ment of stem
steel

(Later)

$$R = \frac{M}{bd^2} = \frac{55.2\,(12000)}{12(16.50)^2} = 203,\qquad p = 1.16\%$$

Flexural   Req'd A_s/ft.= 2.30 □"

Bond Stress   Equals #8's @ 4.13" max.

$$u = \frac{V}{\Sigma_0 jd} = \frac{8380}{12/4.13(\pi)(7/8)(16.50)} = 64\ psi,\ OK$$

< 263 psi of '63 A.C.I. Sec. 1301(c)

○

Req'd Anchorage -A.C.I. Sec. 805 (b), Splices in (Tensile)
Reinforcement, must be consulted.

STABILITY   –Assuming a 1'-7" base slab.

(a) Against Overturning: ΣM about bot. toe pt. $\underline{t}$
RESISTING:

Vertical Forces	Kips	Arm	Moment
			–Clockwise
$W_1 = 1.21\,(14.42)(0.15)$ =	2.62	3.98'	10.43$^{k'}$
$W_2 = 1.58\,(11.25)(0.15)$ =	2.67	5.62	15.00
$W_3 = 6.67(14.42)(0.105) \div 2 =$	5.05	6.81	34.40
$W_4 = 6.67(15.42)(0.105) \div 2 =$	5.40	9.03	48.75
	15.74		108.58

Surcharge (transient)

○

$W_5 = 4.17(9.8)(0.105) =$	4.29	9.17	39.40
	$\Sigma V = 20.03^k$		$\Sigma M_R = 147.98^{k'}$

OVERTURNING:

Horizontal Forces			Counter-clockwise
P_h =	4.48	5.67	25.4
P_s surcharge =	5.16	8.50	43.9
(transient)	$\Sigma H = 9.64^k$		O.T.M.= 69.3$^{k'}$

tion, as in Sheet 3, is then easily corrected because all the original vertical forces have had their moment arms lengthened by the amount of the widening. Reiterating: *The resultant forces will be found to be relatively much nearer the center of the enlarged base, which results in a much smaller Mc/I component of toe pressure.*

Omission of vertical forces. The overburden directly over the toe is always disregarded, except when it is paved. Neither is the soil directly in front thereof (Fig. 11–5) relied upon to resist sliding. Both these earth masses tend to shrink away from the wall.

As in the case of surcharge, the vertical component of inclined backfill pressure, or a portion thereof, is sometimes omitted from calculations when it is conservative to do so; particularly if there is some possibility of settlement of the wall relative to the backfill.

STABILITY PRACTICE PROBLEM

11–4. Calculate how wide the base of the retaining wall of Example 11–3 should be in order to bring the toe stress down to 1.25 tons per sq. ft.

INSTRUCTOR: *See also stability investigation Problem 11–7 at the end of the chapter.*

11–9. THE REINFORCEMENT

The strength design of the stem[10] and toe in Sheets 3 and 4 presented no new problems. Attention is called to the practice of deducting the dead load of the toe when proportioning it and its reinforcement, as in footing design.

The heel strength computations on Sheet 5 pose two new practices. The cantilever bending moment was properly computed about a *support point* $2\frac{1}{2}$ in. inside the stem, where its main reinforcement is centered, as shown in Sheet 6. Also, alternate situations were considered in finding the design shear and bending moment forces. As usually computed, they are (from Sheet 5) 7.95 kips and 44.18 kip-ft. However, Appendix K (AREA Sec. F–1, last paragraph) requires that the allowable unit stresses shall not be exceeded more than 50 per cent if uplift should occur and the upward ground reaction disappear. Accordingly, on Sheet 5, when the "upward" items are disregarded, the design forces become 16.37 kips and 63.73 kip-ft. In the tabulation, directly below these values, two-thirds of each has been set down for direct comparison with the original values ("Total"). Note that in this case the original total moment predominated, and was used in designing the reinforcement, but that the reverse situation prevailed with respect to shear. Also observe that the dead load of the heel itself was purposely included, since it contributes to the tension in the top when there is uplift. Otherwise not.

[10] A possible improvement would be to make the base of the stem thicker than required for a balanced section, resulting in wider bar spacings.

$Ex.11-3$	$Stability, Toe$	$\mathcal{J}.\mathcal{E}.\mathcal{L}.$　$11/9/-$	$\frac{4}{8}$

Net Toe Moment — *to locate resultant force:*

○

$2\underline{|11.25'}$
$3\underline{|5.63}$
$\quad 1.87$

All forces acting:　$x = \dfrac{147.98 - 69.30}{20.03} = 3.93,' or 1.70' to left of$ ₵,

$F. of S. = \dfrac{147.98}{69.30} = 2.13, > 2.0, \therefore O.K.$ $= 0.17'$ inside kern, O.K.

$< 2.2, a 10\%$ economy limit.

$\begin{array}{ll} 5.63 & 5.63 \\ \underline{3.93} & \underline{5.28} \\ 1.70 & 0.35 \\ & 108.58 \\ & \underline{25.40} \\ & \overline{83.18} \end{array}$

If surcharge absent:　$x = \dfrac{108.58 - 25.4}{15.74} = 5.28,' or 0.35' to left of$ ₵, O.K.

$F. of S. = \dfrac{108.58}{25.4} = 4.27, O.K.$

Sec. D2
of A.R.E.A.

(b) Against Sliding　　　　　　A.R.E.A. coeff. = 0.55

—All forces acting:　$F. of S. = \dfrac{0.55(20.03)}{9.64} = 1.14, < 1.5,$ inadequate.

Surcharge absent:　$F. of S. = \dfrac{0.55(15.74)}{4.48} = 1.93$

Must design a base shear key. See later work.

(c) Toe Pressure — All forces acting.

○

$\dfrac{N}{A} = \dfrac{20.03}{11.25} = 1.78$

$I = \dfrac{(11.25)^3}{12} = 119$

$\dfrac{Mc}{I} = \dfrac{20.03(1.70)(5.63)}{119} = 1.61$

$\underline{3.39}\ ksf.$

$11.25'$　$3.0'$　$1.58'$　$6.67'$　0.11　$6.88'$

$1.58(0.15) = 0.24$ ksf base D.L.

A.R.E.A. Sec. D3
and its Fig. 2

≤ 1.7 tsf allowed, O.K.
End of Stability Studies.

TOE STRENGTH

$\begin{array}{l} 3.15 \\ 2.29 \\ 2\underline{|5.44} \\ 2.72 \end{array}$

Diagonal Tension

$d\ req'd. = \dfrac{V}{bv} = \dfrac{2.72(3)(1000)}{12(60)} = 11.34''$

$\begin{array}{l} 3.15 \\ \underline{1.14} + \\ 4.29 + \end{array}$

Bending
$B.M. = \left\{1.575[2] + 1.145[1]\right\}(3) = 12.9\ k.'$

A.C.I.
Sec.
808(a)

$\begin{array}{r} 19.0 \\ \underline{-3.5} \\ d = 15.5 \end{array}$

$d\ req'd. = \sqrt{\dfrac{M}{Rb}} = \sqrt{\dfrac{12.9(12000)}{224(12)}} = 7.6''$

(Later) — Having taken 1'-7" base thickness, and #8 bars:

Ref. '63 A.C.I.
Sec. 911(b)
○ 0.002 min.

p

$R = \dfrac{M.}{bd^2} = \dfrac{12.9(12000)}{12(15.5)^2} = 53.7, p = 0.27\%, > 0.20$

Req'd. A_s/ft. = 0.57 □'' equals #8 bars @ 18.8" c.-c. max. spacing.

Try #8 bars @ 16'' — to splice to stem bars @ 16.''

| *Ex.11-3* | *Toe, Heel* | $\mathcal{H}.\mathcal{E}.\mathcal{L}.$ | *11/9/-* | 5/8 |

Toe, concluded: *Taking #8 bars @ 16"c.c.*

$$\text{Flex. bond, } u = \frac{2.72(3)^{16}\!/_{12}(1000)}{\pi(^{7}\!/_{8})(15.5)} = 255 psi, < 263, O.K.$$

Anchorage: Of upturned toe bar ends by *tensile splicing* them to stem bars. Refer to Art. *11-11* for *calculation* of the 26.1 in. *lap.* Use Code min. of 2'-6".

HEEL STRENGTH

	Forces –*downward*	*Kips*	*Arm* *	*Moment* *
$W_3 = 3.33(14.42)(0.105)$	$=$	5.05	2.44	12.32^k
$W_4 = 3.34(15.42)(0.105)$	$=$	5.40	4.66	25.20
$D.L.= 1.58(6.88)(0.15)$	$=$	1.63	3.44	5.61
SURCHARGE		12.08		43.13
$W_5 = 4.17(9.8)(0.105)$		4.29	4.80	20.60
		16.37		63.73

$$\tfrac{2}{3} \text{ thereof} = \boxed{10.92} \qquad \tfrac{2}{3} = \boxed{42.50}$$

*See Sheet 4*___*Upward*

*About stem reinf. resistance point, $3\tfrac{1}{2}"$ inward

6.88(1.07)	$=$	-7.36	2.29	-16.85
6.88(0.085)	$=$	-0.59	4.59	-2.70
	Total $=$	7.95^k down	Total $= 44.18^{k'}$	

A.R.E.A. Sec. F1 possibility of no ground reaction rules *flexure.*

$$3\underline{|6.88}$$
$$2.29+$$
$$\underline{\times 2}$$
$$4.59$$

Bending

$$d \text{ req'd.} = \sqrt{\frac{M}{Rb}} = \sqrt{\frac{44.18(12000)}{224(12)}} = 14.04"$$
$$\qquad\qquad 0.50 \text{ bar rad.}$$
$$\qquad\qquad \underline{3.00} \text{ cover}$$
$$\text{Req'd. thickness} = 17.54", \text{ rules}$$

$$9.17$$
$$\underline{4.29}$$
$$4.88$$

Diag. Tension

$$d \text{ req'd.} = \frac{V}{vb} = \frac{10920}{(60)(12)} = 15.16", \text{ rules.}$$

6.67	15.16
.29	-3.50
6.96	18.66

Make heel 1'-7" and take #8 bars.

(Later)

$$R = \frac{44.18(12000)}{12(15.5)^2} = 184, \quad p = 1.05\%, A_s/ft. = 1.95^{\circ\,"}$$

$$19.00$$
$$\underline{-3.50}$$
$$15.50$$

Flexural   *Means #8 @ 4.85" or less.*

Bond Stress

$$u = \frac{V}{\Sigma_o jd} = \frac{10920(4.85)}{12(\pi)(7/8)(15.50)} = 104 psi, < \frac{3.4\sqrt{f_c'}}{D} = 186 psi$$
$$\qquad\qquad\qquad\qquad\qquad\qquad O.K.$$

Req'd. Anchorage ~ of top bars, spaced @ 4 in. c.c., per A.C.I. Sec. 1301(b):

$$a = \frac{A_s f_s}{\Sigma_o u_a} = \frac{0.79(20000)\left(\frac{4.00}{4.85}\right)}{\pi(186)} = 22.3" \text{ past the}$$
$$\qquad\qquad\qquad\qquad\qquad\qquad\qquad \text{resistance point.} *$$

Make heel bars 8'-6" long.

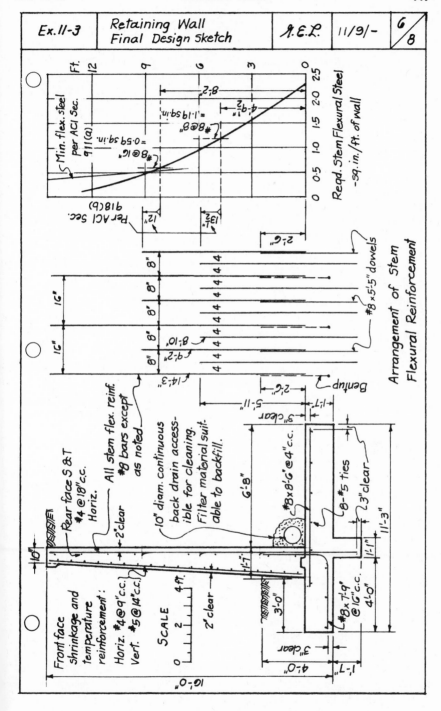

| Ex.11-3 | Retaining Wall Final Design Sketch | A.E.L. | 11/9/- | 6/8 |

As is usually the case, the required heel thickness set the minimum thickness of base slab.

The required steel area per inch of width, the tentatively chosen bar size, and the corresponding embedment required for anchorage were computed for all three of the cantilever elements, for convenient reference in later selecting the final arrangement of the reinforcement.

11-10. BAR ARRANGEMENT

In Sheet 6, the stem reinforcement dominated the arrangement of the rest of the steel.

In *construction*, the base slab (with key) is first placed and allowed to set. The stem forms are then built upon it. The longest stem bars are then set upon the base concrete and laterally secured to the stem forms. They are spliced into the base concrete by straight vertical dowels previously embedded therein, or by bentup extensions of the toe steel, as in this case. Refer to the central portion of Sheet 6.

The stem bar size finally selected was one which, at the top of the wall, could work at some wide spacing divisible by four, and which did not exceed the $3t$ spacing, maximum value 18 in., permitted by ACI Sec. 804(c). As shown on Sheet 6, a spacing decreasing from 16 in. down to 4 in. was used, with all bars being #8's; the lengths thereof varying according to the accompanying diagram of steel area required at each level.

The bars extending only 5 ft. 11 in. above the base were considered to be short enough to support themselves, so the base concrete was cast around them.

Since a base shear key was needed, it was located so that it served as an anchorage block for the 5 ft. 5 in. straight **splicing dowels**, which also reinforce it for bending!

The toe steel size was chosen for a 16-in. spacing so that its bent-up ends could serve as splice material for one-fourth of the stem bars. The heel steel was arbitrarily spaced at 4-in. centers so as to avoid any interference with the rest of the reinforcement.

11-11. SPLICING OF BARS FOR TENSION

At the top of the base slab some of the stem bars must be *tensile-spliced* to bars below. As shown in ACI Sec. 805, the requirements therefor are more demanding than for the anchorage of a single bar end, as taken up in Sec. 1301(b). There must be enough *lap* to hold the anchorage bond stress, u_a, down to $\frac{3}{4}$ of the normal permissible value, and for our **contact splices** the lap must be further increased by 20 per cent. Also, the lap for deformed bars must be at least 30 bar diameters.

To splice a *stem bar* to a 5 ft. 5 in. *base shear key bar* (noting that the stem bars are spaced at 4 in. versus the required 4.13-in. maximum spacing computed on Calculation Sheet 3):

$$\text{Reqd. } a = \frac{A_s f_s}{(0.75 u_a) \Sigma o} (120\%), \qquad \text{min. value } 30D$$

$$= \frac{0.79(20,000)(4.00/4.13)}{(0.75)(263)(\pi)} (120\%) = 29.7 \text{ in.}$$

Make lap 2 ft. 6 in.

The splicing of a *stem bar* to a *toe bar* is the same, except that $(4.00/4.13)$ should be replaced by $(16.0/18.8)$, since the toe bars are spaced at 16 in. versus the required 18.8-in. maximum spacing computed near the bottom of Calculation Sheet 4.   Therefore, $a = 26.1$ in.

Make lap 2 ft. 6 in.
(The Code min.)

11–12. DESIGN OF BASE SHEAR KEY

Calculation Sheet 7 presents a recommended practice [5].   Refer especially to Fig. 11–5, noting that reliance is placed upon the passive resistance of the earth below the toe point.

Base shear keys have sometimes been proportioned for the passive resistance computable at the face of the key, kq, from the base pressure. To so act, the wall would have to lift itself, according to the pictured deformation of the unit cube.   This will not happen if failure can occur more easily along $ptqrji$.   Refer to Appendix Fig. J–2a.

Note that no reliance whatever is being placed upon the upper foot of the toe fill, or upon the *lateral* strength of the earth in front of the toe.

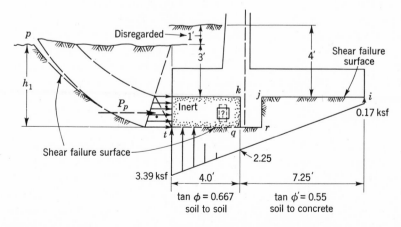

Fig. 11–5.   Passive resistance and shearing action at base shear key.

Ex.11-3	Keys	$\mathscr{Y}.\mathscr{E}.\mathscr{L}.$	11/91-	$\dfrac{7}{8}$

DESIGN OF SHEAR KEYS

Stem Key

This is closely a case of pure shear, for which an allowable of at least $0.08 f'_c$ may be taken: *(Table 1-1, Chapter 1)*

$$V_{max.} = \frac{8380}{6.5(12)} = 108 \text{ psi}, < 240, \therefore O.K.$$

Base Shear Key
Ref. "Sliding" on Sheet 4, and Fig. 11-5.

At incipient leftward sliding of the retaining wall, the value of a key will depend upon how much passive resistance, P_p, can be developed below the toe as a potential failure surface develops. For this purpose, the weight of the upper foot of toe fill earth has conservatively been disregarded.

From fundamentals, or Appendix J, Arts. J-1 and J-4, the *active* hydrostatic pressure ratio is:

$\phi = 33°42'$

$45°\ 0'$
$16°\ 51'$
$28°\ 9'$

$$C_A = \frac{1}{C_p} = tan^2[45° - \phi/2] = tan^2\ 28°\text{-}9' = 0.286$$

Taking $\underline{h}_1$ as in Fig. 11-5, the passive resistance will be:

$$P_p = \frac{\gamma h^2}{2 C_A} = \frac{0.105}{2(0.286)}[h_1^2 - (3)^2] = 0.183 h_1^2 - 1.65\ k/ft.$$

At incipient sliding failure:

$$P_p + tan\ \phi W_{toe} + tan\ \phi W_{heel} = \Sigma H (F.\ of\ S.)$$

*From bottom of Sheet 3.

$$0.183 h_1^2 - 1.65 + 0.667(3.39 + 2.25)\left(\frac{4}{2}\right) + 0.55(2.25 + 0.17)\left(\frac{7.25}{2}\right) = 9.64(1.5)$$

Req'd. $h_1 = 4.54'$, req'd. key depth = $1.54'$, make 1'-7."

Refer to Sheet 6. Study has shown that the existing large dowel bars will safely reinforce the key for bending if its horizontal dimension be only 7 inches. Conveniently make it at least 12 in. and cleanly trim the trench to undisturbed surfaces.

The reader is cautioned against the use of a deep base key, the need for which always reflects foundation weakness. See also note on sheet 8.

| Ex. 11-3 | S. & T. Reinf | | 4. E. L | 11/91- | 8/8 |

SHRINKAGE & TEMPERATURE REINFORCEMENT

Stem — Refer to A.C.I. Sec. 2202(f) & (g)

Horizontally

14' $(1.2'_{av.})(144)(0.0025) = 6.0$ sq. in. total.
In front face, $20 - \#4 @ 9"c.-c. = 4.0$ sq. in.
In rear face, $10 - \#4 @ 18"c.-c. = 2.0$ sq. in.

Vertically

In front face:
$1.2'av.(12)(12)(0.0015) = $ 0.26 sq. in. per ft.
Use $\#5 @ 14"c.c.$
In rear face, the flexure reinforcement serves.

Base Slab See text Art. 11-13.

Provide about 0.1% as ties.
$11.25'(1.58')(144)(0.001) = 2.56$ sq. in.
$8 - \#5's$ will do.

NOTE: This example illustrates the design proceedure for the retaining wall proper only. The more important problem of foundation stability has not been attempted. This would require the consideration of the equilibrium, not only of the wall alone, but of the wall and the backfill acting together as a unit, as in the case of an unretained earth slope.

First, there may be a possibility of sliding on a weak substratum in the foundation rather than sliding on the base of the wall itself. There also exists a possibility of general settlement of the entire area, although this can usually be minimized by avoiding overstress at the toe of the wall. Finally there remains the possibility of a deep-seated rotational-sliding failure of the foundation.

On these questions, refer to B.K. Hough's Basic Soils Engineering (2d ed.), The Ronald Press Co., 1969.

For the key to be effective, the trench must be cleanly cut and the shoulder at kq firm and free of root holes. If such is not the case, the unsound portion may be removed, a form placed, and the earth replaced by thorough compaction of thin layers. If the earth is not cohesive enough to compact properly, it should be stabilized by the addition of not over 10 per cent of clay. After drying, the form is removed and the concrete of the key placed integrally with the base concrete.

BASE SLIDING PRACTICE PROBLEMS

11–5. For the retaining wall of Example 11–3 above, calculate the required depth of base shear key if the passive resistance computable at the face of the key from the foundation pressure were relied upon for the additional shearing resistance needed. Comment upon your result.

11–6. For the retaining wall of Example 11–3, endeavor to get along without a base shear key by making the heel (and base) longer, and discuss your findings.

11–13. SHRINKAGE AND TEMPERATURE REINFORCEMENT

This reinforcement is needed to control expansion and contraction perpendicular to the direction of the flexure steel in structures that are extensive in that direction. Refer to Calculation Sheet 8.

For the stem portion, ACI Sec. 2202(f) and (g) for the walls of buildings was followed, since there is no section on retaining walls. It requires a minimum of 0.25 per cent of *horizontal reinforcement,* spaced at not over 18 in. About two-thirds of it is ordinarily located near the exposed front face.

The above requirement exceeds that of AREA Sec. F–1, which calls for a minimum of 0.25 sq. in. per ft. of wall height.

Vertically, the Code-required 0.15 per cent was provided near the front surface. The rear one is taken care of by the flexure reinforcement.

The base slab is primarily a buried footing which is little subject to temperature or moisture variations. About 0.1 per cent of reinforcement was provided longitudinally of the structure to serve principally as ties for the flexure bars. As much as 0.3 per cent is *sometimes* provided to reinforce the base against possible soft spots in the foundation soil.

Expansion Joints. Keyed *expansion joints* should be located about 80 ft. apart or more, depending upon the climate. At intermediate 20-ft. intervals, weakened plane *contraction* joints should also be provided.

11–14. DRAINAGE FEATURES

The *continuous back drain* covered with filter material, pictured on Calculation Sheet 6, is satisfactory for chart-designed walls up to 20 ft. high. An alternate scheme is the provision of *weep holes* through the lower portion of the stem. They are less satisfactory because (a) they cannot be gotten low enough to drain the full height of the backfill, (b) they tend to become clogged with snow, ice, and debris, and (c) the emerging water tends to soften the foundation soil at the critical toe point.

Retaining walls higher than 20 ft. not only require the determination of the earth pressure forces by accepted soil mechanics theory, but also "that the backfill and drainage system be constructed in strict compliance with the conditions imposed by the theory" (see Art. 11–6). Their drainage should include such features as a sloped impermeable top layer of backfill, a vertical gravel (French) drain[11] covering the entire back surface of the stem (or wall) and/or an inclined drainage layer conforming roughly to the backfill failure plane. Refer to Chapter 8 of Reference 1, this chapter.

11–15. COUNTERFORT RETAINING WALLS

The high cantilever type of walls are most economically proportioned if the stem and heel are tied together at intervals by ribs called **counterforts,** as illustrated in Fig. 11–1c. Both stem and heel are designed as continuous slabs extending longitudinally of the wall. Their bending moments and thicknesses are thereby much decreased, but this saving is partially offset by the cost of the counterforts. The *buttress* type of wall, also pictured, is a variation thereof. For the designing of these walls, see *Reinforced Concrete Structures* by Dean Peabody, Jr., published by John Wiley and Sons, Inc., New York.

11–16. SUMMARY OF RETAINING-WALL DESIGN

Structurally, a cantilever retaining wall is a vertical cantilever anchored to a footing. Such walls are relatively light, so the weight of the front portion of the backfill is much relied upon for their stability.

The process of determining the dimensions of the members is a simple one, but the great differences in the pressures exerted by the various soils, together with the vagaries of weather conditions, combine to make an accurate determination of the forces acting an impossibility.

One of the most enlightening approaches to retaining-wall design is that of Coulomb, who many years ago visualized a sliding wedge of granular soil, the weight of which was partially supported by an inclined upward ground force, and more importantly, by the lateral resistance of the wall.

From an engineering standpoint *internal friction* is probably the most essential attribute of a granular soil, since it is responsible for the *shear*

---

[11] The Terzaghi and Peck design charts of Fig. 11–4 include an allowance for the increase in backfill pressure due to the imperfect drainage features of low retaining walls.

Plate 11–2. Workmen setting and tying the stem reinforcement for a cantilever retaining wall. Note the horizontal shrinkage and temperature steel.

resistance, the most important strength property.   All the usual methods of retaining-wall design rely upon the presence of an active internal friction between the soil grains.   When it does not exist, the wall must be a great deal larger and stronger.   Refer to Appendix J.

To determine the trial dimensions needed in the initial stages of the *designing* process, employ the Terzaghi and Peck semiempirical charts, the simplified Coulomb formula of Eq. J–1, Appendix J, or the Rankine formula to approximate the earth pressure.   High or complexly loaded walls should be designed, or at least checked, by the Culmann graphics or some other acceptable trial wedge procedure.

A retaining wall may fail in four ways; namely, by sliding, overturning, settlement, or by breaking apart.   Such fracturing can be due to overstress in bending, shear or diagonal tension, bond or anchorage.

Tilting and settlement of a retaining wall on granular soil is forestalled by proportioning it so that (1) the resultant foundation reaction is within the middle third of the base, and (2) the allowable foundation pressure is not exceeded.   For poorer soils the foundation reaction should be near the center of the base.

When attempting to laterally deform a soil mass against gravity forces, its high *passive resistance* is encountered.   This property is used advantageously in designing abutments and base shear keys.

RETAINING WALL PROBLEMS

11–7. For the retaining wall of Fig. 11–6 make a complete stability investigation, including a diagram of foundation pressure.   Use the Terzaghi and Peck earth pressure chart.   Follow the AREA Code and prepare a brief report of your findings:

    (a) Taking AREA Type 1 backfill and foundation soil.

    (b) Taking AREA Type 2 backfill and foundation soil.

11–8. Additionally for the retaining wall of Fig. 11–6, make a complete strength

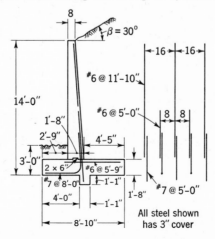

Fig. 11–6

investigation, including the base shear key and all bar anchorages.   Take 2500-lb. concrete and the ACI Code for its allowable stresses.   The reinforcement is intermediate grade, high bond, deformed bars.   Follow the AREA Code for the retaining wall requirements and prepare a brief report of your findings:
  (a) Taking AREA Type 1 backfill and foundation soil.
  (b) Taking AREA Type 2 backfill and foundation soil.

11–9. (a) Design a cantilever retaining wall of 20-ft. total height for Cooper's E-70 railway loading.   Take AREA Type 2 backfill and foundation soil properties and follow this retaining wall specification throughout.

For concrete and steel take the ACI Code, 3750-lb. concrete and high bond, intermediate grade, reinforcing bars.

For any additional starting information consult the instructor.

(b) Make an independent check upon the stability of the retaining wall by the best available method.

11–10. Given the reinforced concrete box culvert of Fig. 11–7.   Investigate the safety thereof considering it as a rigid frame subject to 300-psf highway vehicle surcharge loading, the overburden and the lateral pressure of the earth.

Take AREA Type 2 soil and specification.

Take ACI 3000-lb. concrete and specification, also high bond deformed bars.

NOTE: Consult the instructor for any additional starting information needed.

11–11 (Individual). Determination of the Concrete Dimensions of a Cantilever Retaining Wall.

Given: AREA Type 1 soil and specification, and a backfill slope of 33°42′ (no surcharge).   For concrete take ACI 3000-lb. concrete and specification, and high bond deformed bars.   The aggregate maximum size is $1\frac{1}{2}$ in.

Required: Taking your assigned total height and the Peck charts for earth pressure, follow the old rules and the general procedure of the calculation-sheet pages of the chapter.

Further, in order to meet the quite conservative value of maximum toe pressure dictated by Fig. 2 of the AREA Specification (reproduced as Appendix Fig. K–1 in this text), design to have the resultant vertical earth force at $0.15B$ from the center of the base for the first trial, and not over $0.167B$ for the final position.

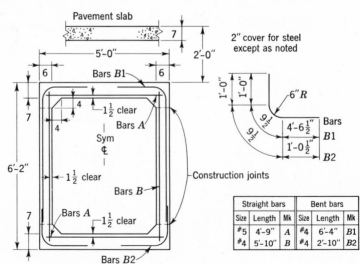

Fig. 11–7

In addition, ensure that your design has satisfactory stability whether or not the vertical component of earth pressure, P_v, acts.   The probabilities are that a greater base width, B, will be required when P_v is absent.   Therefore:

1. In your first calculation for required B, stem thickness and toe pressure, consider P_v absent.
2. Check the structure evolved in (1) above with P_v present, and revamp if necessary.

If a toe pressure proves too great, refer to Art. 11–8 for guidance.   To avoid wastefully wide base slabs see that the overturning moment factor of safety does not exceed 2.2 under the controlling loading condition.

Group	Total Height of Wall
	18 ft.
	15 ft.
	13 ft. 6 in.
	12 ft.

If the stem thickness required for strength differs by more than 2 in. from that originally taken, recalculate the required B dimension, as on Sheet 2/8.

Finally, draw an end view sketch of your wall at the left end of a sheet, as in Sheet 6/8, to the scale 1 in. = 4 ft.

11–12 (Individual). Design of the Reinforcement for the Cantilever Retaining Wall of Problem 11–11.

Given the cantilever retaining wall with an inclined backfill surface, the concrete dimensions of which were designed in the preceding problem for Type 1 soil, following the 1953 AREA *Retaining Wall Specification*, and the ACI Code for reinforced concrete design.

Required to design the steel for the structure, following the ACI Code and Chapter 11 of the textbook.   The aggregate maximum size is $1\frac{1}{2}$ in.

Systematically arrange your calculations, taking up the stem, toe, heel, and base shear key in order, and making the following subheadings:

1. List your shear and moment forces (from the preceding problem).
2. Study diagonal tension and shear, including the stem key designing.
3. Study bending.
4. Study bond.
5. Study anchorage (including also that of the dowel bars).

Indicate in each case what steps you have taken to ensure a safe design, whether or not P_v is acting.

Also calculate the shrinkage and temperature reinforcement, following the Chapter 11 work, and locate it properly.

Finally make a *final design sketch* to the scale 1 in. = 4 ft. showing the (a) position, (b) bar size number, (c) length, and (d) spacing of all steel.   Include the two stem steel diagrams, as in Sheet 6/8 of Chapter 11 *in projection therewith, and on the same sheet,* neatly pasting on more paper if necessary.

Indicate the clear distance of all flexure steel from the face of the concrete, or cover with a general note.   The shrinkage and temperature steel is to be identified as such.

Also be sure to include all the concrete dimensions, the class of the concrete, and the type of soil on the drawing.

QUESTIONS

1. Define *retaining wall*. Distinguish between the five types. Indicate under what circumstances each should be used.

2. Name and discuss the many factors that affect the forces which come upon retaining walls.

3. State the Coulomb theory of earth pressure.

4. Taking a level backfill of sand, what portion of it presses against a wall? Is the angle ϕ a factor? Explain.

5. Enumerate all the factors which influence the presence or absence of friction between a wall and a backfill. What usually is the effect of disregarding it?

6. Enumerate the ways in which a retaining wall might fail. State reasonable specification requirements to prevent each.

7. Define *hydrostatic pressure ratio*. Explain whether it can ever exceed unity. What is the hydrostatic pressure ratio of mercury? See Appendix J.

8. State clearly how to compute the factors of safety against sliding, overturning and soil bearing failure.

9. If a retaining wall is securely fastened to some other large structure at its ends, will it require more material or less material than in the usual case? Explain.

10. To what extent will muddy water press more heavily upon a wall than clean water? Illustrate with a numerical example. Is the method the same for a saturated backfill?

11. How may the required base width of a gravity wall be determined systematically?

12. Explain *passive resistance*. What is wrong with the term *passive pressure?* What is the fundamental difference in action along the failure plane as between active and passive cases? What use is made of the principle in designing?

13. What is the advantage in having a foundation bed consist of undisturbed earth? Is it impossible to produce equal or greater strength by compaction of loose material? Explain.

14. Which is better: to have a uniform foundation pressure at the allowable bearing value, or widely varying edge pressures both of which are appreciably below the allowable value?

15. What precautions need to be observed in designing the reinforcement for retaining walls? Which reinforcement is likely to be overlooked in designing?

16. Which end of the base slab would you lengthen if (a) the toe pressure is too great? (b) the sliding factor of safety is too low? Explain.

REFERENCES

1. TERZAGHI, KARL, and PECK, RALPH B. *Soil Mechanics in Engineering Practice.* New York: John Wiley & Sons, Inc., 1948. Chap. 8.
2. TAYLOR, DONALD W. *Fundamentals of Soil Mechanics.* New York: John Wiley & Sons, Inc., 1948. Chap. 17.
3. PECK, R. B., HANSON, W. E., and THORNBURN, T. H. *Foundation Engineering.* New York: John Wiley & Sons, Inc., 1953. Chaps. 11, 15, 22.
4. WILBUR, JOHN B., and NORRIS, CHARLES H. *Elementary Structural Analysis* (2d ed.). New York: McGraw-Hill Book Co., Inc., 1960. Chap. 1.
5. FISHER, G. P., and MAINS, R. M. "Sliding Stability of Retaining Walls," *Civil Engineering,* July, 1952, p. 54.

TIME-DEPENDENT STRAINS: CREEP OF CONCRETE

12–1. TERMS AND DEFINITIONS

As mentioned in Arts. 1–13 and 1–14, loaded concrete, like other building materials, immediately develops an *elastic deformation* proportional to the magnitude of the load. In addition, it continues to deform with lapse of time, though at a gradually decreasing rate, until the action finally ceases. Because this latter continuing deformation did not at first appear to be proportional to the magnitude of the applied load or stress, early investigators called it *plastic deformation*. The term *plastic flow* also was used for many years to designate this unusual property of concrete.

In recent years it has been shown experimentally [1] that the delayed deformation which takes place within the lower half of the stress-strain

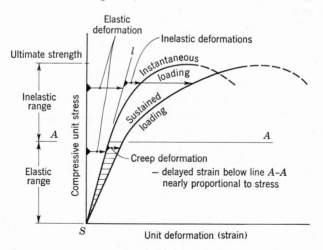

Fig. 12–1. Creep and inelastic unit deformations of concrete.

diagram for concrete (Fig. 12–1) is nearly proportional to the loading [2], and is best called **creep** deformation. Therefore this lower portion of the diagram may, without serious error, be called the *elastic range* of the material. The sum of the elastic and creep unit deformations is sometimes used to compute an elapsed time modulus of elasticity, E_{ct}, of decreased value, called the *sustained modulus*, for the particular concrete age and loading duration involved. The subscript t is used to indicate that *time* is a factor therein.

Thus *creep* of concrete is the delayed, or *time-dependent*, portion of the total unit deformation, or *strain*, resulting from stress within the proportional elastic range of the material. It may become considerably greater than the instantaneous, or immediate, elastic unit deformation. It is partially recoverable, depending upon the duration of the load.

J. R. Shank (1887–1963) was Research Professor of Structural Engineering at The Ohio State University and an early experimenter in creep and inelasticity. After careful analysis of all available world data, he evolved creep formulas for American engineers, and showed by numerical examples their application to everyday design of reinforced concrete members. During the 1930's he perfected a rapid method of securing creep-free straight-line stress-strain test data, the results of which anticipated by many years the E_c values of the present Code. (Refer to Fig. 1–3.) His paper, "The Mechanics of Plastic Flow of Concrete," won him the Wason Medal of the American Concrete Institute.

In the upper half of the stress-strain diagram of Fig. 12–1, a small increment of stress quickly produces a disproportionately large increment of strain[1] which is nonlinear in nature and largely *independent of time*, now called **inelastic** deformation. Obviously this is the region of large stress adjustments due to slippage between particles as the ultimate strength is reached at the highest point of the curve. This stage is usually followed by a destructive breakdown, which occurs so quickly that there is a falling off of the test machine load. In today's concrete nomenclature the term *inelastic range* is applied to this locality of large deformations which develop rapidly within the upper region of stress approaching failure. They cause stress redistributions, are nonlinear in nature, and nonrecoverable upon removal of the load.

12–2. CREEP DIAGRAMS AND ELASTICITY

Figure 12–2 shows some typical creep data curves.[2] Specimen A was loaded to 1500 psi at 28 days. Specimens B and C were loaded to 750 psi at the 28-day age. Specimen C was unloaded 62 days later and its *creep*

---

[1] It is almost wholly recoverable if the duration of the loading approaches zero.

[2] Students of soil mechanics and foundations will recognize the similarity of the shape of typical creep-time curves to that of consolidation-time graphs of data from soil settlement tests made under constant load.

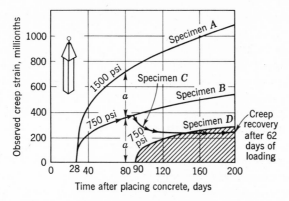

Fig. 12–2. The time element in creep and creep recovery (sustained stress and stress removal).

strain recovery observed. Specimen D was first loaded to 750 psi at the 90-day age. Note that the creep ordinates of specimens A and B that were loaded at the 28-day age for 172 days were proportional to the imposed stresses, thus justifying the linear relationship depicted in the lower portion of Fig. 12–1.

To simplify the presentation, the *elastic strain*, 250 millionths in the 750-psi specimens, was omitted from the lower portion of the figure, leaving only the creep.

Elastic materials return to their original form instantaneously when all load is removed, so they are said to *recover*. In the case of concrete the effect of the *duration* of the load must be recognized in discussing recovery, since the *rate* of both creep and *creep recovery* is much slower at the later load-removal ages. Note in the lower portion of Fig. 12–2 the relatively small creep that occurred in specimen D when the 750-psi stress was applied at the 90-day age. On the other hand, consider specimen C, which was loaded at the 28-day age and *unloaded* at the 90-day age. The effect of this operation may be visualized by conceiving the 28-day *compressive* load to remain on, then applying an equal additional *tensile* one at the 90-day age, and adding the two effects. This has been done geometrically in the figure by subtracting each specimen D creep-time ordinate from that of the corresponding specimen B. The arrows indicate that the creep became considerably less after the unloading, but the large remainder accounts for the common unqualified statement that concrete structures do not recover well.

12–3. EFFECT OF IMPULSIVE LOADS VERSUS DEAD LOAD

By transferring our attention from the 90-day age to the 28-day one, Fig. 12–2 will show that, had the 750-psi load been removed immediately after being applied, instead of 62 days later, the specimen would have fully recovered, since *there can be no creep under load without a lapse of time.* This means that the design live loads of fast-moving vehicles, if applied without impact and quickly removed, seldom cause permanent strains in well-cured concrete bridge members.

On the other hand, the *dead load* of a member, relatively large in concrete structures, comes on only once; and is not removed in service. It usually comes upon the member at the early age of form removal, and so adds a great deal of creep strain to the elastic strain.

It should by now be apparent that the prediction of the deformation or deflection of concrete members is not a simple matter. (It involves other variables yet to be discussed.) To make even an estimate of the expected deformation one needs the whole *stress history* of the member. Formulas for estimating creep effects will be presented in succeeding articles.

Concrete is different from the other structural engineering materials. As Dr. Freyssinet has said:

Concrete is far more like a living tissue. Like the latter, it is affected by any external action—variation of pressure, temperature, or humidity—and since part of the effect is irreversible there remains a part which is never completely effaced. Thus it has a memory, and I think that the memory—even in its highest manifestations—is no more than a hysteresis phenomenon as in the case of cement. It has its age; when the circulation canals have reduced their sections to the extreme, its properties approach those of true solids. It has its sleep, for its activity may be slowed down or stopped by lack of water, and restarted by wetting.

Of all its similarities to a human being, that which interests us most is its faculty of healing its wounds, and its ability to overcome causes of failure.

12–4. THE NATURE OF CREEP

The hydration of portland cement proceeds with the formation of a jelly-like *gel* around each particle. It continues until the entire particle has finally been completely hydrated. The time required varies greatly, depending upon the size of the cement particles, the availability of sufficient water and the influence of retarders; it is believed by some that the gel in time changes to crystalline forms.

Creep is due to compression of the gel by load. It may be due partly to an actual loss of water volume forced toward the outside surface through capillary channels, since the rate of creep is faster in a dry curing atmosphere.

The *rate* of creep is greater for a small member, of low strength concrete, of high water/cement ratio, low cement factor and large slump, when hand placed, cured in a dry atmosphere, then loaded at an early age, considering the other influences constant in each instance. The rate is greatest immediately after load application, but decreases quite fast, asymptotically.

For cured-in-air concretes, about one-fourth of a 5-year creep takes place during the first 14 days of loading, one-half during the first 3 months and three-fourths during the first year. Concrete loaded at the 4-year age creeps very little, so it recovers almost completely after being unloaded. It is believed that it reaches this stable state due to solidification of the gels.

12–5. THE FORMULA FOR CREEP UNDER SUSTAINED STRESS

Although good expressions have been devised by Straub, Thomas, and others for predicting the ordinates, δ_t, of a creep-time curve of concrete, as in Fig. 12–2, only Professor Shank's [3, 4] will be briefly illustrated here, namely:

$$\delta_t = C \sqrt[r]{t} \qquad (12\text{--}1)$$

where δ_t = *specific creep*, the *time*-dependent unit creep strain of concrete per psi of sustained compressive stress, in millionths

C = the *first day's creep strain* under a stress of unity, also expressed in millionths (from tests)

r = a root index deduced from tests

t = the *duration of the loading*, in days after the age, a, at loading.

For *ordinary strength concretes*, i.e., in the 2500- to 4000-lb. range, made with normal standard portland cement and good limestone aggregates, or equivalent, loaded in air at the 28-day age, Shank recommended

$$\delta_t = 0.13 \sqrt[3]{t} \qquad (12\text{--}2)$$

This formula is satisfactory up to one year of loading. For longer periods he applied the following multipliers to the value of δ_t at one year.

Number of Years Loaded	Multiplier m
1	1.00
2	1.17
3	1.26
4	1.30
5 or more	1.33

When normal standard portland cement concrete was loaded at ages other than the 28-day one, Shank modified C in Eq. 12–1 to

$$C = \frac{0.500}{\sqrt[2.5]{a}}$$

where a is the age when loaded, in days.

The following table has been prepared from Shank's recommendations, assuming good limestone aggregate concrete loaded in air.

		Shank's C-value, in millionths	
Class of Concrete	a = Age When Loaded in Air, in days	Normal Standard Portland Cement	High Early Strength Portland Cement
For ordinary strength concretes:	4	0.29	[3]0.13
f'_c = 2500 to 4000 psi	7	0.23	0.10
	14	0.17	0.07
	28	0.13	0.049
	60	0.10	0.034

For different aggregates, cements, ages when loaded, and curings studied by Shank, see page 51 of Reference 4.

12–6. LONG-TIME CREEP PREDICTIONS FROM THE RESULTS OF TESTS

Since the prediction of *long-time* creep values is of most interest to designers, Fig. 12–3 was prepared to clarify the relationship of the previously mentioned terms involved. Note that it was necessary to show two different "breaks" in the curve of creep strain in order to include the 5-year long-time value.[4]

In Table 12–1 are shown the end results of tests *made independently* by Shank [4], Shideler [5], and Glanville [6]. They included both normal standard and high early strength portland cement concretes, from which it may be seen, in column 7, that satisfactory strengths are possible at the early age of 4 days even when lightweight aggregates are used.

In the upper portion of the table, the long-time creep of the standard portland cement concretes consistently varies inversely with the concrete strengths. In the lower portion, the variation of both factors is relatively less. But note that the creep values of high early strength concretes

---

[3] This 0.13 value is from $C = 0.26/\sqrt{a}$ of Reference 4, p. 51 thereof.

[4] Since the publication (in 1958) of ten creep-time graphs of test data secured by Troxell, Raphael, and Davis [10] over durations up through 20 years, the term "long-time" has been extended by 15 years! The 20-year values run about 10% greater than the 5-year, and may be referred to as δ_{ttt}. Twenty-year data were also secured on drying shrinkage.

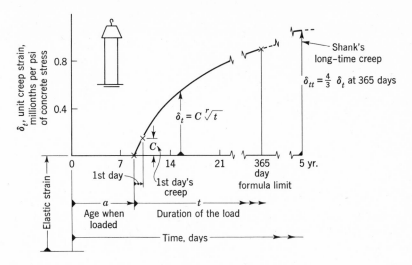

Fig. 12–3. The graphics of Shank's prediction of unit creep strain, from tests.

average smaller than in the upper part of the table, in spite of their being loaded earlier, cured for shorter periods, and, in the last case, containing the weaker lightweight aggregates.

In the designing of precast pretensioned beams and slabs, as in Chapter 14, a long-time unit creep strain, δ_{tt} of 0.40×10^{-6} is widely used.

Creep in Axially Loaded Members

EXAMPLE 12–1

Given a 3000-lb. standard portland cement unreinforced stone concrete pier loaded in air to 700 psi at the 14-day age.

It is required to compute the unit creep strain after two years of loading. Calculate also the instantaneous elastic strain, and compare.

Solution. Referring to the formulas and tables of Art. 12–5: Basically,

$$\delta_t = C \sqrt[3]{t}$$
$$\delta_t = 1.17(0.17) \sqrt[3]{365} = 1.42 \text{ millionths per psi}$$

So,   700-psi unit creep strain $= 700(1.42 \times 10^{-6}) = \underline{0.00099 \text{ in./in.}}$

and   Corresp. elastic strain $= \dfrac{f_c}{E_c} = \dfrac{700}{3,150,000} = \underline{0.00022 \text{ in./in.,}}$
ACI Sec. 1002(a)

so the creep strain is over four times the elastic in this case.

CREEP PRACTICE PROBLEMS

12–1. A 3500-lb. high early strength portland cement stone concrete pedestal is loaded to 800 psi at the 7-day age. Compute the unit creep strain after one and four

Table 12–1. Predictions of Long-Time Unit Creep Strains, δ_{tt}, from Tests

(1) Cement Used	(2) Investigation	(3) Aggregate Used	(4) Curing	(5) Age a at Loading in Air, days	(6) Unit Creep Strain from 5-yr. Long-Time Loading Duration: $\delta_u = C \sqrt{t}(\frac{2}{3})$, 10^{-6}/psi	(7) Ultimate Compressive Strength of Cylinders
Normal standard portland	Shank's prediction from his tests	Good limestone	Moist-cured for 7 days	28	$\delta_u = 0.13 \sqrt[3]{365}(\frac{2}{3}) = 1.24$	1930 28-day 2500-3750-psi strengths
	From Shideler's test data*	Good natural stone	Moist-cured for 7 days at 74°F	28	$= 0.76$	Recent 28-day 5410 psi
	5-test avg.	Lightweight	Moist-cured for 7 days at 74°F	28	$= 0.80$	Recent 28-day 4980 psi avg.
High early strength portland	Shank's prediction from Glanville's tests†	Good limestone	Moist-cured	28	$\delta_u = 0.049 \sqrt[3]{365}(\frac{2}{3}) = 0.47$	1933 28-day 4000-psi avg.
	From Shideler's test data*	Good natural stone	Moist-cured for 1 day at 74°F	4	$= 0.74$	Recent 4-day 4250 psi
		Good natural stone	Steam-cured for 15 hr. at 160°F	4	$= 0.46$	Recent 4-day 4050 psi
	5-test avg.	Lightweight	Steam-cured for 15 hr. at 160°F	4	$= 0.54$	Recent 4-day 5270-psi avg.

* Reference 5, this chapter.
† Reference 6, this chapter.

years of loading.   Calculate the elastic strain also.

Partial Ans.   0.00057 in./in., at 1 year
0.00074 in./in., at 4 years.

12–2. A 3000-lb. standard portland cement stone concrete pier 30-ft. high is loaded in air to 900 psi at the 14-day age, and unloaded at the 60-day age. Compute the creep strain in inches at the 90-day age. Refer to Fig. 12–2.

Ans.   0.133 in.

12–3. Same as Problem 12–2 except that the pier is reloaded at the 90-day age. Compute the creep strain at the 1-year age.

Creep in Columns

EXAMPLE 12–2

Given a 20-in. diameter R/C column with 12-#9 vertical bars, to carry 400 kips. Have high early strength portland cement concrete, $f'_c = 3000$ psi, $n = 9$, per Sec. 1002(a); $f_y = 40,000$ psi.

Required to find f_c and f_s therein after creep if loaded with 400 kips at the 7-day age (a) for a 125-day duration; also (b) if 5-year long-time loaded, and (c) to comment thereupon.

Solution.   (a) Must calculate E_{ct} and n_t for 125-day load duration, and compute the corresponding stresses elastically (WSD).

Taking a 1-psi concrete stress: $E_c = E_s/n = 29 \times 10^6/9 = 3.22 \times 10^6$ psi,

$$\text{Elastic strain, } \delta_e = 1 \text{ psi}/3.22 \times 10^6 = 0.31 \times 10^{-6}$$
$$\text{Creep strain, } \delta_t = C \sqrt[3]{t} = 0.10 \sqrt[3]{125} = \underline{0.50}$$
$$\text{Total} = \overline{0.81 \times 10^{-6}}$$

Corresp. $E_{ct} = \dfrac{1 \text{ psi}}{0.81 \times 10^{-6}} = 1.235 \times 10^6$, the "sustained modulus."

$$n_t = \frac{E_s}{E_{ct}} = \frac{29}{1.235} = \qquad\qquad \underline{23.5, \gg 9}$$

Calculation of 125-day stresses:

$$314 f_{ct} + 22.5(12) f_{ct} \equiv 400,000 \text{ lb.} = 584 f_{ct}$$
$$f_{ct} = 400,000/584 = 685 \text{ psi}, \quad f_{st} = 23.5 f_{ct} = \qquad \underline{16,100 \text{ psi}}$$

From the WSD axial column formula of Code Sec. 1402:

$$\text{Safe } P = A_g(0.25 f'_c + 0.4 f_y p_g)$$
Allowed $f_c = 750$ psi,   allowed $f_s = $ 16,000 psi
Column could be considered safe.

Solution.   (b) If column is 5-year long-time loaded:

Elastic strain, δ_e, as before $=$ 0.31×10^{-6}

Creep strain, $\delta_t = 0.10 \sqrt[3]{365}(4/3) = $ 0.953
(long-time)

1.263×10^{-6} due to 1 psi

Corresp. $E_{ct} = \dfrac{1 \text{ psi}}{1.263 \times 10^{-6}} = 0.792 \times 10^6$

$$n_t = \frac{E_s}{E_{ct}} = \frac{29.0}{0.792} = \qquad\qquad \underline{36.6, \ggg 9}$$

Calculation of 5-year long-time stresses:

$\frac{314}{427}$
$\overline{741}$

$$314f_{ctt} + 35.6(12)f_{ctt} \equiv 400,000 \text{ lb. } = 741f_{ctt}$$
$$f_{ctt} = 400,000/741 = 539 \text{ psi}, \quad f_{stt} = 36.6f_{ctt} = \qquad \underline{19,700 \text{ psi}}$$

These also may be considered safe stresses.

Comment (c). On comparing the stress results of the 125-day loading with those of the long-time loading, one sees that the creeping concrete keeps "passing the buck" to the steel as time elapses, although at a decreasing rate.

A re-examination of the long-time case will show that had the column been loaded when only 4 days old, the steel stress would be about 21,300 psi.

Because the continuing creep of concrete increases the stress in compressive steel, its WSD allowable stress has long been held lower than the tensile.

Creep in Flexural Members

12–7. BENDING STRESSES AND DEFLECTIONS OF SINGLY REINFORCED BEAMS WITH LAPSE OF TIME

Here we principally wish to make a reasonably accurate prediction of the elastic plus creep deflection of R/C beams under long-continued loads which cause stresses in the so-called "Elastic Range" of performance depicted earlier in Fig. 12–1. The current trend toward longer spans is making it imperative that beam and slab constructions be designed to meet the rather strict test deflection limitations of Sec. 909.

Our ability to predict longtime R/C beam deflections, as originally presented in the United States by Shank [4], has lately been strengthened by studies of the results of Washa and Fluck's [7] beam creep deflection tests, and, more recently, Yu and Winter's [8], which enable one to evaluate the *additional* deflection due to shrinkage warpage (Fig. 12–5) with reasonable confidence.

EXAMPLE 12–3

Singly Reinforced Beam Investigation

Given the Washa and Fluck test beams B-3 and B-6 of Reference 7 and pictured in Fig. 12–4. Assuming ACI 3500-lb. concrete and specification, the beams were designed in the usual manner for a total load of 107 plf over a 20-ft. simple span. The ones tested, actually of 3680-lb. strength, were loaded at the 14-day age for $2\frac{1}{2}$ years. Standard portland cement and good stone aggregates were used. The f_y was 40,000 psi.

It is required to investigate (a) the flexural unit stresses and (b) the deflection after the $2\frac{1}{2}$ years by Shank's creep method. Also to compare the computed total deflection with that observed by Washa and Fluck.

Solution. From Code Sec. 1102(a):

$$E_c = 33(w)^{3\!/_2} \sqrt{f'_c} = 33(145)^{3\!/_2} \sqrt{3680} = 3,500,000 \text{ psi}$$

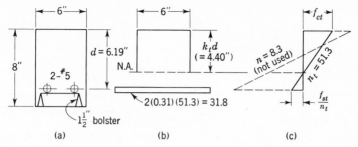

Fig. 12-4. Beam investigation for stress and deflection, after creep.

Unit elastic strain:

$$\delta_e = \frac{1 \text{ psi}}{3,500,000} = \qquad 0.286 \times 10^{-6}$$

Referring to Eq. 12-1 of Art. 12-5, and the tables adjacent thereto:

Unit creep strain:

$$\delta_t = C \sqrt[r]{t}(m) = 0.17 \sqrt[3]{365}(1.22) = \qquad 1.485 \times 10^{-6}$$
$$\text{Total} = \qquad 1.771 \times 10^{-6}$$

Note that for this concrete and early loading $\qquad$ the creep strain is over
$\qquad \qquad \qquad \qquad \qquad \qquad \qquad \qquad \qquad \qquad$ 5 times the elastic.

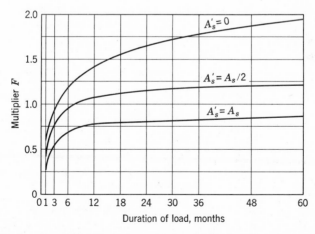

Fig. 12-5. Yu and Winter's multipliers [8] for time-dependent beam deflection, additional to the immediate (elastic) deflection. (This additional deflection is due to creep plus shrinkage of the concrete. Refer also to Fig. 1, page 21 of the 90-page "Commentary" [9] on the Code, published by the American Concrete Institute.)

Sustained modulus:

$$E_{ct} = \frac{1 \text{ psi}}{1.771 \times 10^{-6}} = 565{,}000 \text{ psi}$$

$$n_t = \frac{E_s}{E_{ct}} = \frac{29 \times 10^6}{0.565 \times 10^6} = 51.3$$

(a) **Stresses.** Refer to Fig. 12–4.

To find the decreased value of maximum f_c after creep, calculate the N.A., I, and Mc/I:

Get k for such unusual values of n from Chart L–5 of Appendix L (singly reinforced beams only):

$$pn_t = \frac{2(0.31)(51.3)}{6(6.19)} = 0.856, \text{ find } k_t = 0.71, \, k_t d = 4.40 \text{ in.}$$

$$M = wL^2/8 = 107(20)^2/8 = 5350 \text{ lb.-ft.}$$

Get I_{ct}:

$$6(4.40)^3/3 = 171.0$$
$$31.8(1.79)^2 = \overline{101.9}$$
$$I_{ct} = \overline{272.9} \text{ in.}^4$$

$$\text{Max. } f_{ct} = \frac{Mk_t d}{I_{ct}} = \frac{5350(12)(4.40)}{272.9} = 1035 \text{ psi,}$$

$$< 1610 \text{ of the Washa elastic designing.}$$

Since $(1 - k_t)d = 6.19 - 4.40 = 1.79$ in.,

$$f_{st} = \frac{n_t M(1 - k_t)d}{I_{ct}} = \frac{51.3(5350)(12)(1.79)}{272.9} = 21{,}600 \text{ psi,}$$

$$> 19{,}250 \text{ of the Washa elastic designing.}$$

(b) **Deflection.** Refer to Code Sec. 909(a) through (d).

The formulas for the *elastic* deflection, y, of beams all have the product EI in the denominator thereof, the one for a uniformly loaded simple span being $y = 5wL^4/384EI$. It has been found that the large *creep* deflection will also be embraced if:

1. The *sustained* modulus of elasticity, E_{ct}, computed after a loading duration t, and
2. The sustained moment of inertia, I_{ct}, computed from the section still effective at the time t, are used.

The deflection is *required* to be computed in this case, since, from Code Sec. 909(b) our total depth, $t = 8$ in., is less than $l/20$, which is 12 in.

As to what section is to be used to calculate the moment of inertia to be used in computing deflection, Code Sec. 909(c) states that if $pf_y > 500$ psi, the transformed cracked section[5] is to be taken; as it is in this case, since $pf_y = 0.0167(40{,}000) = 668$ psi.

Calculated deflections. Refer to Fig. 12–6.

[5] As stated in the ACI "Commentary" [9], the reasoning behind the above simple approximation is that the magnitude of the *effective* deflection moment of inertia depends upon the amount of hairline tensile cracking which has taken place. If the

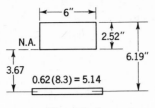

Fig. 12–6

Elastic + creep deflection from 2½-year duration:

$$\Delta = \frac{5wL^4}{384E_{ct}I_{ct}} = \frac{5(107)(20)^4(12)^4}{384(12)(565,000)(272.9)} = \qquad \underline{2.50 \text{ in.}}$$

Instantaneous-elastic only: $E_c = 3,500,000$ psi, $n = E_s/E_c = 29/3.5 = 8.3$.

$$pn = \frac{0.62(8.3)}{6(6.19)} = 0.138, \quad k \text{ (from Appendix L chart)} = 0.408, \quad kd = 2.52 \text{ in.}$$

Get I_c for elastic condition:

$$
\begin{array}{rl}
6(2.52)^3/3 = & 32.0 \\
5.14(3.67)^2 = & 69.3 \\
\hline
I_c = & 101.3 \text{ in.}^4
\end{array}
$$

$$\Delta = \frac{5wL^4}{384E_cI_c} = \frac{5(107)(20)^4(12)^4}{384(12)(3,500,000)(101.3)}, \qquad \text{elastic only} = \underline{1.08 \text{ in.}}$$
$$\text{Therefore,} \qquad \text{due to creep only} = \underline{1.42 \text{ in.}}$$

Corresponding WSD design stresses:

$$f_c = \frac{Mc}{I} = \frac{5350(12)(2.52)}{101.3} = \qquad \underline{1,594 \text{ psi}}$$

$$f_s = \frac{nMc}{I} = 8.3\left[(1594)\left(\frac{3.67}{2.52}\right)\right] = \qquad \underline{19,200 \text{ psi}}$$

Comment upon Example 12–3. Table 12–2 presents a comparison of computed stresses. It shows the 1594-psi WSD concrete stress to be close to the $0.45f'_c$ design allowable of 1656 psi, which the ACI sets high, in anticipation of later decrease to the 1100- to 1000-psi range for the 3680-lb. concrete, due to creep.

Regarding deflections, the elastically computed one of 1.08 in. checks well with the 1.04 in. observed in test, but the predicted total deflection of 2.94 in. is about 14 per cent less than that actually observed, even though it includes the Fig. 12–5 projected deflection due to *shrinkage warpage,* to be taken up in Chapter 13.

---

calculated tensile (concrete) bending stress at service design load exceeds the plain concrete modulus of rupture (bending) strength of the section, the *effective section* will be that remaining after the cracking of the concrete; in which case the "*I*" of the (one *n*) *cracked transformed section* should be used in *deflection* calculations.

Table 12–2. Comparison of Long-Time Stress and Deflection Values

Singly reinforced 6-by-8-in. beam with 2–#5 bars
Design-loaded at 14-day age for 2½ years

For Actual f'_c of 3680 psi Used	Calculated Stresses (psi) and Deflections (in.) Using Transformed Cracked Sections		Average Test Deflections Observed by Washa and Fluck‖ (in.)
	By Shank's Sustained Modulus Creep Method (n_t = 51.3)	By ACI WSD Elastic Method (Creep Disregarded) (n = 8.3)	
Stresses:			
f_c	1,035	1,594	—
f_s	21,600	19,200	—
Deflections:			
Elastic	(1.08)	1.08	1.04
Creep	1.42†	—	—
Shrinkage*	0.44‡	—	—
Total	2.94§		3.40§

* See Reference 8, this chapter.
† Shank's calculated elastic + creep = 2.50 in.; see preceding calculation.
‡ From Fig. 12–5, creep + shrinkage = 1.72(elastic) = 1.72(1.08 in.) = 1.86 in., so deduced shrinkage = 1.86 − 1.42 = 0.44 in.
§ Compare these two values.
‖ See Reference 7, this chapter.

There are other contributory minor variables not usually considered, so such a predicted deflection may be in error by as much as 20 per cent, which is usually acceptable for most practical purposes.

In the $\frac{1}{4}E_c$ *approximation*, used by McMillan [12] as early as 1915, $4n$ is used in transforming all sections, and the stresses are then computed as if creep were nonexistent.

For calculating deflections we ought to use E_{ct} to find the deflection due to the permanent loads, such as dead load, and the much greater common value, E_c, for that due to transient loads. In such cases, the dead load deflection will usually prove to be much the larger item.

In Example 12–3 the dead and live loads were not separately designated. Therefore the deflection found should be thought of as representing a case where both loadings were on for the whole period.

BEAM CREEP PRACTICE PROBLEMS

12–4. Recalculate Example 12–3, assuming that 3680-lb. high early strength portland cement concrete is to be used, loaded at the 7-day age, and carry the loading for 5 years.

12–5. A one-way simple span stone concrete slab is 6 in. thick, and has #5 bars with 1-in. cover, spaced at 3½ in. center to center. It was designed for 250-psf live loading over an 11-ft. span. The WSD specification was 18,000–1200–10, f'_c = 3000. High early strength portland cement was used. It was loaded at the 4-day age.

Find the 5-year steel and concrete unit stresses, and the total deflection by Shank's method, including the allowance for shrinkage warpage deflection.

12–8. CREEP OF DOUBLY REINFORCED BEAMS

Since the large creep deflection of beams is due to the continued compressing of the concrete of the compression side, it may be effectively decreased by the addition of compression reinforcement. This case differs from the preceding example only in that there is also top steel to be transformed into a strip of equivalent crept concrete and included in neutral axis and moment-of-inertia calculations.

EXAMPLE 12–4

Doubly Reinforced Beam Investigation

Given the same beam and loading conditions as studied in Example 12–3 except that 2–#5 compression bars have been added, as Washa and Fluck did in their B–1 and B–4 test beams [7]. Consider the bars centered 1.81 in. from the top.

It is required to compute the stresses and the deflection by Shank's creep method, and to compare it with the test data, etc.

Intermediate results: $E_{ct} = 565{,}000$, $n = 51.3$, $kd = 3.46$, $I_{ct} = 414$. See Table 12–3 for the remaining data.

Comments. In Table 12–3, the compressive stresses found in column 2 by Shank's method may be compared with those gotten by three other methods, including the ACI $2n$ approximation to *compression steel stress after creep*.

Note that the stresses of McMillan's $\frac{1}{4} E_c$ approximation [12] of column 3 agree well with Shank's method as a standard.

The methods of columns 4 and 5 disregard the effect of creep upon f_c values, giving top fiber stresses that are fictitiously *high*. On the other hand, they give compressive steel stresses which are far too *low*. For the usual conditions, the $\frac{1}{4} E_c$ *method* (or $4n$ method) is recommended as a good quick stress approximation.

Studies made of *balanced* doubly reinforced beam designs indicate that the allowable concrete stress should be limited to about $0.25f'_c$ when good methods recognizing creep are used.

A study of columns 2 and 6 in comparison with Table 12–2 shows that the arbitrary introduction of the same amount of reinforcement into the top of the beam as exists in the bottom approximately *halves* the f_c stress, and correspondingly the deflection: 536 psi vs. 1035 psi, 1.64 in. vs. 2.94 in., and 1.62 in. vs. 3.40 in.

DOUBLY REINFORCED BEAM CREEP PRACTICE PROBLEMS

12–6. Verify the findings of the solution of Example 12–4 which appear in column 2 of Table 12–3, and elsewhere.

Table 12–3. Comparison of Creep Stress and Deflection Values

Doubly reinforced 6-by-8-in. beam with 2–#5 bars in top and in bottom
Design-loaded at 14-day age for 2½ years

	Calculated Stresses (psi) and Deflections (in.) Using Transformed Cracked Sections				
For Actual f'_c of 3680 psi Used	Sustained Modulus Methods		By the ACI 2n Compressive Steel Stress Approximation of Sec. 1102(c)	By the Common Elastic Method (Creep Disregarded) $n = 8.3$	Average Test Deflection Observed by Washa and Fluck (in.)
	By Shank's Creep Method	By the ¼ E_c Creep Stress Approximation			
(1)	(2)	(3)	(4)	(5)	(6)
Stresses:					
f_c	536	733	1,420	1,492	
f_s comp.	13,480	10,540	4,760	2,875	
f_s tens.	22,300	21,700	19,800	19,600	
Deflections:					
Elastic	—	—	—	—	0.92
Creep	—	—	—	—	0.70
Total*	1.64†	1.48	1.01	1.03	1.62†

* There is no shrinkage (warpage) deflection because the steel is symmetrically arranged in this case.
† Compare these two values.

12–7. Reinvestigate the creep stresses and deflection of the beam of Example 12–4, assuming the same span and loading, but that the added reinforcement is placed in the bottom instead of in the top. Take a total bottom steel content of exactly 1.24 sq. in. at the same 6.19-in. distance from the top. Make a tabular comparison of your findings with those of Example 12–4 and comment.

12–9. PREDICTION OF LONG-TIME SLAB OR BEAM DEFLECTIONS FROM 24-HOUR EXPERIMENTAL DATA

The creep of concrete takes place at a gradually decreasing rate, following a power curve variation (Fig. 12–2) which has been well established by several investigators from many experimental data. Table 12–4 prepared from Shank's creep formula shows, for example, that 10.5 per cent of the total creep takes place during the first 24 hr. of loading. Such relationships can be used to predict deflections at later ages *provided* that the loading and atmospheric conditions prevailing during the short-time period of observation are typical of the service period.

Plate 12–1.   Use of a lifting cradle to set precast channel-slab roof panels.

EXAMPLE 12–5

A slab weighing 50 plf deflected 0.30 in. immediately due to the application of the design live loading of 80 plf, and 0.07 in.[6] more within 24 hr. **Predict** the long-time total elastic plus creep **deflection** due to dead plus uninterrupted live loading.

Solution.

$$\text{Live load deflection}$$
$$\text{Elastic} = 0.30 \text{ in.}$$
$$^{7}\text{Creep}\left(\frac{0.07}{0.105}\right) = 0.67 \text{ in.}$$

$$\text{Total} \qquad\qquad = 0.97 \text{ in.}$$
$$\text{Dead load deflection}$$
$$\text{Elastic} + \text{creep} = {}^{50}\!/_{80}(0.97) = 0.61 \text{ in.}$$
$$\text{Long-time total deflection} = 1.58 \text{ in.} \qquad\qquad \text{Ans.}$$

---

[6] Normally, a member will have supported its dead load for some time before the test load is applied, so little dead load creep will occur during the 24 hr. Its value may be deduced from Art. 12–5 as a percentage of the live load creep and deducted, when appreciable.

[7] Subject to being decreased if the live loading is intermittent.

Table 12–4. Percentage Early Creep of Concrete, $\delta_t \propto \sqrt[3]{t}$, Up to 1 Year, Deduced from Experimental Data

For cured-in-air portland cement concretes* and at whatever age first loaded—after Shank

Duration of Loading	Creep in Percentage of Long-Time Total
1.15 min.	1.0
2	1.2
10 min.	2.0
1 hr.	3.7
6	6.6
12 hr.	8.4
1 day	10.5
3	15.1
7	20.2
14	25.0
28 days	32.0
2 months	41.0
3	47.4
6	59.5
9 months	68.0
1 year	75.0
2	88.0
3	95.0
4	98.0
5 years or more	100.0

* Except granite aggregate concretes. Refer to Shank's bulletin [4].

12–10. SUMMARY OF CREEP OF CONCRETE

Creep is now defined as "the delayed portion of the total unit deformation resulting from stress within the proportional elastic range of the material." It is mostly or partially recoverable, depending upon the duration of the load [11].

The hydration of portland cement develops a gel around each particle. Creep is due to compression of the gel and is greatest in a dry curing atmosphere. Low strength concretes creep more than high strength ones. Creep practically ceases after five years.

Creep-time data for the first year of loading are well represented by power curves. For ordinary strength portland cement concretes made from good natural stone and loaded in air, Shank found the curve to be a third-power one.

When concrete is loaded at the later ages, the creep is much less. By conceiving such loading to be applied in reverse sense (e.g., tensile instead of compressive) at the later age, the effect of removing the same load applied earlier can be followed. Refer to Fig. 12–2.

The compressive stresses in reinforced concrete beams after creep under sustained load may be found by computing a decreased value of E_c from the sum of the unit creep and instantaneous elastic strains, and using it to make conventional beam stress calculations. In the absence of creep data, $\frac{1}{4} E_c$ may be assumed for loading durations of a year or more. The term *sustained modulus of elasticity*, E_{ct}, is applied to all such decreased values. The corresponding n_t value may be from 3 to 6 times a normal one.

Because of the great influence of the time element, live loads cause a great deal less creep than dead, since the former seldom act for prolonged periods. To predict the deflection of reinforced concrete beams, the full value of E_c may be used to get the live load deflection, but for the dead load deflection the much smaller elapsed time *sustained modulus*, E_{ct}, should be taken.

When a sustained strain is maintained upon a concrete member, instead of a sustained stress, creep causes a decrease in concrete stress. This is the beneficial *relief of stress* which often takes place in the restrained members of continuous structures.

A method has been presented for investigating the effect of creep upon the stresses in an axially loaded reinforced concrete column. In Example 12–2, after 4 months of creep, the n-value had increased to about $2\frac{1}{2}$ times the elastic value, and the f_c and f_s values then matched those of ACI WSD Column Formula 14–1, Sec. 1402(a).

In columns and doubly reinforced beams, wherein the compressive steel and concrete *share* in the resistance to compressive force or load, creep [11] was found to cause a two- to fourfold increase of the common elastically computed compressive steel stress, or even more. Refer to Table 12–3. Such steel must be well held in place by spirals, ties or stirrups.

CONTINUATION PROBLEMS

12–8. A plain concrete pier of normal standard portland cement concrete was first safely loaded in air at the 30-day age for a period of 30 days. It was then alternately unloaded and loaded at 30-day intervals until the 150-day age.

Compute the ratio of the creep at the 150-day age to what it would have been had the load never been removed. Make a scale creep-time diagram of the 120-days of movements involved in the two cases.

12–9. If the column of Example 12–2 is 15 ft. high, calculate the long-time shortening thereof, considering creep. What then will be the steel and concrete unit stresses?

QUESTIONS

  1. Define *elasticity*, *creep*, and *inelasticity*, distinguishing between them.
  2. Sketch the stress-strain curves of concrete, subdividing and identifying all major divisions thereof.
  3. Define the *instantaneous*, *straight-line*, and *sustained moduli of elasticity*. Refer to Chapter 1 also.

4. What is the characteristic shape of creep-time curves? Delineate a creep recovery-time curve and tell how they may be deduced without experimentation.
5. Describe the nature of creep. Enumerate the factors which affect it, stating whether they increase or decrease it.
6. Enumerate all the advantages and disadvantages of the creep phenomenon.
7. Why should high early strength portland cement concrete creep less than standard portland cement concrete if they are loaded at the same age?
8. Describe two methods for predicting the compressive stress in a singly reinforced concrete beam after creep has taken place.
9. In doubly reinforced beams, which stresses are most inaccurate if calculated by the conventional method? Explain how this situation arises.
10. Explain the deficiencies of the ACI $2n$ approximation to the final compressive stress in doubly reinforced beams.
11. Explain the inelastic property of concrete as presently defined, and tell why it is becoming of increasing importance. Are stress diagrams and strain diagrams ever identical? Explain.

REFERENCES

1. McHenry, Douglas. "A New Aspect of Creep in Concrete and Its Application to Design," *Proc. ASTM*, 1943, Vol. 43, p. 1069.
2. U.S. Department of the Interior. *Concrete Manual* (5th ed.). Washington, D.C.: Government Printing Office, 1951. P. 31.
3. Shank, J. R. "The Mechanics of Plastic Flow of Concrete," *Proc. ACI*, 1936, Vol. 32, p. 149.
4. Shank, J. R. "The Plastic Flow of Concrete," *Bulletin No. 91*, Ohio State University Engineering Experiment Station, 1935.
5. Shideler, J. J. "Manufacture and Use of Lightweight Aggregates for Structural Concrete," *Bulletin D40*, Development Department, Research and Development Laboratories, Portland Cement Association, Chicago, January 1961.
6. Glanville, W. H. "The Creep or Flow of Concrete Under Load" (Studies in Reinforced Concrete III), *Department of Scientific and Industrial Research Technical Paper No. 12*, Building Research Station, Garston, England, 1930.
7. Washa, George W., and Fluck, P. G. "Effect of Compressive Reinforcement on the Plastic Flow of Reinforced Concrete Beams," *Proc. ACI*, 1953, Vol. 49, p. 89.
8. Yu, Wei-Wen, and Winter, George. "Instantaneous and Long-Time Deflections of Reinforced Concrete Beams Under Working Loads," *Proc. ACI*, 1960, Vol. 57, pp. 29–50.
9. American Concrete Institute. "Commentary on Building Code Requirements for Reinforced Concrete (ACI 318-63)," *ACI Publication SP-10*, 1965.
10. Troxell, G. D., Raphael, J. M., and Davis, R. E. "Long-Time Creep and Shrinkage Tests of Plain and Reinforced Concrete," *Proc. ASTM*, 1958, Vol. 58, pp. 1101–20.
11. Neville, A. M. (ed.). "Symposium on Creep of Concrete," *ACI Publication SP-9*, 1964.
12. McMillan, F. R. "Discussion of the Paper by A. C. Janni: Method of Designing Reinforced Concrete Slabs," *Trans. ASCE*, 1916, Vol. 80, p. 1738.

EFFECT OF SHRINKAGE AND TEMPERATURE CHANGE

13–1. INTRODUCTION

In this chapter we are concerned with the time-dependent deformations and stresses which may develop in the members of concrete structures due to influences other than externally applied loads. These factors are **drying shrinkage,** or expansion, resulting from changes in moisture content, and similar movements caused by **temperature change.**[1]

Although these topics are controversial due to the multiplicity of variables often involved, an effort will be made to develop them, and to evaluate quantitatively the stress-strain effects which may be expected in the cases presented.

A. Axial Shrinkage

13–2. EFFECT OF CHANGE IN MOISTURE CONTENT

Concrete shrinks [13] with loss of moisture and expands with gain thereof. It also contracts somewhat due to the chemical reactions of hardening. Most of the original shrinkage takes place during the curing period of the first few months and is known as **drying shrinkage.** It coincides with the period of most active creep, to which shrinkage is inextricably related.

Excessive shrinkage is a serious concern of the engineer. It is often traceable to such factors as poor aggregates, poor proportioning, neglected curing, or a particular source of cement. Moreover, the external

---

[1] The general term "volume change" is often used to refer to the following four phenomena as a group: creep, shrinkage, temperature change effects, and possible chemical disintegration.

restraints which often develop therewith cause tensile stresses in the concrete which sometimes result in cracking.   Oft-repeated shrinkage and expansions gradually tend to cause a breakdown of the internal structure of the hardened cement-water paste and its bond to the aggregate particles, resulting in disintegration of the concrete.   The engineer decreases shrinkage and expansion somewhat by introducing *shrinkage reinforcement*, and he provides suitable *joints*, contraction and/or expansion, which are designed to adjust to the expected movements.   Refer to Figs. 13–6 and 13–7.

A well-proportioned mix of concrete is a cohesive plastic mass that is fully saturated with water.   As the cement sets, it takes up water, or *hydrates*.   Additional water, called *curing water*, must be furnished to ensure complete hydration.   If such is adequately provided the concrete mass will expand slightly, and little if any shrinkage[2] will occur so long as the wet curing is maintained.   Schorer's formula [14] for predicting the unrestrained shrinkage unit deformation,[3] ϵ_{fs}, which he called the *free shrinkage* "coefficient," is:

$$\epsilon_{fs} = \frac{0.125(0.90 - h)}{100} \tag{13-1}$$

wherein h is the relative humidity of the surrounding atmosphere, expressed as a decimal.

For a fully saturated curing condition (fog or water), $h = 1.00$, and $\epsilon_{fs} = -0.000125$, namely, expansion.

When curing is omitted or withdrawn, assuming an average relative humidity of 50 per cent ($h = 0.50$), ϵ_{fs} turns out $+0.0005$, which is the well-established average value of total free shrinkage; namely, from the quite wet to the completely dried-out condition.   Most of it can be recovered (erased) by a thorough rewetting.

Note that the above value of total shrinkage is equivalent to an 83° temperature drop, assuming a thermal coefficient, α, of 0.000006.

It has been found that shrinkage is approximately proportional to the paste content, $c + w$, per unit volume of concrete; and that the water is responsible for about 80 per cent of the shrinkage.   "Thus any factor which increases the water requirement of the paste, such as wetter consistencies, finer sands or smaller coarse aggregates, will increase the shrinkage" [13].   Furthermore, although rich concrete tends to shrink more than lean, it may be very little more, provided the consistency is no wetter.   For pretensioning the reinforcement of prestressed concrete

---

[2] Concrete does not exhibit drying shrinkage while still plastic, except that the water which may rise to the surface during the first hour or so after placing (due to being displaced by the settling of the aggregate) may be allowed to evaporate before it sinks again to feed the hydration of the cement, thus decreasing the volume of the mass.

[3] Throughout this chapter, ϵ_{fs} is the unit deformation, or strain, due to free shrinkage.

beams, fairly accurate estimates of the amount of concrete shrinkage expected are needed in order to properly allow for the corresponding loss of steel prestress.   Refer to Chapter 14.

The shrinkage of concrete is advantageous in one respect: It causes the concrete to grip the steel tightly, thus decreasing the possibility of bar slippage.

13–3. CALCULATION OF SHRINKAGE STRESSES

Shrinkage stresses are caused by *external* or *internal* restraints upon the free contraction of the concrete.   If the shrinkage strain can be estimated, the axial stress due to the shrinkage can be computed by multiplying the strain by the sustained modulus of elasticity, E_{ct}, first used in the creep calculations of Example 12–2.

The marked similarity of the time-dependent actions of *shrinkage* and *creep* is shown in Fig. 13–1.   Since most of the shrinkage takes place during the first few months, while the time-dependent modulus of elasticity, E_{ct}, still is relatively large, high shrinkage stresses of the order of $\epsilon_s E_c$ can develop in an unreinforced restrained member.   As time passes, creep causes the effective modulus to decrease to E_{ct}, a very much smaller value, while ϵ_s increases only moderately toward ϵ_{fs}, the maximum value; so the shrinkage tensile stress decreases.   This accounts for the common observation that creep *relieves* shrinkage and temperature stresses; and that *shrinkage* cracking seldom occurs after the first few months.

EXAMPLE 13–1

External Restraint

Consider a new plain concrete wall extending between two large fixed concrete masses 16 ft. 8 in. apart.   The wall is integral therewith, and fully restrained thereby, as indicated in Fig. 13–2.

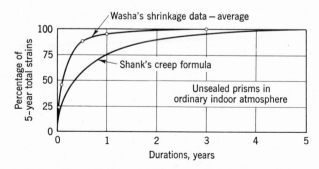

Fig. 13–1. Typical accumulations of shrinkage and creep.

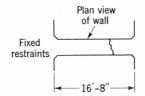

Fig. 13–2.   Externally restrained wall.

What **shrinkage stress** will develop if the wall dries out completely? Take ACI 3000-lb. concrete, with a 5-year sustained modulus[4] of elasticity, E_{ct}, of only 400,000 psi.   Use 0.0005 in./in. as the *free shrinkage*, ϵ_{fs}.

Solution.   Shrinkage unit stress equals shrinkage unit strain times the sustained modulus of elasticity:

5-year shrinkage stress $f_{cs} = \epsilon_{fs}E_{ct} = 0.0005(400,000) = 200$ psi, tensile in the concrete.   Ans.

Comment.   At an earlier age when the modulus was larger, the stress might well have reached 300 psi, causing cracking of the concrete.   Such a crack could be expected to become 0.0005(16.7)(12) = 0.10 in. wide.

The free shrinkage of concrete can be decreased somewhat by providing properly located *shrinkage reinforcement* therein, *in the direction of the expected contraction*.   Such steel knits a member together, but becomes compressed because of its bond to the contracting concrete, and induces a small corresponding tension into the concrete.   Thus the *potential free shrinkage* of the concrete is decreased by the opposing *internal restraint* of the reinforcement.   The problem is to find the internal *shrinkage force*, P, acting between the steel and the concrete, from which the shrinkage stresses and the shrinkage deformation are easily computed.

EXAMPLE 13–2

Axial Internal Restraint

Given the same 16 ft. 8 in. wall as in Example 13–1 except that it is now reinforced with two #4 horizontal bars at 5-in. intervals of its height, as indicated in Fig. 13–3b.

It is required to calculate the shrinkage force, P, and the shrinkage stresses after 6 months of drying.   Also to calculate the restrained shrinkage strain and compare it with the free shrinkage strain found in Example 13–1.   Take the same 3000-lb. concrete, $\epsilon_{fs} = 0.0005$ and a 6-month $E_{ct} = 1,000,000$ psi, $n_t = 29$.   For clarity, visualize the steel as unbonded to the concrete except at the ends of the member, and opposing the shrinkage contraction of the concrete.

---

[4] Since shrinkage develops after moist curing is withdrawn, that age can be taken as the *age when loaded with shrinkage stress*, for purposes of calculating an E_{ct} for shrinkage calculations.

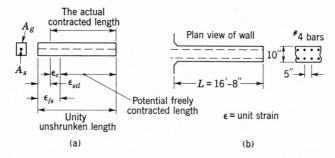

Fig. 13–3. Internally restrained shrinkage.

Derivation of the axial shrinkage formula. Employing the notation of Fig. 13–3a:

$$\epsilon_{stl} + \epsilon_c = \epsilon_{fs} = free \text{ shrinkage} \qquad (13\text{–}2)$$

Let P be the total force compressing the steel and tensioning the concrete [3].

Then $\qquad \epsilon_{stl} = \dfrac{P}{A_s E_s} \qquad$ and $\qquad \epsilon_c = \dfrac{P}{A_c E_{ct}}$

Also $\qquad A_s = p_s A_g \qquad$ and $\qquad A_c = (1 - p_s)A_g$

wherein A_g is gross concrete area.[5]

Substituting in Eq. 13–2, and rearranging:

$$P = \epsilon_{fs} E_s A_g \left[\frac{p_s(1 - p_s)}{1 + (n_t - 1)p_s} \right] \qquad Axial \text{ shrinkage of } R/C \qquad (13\text{–}3)$$

wherein p_s is the steel ratio stated with respect to A_g, as for shrinkage and temperature change calculations *only*.

Knowing P, the shrinkage stresses and the deformation follow easily.

Solution. Conveniently take $A_g = 50$ sq. in., and $A_s = 0.40$ sq. in. Then,

$$p_s = A_s/A_g = 0.40/50 = 0.8\%$$

$$P = 0.0005(29 \times 10^6)(50) \left[\frac{0.008(0.992)}{1 + 28(0.008)} \right] = \underline{\quad 4700 \text{ lb.}}$$

f_s (due to shrinkage) $= P/A_s = 4700/0.40 \qquad = \underline{\quad 11{,}750 \text{ psi compressive}}$

f_c (due to shrinkage) $= P/A_c = 4700/0.992(50) = \underline{\quad 95 \text{ psi tensile}}$

Total shrinkage strain $= L\epsilon_{stl} = \dfrac{PL}{A_s E_s} = \dfrac{4700(200)}{0.4(29 \times 10^6)} = \underline{\quad 0.081 \text{ in.} \quad} $ **Ans.**

Comment. Having noted that the free shrinkage of 0.10 in. has been decreased only 20 per cent by the introduction of 0.8 per cent of shrinkage reinforcement, an examination of the algebraic expressions shows that no greater quantity of steel will *eliminate* the shrinkage of the wall, so a contraction joint must be provided. Refer to Art. 13–7.

[5] Herein, A_g is computed by traversing the perimeter of the concrete section, whatever its shape.

AXIAL SHRINKAGE PRACTICE PROBLEMS

13-1. Derive, in detail, the P of Eq. 13-3 for axial shrinkage of R/C members.

13-2. A plain concrete wall is fully restrained at both ends by large concrete masses.
(a) Assuming that it was wet cured for the first 14 days, compute the shrinkage tensile stress therein one year after the withdrawal of curing. Take a 5-year free shrinkage strain of 0.00045 and refer to Fig. 13-1. Compute your sustained modulus of elasticity, E_{ct}, as in creep Example 12-2, assuming 3000-lb. standard portland cement concrete. <u>Ans. 275 psi.</u>
(b) Compute the shrinkage stresses after several other assumed shorter durations and deduce the early age at which the cracking tendency is the greatest.

B. Eccentric Shrinkage (Warpage)

13-4. EFFECT OF CONCRETE SHRINKAGE UPON THE STRESS IN THE TENSILE REINFORCEMENT OF BEAMS AND SLABS

In flexural members, the effect of shrinkage is to introduce a considerable amount of compression into the flexure steel, thus decreasing the design tensile stress. At the same time, the concrete of the tension side is subjected to additional tension, which causes it to crack[6] at a lighter load than if there were no shrinkage. This latter condition is accentuated because beam flexure steel is nearly always *eccentric* to the centroid of the whole concrete area; and its opposition to the shrinkage of the concrete causes shrinkage *bending* tensile stresses in the concrete in addition to the shrinkage *axial* tensile ones.

The topic of eccentric shrinkage is being introduced partly because of its great importance in evaluating the losses of pretension from the reinforcement of prestressed beams, the design of which is taken up in Chapter 14.

EXAMPLE 13-3

Eccentric Internal Restraint—Prediction of the Shrinkage Warpage of a Singly Reinforced Concrete Beam

Given the Washa and Fluck [7] test beam of Fig. 13-4, and creep Example 12-3. The actual f'_c was 3680 psi. Take 0.0005 free shrinkage strain. Normal standard portland cement was used. The beam was loaded at the 14-day age,[7] and for $2\frac{1}{2}$ years thereafter.

Required. To calculate (a) the $2\frac{1}{2}$-yr. shrinkage stresses and strains, and (b) the deflection.

Find in Example 12-3, for the same conditions as above: $E_{ct} = 565,000$ psi, and $n_t = 51.3$.

---

[6] Numerous tests have shown that reinforced concrete beams that have been designed in the usual manner normally develop very fine "hairline" cracks before all the design safe service load has been applied.

[7] At which time moist curing was discontinued.

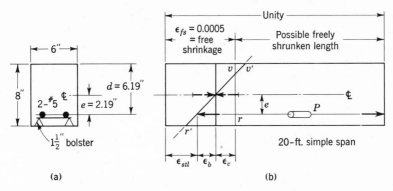

Fig. 13–4.   The eccentric shrinkage of beams (warpage).

Derivation of the eccentric shrinkage formula [3].   Utilizing from Fig. 13–3 the notation for the *axial* shrinkage unit deformations ϵ_{stl} and ϵ_c, consider in Fig. 13–4b that ϵ_b is the additional bending unit deformation at the level of the steel due to the bending moment Pe resulting from the eccentricity of the reinforcement, so:

$$\epsilon_{stl} + \epsilon_b + \epsilon_c = \epsilon_{fs} \qquad (13\text{–}4)$$

As is usually conceived when dealing with eccentric loadings, two equal and opposite (dashed line) P forces have been inserted in Fig. 13–4b at the middepth of the section.   One of them is considered to cause the uniform axial tensile strain in the concrete, ϵ_c.   The other is teamed with the actual P force to produce the couple Pe which causes the bending strain ϵ_b.

Consider the steel bar to be unbonded to the concrete and pressing eccentrically against section v-r as the concrete shrinks, causing it to get into the tilted position v'-r', as shown by the arrows.   Then:

$$\epsilon_{stl} = \frac{P}{A_s E_s}, \qquad \epsilon_b = \frac{Pe^2}{I_c E_{ct}}, \qquad \epsilon_c = \frac{P}{A_g E_{ct}}$$

wherein the concrete area, A_g, and the moment of inertia, I_c, are conveniently those of the uncracked gross plain concrete section.

Substituting in Eq. 13–4 and rearranging:

$$P = \frac{\epsilon_{fs} E_{ct}}{\dfrac{1}{A_g}\left(1 + \dfrac{1}{n_t p_s}\right) + \dfrac{e^2}{I_c}} \qquad \textit{Eccentric shrinkage force} \qquad (13\text{–}5)$$

wherein p_s states the flexure steel content in terms of A_g for shrinkage calculations only, and n_t and E_{ct} are elapsed-time values.

Solution.   (a) *For stresses and strains.*

Calculating the 2½-year sustained modulus of elasticity, E_{ct}, for a beam loaded at the 14-day age:

From the same conditions of Example 12–3: $E_c = 3,500,000$, $E_{ct} = 565,000$, and $n_t = 51.3$.

For Eq. 13–5:

$$p_s = A_s/A_g = (2)(0.31)/(6)(8) = 1.29\%$$
$$I_c = (bh^3)/(12) = (6)(8)^3/(12) = 256$$

Then,

$$P = \frac{0.0005(565,000)}{\frac{1}{48}\left[1 + \frac{1}{51.3(0.0129)}\right] + \frac{(2.19)^2}{256}} = 3980 \text{ lb., the shrinkage force.}$$

Shrinkage stresses.

Steel.

$$f_{ss} = \frac{P}{A_s} = \frac{3980}{2(0.31)} \qquad = 6420 \text{ psi, comp.}$$

This shrinkage compressive stress will decrease Washa's original design tensile steel stress of 19,250 psi to 12,830 psi (Example 12–3).

Concrete.

Concrete
unit stress

Top fiber:

$$\text{Direct stress} = \frac{P}{A_g} = \frac{3980}{6(8)} \qquad = \quad 83 \text{ psi, tens.}$$

$$\text{Bending stress} = \frac{Pec}{I} = \frac{3980(2.19)(4)}{256} = \quad 136 \text{ psi, comp.}$$

$$f_{cs} = \overline{\quad 53} \text{ psi, comp.}$$

Bottom fiber:
Direct stress = (as before)   83 psi, tens.
Bending stress = (as before)   136 psi, tens.
$$\overline{219} \text{ psi, tens.}$$

The bottom fiber tensile stress of 219 psi is less than the 368 psi axial tensile strength of 3680-lb. concrete of Table 1–1; and less than its 460-psi minimum bending modulus of rupture, as determined from Kesler's tests of 1954. (Refer to Fig. 2–23.)

Shrinkage strains. All are contractile, and measured from the left end of Fig. 13–4b.

Steel.

$$\frac{6420}{29 \times 10^6} = \qquad 222 \times 10^{-6}$$ Students: Check

Concrete.   the *linearity* by
Top fiber: drawing the strain

$$0.0005 + \frac{53}{565,000} = \qquad 594 \times 10^{-6}$$ diagram, as in Fig. 13–4b, but to large

Bottom fiber: scale.

$$0.0005 - \frac{219}{565,000} = \qquad 112 \times 10^{-6}$$

Solution. (b) *For 2½-year midspan shrinkage deflection.* The shrinkage moment in the slab is, from Fig. 13–4 and Solution (a), $Pe = 3980(2.19) = 8720$ in.-lb. over its full length.

By the moment-area law of the tangent, the midspan shrinkage deflection will be the moment of the area of half the moment diagram about one end, and divided by $E_{ct}I_c$:

$$\Delta = \frac{M(L/2)[L/4]}{EI} = \frac{8720(120)[60]}{565,000(256)} = \underline{0.434 \text{ in.}}$$

Washa's observed deflection = 0.44 in. (Table 12–2)
Branson's calculated deflection [15] = 0.37 in.

Comment. Note that the preceding computations, and Table 12–2, separate the shrinkage deflection from that due to creep; which the Yu and Winter tests did not do [8].

Usually, the *total* deflection, with the shrinkage component computed as above, will check with *test data*, almost as well as that computed by Branson, who has developed a more precise, but much longer method [15].

ECCENTRIC SHRINKAGE PRACTICE PROBLEM

13–3. Compute the shrinkage deflection of the beam of Example 13–3 for a 5-year loading duration.

C. Temperature Change

13–5. RESEMBLANCE OF TEMPÉRATURE CHANGE TO SHRINKAGE

As indicated briefly in Art. 1–19, the thermal coefficient of expansion of concrete, α, has an average value of about six millionths per Fahrenheit degree of temperature change, but varies between four and seven millionths depending upon the kind of aggregate used [16]. Since the corresponding value for steel is 0.0000065, the justification for reinforced concrete construction is obvious. For outdoor concrete in severe climates the importance of careful aggregate selection with respect to the thermal property is very great, since bar slippage cannot be allowed to occur.

During the early part of the curing period the temperature of concrete rises well above its temperature at the time of placing, due to the heat generated by the chemical action of hydration. Within the *mass concrete* of large dams much heat is so evolved at interior points, far from any exterior cooling surface. Elaborate measures, including the embedding of refrigeration pipe systems have often been taken to prevent excessive temperature rise [16].

In winter a progressive cooling and contraction occurs which tends to be highly detrimental because the temperature stresses then induced in the outside surfaces of the concrete are tensile. Because concrete's ultimate axial tensile strength is only about $\frac{1}{10}$ of the compressive, a 10-degree fall in temperature can produce as critical a strain as a 100-degree summer time rise. (Refer to Table 1–1.) *So far as temperature change alone is concerned*, it is advantageous to place concrete in cool weather, so that the fall to the wintertime low will be much less than the rise to the summertime high.

Repeated cycles of *sudden change* in temperature are the most detrimental to concrete because the temperature differential so created between its interior and the exterior surface causes large temperature stresses. Although they disappear as soon as the temperature has again become uniform throughout, the member will have contracted (or expanded) accordingly.

Although the greatest drying *shrinkage* usually occurs early, contraction due to a fall in *temperature* may occur at any time. Because the commonly used mathematical relationships are fundamentally the same, it is customary in designing to assume a *combined* shrinkage plus temperature coefficient when both influences are expected to be active at the same time. A case in point would be outdoor concrete which conceivably might become thoroughly dried out during a drouth, and then be subjected to a sudden severe drop in temperature.

In designing, engineers generally use a lowered shrinkage coefficient between 0.0003 and 0.00035, since in most structures complete drying out never occurs. Similarly, for temperature change, the 0.000006 thermal coefficient may be multiplied by one-half to two-thirds of the expected degree change to get a temperature strain component to add to the shrinkage strain.

Designers with unusual temperature problems should consult References 16 and 17.

Shrinkage and temperature reinforcement. In wide structural elements such as walls and one-way footings, as well as in floor and roof slabs that are reinforced for flexure in only one (the spanwise) direction, shrinkage and temperature reinforcement must be provided in the direction of the width, i.e., perpendicular to the flexural span and the direction of the principal reinforcement, as illustrated in Fig. 13–5.

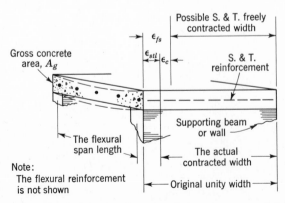

Fig. 13–5. Idealized slab shrinkage and temperature reinforcement.

PRACTICE PROBLEM

13–4. A 60-ft. wall of 3750-lb. standard portland cement concrete containing 0.30 per cent of horizontal temperature reinforcement was placed and wet cured for 28 days at 80°F. If the annual range of change to be considered is 0° to 120°, calculate the required freedom of joint adjustment in each direction, and the total travel to be provided for so far as temperature change is concerned. Take $\alpha = 0.0000065$ for both materials. HINT: Adapt Eq. 13–3 to your purpose.

EXAMPLE 13–4

Shrinkage plus Temperature Stresses

Given the floor slab of Fig. 13–5, consisting of 3000-lb. concrete. Considering the design free shrinkage coefficient to be three-quarters of the 0.0005 value, and that 50 degrees of temperature drop is also to be taken into account, **compute** the shrinkage plus temperature stresses if 0.2, 0.3, 1, and 4 per cent of such reinforcement, p_s, is used. Take the thermal coefficient, α, at 0.000006, and a 6-month $E_{ct} = 1,000,000$ psi; $n_t = 29$.

Solution. Conveniently consider an A_g of 100 sq. in.

$$\epsilon_{fs} = 0.75(0.0005) + 50(0.000006) = 0.00067 \text{ in./in., free S. + T. strain}$$

$$P = \epsilon_{fs} E_s A_g \left[\frac{p_s(1 - p_s)}{1 + (n_t - 1)p_s} \right] \quad \text{(from Example 13–2)} \qquad (13\text{–}3)$$

Sample calculation, with $p_s = 0.2\%$:

$$P = \frac{0.00067(29 \times 10^6)(100)(0.002)(0.998)}{1 + 28(0.002)} = 3680 \text{ lb.}$$

$$f_s = 3680/0.002(100) = \underline{\underline{18,400 \text{ psi, compressive}}}$$

$$f_c = 3680/99.8 \qquad = \underline{\underline{37 \text{ psi, tensile}}}$$

Comments. Table 13–1 demonstrates that the small percentages of shrinkage and temperature reinforcement ordinarily used are consistent with accepted shrinkage calculations. Unfortunately, the nature of the algebraic expression is such that the calculated steel stress hardly rises to 20,000 psi when even smaller percentages are used, so the actual content to be used must be based largely upon experience.

Note in the lower portion of Table 13–1 that *symmetrical arrangements of high percentage longitudinal reinforcement*, such as in columns, tend to cause high concrete tensile stresses as contraction takes place. However, it is believed that this elastically computed condition seldom develops, due to (a) the relief of concrete stress provided by the creep of the concrete and (b) the early application of superimposed dead load to columns as construction progresses, which prevents tensile cracking. Nevertheless, columns have been known to develop such tensile cracks many years later when, due to remodeling operations, a large portion of their superimposed dead load was removed!

As shown by Pickett [17] there is a great deal more mathematics involved in precise studies of shrinkage than can be presented here. Those with highly important shrinkage problems should refer to his work.

Table 13–1. Calculated Shrinkage plus Temperature Stresses, psi

Slab Shrinkage plus Temperature Steel Content p_s, in per cent	In Steel, f_s, Compressive	In Concrete, f_c, Tensile	Remarks
0.2	18,400	37	Requires #4's at 14 in. c.c. in a 7″ slab.
0.3	17,850	54	Ref. ACI Sec. 807.
Column or Wall Principal Vert. Steel Content			
1.0	15,000	152	
4.0	8,800	367	367 > 300, so concrete tensile failure; but see *Comments*.

13–6. THE CODE REQUIREMENTS FOR SHRINKAGE AND TEMPERATURE REINFORCEMENT, SECTION 807

The minimum S. & T. steel ratios of 0.0025 for plain bars and 0.0020 for deformed bars as set by the ACI Code are not inconsistent with the findings of Table 13–1.

The reader should remember that the Code ratios are *minimums*. In case the concrete is to be placed and cured at quite high summer temperatures, 150 per cent of the above values will be good insurance.

I. E. Morris[8] would distinguish considerably between the degrees of exposure; for outdoor slabs of unheated structures, porches and canopies wholly exposed to the winter climate of northern United States, he considers that the Code minimum steel percentages should be fully doubled. "The added cost would be small, and will usually prove to be money well spent."

13–7. CONTRACTION AND EXPANSION JOINTS

As indicated in earlier articles, shrinkage and temperature reinforcement decreases the free contraction or expansion of concrete members only slightly. The actual movements must be provided for by joints especially introduced for the purposes, since concrete structures are typically integral, or jointless.

Contraction Joints. The general philosophy of joint design may be illustrated by the 150-ft. section of pavement or basement floor pictured

[8] A consulting structural engineer of Atlanta, Georgia.

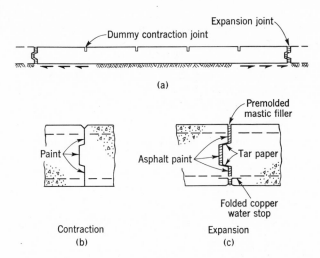

Fig. 13–6. Major contraction and expansion joints.

in Fig. 13–6a.   As it contracts due to drying shrinkage and/or fall in temperature, the friction of the subgrade develops the tensile forces shown, and possible tensile cracks.   To prevent their being unsightly, the four weakened plane *dummy contraction joints* ensure that possible cracks will be straight and largely hidden in the groove.   Moreover, since the total contraction will be distributed among five sections, each will hardly be noticed.   The interlocking of the rough surfaces at a fracture is relied upon to transmit vertical shear.   The *keyed contraction joint* at (b) is much better in this respect.   Less shrinkage will develop if alternate slabs can first be placed and well cured.   The key is sometimes replaced by plain-bar dowels about 60 diam. long, one-half of each of which is embedded in the slab or wall first cast; the other is greased or fitted with a noncorrosive sleeve to facilitate movement.

Expansion Joints.   When slabs or walls *expand* due usually to temperature rise, an *expansion joint* consisting of a relatively wide gap filled with slabs of mastic filler, as in Fig. 13–6a and c, is needed at intervals of 100 to 200 ft. in buildings, assuming $\frac{1}{2}$- to 1-in. filler material.   Such a joint can also function as a contraction joint.   If a wall must be completely watertight, the folded sheet copper *water stop* pictured in (c) can accommodate to the movement and also help hold the mastic in place.   Refer also to Fig. 13–7.

Temperature Change Demands.   As stated previously, most of the concrete shrinkage takes place at an early age, but temperature change continues indefinitely.   Sudden weather changes are the most detrimental.   Concrete foundations, being buried in the ground, expand and contract very little.   Brick masonry building walls bearing thereon can usually accommodate to them, but a long exposed concrete wall, with twice as great a thermal coefficient, cannot.   Therefore, in concrete structures, vertical joints should make a complete separation all the way to the ground, and preferably be not over 100 ft. apart for average exposures.   Joints should be provided between wings and the parent structure, and at the beginnings of extensions.

Wide Ranges of Temperature Change.   The usual winter to summer temperature range visualized is 100°F.   But roofs pass through a wider range than most walls, so there tends to be relative movement between them.   In summer the range will be even greater between the inside and outside of cold storage plants and similar installations.   The amount of thermal movement is easily estimated and must be accommodated.

General.   The range of travel needed at a given joint can be lessened by more judicious locating of S. & T. reinforcement.   Although theory says in Table 13–1 that it is possible to cause cracking by having *too much* reinforcement, this condition seldom occurs.   Extra bars should be provided around large openings in floors and walls to offset concrete's tensile weakness thereabout.   More effective moist curing of the concrete enables it to develop greater tensile strength before shrinkage and temperature strains accumulate.

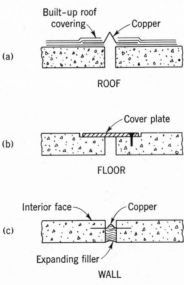

Fig. 13–7.   Joints in buildings.

13–8. SUMMARY OF SHRINKAGE AND TEMPERATURE CHANGE

With lapse of time the dimensions of extensive concrete members may change without the application of any external force, due to shrinkage or a change in temperature.

The initial shrinkage of concrete accompanies the drying which occurs when moist curing is withdrawn, and finally reaches a maximum value of about one in two thousand. After such a member has been expanded by a thorough rewetting, it will again shrink, but to a lesser extent.

Since steel and concrete must expand and contract the same amount in order to adhere permanently, the thermal coefficient of expansion of cured concrete should approach steel's value of 0.0000065 per degree Fahrenheit. Suitable aggregates are an important factor.

As moisture or heat enters or leaves a concrete member, unequal strains develop as between the outer shell and the inner portion, due to the time required for complete penetration. These differential strains cause

Plate 13–1. Erection of pretensioned prestressed double-floor panels of 8-ft. width. Refer to Fig. 14–17 and to Art. 2–18. Note the plant-precast wall sections, 12 ft. wide. (Courtesy of Portland Cement Association)

internal stress, the magnitude of which would be great were it not for the mitigating effect of shear deformation between layers, and the creep property of the concrete.

In slabs and walls, the destructive effect of repeated cycles of contraction and expansion may be greatly reduced by providing suitable amounts of shrinkage-temperature steel in the directions not already reinforced for the purpose of carrying the design loads. The movements will thereby be somewhat decreased; but long members still must be provided with joints which can adjust to them.

In singly reinforced beams, due to the eccentricity of the flexure reinforcement, shrinkage is accompanied by a warpage of the beam as the compressed steel minimizes the contraction of the tension side. The design flexural tensile stress in the reinforcement is thereby appreciably decreased; but the adjacent concrete is subjected to shrinkage tension, which may cause hair-line tensile cracks to develop at lighter loads than would otherwise be the case.

Since shrinkage and temperature effects are considerably *time-dependent*, estimates of the magnitudes of the corresponding stresses and deformations should be made, utilizing a *sustained* modulus of elasticity of the concrete, which has been computed for the period of time involved, as in the creep calculations of Chapter 12.

In designing the prestressed beams of Chapter 14, one must be able to closely estimate the shrinkage, creep, and elastic deformations of the concrete of the tension side in order to predict the magnitude of the losses of steel prestress due thereto.

CONTINUATION PROBLEM

13-5. Shrinkage Warpage of a Doubly Reinforced Concrete Beam. Recalculate the 5-year shrinkage stresses, strains and midspan deflection of the beam of Example 13-3 if compressive reinforcement, centered 1.81 in. from the top is added, as follows:

(a) One-half of the tensile A_s, namely, one #5 bar.
(b) Closely one-third of the tensile A_s, namely, one #4 bar.

Make a tabular comparison of both sets of results with those of Example 13-3, and comment.

SHRINKAGE AND TEMPERATURE CHANGE QUESTIONS

1. Distinguish clearly between *shrinkage* and *creep* in the most important fundamental respect by defining each carefully.

2. If a shrinkage crack develops, it is usually at a relatively early age. Explain.

3. Distinguish clearly between *external* and *internal restraints* upon contraction and expansion. Are they both undesirable? Explain.

4. Why are shrinkage and expansion sometimes destructive? Enumerate and explain what preventive measures may be taken.

5. What property of concrete sometimes prevents shrinkage and temperature stresses from becoming excessive? Describe how and when this is possible.

6. Sketch the localities of a concrete test cylinder which become stressed (a) in tension and (b) in compression under each of the following:

drying	external cooling
external heat	rewetting
heat of hydration	

7. Will strain gage readings taken upon the flexure reinforcement of a simple span beam before and after loading reveal the true tensile stress therein? Explain. Suggest a much better technique.

8. Derive a fundamental formula for the force induced in temperature steel. State your notation clearly.

9. Is it possible for an excessive amount of shrinkage and temperature steel to be positively detrimental as well as wasteful? Demonstrate how.

10. Distinguish between *axial* and *eccentric shrinkage*. In what type of designing does the amount of the latter become quite important?

11. Discuss at length the effects of temperature change upon concrete structures and what measures can be taken to mitigate or eliminate them.

12. Outline, in order, the steps necessary to predict by calculation the shrinkage deflection (warpage) of a singly reinforced concrete slab. How could you check your results experimentally?

REFERENCES

For References 1 through 12, see References at end of Chapter 12, on creep.

13. PORTLAND CEMENT ASSOCIATION, STRUCTURAL BUREAU. "Volume Changes of Concrete," *Modern Developments in Reinforced Concrete, No. 18.* Chicago: The Association.

14. SCHORER, HERMAN. "Prestressed Concrete, Design Principles and Reinforcing Units," *Proc. ACI*, 1943, Vol. 39, pp. 493, 501.

15. BRANSON, DAN E. "Deflections of Reinforced Concrete Flexural Members," *Report of ACI Committee 435, Dan E. Branson, Chm.,* January 1965, p. 34.

16. RAWHOUSER, CLARENCE. "Cracking and Temperature Control of Mass Concrete," *Proc. ACI*, 1945, Vol. 41, p. 305.

17. PICKETT, GERALD. "Shrinkage Stresses in Concrete," *Proc. ACI*, 1946, Vol. 42, pp. 165, 361, 375.

14

PRESTRESSED CONCRETE BEAMS

14–1. INTRODUCTION

A fully prestressed concrete beam is one into which sufficient *initial compression* has been introduced to counteract the anticipated tensile concrete stresses resulting from the service loads. Such beams are dependably crack-free[1] in normal service. The precompression is usually accomplished by initially tensioning high strength steel bars, straight wires, or helically laid wire (strands) located principally within the tensile portion of the beam.

Although prestressed concrete has been used in Europe for 30 years or more, its engineered use in the United States began in 1949 with the construction of the Walnut Lane Bridge, in Philadelphia. See Plate 14–1.

Strictly speaking, a prestressed concrete beam is not reinforced concrete because

1. The reinforcement need not be bonded to the concrete if securely end-anchored by mechanical means, and
2. The initially compressed concrete resists the bending tension.

Because the whole sectional area of the concrete is effectively utilized to resist the service loads, prestressed beams are of about two-thirds the size and weight of corresponding reinforced concrete ones. Furthermore, the longitudinal steel may be only one-fourth as much, though it must be of very high tensile strength.

The precompressing of the concrete increases its resistance to the weather, i.e., its *durability*, because the entrance of moisture is largely prevented thereby.

---

[1] Numerous tests have shown that *conventional* reinforced concrete beams develop small "hair-line" flexural tensile cracks before all the design safe service load has been applied. The common practice of omitting the tensile concrete from bending calculations is consistent therewith.

Plate 14–1. The Walnut Lane Bridge in Philadelphia, Pennsylvania. Completed early in 1951, it was the first engineered construction of a prestressed concrete bridge undertaken in the United States.

Some surprising characteristics that will be revealed in designing prestressed beams are that:

1. The amount of (prestressing) steel required is not directly dictated by the load to be carried, but by the need to have enough to precompress the whole concrete sectional area to the desired degree,
2. All or most of the dead load of the beam can be carried "free" by proper designing,
3. A simple span beam that is safe in flexure at midspan may be unsafe therein at the supports,
4. When the design service load is finally applied, the then-existing unit stress in the steel is then actually less than before any load was applied,
5. The factor of safety under any chosen loading cannot be deduced by comparing unit stresses, but
6. The *ultimate* flexural strength is closely the same as if the beam were un-prestressed, although the crack-free safe working load is much increased.

Since the characteristics mentioned above bear little resemblance to those of other beams, it probably will be another surprise to learn that the *ultimate* strength of prestressed beams is predicted closely as in Chapter 2 for conventional reinforced concrete beams. This is because such beams lose their prestress in the inelastic range of high overload approaching failure. Refer to Fig. 14–11.

14–2. CONCEPT OF A PRESTRESSED BEAM

A prestressed beam is like a rectangular section *plain concrete* pier, as in Fig. 14–1, eccentrically loaded with an external axial compressive force *F*, to which a lateral loading *w* has later been added without causing any cracking. The typical unit stress diagrams pictured are all com-

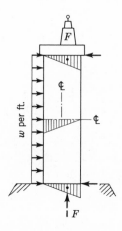

Fig. 14–1. Action of a prestressed beam standing vertically.

pressive.   By rotating the book clockwise through a right angle it will be evident that there is no tension in the bottom fiber of this "beam."

In actual prestressed beams the internal pretensioning steel should be regarded primarily as a convenient means of applying the compressive force F to the concrete.

14–3. THE BASIC MECHANICS OF PRESTRESSING

As indicated in Fig. 14–2a, one might precompress the 5000-lb. concrete of a beam by pretensioning a centrally located rod or wire, thus inducing a uniform precompression (1000 psi in this case).   If, thereafter, enough design live load is applied to create an additional 1000 psi of bending stress in this uncracked section, the maximum combined stress will

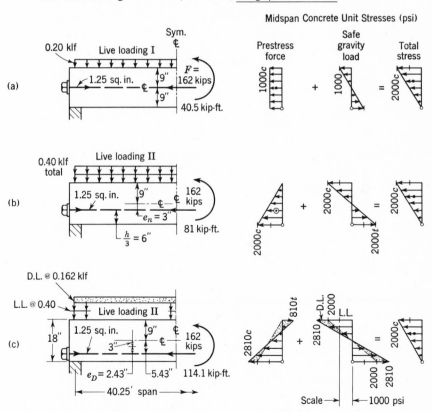

Prestressed 9″ × 18″ Rectangular Beam

In all cases the longitudinal forces, or stresses, acting upon the concrete, are shown

Fig. 14–2. Magnitude and sense of concrete unit stresses under service loadings, accompanied by increasing eccentricity of the same prestressing force.   Consider $f'_c = 5000$ psi.

become 2000 psi compressive in the top fiber, as shown at the extreme right. Note that the triangular distribution thereof leads to zero total stress in the bottom fiber.

In (b), the capacity of the beam for carrying design live load was *doubled* simply by moving the prestressed steel downward 3 in., one-sixth of the depth, until the precompression in the top fiber of concrete became zero. The 2000-psi total stress is the same as in (a).

Now looking at Fig. 14–2c in a general way, we see that the dead load of the beam, heretofore disregarded, has been added to Live Loading II used in (b). Furthermore, looking at the stress diagrams at the right, we note that the middle one, representing the effect of uniformly distributed load, has had its extreme fiber stress value increased from 2000 psi to 2810 psi, due to considering the dead load. Nevertheless the "Total," or *combined,* stress at the extreme right is the same as in (b), namely, 2000 psi. Returning to the side view sketch of (c), we see that this astounding result has been achieved simply by moving the prestressed steel 2.43 in. farther down,[2] until $e = 5.43$ in., and at no additional cost in materials! (The values of the dead and live loading, together with the span distance, have been shown in (c) to enable the reader to check the stresses just discussed.) Due to the increased eccentricity of the prestressing force, the left-hand stress diagram in (c), representing prestress combined unit stress in the concrete, has become 810 psi tensile at the top, but it is immediately erased by the corresponding dead load compressive stress. This matter will be taken up again later.

The Kern Points. The student is assumed to be familiar with the fundamental mechanics of direct stress plus bending situations in rectangular sections as reproduced in Fig. 14–2a. The key situation for our purposes is that of (b) of the figure, wherein the axial prestress force is at the lower "edge of the middle third" of the section, causing the triangular distribution of stress pictured nearby. This elevation is the *lower kern point* of the section, as defined by the centroid of the triangular stress diagram, and the corresponding (3 in.) eccentricity, e_n, of the prestress force will hereinafter be called the *normal eccentricity.*

The Dead and Live Load Ranges. The lower kern point of a prestressed section is a base elevation, *downward* from which the additional eccentricity required to offset the dead load bending moment may be laid off in designing. In the case shown in Fig. 14–2c, the bending moment involved is $0.162(40.25)^2(12)/8 = 393$ kip-in. This, when divided by the 162-kip prestress force, gives 2.43 in. of additional downward displacement, which is known as the *dead load eccentricity* (Fig. 14–3) for

---

[2] In shallow long-span prestressed beams and slabs not all the dead load can be so taken care of. Part of it must be included with the live load when proportioning the member.

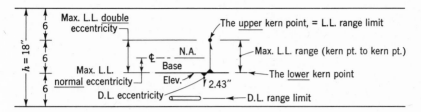

Fig. 14–3. Example of the relationship of the kern points to dead load and live load ranges and eccentricities (beam of rectangular section).

the particular dead load that we have. Obviously we *could* have compensated for some maximum dead load, the displacement of which would be defined by the lowermost $h/3$ measurement minus the centroidal elevation of the steel, known as the *dead load range limit*.

Note in Fig. 14–2b that the application of the chosen live load converted the prestress stress triangle with base *downward* to an identical one with its base *upward*; and that the centroid moved upward 6 in., or $h/3$, in the process. This distance is called the *double eccentricity*, $2e_n$ of the live load. Its value should not exceed the vertical distance from the lower kern point to the upper kern point of the section, called the *live load range*. Note that the eccentricities referred to are related to the *loadings*, while the kern limits are properties of the *cross section*.

For rectangular-shaped beams the live load range is always the $h/3$ distance between kern points. It may be increased to $0.50h$ or even $0.55h$ by designing a suitable I-section, thus increasing the live load capacity without increasing the beam depth or cross-sectional area.

Live Loading Versus Beam Size. Reference to the stress diagrams of Fig. 14–2b and c will show that neither the addition of the prestress force nor of the dead load increased the maximum total stress on the section. Therefore the required *concrete* dimensions of prestressed rectangular sections may be quickly proportioned from the live load bending moment only,[3] $(w_L L^2)/8$ in this case, so far as safe working strength is concerned.

EXAMPLE 14–1

The Working Stress Design of a Pretensioned Concrete Slab

Given a simple span of 15 ft. and a live loading of 0.72 ksf.

It is required to design the slab thickness (to some whole inch), and the pretensioned steel content at midspan.

Concrete data. Take 6250-lb. concrete, allowable $f_c = 0.4f'_c = 2500$ psi in compression, zero in tension in the bottom fiber. Take the weight of *prestressed* concrete at 147 pcf. Provide not less than ¾-in. fire-proofing (cover) for the strands.

---
[3] Except when the dead load is relatively large.

Steel data. Take Roebling's uncoated stress-relieved twisted steel pretensioning strand at 250,000-psi ultimate tensile strength. The design final pretension is 140,000 psi. See the table in Fig. 14–6 for strand sizes and areas. $E_s = 27,000,000$, $E_c = 4,560,000$, $n \cong 6$.

Solution. By the kern points method suggested at the end of Art. 14–3:

(a) Calculation of the *F*-force required to suit the live load range:

Taking a 12-in. slab width, and a total thickness of h inches:

$$M_L = 0.72(15)^2/8 = 20.25 \text{ kip-ft.}$$
$$F = M_L/(h/3) = 20.25(12)/(h/3) = 730/h \tag{1}$$

(b) *F*-force required to fully precompress the section, as in Fig. 14–2b:

$$F = \frac{f_c}{2}(A_g) = \frac{2.5 \text{ ksi}}{2}(12)h = 15(h) \text{ kips} \tag{2}$$

Solving Eqs. 1 and 2, reqd. $h = 6.98$ in. Selecting h at 7 in.,

$$F = 15(7) = 105 \text{ kips.}$$

(c) Live and dead load stresses:

Plain concrete sec. modulus, $Z = 12(7)^2/6 = 98$ in.[3]

In Fig. 14–4b, $\qquad f_{c_L} = \dfrac{M_L}{Z} = \dfrac{20.25(12,000)}{98} = \qquad 2480 \text{ psi.}$

$$W_D = \frac{12(7)}{144}(0.147) = 0.086 \text{ kips}, \quad M_D = \frac{0.086(15)^2}{8} = 2.41 \text{ kip-ft.}$$

$$f_{c_D} = \frac{2.41(12,000)}{98} = \qquad 295 \text{ psi.}$$

(d) **Required depth of the steel.** Since $e = h/6$ when $Mc/I = F/A$ (fundamental):

$$\text{Reqd. } e = {}^{1525}\!/_{1250}(\tfrac{7}{6}) = \qquad 1.42 \text{ in. from middepth.}$$

(e) **Steel area.** (Refer to Fig. 14–5.)

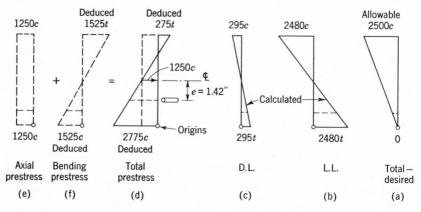

Fig. 14–4. Graphical deducing of required axial and bending prestress unit stresses from the dead and live load stresses at midspan of the pretensioned slab.

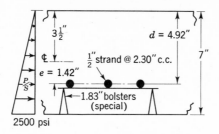

Fig. 14–5. Final design sketch for Example 14–1.

$$\text{Reqd. } A_s \text{ per one-foot width} = \frac{105,000}{140,000} = \underline{0.75 \text{ sq. in.}}$$

For available strand sizes and strengths, see Fig. 14–6.
Trying ½-in. strand at 0.1438 sq. in.:

$$\text{Maximum c.c. spacing} = \frac{(0.1438)(12)}{0.75} = 2.30 \text{ in.}$$

Use one layer of ½-in. strand at 2.30 in. c.c.
Make 1.83-in. special bolsters.

14–4. DISCUSSION OF THE PRESTRESSED SLAB DESIGN

In Example 14–1, the required 7-in. depth of the section was computed from the live loading only, as earlier directed. The live and dead load unit stresses were then easily computed and the corresponding diagrams (b) and (c) of Fig. 14–4 were constructed therefrom. *Diagram (a)*, at the right, is *the desired final stress situation*. Diagram (d) shows the corresponding required prestress deduced leftward from (a), (b), and (c). The algebraic average abscissa on (d) is the 1250 axial prestress shown at (e), which checked with the $f_c/2$ value it must have if the final distribution at (a) is to be triangular. The undesirably high stresses of diagram (d) exist only in combination with the mitigating dead load stresses of diagram (c) of reversed sense, as will be discussed in a succeeding article.

The prestress bending stress of 1525 psi at (f) of the figure resulting from the still undetermined eccentricity of the prestress force, was gotten from (e) and (d) of the figure by simple arithmetic.

The 1.42-in. required eccentricity, *e*, of the strand was found in calculation item (d) by recalling that when the axial and bending stresses in a rectangular-shaped column are *equal*, the load must be at "*the edge of the middle third*" of its depth; and proportionately therefrom when the stresses are *un*equal.

Roebling's Uncoated Prestressed Concrete 7-Wire Strand
for Bonded Pretensioned Designs

The basic unit of Roebling 7-wire strand for pretensioning is uncoated prestressed concrete wire. Excellent bonding properties are afforded by these strands because of the relatively small diameter of the wires, and the mechanical bond that is provided as the concrete sets in the valleys between the outside wires.

The strands are stress-relieved to remove the internal stresses that are set up by the wire drawing and stranding operations, so that stress relaxation at the design loads is reduced to a minimum. Additional advantages of the stress-relieving process are an improvement in the bonding properties of the wire as well as in the flexibility and ease of handling the strand in the field.

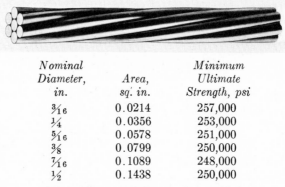

Nominal Diameter, in.	Area, sq. in.	Minimum Ultimate Strength, psi
³⁄₁₆	0.0214	257,000
¼	0.0356	253,000
⁵⁄₁₆	0.0578	251,000
³⁄₈	0.0799	250,000
⁷⁄₁₆	0.1089	248,000
½	0.1438	250,000

The average modulus of the strands in the above table is 27,000,000 psi. Observe 4 diameters minimum c.c. spacing.

Steelcase Strandvise

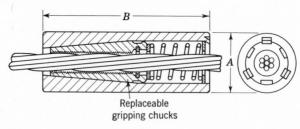

Replaceable gripping chucks

Wire Range	A	B
8 BWG. (0.144–0.165 diam.)	⅝	2⅛
6 BWG. (0.180–0.206 diam.)	¾	2¹¹⁄₃₂
4 BWG. and ¼ (7 str.) (0.230–0.260 diam.)	⅞	2⁴⁷⁄₆₄
⁵⁄₁₆ (7 str.) and rod (0.280–0.320 diam.)	1¹⁄₁₆	3³⁄₆₄
³⁄₈ (7 str.) and rod (0.340–0.380 diam.)	1³⁄₁₆	3²⁹⁄₆₄
⁷⁄₁₆ (7 str.) and rod (0.430–0.445 diam.)	1¼	3⁹⁄₁₆

Fig. 14–6. Strand and "Strandvise" data: *upper,* courtesy of John A. Roebling's Sons Corporation; *lower,* courtesy of Reliable Electric Company.

Comparison. As a matter of interest, a conventional un-prestressed slab was designed by WSD for the same span, loading, and class of concrete. It required 22 per cent more concrete, and 198 per cent more steel.

Members of rectangular cross section are rather disadvantageous for prestressing because the portion of the section that is within the middle third of the depth (a) contributes very little to bending strength and (b) requires additional steel to compress it. An I-section is much more suitable, as will be seen in Example 14–2.

14–5. FINAL COMMENT ON THE PRESTRESSED SLAB DESIGN

Referring to Fig. 14–4d, the *bottom* fiber concrete stress is 2775 compressive, which is greater than the 2500 psi allowable. Moreover, at the ends of the span, where the tensile dead and live load stresses are always zero, this compressive stress does not get mitigated any, as it does elsewhere along the span. Such end locality difficulties are common, and will be dealt with later in this chapter.

In this particular member, the top fiber *tensile* stress of 275 psi at the end section is safely well below the $6\sqrt{f'_c}$ allowed value of 424 psi of Code Sec. 2605(b)(2).

PRESTRESSING PRACTICE PROBLEMS

14–1. Design a prestressed slab for the same conditions as those of Example 14–1 except that:
  (a) The span is 33 ft. and the live load 0.54 ksf.
  (b) The span is 45 ft. and the live load 0.29 ksf.
Comment upon any new situations encountered, and how they were met.

14–2. Verify or disprove the statement that the prestressed slab of Example 14–1 has only 82% as much concrete and only 34% as much steel as the corresponding conventional WSD reinforced concrete slab.

14–3. Recompute the stresses in the slab designed in Example 14–1 under the design loading, assuming that the amount of the pretension has decreased by 35 kips. Investigate the possibility of tensile cracking of the concrete, and the extent thereof.

14–4. Investigate the prestressed slab design of Example 14–1, studying the midspan section.

Set up the *algebraic expressions* for (a) top, and (b) bottom fiber stress in terms of F and e as unknowns, and evaluate them. Also calculate therefrom the unit axial prestress and the bending prestress at the bottom fiber, and compare with Fig. 14–4.

14–6. TYPES OF PRESTRESSED BEAMS

Table 14–1 shows the two principal types of prestressed flexural members. The essential distinction is: *was the steel tensioned before or after the concrete had gained a working strength?*

Table 14–1. Classification of Typical Prestressed Beams

Type of Prestressed Beam or Slab	Materials		Concrete
	Prestressing Steel		
	When Tensioned?	How Anchored?	Where Usually Cast?
Pretensioned*	Prior to placing the concrete	*By bond*, effective principally at the ends, sometimes supplemented by mechanical devices	*Precast* at a factory or casting bed, and transported (joists and small beams, ordinarily)
Posttensioned*	After concrete has hardened and the steel has been pulled through	*Mechanically*, at the ends of the beam	*In place* in the structure if large beams, or precast if small

* See footnote 4.

Pretensioned Beams. When the steel is to be pretensioned,[4] fixed abutments, as in Fig. 14–7, are needed to resist the large pretensioning force. In some systems the force is resisted by heavily constructed forms. After the concrete has been placed around the tensioned steel, and has gained a satisfactory strength, the prestress is *transferred* to it as compression, by releasing the jacks or anchorage devices. The pretension in the steel must thereafter be maintained either (a) entirely by the *bond* to the concrete at the ends of the beam, or (b) with the aid of some mechanical device which bears upon the concrete at the ends of the beam. In all cases the steel is bonded over its full length. If this final anchorage is to be achieved by bond alone, small diameter wire, or seven-wire strands not over $\frac{1}{2}$ in. in diam. must be used in order to get enough perimeter per square inch of steel cross-sectional area. Such pretensioned beams

[4] It is unfortunate that more illuminating terms such as *precompressing* and *post-compressing* are not used. After all, the central thought is to get compression into the concrete before any tension from the dead plus live loading develops.

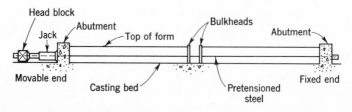

Fig. 14–7. Schematic arrangement for multiple production of bonded pretensioned prestressed beams.

are often produced end to end on a casting bed several hundred feet long, the tensioned wire being continuous, as suggested by Fig. 14–7. Such assembly line production is economical because the labor cost of pretensioning is spread over several beams. Pretensioning is also advantageous because plant labor is less expensive than field labor.

A disadvantage to pretensioned beams is that after records have been lost there is no way to tell how much prestress remains therein except by proof-testing to the cracking load.

Pretensioned beams nearly always have to be transported to their position in a structure, so some top steel is provided to resist the tensile stresses due to the handling. It may or may not be prestressed.

Pretensioned beams are subject to considerable **loss of prestress** from progressive shortening of the member due principally to concrete shrinkage, elastic shortening, and creep. The total loss of steel stress may be as much as 50,000 psi, depending upon conditions. Consequently, high tensile strength wire (Fig. 14–6) with ultimate strengths in the 250,000 psi range, and proportionality limits approaching 150,000 to 180,000 psi must be used if the final working stress pretension is not to fall below 100,000 to 130,000 psi, respectively. Obviously, mild steel with a proportionality limit stress (yield point) of 40,000 to 60,000 psi is entirely unsuitable. Refer to Fig. 14–11.

Since conditions vary considerably from case to case, the loss of prestress due to each influence should be separately computed and reconsidered from time to time, rather than assumed at some fixed percentage of the initially applied prestress.

See Example 14–2 for the designing of a bonded prestressed beam having pretensioned reinforcement, for which the losses of prestress were initially considered in detail.

Posttensioned Beams. This type of prestressed beam is commonly cast with channels therein, through which the prestressing steel is finally inserted. No abutments are involved, as the steel is posttensioned against the fully hardened concrete, and mechanically end-anchored, since there is often no bond to the concrete.[5]

Posttensioned beams have the advantage of being subject to less *loss of prestress* than pretensioned ones because (a) there is no loss due to concrete elastic deformation, (b) part of the loss due to concrete shrinkage will already have taken place before the posttensioning, and (c) the concrete creep loss will be less because posttensioning is usually done at a later concrete age.

An important advantage of ungrouted posttensioned beams is that, theoretically, it is possible to determine at any time the existing tension in straight reinforcement, and to adjust it if necessary.

---

[5] Except when post-bonded by grouting.

The other characteristics and advantages of posttensioning are taken up in Art. 14–26.

14–7. THE LOADING STAGES OF PRESTRESSED BEAMS

In prestressed designing, the loading conditions considered are called *loading stages*. At present we are concerned with two principal ones, which are:

Stage 1: Prestress plus dead load, the condition immediately following *transfer* of the prestress to the concrete,[6]

Stage 3: Prestress plus dead load and live load, the *final condition* in service, after *all* losses of prestress have taken place.

Ordinarily the beam's own dead load comes upon it at an early age as the prestress is **transferred** to it, and before the design f'_c is fully developed. This is because the precompressing of the lower fibers of concrete cambers the beam off its casting bed, bringing the counteractive dead loading into action.

After transfer, the concrete is considered to have tightly seized the steel. For the subsequent live loading investigations of Stage 3, and for predicting the initial (virgin) cracking load, the *uncracked transformed* section should be used, instead of the *uncracked plain concrete* section conveniently taken earlier in trial designing.

Figure 14–8, prepared from Fig. 14–4, shows at (b) and (c) the stresses in the pretensioned slab *at midspan*, under Stages 1 and 3 loadings, respectively. Note that the addition of the live load bending stress of 2480 psi caused an inverting of the stress distribution diagram at (b) to the position at (c).

[6] Stage 2 is during any handling which does not comply with Stage 1.

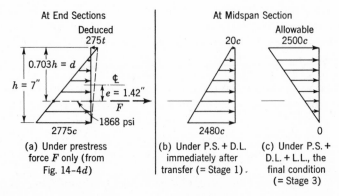

At End Sections	At Midspan Section

Deduced 275t

20c   Allowable 2500c

0.703h = d
h = 7″
e = 1.42″
F
1868 psi
2775c

2480c   0

(a) Under prestress force *F* only (from Fig. 14–4*d*)

(b) Under P.S. + D.L. immediately after transfer (= Stage 1).

(c) Under P.S. + D.L. + L.L., the final condition (= Stage 3)

Fig. 14–8. Summary of concrete stress totals in the pretensioned slab, *at transfer* and *at the final condition*, end section versus midspan section. (From Fig. 14–4.)

At (a) is shown the corresponding stress distribution at the end supports of the slab, which is the same for all loading situations because of the absence of dead and live load bending stresses.   Recall, or note from Fig. 14–4, that it was necessary to throw the top fiber into tension under prestress only, in order to counteract the 295-psi dead load compressive stress.   Note also that the prestress values shown in Fig. 14–8a are rather high.   Since some loss of pretension is presumed to have occurred already, the initial values of these stresses must have been still greater.

It will now be apparent that Example 14–1 and Figs. 14–4 and 14–8 illustrate an elementary prestress calculation which did not require an evaluation of the losses.   Before taking up our next designing example, these losses will be computed from fundamental considerations.   Their values will then be used in Example 14–2 from the beginning of the calculations, i.e., at both loading stages.

A. The Losses of Steel Pretension

14–8. INTRODUCTION [2]

In pretensioned beams, the extent to which the end surfaces of a beam approach each other at the level of the centroid of the pretensioned reinforcement due to *concrete's* properties of shrinkage, creep, and elastic deformation, is a measure of the loss, Δf_s, of steel pretension.   The possible additional losses resulting from the individual characteristics of the *steel* are the relaxation of the reinforcement and that due to the seating of mechanical end anchorages.

More insight is required to evaluate the probable losses of pretension for a given case than is required to design the beam!   Consequently some designers conveniently assume a flat 20 per cent loss of the 175-ksi initial pretension for all cases (175 ksi is the recommended initial tension in Roebling's strands, and equals 0.7 of their 250-ksi minimum ultimate strength on the average).   A better approximation would be to assume a 40,000-psi loss, since the total loss is almost independent of the amount of initial pretension in the steel, as will be seen.

The Early Losses—At Transfer

14–9. THE LOSS DUE TO THE RELAXATION OF THE STEEL

The common practice of initially pretensioning steel strands to a high *strain* approaching the proportionality limit, and maintaining it, causes a slow reduction in *stress* which is called *relaxation*.

In the case of Roebling's 250,000-psi stress-relieved pretensioning strands, the recommended initial tensioning to 0.7 of the ultimate strength, namely, 175,000 psi, looking toward a final tension of 0.8 thereof, or 140,000 psi, is stated by the manufacturer to be accompanied by a maximum relaxation of about $2\frac{1}{4}$ per cent of the initial tensioning value, or 4000 psi; which value has been included in our later table. Considerably higher values have been reported for other strands, so the matter needs some attention. (In posttensioned beams, the relaxation can be offset by later retensioning.) So

$$\Delta f_{sr} = 0.0225(f_{si}) = 4000 \text{ psi} \quad \text{(Roebling's relaxation loss)} \quad (14\text{--}1)$$

Also refer to Art. 14–26.

14–10. THE LOSS DUE TO THE ELASTICITY OF THE CONCRETE

This is the loss of steel pretension which occurs in Stage 1 as the prestress force is transferred to the concrete. Such elastic shortening of the concrete is due only to the prestress force[7] F of Fig. 14–8a, at its eccentricity e. The value of steel prestress loss due thereto may be found from the figure by first computing the compressive stress, f_{cd}, in the concrete *at the level of the centroid of the pretensioning steel*, then:

$$\Delta f_{se} = n f_{cd} \quad \text{(elastic loss)} \quad (14\text{--}2)$$

For the 6250-lb. slab concrete of $n = 6$, and $f_{cd} = 1868$ psi:

$$\Delta f_{se} = 6(1868) = \underline{11,200 \text{ psi.}}$$

For preliminary estimates use $n(d/h)f_{c\,\text{allow}}$.

The Later Losses[8]

14–11. THE LOSS DUE TO SHRINKAGE OF THE CONCRETE

As mentioned in Art. 13–5, concrete members are usually considered to be subject to a design free *axial* shrinkage of about 0.0003 of their length. In the case of a beam, the eccentricity of the reinforcement with respect to the gravity axis thereof results also in an *eccentric* shrinkage, or *warpage*, as the concrete contracts against the opposition of the steel. Consequently, the resulting shrinkage strain line is considerably inclined, and the net shrinkage coefficient *at the level of the reinforcement* turns

---

[7] Only the F-force and its eccentricity produce *prestress strain interaction* between the steel and the concrete.

[8] At this point the student is presumed to be already familiar with Chapters 12 and 13.

out somewhat less than the free axial shrinkage value. Compare, from the last table of Example 13–3(a), the value of 0.000222 with the given 0.00050 free value.

In prestressed beams the difference is not so great, due principally to their much smaller steel content. Taking a design shrinkage strain of 0.00028 and an E_s for pretensioning strand of 27,000,000 psi, the corresponding loss of steel prestress will be:

$$\Delta f_{ss} = \epsilon_s E_s \qquad \text{(shrinkage loss)} \qquad (14\text{–}3)$$

For the case at hand:

$$\Delta f_{ss} = 0.00028(27 \times 10^6) = \qquad \underline{7550 \text{ psi.}}$$

One-third of this shrinkage loss is sometimes considered to take place in Stage 1, at transfer. A more realistic practice, when moist curing has been maintained until transfer, is to consider that all of it occurs thereafter. Such a practice also is consistent with that of deliberately underestimating the total of the losses which occur before transfer, so that any high initial stress in the concrete at the ends of the beam will be fully recognized.

14–12. THE LOSS DUE TO CREEP OF THE CONCRETE

Of all the losses of prestress, that due to the creep of the concrete is the greatest, and probably the most uncertain.

The concrete unit creep strains, δ_t in Eq. 12–1 and Art. 12–5, now being used in calculating prestress losses, are considerably smaller than those found by Shank and others forty or more years ago. They are based largely upon the more recent findings of English and European investigators [2, 3] who studied the high strength concretes used in prestressed members. See Table 14–3 for Ross' guide to prestress loss due to creep.

For *pretensioned* beams a common American practice is to take the long-time concrete unit axial creep strain at 0.4 millionth per psi of concrete stress [3], or at about 40 per cent of the 1.0 millionth value of years past, because:

1. The 5000- to 8000-lb. concretes now used creep less,
2. The almost universal practice of placing by vibration results in lower cement factors and correspondingly less creep,
3. The increased concrete densities resulting from vibration, and possibly from the compacting effect of early transfer of stress thereto, decrease the creep, and
4. The creep, related as it is to drying out, has been found to be less in full-sized members and structures than in the small laboratory specimens ordinarily used in research. Refer to Table 14–3.

It may be added that high early strength portland cement and hot moist curing when used, both tend to decrease further the total creep below the 0.4 millionth value deducible from Professor Ross' Table 14–3.

The urgent need for more comprehensive test data upon the creep losses of present-day high-strength concretes is universally recognized both here and abroad. In the meantime it is convenient to remember that since the unit service level elastic strain of high-strength concrete is roughly 1/5,000,000, or 0.2 millionth, the longtime *total* (elastic plus creep) strain will be about 0.5 millionth, or $2\frac{1}{2}$ *times the elastic strain*.

Referring again to Fig. 14–8b, the corresponding time-dependent loss of steel pretension will be closely equal to the long-time creep strain times the modulus of elasticity of the steel strand:

$$\Delta f_{st} = \delta_t (d/h) f_{ct} E_s \qquad \text{(creep loss)} \qquad (14\text{--}4)$$

with the steel centroid at distance d from the top of the beam, and the D.L. tension[9] recognized, as at (b).

Since in Fig. 14–8 the live loading is transient, and is often not first applied until some late age,[10] we cannot safely rely upon its contribution to the total tensile deformation pictured in (c) to further decrease the creep loss already accumulated under prestress *minus* dead loading. Consequently, it is conservative to compute the creep loss from the Stage 1 diagram at (b), and to consider its value as the total creep loss. For our case, using $d/h = (4.92)/(7.00) = 0.703$,

$$\Delta f_{st} = 0.4 \times 10^{-6}(0.703)(2480)(27 \times 10^6) = \text{creep loss} = \underline{18,800 \text{ psi.}}$$

14–13. TOTAL LOSSES

Note in the summary of computed losses (Table 14–2) that for pretensioned members the total loss of steel pretension can be fully 41,550 psi, of which over 45 per cent is due to the creep of the concrete. Note also that the 15,200-psi loss taken "after transfer" is a deliberate underestimate gotten by considering that all the concrete shrinkage and creep losses occur later. This is a correct procedure because it will prevent one's early deducting of such a large share of the total loss of steel pretension that high *end section* concrete stresses, like 275 tensile and 2775 compressive of Fig. 14–8a, may be obscured. On the other hand, the *total* loss of steel prestress, which affects the performance in service,

[9] The dead and live load strains arise from the bending effect of downward (gravity) loads, and neither increase or decrease the pretension. Visualize their stresses as *separate* additional ones.

[10] On the other hand, if the live load is applied at an early age and is relatively permanent (the beam supporting a water storage tank, for example), credit may be taken for the corresponding reduction in creep loss in the manner indicated for load removal in Art. 12–2 and Fig. 12–2.

should never be underestimated, because undesirable *midspan* bottom concrete tension could thereby be overlooked.

The authors consider that the "Totals" of Table 14–2 show "minimum to above average" loss values, and that the AASHO's (American Association of State Highway Officials) permitted totals of 35,000 and 25,000 psi for pretensioned and posttensioned beams, respectively, are certainly not too high.

In addition to the four losses considered in Table 14–2 there may be *anchorage loss* at the beam ends, and deflected strand *frictional loss*, which occur principally in the posttensioned type of beam, and are not taken up in detail in this textbook. Refer to the ACI, PCI (Prestressed Concrete Institute), and AASHO regulations.

14–14. THE NATURE OF THE LOSSES OF STEEL PRETENSIONING

An examination of Eqs. 14–2, 14–3, and 14–4 for the principal losses of steel prestress due to concrete's elasticity, shrinkage, and creep,

Table 14–2. Summary of Computed Losses of Slab Steel Prestress

6250 psi concrete, $n = 6$　　　250,000-psi strand centered
(Pretensioned) transfer at　　　at about 0.7 beam depth
7-day age　　　　　　　　　$E_s = 27 \times 10^6$ psi
Allowable $f'_c = 2500$ psi

		Totals (psi)	
Sources of Loss		Pretensioned Member	Posttensioned Member
Early losses:			
Steel relaxation	4,000		0*
Concrete elastic	11,200		0
Total after transfer		15,200	0
Later losses:			
Concrete shrinkage	7,550	7,550	5,000†
Concrete creep	18,800	18,800	14,100‡
Total steel stress loss at final condition		41,550	19,100
Estimated possible range		⎰15,000 to 50,000	5,000 to 25,000
The AASHO permits		35,000	25,000

* If retensioned.
† Considering ⅓ of the shrinkage to have already taken place.
‡ Equals ¾ of 18,800.

respectively, will reveal that in no case are these losses directly related to the high initial tensile stress induced in the reinforcement.

The *elastic loss* varies principally with the relative depth of the reinforcement, since n times $f_{c\,\text{allow}}$ is nearly a constant. For well-proportioned and properly built beams, the *shrinkage loss* approaches a constant. The *creep loss* varies directly with the concrete unit stress and the relative depth of the reinforcement.

Consequently, losses should not be stated in percentage of the 175-ksi initial pretension, and used repeatedly and *unthinkingly*. Even for beams of the same depth, but varying in span, load, and steel ratio, the total loss can vary all over the "possible range" shown at the bottom of Table 14–2.

Loss values should be reconsidered from time to time as better experimental data become available.

As may be seen in Table 14–3, the creep loss also varies inversely, and widely so, with (1) the strength of the concrete, (2) its age when first loaded, and (3) with the area/perimeter ratio of the cross section of the member.

Table 14–3. Prof. A. D. Ross' Concrete Creep Prestress Loss Guide*

Concrete: English standard portland cement
and good natural stone aggregates
70% mean relative humidity

Cement and Water Ratios		Magnitude of Long-Time Unit Creep Strain, δ_t, in millionths per psi of Concrete Compressive Stress								
		Loaded at 7 Days			Loaded at 28 Days			Loaded at 91 Days		
Volumetric W/C	Weight C/W	\multicolumn{9}{c}{Area/Perimeter Ratio of Specimen, in inches}
		1.0	2.0	2.5	1.0	2.0	2.5	1.0	2.0	2.5
0.50	3.02	0.50	0.36	0.26	0.39	0.30	0.20	0.24	0.16	0.10
0.60	2.52	0.67	0.50	0.38†	0.49	0.38†	0.28	0.37†	0.27	0.19
0.70	2.16	0.86	0.67	0.50	0.64	0.50	0.38	0.51	0.38	0.28
0.80	1.89	1.06	0.84	0.64	0.80	0.64	0.50	0.69	0.52	0.40
0.90	1.68	1.35	1.05	0.82	1.08	0.84	0.65	0.92	0.70	0.54
1.00	1.51	1.65	1.25	1.00	1.43‡	1.11	0.83	1.22	0.91	0.71

SOURCES: Deduced from test data from hand-placed ordinary strength concretes by projecting the effect of W/C upon creep, and confirmed by Dr. Magnel's tests on beams of high-strength concrete.

* See Reference 3.

† Close to the commonly used value of 0.4.

‡ Compare with 1.23 obtainable after 5 years of loading by Shank's Eq. 12–1 of Chapter 12, deduced from 4-by-4 in. hand-placed compression specimens.

PREDICTION-OF-LOSSES PROBLEM

14–5. Recalculate the four basic losses of prestress for the 7-in. slab design of Ex. 14–1 and Fig. 14–5 if the strands had conveniently been laid on $1\frac{1}{2}$-in. standard bolsters.

EXAMPLE 14–2

The Design of a Pretensioned Fully Prestressed Concrete Girder

It is desired to design an economical pretensioned girder of symmetrical I-shape to carry a uniformly distributed loading over a long span, as taken up in detail below.

DESIGN GUIDES

Follow Code Chapter 26.   Design for flexure by WSD, and check the stresses thereby.   Then **investigate** for M_u by USD, and finally design the stirrups.

Loading and span data.   The service live loading is 1.36 klf over a 58-ft. simple span, center to center of 16-in. supports.   Estimate the dead load at 25% of the live, and use as a design[11] trial.

CONCRETE

The ultimate compressive strength of the concrete, f'_c, is to be 5000 psi.   Aggregate max. size < 1 in. $n = 7, f_c = 2250$.   Initially, $f'_{ci} = 4000$.   Modulus of rupture $= 7.5 \sqrt{f'_c}$.

WSD allowable stresses.

(a) *At Stage 1*, immediately after transfer:
   Compressive, at beam ends, $0.6f'_{ci}$
   Tensile, at beam ends, $3 \sqrt{f'_{ci}}$, but see Code.
(b) *At Stage 3*, the final condition in service:
   Compressive, at midspan, $0.45f'_c$
   Tensile, at midspan, $6 \sqrt{f'_c}$

STEEL

For prestressing take Roebling's uncoated stress-relieved $\frac{7}{16}$-in. seven-wire pretensioning strand at their stated 248,000-psi minimum ultimate strength, f'_s.   Take E_s of strand at 27×10^6 psi.   Refer to Fig. 14–6.

WSD allowable stresses.

   Max. pretension immediately after transfer: $0.7f'_s$
   Max. pretension at final condition: $0.6f'_s$

Flexural steel ratios.

   Max.: $p \le 0.3(f'_c/f_{su})$ [Code Sec. 2609(a)]
   Min.: Enough to exceed the modulus of rupture by 20%   [Code Sec. 2609(c)].

---

[11] Include the D.L. bending moment to compute the reqd. depth h for I-beams, since their lower kern point is only about $h/4$ from the bottom.   See Fig. 14–3.

Assigned losses of steel pretension (similar to those of Table 14–2).

Immediately after transfer:
Concrete elastic = 12,000 psi
Steel relaxation = 4,000
Later additional:
Concrete shrinkage = 8,000
Concrete creep = 21,000

Grand total = 45,000 psi

USD final flexural investigation.

Using f_{su} from ACI Formula 26–6:
Get M_u using ACI Formula 26–5 and others.

USD web reinforcement.

Use A305 bar stirrups of 50,000-psi yield point.
Provide cover per Code Sec. 2616.

Initial Dimensions

Expect the (whole-inch) depth h to be about $\frac{1}{15}$ of the span.
Design all other outside dimensions by half-inches.
Try $0.52h$ as kern-to-kern distance between F-forces. Refer to Fig. 14–9.
Refer to Sec. 2617(b) for min. strand spacing, and to Sec. 2616 for cover [4].
Note at bottom of Fig. 14–9 that 3 layers of strand demand a 7-in. thick flange. Refer to Fig. 14–6.

B. WSD Pretensioned Girder Designing

14–15. PROPORTIONING THE GIRDER

(a) F_i-force required by M_{D+L}: First compute the moments.

	w, klf	M, kip-ft.
Live	1.36	573
Dead	0.34 (est.)	143
Total	1.70	716

Hence,

$$F_i = \frac{716(12)}{0.52h} = \frac{16,530}{h} \tag{1}$$

The flange width, b, required for the 21 trial strands of Fig. 14–9 will be: $7(7/16) + 6(3)(7/16) + 2(1\frac{1}{2}) = 13.94$ in.

Means a 14-in.-wide flange.

(b) The force required to precompress the whole concrete section to an average stress of $0.45f'_c/2$, or 2.25 ksi/2, will be:

$$F_i = (2.25/2)\{2(7)(14) + [h - 2(7)](3.5)\} = 3.94h + 165.4 \tag{2}$$

Equating (1) and (2):

$$\text{Reqd. } h = 47.10 \text{ in.}$$

As a trial, make h conservatively larger at 48 in., or 4 ft.

Then F_i for $h = 48$ in. and 7-in.-thick flange is

$$(1.125 \text{ ksi})[2(7)(14) + 3.5(34)] = 354 \text{ kips}$$

Trial number of strands reqd. to precompress $= 354/(175 - 45)(0.1089)$
$= 25.0$

Tentative strand design $\begin{cases} 4 \text{ in top flg., for handling, etc.} \\ \underline{21} \text{ in bot. flg. } (= 2.284 \text{ sq. in.}) \\ \overline{25} = \text{trial total number pre-} \\ \qquad \text{compressing the concrete.} \end{cases}$

Corresp. L.L. double eccentricity $= 573$ kip-ft.$(12)/354 = 19.40$ in. $= 2e_L$. Refer to Fig. 14–9.

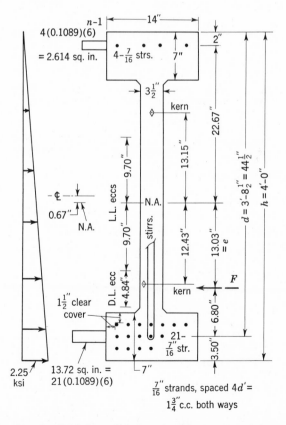

Fig. 14–9. Precise W-S investigational check on the girder designing.

(c) The *web thickness* of $3\frac{1}{2}$ in. was dictated by the $1\frac{1}{2}$-in. cover demanded for the strand by Code Sec. 2616. Another guide (rough) is that the maximum vertical shear in the web should not exceed $0.06f'_c$.

14–16. W-S INVESTIGATION OF PRETENSIONED GIRDER STRESSES

In the investigational calculations, presented below as Example 14–2 (continued), the designing approximations of Art. 14–15 are absent. The contribution of the steel to the transformed section properties, including the displacement of the neutral axis, was taken into account. Note that the live load eccentricities lie well within the kern limits (Fig. 14–9). Also note that the top strands are contributing to the pre-compressing of the concrete.

As will be seen in the continuation of Example 14–2 below, the *concrete stress* investigations, showing the action immediately *after transfer*, and at the *final condition*, attest to the safety of the design, except for the high compressive stress at the ends *after transfer*, which is greatly decreased by an *end block* detail such as is shown in Fig. 14–15.

EXAMPLE 14–2 *(Continued)*

W-S Investigation of Pretensioned Girder Section

(a) **Get N.A. by ΣM about the centerline.**

Gross concrete: 14(14) = 196 3.5(34) = 119 ─── 315 sq. in.	Area	Arm	Moment
	315.0	0	0
	2.61	−22.0	−57.4
	13.72	0.5	281.2
	331.3		223.8

So N.A. is $223.8/331.3 = 0.67$ in. below the centerline.

(b) **Get I_{NA}.**

$$\text{Concrete:}$$
$$14(48)^3 \div 12 = 129{,}200$$
$$10.5(34)^3 \div 12 = -34{,}400$$
$$\overline{94{,}800}$$
$$315(0.67)^2 = \phantom{-129{,}}142$$

$$\text{Transformed steel:}$$
$$2.61(22.67)^2 = 1{,}343$$
$$13.72(19.83)^2 = 5{,}400$$
$$I = \overline{101{,}685 \text{ in.}^4}$$

(c) **Actual kern points.**

$$\frac{F}{A} = \frac{Fec}{Ar^2} \equiv 1, \quad e = k = \frac{r^2}{c}, \quad r^2 = \frac{I}{A} = \frac{101{,}685}{331.3} = 306.6$$

Distances of kerns from N.A.:

$$\text{Upper, } k_t = 306.6/23.33 = 13.15 \text{ in.}$$
$$\text{Lower, } k_b = 306.6/24.67 = 12.43 \text{ in.}$$

Actual L.L. range = 25.58 in. = $0.53h$, compare with $0.52h$ originally tried.

(d) **Live and dead load eccentricities.**

$$2e_L = \frac{573 \text{ kip-ft.}(12)}{1.125(315)} = 19.4 \text{ in.}$$

$$e_D = \frac{143 \text{ kip-ft.}(12)}{1.125(315)} = 4.84 \text{ in.}$$

(e) **Final live plus dead load unit stress.** At midspan, $M_{L+D} = 716$ kip-ft. Therefore,

$$\text{Top fiber, } f_{c_{L+D}} = \frac{Mc}{I} = \frac{716(12,000)(24.67)}{101,685} = 2085 \text{ psi}$$

But there are yet axial and eccentric prestress to be added.

(f) **Actual eccentricity of the precompressing force F.** Summing moments about the bottom centroid, 3.50 in. up from the bottom of the beam:

$$\frac{(4 \text{ strands})(48 - 2 - 3.50)}{(4 + 21) \text{ strands}} = 6.80 \text{ in. therefrom}$$

or, $\qquad\qquad\qquad\qquad e = 13.03$ in.

(g) **Concrete stresses immediately after transfer.**

$$F_t = (175 - 16)(25)(0.1089) = 433 \text{ kips} \qquad f'_{ci} = 4000 \text{ psi}$$

	Unit stresses	
	Top	Bottom
At centerline of girder end supports	$c = 24.67$ in.	$c = 23.33$ in.

Due to the prestress force F_t:

$\dfrac{F_t}{A} = \dfrac{433,000}{331.3} =$	1310 comp.	1310 comp.
$\dfrac{F_t ec}{I} = \dfrac{433,000(13.03)(c)}{101,685} =$	1370 tens.	1295 comp.
	60 tens.	2605 comp.
	$< 3 \sqrt{f'_{ci}}$	$> 0.6f'_{ci}$
	$= 190$ psi	$= 2400$ psi
	O.K.	But the end block increases I by over 27%; total there is then only 1666 psi.[12]

[12] End block $I = 14(48)^3/12 = 129,000$ in.^{4} and more. Refer to the "final design sketch," Fig. 14–15. See also the Art. 14–25 discussion of end anchorage *prestress transfer distance L_t.*

The D.L. and L.L. stresses are zero at the ends.

At midspan (F_t still 433 kips)	Top	Bottom

Due to the axial + eccentric prestress
total above   60 tens.   2605 comp.
Due to the D.L. activated by the
cambering:

$$\frac{M_{DC}c}{I} = \frac{143,000(12)(c)}{101,685} =$$

	Top	Bottom
	417 comp.	394 tens.
	357 comp.	2211 comp.

Both < 2400 psi, O.K.

(h) **Concrete stresses at the final condition.** $f'_c = 5000$, and under the design service loading:

$$F_f = (175 - 45)(25)(0.1089) = 354 \text{ kips}$$

	Unit stresses	
At midspan only	Top $c = 24.67$ in.	Bottom $c = 23.33$ in.

Due to prestress:

$$\frac{F_f}{A} = \frac{354,000}{331.3} =$$

1068 comp.   1068 comp.

$$\frac{F_f ec}{I} = \frac{354,000(13.03)(c)}{101,685} =$$

1118 tens.   1059 comp.
$\Sigma = 50$ tens. $\Sigma = 2127$ comp.

Due to D.L. + L.L.:

$$\frac{Mc}{I} = \frac{716(12,000)(c)}{101,685} =$$

2088 comp.   1974 tens.
2038 comp.   154 comp.

Both < 2250 psi, O.K.
If bottom is tensile, see ACI
Sec. 2605(b)(2). See also
second paragraph of Art. 14–17.

Comment. Note that the compressing of the concrete by the pretensioned steel prevents high *combined* stresses in the concrete.

PRESTRESSED BEAM DESIGN PROBLEM

14-6 (Individual). (a) Design by WSD an *alternate* I-shaped pretensioned girder for your assigned flange width, following both Example 14–2 and the Code closely. Make the flange thicknesses 7 in. Use any (single) suitable Roebling strand size. Take the same steel and concrete strengths.

(b) Draw a *design sketch* of your section, as in *Fig. 14–9*, and submit your sheet of supporting calculations.

Name	Flange Width, in.
	16
	18
	$19\frac{1}{2}$
	21, etc.

14–17. MAXIMUM AND MINIMUM FLEXURAL STEEL CONTENTS

The limiting *maximum steel* clause of Sec. 2609(a) for *prestressed beams*, and the $(\frac{3}{4})p_{bal}$ maximum value used in Example 2–3 to design *conventional R/C beams*, both exist to insure that the steel content will be **small enough that a slow-yielding tensile failure will occur** therein in case of overloading.

The *minimum steel* clause of Code Sec. 2609(c) demands that the prestressed steel content be *large enough*[13] that the **shock** accompanying *sudden deep concrete cracking*, as occurred in Example 2–12, would not also cause actual **fracturing** of the steel, and a **falling apart of the member!**

This latter Code clause demands adequate steel resistance to potential concrete flexural tensile failure; as determined by a flexural force T_{min} calculated from 1.2 times the $7.5 \sqrt{f'_c}$ (plain concrete) modulus of rupture, which for 5000-lb. concrete is 636 psi [6] at the extreme tensile fiber of concrete.

Thus both the "Max." and the "Min." permissible steel clauses exist for the same general purpose, namely, to prevent a destructively sudden fracturing type of ultimate failure, whether via compression in the concrete or tension in the steel.

14–18. COMMENTS UPON THE FLEXURAL INVESTIGATION

Figure 14–10 shows principally the top and bottom *concrete stresses* taken from the stress tables of Example 14–2 (continued), and *those at the level of the steel*, also deduced therefrom. Note also at (a) the shaded locality representing prestress loss. Its abscissae are proportional to those of the parent diagram, namely 16/175 thereof.

Concrete stresses at midspan (Fig. 14–10 and the preceding stress tables). At (f) of the "final condition," the trapezoid's low stresses of 2038 compressive and 153 compressive are no problem.

At (c) at "transfer," with the trapezoid inverted, there exist approximately the same low stresses.   *O.K.*

---

[13] Expect trouble when the section modulus of the tension side of a transformed section turns out less than if the member were unreinforced!

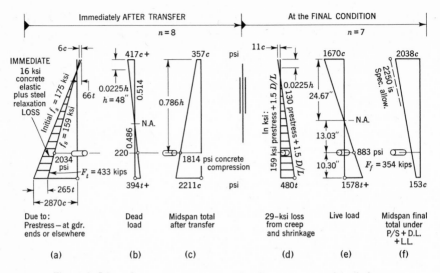

Fig. 14–10. Summary of stresses in the prestressed I-girder.

Concrete stresses at girder end (Fig. 14–10 and the preceding stress tables). At (a), after transfer, the high bottom stress of 2605 compressive has been reconciled. The 60 tensile one is safe. Both also appear in item (g) of Example 14–2 (page 521).

Steel stresses. It is usually a surprise to learn that the application of the service dead and live loads *increases* the tension in the prestressed steel comparatively little. The *decrease* due to the losses of prestress is a much larger item, so the final stress still is less than the initial one!

Let us determine the final stress in the steel by progressing from left to right on the stress diagrams of Fig. 14–10 and *at the level of the centroid of the steel.*

At (a) the initial 175-ksi steel pretension decreased almost instantaneously to 159 ksi, due to the concrete elastic plus steel creep loss of 16 ksi. Next, the concrete compressive stress at the level of the steel dropped from 2034 psi to 1814 psi due to the 220 psi dead load tensile stress developed from the cambering (rise) of the central part of the beam from the casting bed. The bonding of the concrete to the steel had then increased the tension therein by $(n = 7)(220) = 1.54$ ksi, for a total of 160.5 ksi.

At (d), the 29-ksi loss decreased the above total to 131.5 ksi, but the 883-psi live load concrete stress added $7(0.883) = 6.2$ ksi, making the final total 137.7 ksi, which is considerably *less* than the unloaded beam initial stress of 175 ksi!

14–19. PREDICTION OF THE ULTIMATE RESISTING MOMENT, M_u, OF PRESTRESSED FLEXURAL MEMBERS

The relationship between the ultimate resisting moment of a prestressed flexural member and its safe working moment is not a linear one computable from the ratio of the failure stress to safe working stress of the materials involved.   This is because one or both of our materials get into the curving *inelastic range* of performance depicted in Fig. 14–11 as beam failure is approached.   The corresponding large *inelastic* deformations of the steel *erase* the prestress therein, so that shortly before failure a prestressed beam functions substantially as a conventional reinforced concrete beam.

Neither the yield-point strength f_y, nor the *nominal* yield strength f_{sy} improvised by $\frac{1}{500}$ set strain geometry for steels (such as our strand) having no well-defined yield point, is used by the Code to predict the ultimate moment, M_u, of *prestressed* beams.

A higher stress, f_{su}, pictured in Fig. 14–11, must be computed from Formula 26–6 of Sec. 2608, and used to find M_u for the pretensioned I-girder.

EXAMPLE 14–3

Independent Investigation for the Ultimate Resisting Moment, M_u, of the Pretensioned I-Girder Designed in Example 14–2

Refer to Code Secs. 2608 and 2609.   The ultimate strengths are $f'_c = 4000$ and $f'_s = 248,000$ psi.   (Review Example 2–5 and Art. 2–14.)

Solution.   *Introduction.*   Examination of the above-mentioned Code sections

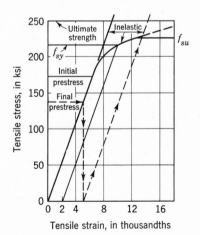

Fig. 14–11.   Loss of steel prestress within the elastic range approaching failure.

will show that much depends upon the value of the bottom prestressing steel ratio, p, of Sec. 2609(a). It "develops" part, or most, of the compressive strength of the web, and is sometimes designated as p_w, because only the web dimensions are used in computing it.

Note from Formula 26–6 that f_{su} varies inversely with p. A high p-value leads to a conservatively low value of f_{su} and to the desired low M_u.

Referring to Sec. 2609, the maximum permissible value of p_w is

$$0.30 \frac{f'_c}{f_{su}} = \frac{0.30 f'_c}{f'_s \left(1 - 0.5p \frac{f'_s}{f'_c} \right)}$$

For our two failure strengths of 5000 and 248,000, this quadratic in p yielded $p_{max} = 0.744\%$; and from Formula 26–6 the corresponding $f_{su,min}$ was 202.3 ksi.

Devising the resisting couples. The ultimate resisting moment of a common doubly reinforced section is most easily found by separating it into consistent *component* resisting couples; and summing the corresponding *resisting moments* thereof. Figure 14–12 shows at (b) a **steel couple** that has been "spun off" of the girder at (a). The steel area removed is indicated.

Next, in (c), the overhanging **compression flange** area was removed, together with enough bottom steel to make its T_u equal the C_u. At (d) the **remaining steel** works with its required (balancing) web concrete area.

The (c) and (d) steel areas were computed before trying to write the final M_u expressions. At this point, since f_{su} still was indeterminate, a trial value of 230 ksi was taken (later corrected) in order to get the corresponding 1.36 sq. in. trial value of flange bottom steel at (c). The subtraction of the (c) plus (b) steel area from the given 2.287 sq. in. total gave a 0.491 sq. in. *tentative* tensile steel area for web element (d).

It was found that after substituting $p_w = (A_{sw})/(b'd_w)$ into Code Formula 26–6, an improved value of 228 ksi for f_{su} satisfied the fixed requirement that $A_{sf} + A_{sw} \equiv 1.851$ sq. in. in this case. The correspondingly corrected p_w was

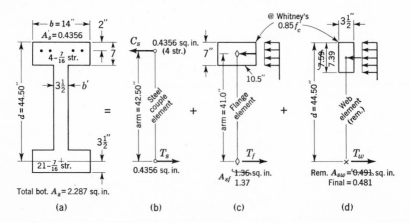

Fig. 14–12. Investigation for *resisting* M_u by summing couples. Refer to Fig. 14–9 of Example 14–2.

$0.481/(3.5)(44.5) = 0.309\%$,[14] which was safely less than the 0.744% maximum computed earlier.

Calculation of the component M_u's.

Source	ϕ	A_s	f_{su}	Arm		
Steel couple:	0.9	(0.4356)	(228)	$\left[\dfrac{42.50}{12}\right]$	=	317 kip-ft.
Flange element:	0.9	(1.37)	(228)	$\left[\dfrac{41.0}{12}\right]$	=	962
Web element:	0.9	(0.481)	(228)	$\left[\dfrac{40.80}{12}\right]$	=	336

$$\text{Total USD investigational } M_u = \underline{\underline{1615 \text{ kip-ft.}}} \quad \text{Ans.}$$

$$\text{Avg. factor of safety} = \frac{1615}{\underset{D}{143} + \underset{L}{573}} = 2.26$$

PRESTRESSED BEAM INVESTIGATION PROBLEM

14–7. Investigate the rectangular pretensioned prestressed beam of Fig. 14–13 for the pertinent concrete stresses (a) at transfer, and (b) at the final condition.   Compare with the allowables *and comment.*

Refer to the continuation of Example 14–2 (page 520).

The material strengths, Code allowables, and the losses are the same as in Example 14–2 (page 517).   The live load is 0.40 klf over a 28-ft. simple span.

Finally, comment upon the effect of the *shape* of the section.

14–20. RESISTANCE TO INITIAL CRACKING

Once the design live loading has been applied, the additional bending moment required to *initially* crack a beam in flexure will be:

1. That required to decrease the compressive stress in the bottom fiber to zero, *plus*
2. That required to crack the beam if it were unreinforced, i.e., the (minimum) modulus of rupture bending moment.

[14] The high strength strand steel p ratios required to develop the compressive strength of the top concrete run only about $\frac{1}{4}$ to $\frac{1}{6}$ of those for mild steel bars of correspondingly lower strength.   Refer to the table of Problem 2–3, and to the WSD beam charts of Appendix L.

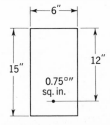

Fig. 14–13

Solution. For the I-girder of Example 14–2, and referring to items (b) and (h) of the "Investigation" in Example 14–2 (continued):

1. From the calculations referred to:

$$M_a = \frac{sI}{c} = \frac{153(101,685)}{23.33(12,000)} = 55.5 \text{ kip-ft.}$$

2. From Code Sec. 2609(c), 7.5 $\sqrt{f'_c}$ of Fig. 2–23, and Ref. [5], = 530:

$$M_b = \frac{sI}{c} = \frac{530[14(48)^3 - 10.5(34)^3]}{24(12)(12,000)} = 174.0 \text{ kip-ft.}$$

Total initial cracking moment =   229.5 kip-ft.

The corresponding D.L. + L.L. average factor of safety against *initial* cracking is, comparing bending moment values,

$$\frac{143 + 573 + 229.5}{143 + 573} = 1.32$$

Once a girder has so cracked, the modulus of rupture strength disappears. Thereafter the factor of safety against *repeated* opening of a crack will be in this case,

$$\frac{143 + 573 + 55.5}{143 + 573} = 1.08$$

When greater factors of safety against cracking are desired, plan from the beginning to have a greater concrete compressive stress at the bottom fiber under the design loading.

PRETENSIONED BEAM PRACTICE PROBLEM

14–8. One day a series of pretensioned beams were cast, for which the gage on the strand pretensioning device was later found to have been out of adjustment from the beginning.

You have been retained to "rate" these beams by experimentally determining what their safe live load is, using one or two of them, but without destroying their usefulness.

All the pertinent designing calculations are at hand, including the strength of the steel and concrete, but the value of the actual prestress force *F*, is unknown.

What to do? State, in order, the several steps you would take. Then elaborate on each, giving reasons, and possibly citing the girder calculations of Example 14–2 to illustrate your points.

14–21. ALTERNATE SECTIONS FOR PRESTRESSED I-GIRDERS

A dashed-line I-section, as in Fig. 14–14a, consisting of three simple rectangles was very convenient in the early designing of Art. 14–15 for establishing trial dimensions, such as flange width and total depth, also the strands required. It was also convenient for the later WSD calculation of the eccentricity of the prestress force, and the concrete stresses of Art. 14–16 and Fig. 14–9.

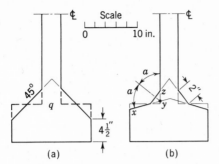

Fig. 14—14. Relief of re-entrant corner stress.

Unfortunately, the two 90° lower re-entrant corners at q are what have sometimes been labeled as "stress raisers," since they have been the cause of *early* cracking of concrete, as well as *later* failures under test overloads, due partly to a poor combined stress situation at q.

It has been found that the *dashed-line* shape at (a) may be converted into the *broken line* xz at (b), while maintaining the same 14-by-48 in. outer dimensions (but of slightly greater concrete area), without appreciably sacrificing overall strength. Of course the bottom steel has to be rearranged, with some of it located in the lower portion of the web, and the section thoroughly re-investigated beginning with the methods of Art. 14–16.

However, satisfactory action has sometimes been achieved simply by sloping the re-entrant surfaces of the flanges to follow a course xyz.

PRACTICE PROBLEM

14–9. Redesign the I-section of Example 14–2 and Fig. 14–14 to have sloping flanges and fillets as in Figs. 14–14b and 14–15.
(a) Check its concrete working stresses, per Art. 14–16, (a) through (h) and report.
(b) Check its ultimate moment M_u according to Example 14–3, and report.

14–22. THE WEB REINFORCEMENT OF THE PRETENSIONED GIRDER

It is sometimes erroneously assumed that the precompression induced in the concrete by the prestress force prevents the development of the diagonal tensile stresses associated with conventional reinforced concrete beam designing, and that, consequently, stirrups are unnecessary in a prestressed member.

The greatest error in the above assumption is that in the high loading range approaching the ultimate strength of the beam the prestress disappears, due to the inelastic action of the reinforcement, as depicted in Fig. 14–11, and the beam action thereafter is closely that of a conventional reinforced concrete beam.   If the resulting *diagonal tensile stresses* are high, some diagonal tensile reinforcement must therefore be provided to prevent a sudden and disastrous *shear-related* failure at a loading that is less than the flexural ultimate load.

The Code clauses are partly based upon tests of about 250 beams, the failures of which were shear-related, including some prestressed ones. As such tests progressed there was a tendency for the principal (diagonal) tension[15] to greatly outrun the increase in unit vertical shear, while the normal stress (axial compressive) was decreasing. This is why the stirrups of prestressed beams are now required to be designed at the *ultimate strength* level.

14–23. A SUMMARY OF STIRRUP DESIGNING

In Fig. 14–15 the shear diagram for the W-S designed I-girder was prepared on a U-S basis by increasing the service-level loads in the table at the beginning of Art. 14–15. Thus, the ultimate uniform load, w_u, was $1.5(0.34) + 1.8(1.36) = 2.96$ kips per ft. The *load-factored* beam shear, V_u, at the *key point*, $d/2$ distant from the face of support [Sec. 2610(c)], was found to be 78.44 kips.

According to Sec. 2610(a), the required area of vertical stirrups is given by:

$$A_v = \frac{(V_u - \phi V_c)s}{\phi d f_y} \qquad \text{[ACI Formula 26–10]}$$

In the above formula, ϕV_c is the shear carried by concrete, V_c being the corresponding value for *ideal* conditions. Therefore, $(V_u - \phi V_c)$ is that part of the beam shear to be carried by stirrups, and is similar to V'_u in ACI Formula 17–4 for conventional R/C beams, except that the ϕ-factor has been introduced in an alternative fashion.

According to Sec. 2610(b), the V_c value to be used in Formula 26–10 is the *smaller* of the two values: V_{ci} and V_{cw}. V_{ci} is the shear at diagonal cracking related to flexural cracking, and V_{cw} is the shear in the non-flexurally cracked part of a beam when diagonal cracking occurs. For normal-weight concrete, V_{ci} and V_{cw} are given by the following formulas:

$$V_{ci} = 0.6b'd\sqrt{f'_c} + \frac{M_{cr}}{\dfrac{M}{V} - \dfrac{d}{2}} + V_d \qquad \text{[ACI Formula 26–12]}$$

with a minimum value equal to $1.7b'd\sqrt{f'_c}$.

$$V_{cw} = b'd(3.5\sqrt{f'_c} + 0.3f_{pc}) + V_p \qquad \text{[ACI Formula 26–13]}$$

---

[15] The *direction* of principal (diagonal) tension associated with axial *compression* may be shown to be much nearer the vertical than at 45°, and indicates the ideal alignment of such reinforcement.

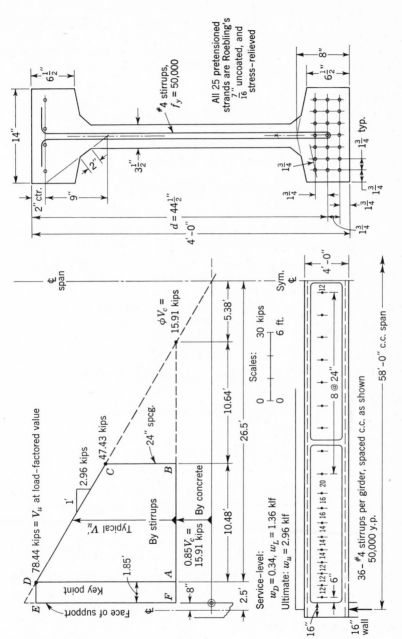

Fig. 14–15. Final design sketch of pretensioned I-girder.

For the present example, V_{ci} was taken to be conservatively equal to its minimum value, namely, $1.7b'd\sqrt{f'_c} = 1.7(3.5)(44.5)\sqrt{5000} = 18.72$ kips. It is obvious then that this value is always less than V_{cw} as given by Formula 26–13. Therefore, $V_c = 17.82$ kips, and $\phi V_c = 15.91$ kips. Figure 14–15 shows this point, beyond which stirrups were theoretically not required.

Section 2610(c) stipulates a maximum stirrup spacing of 24 in. or three-fourths of the depth of a member, whichever is the smaller. For the present example, three-fourths of d came to about 33 in., and therefore the 24-in. maximum was observed. Based on this spacing, the required area of stirrups was calculated using the minimum A_v of ACI Formula 26–11:

$$\text{Min. } A_v = \frac{A_s}{80}\left(\frac{f_s}{f_y}\right)\left(\frac{s}{d}\right)\sqrt{\frac{d}{b'}} \qquad \text{(ACI Formula 26–11]}$$

$$= \frac{2.7225}{80}\left(\frac{250}{50}\right)\left(\frac{24}{44.5}\right)\sqrt{\frac{44.5}{3.5}}$$

$$= 0.33 \text{ sq. in.}$$

Therefore #4 stirrups with A_v of 0.40 sq. in. were adopted, and the corresponding $\phi A_v f_y d = 0.85(0.40)(50)(44.5) = 756.5$ kip-in.

The application of Formula 26–10 at the key point yielded a required spacing of 12.1 in. By the same formula, the 24-in. maximum spacing was found to develop at the 47.43-kip ultimate shear. This 24-in. spacing was used throughout the central 32 ft. of the girder, following the long paragraph of Sec. 2610(c).

Referring to Fig. 14–15, the theoretical number of stirrups required between E and B was given by:

$$N = \frac{\Sigma s V'_u}{s V'_u \text{ of one stirrup}}$$

$$= \frac{\Sigma(V'_u \text{ areas } ABCD \text{ and } ADEF)}{\phi A_v f_y d}$$

$$= \frac{[(10.48/2)(62.53 + 31.52) + 1.85(62.53)](12)}{756.5}$$

$$= 9.65$$

Knowing the stirrup spacings at A and B, the intermediate spacings were worked out in the same manner as in Chapter 3, and they are shown in the lower view of Fig. 14–15, including the eight additional "arbitraries" necessary to reach midspan.

STIRRUP PRACTICE PROBLEM

14–10. Referring to Fig. 14–15, produce the detailed *supporting calculations* for the designing of all the stirrups, together with clear references to the corresponding Code clauses followed. Include a well-drawn *large scale* layout on 8½-by-11-in. *good* *coordinate paper* sheet which shows a *verification* of the development of all the stirrup spacings involved.

14–24. THE PREDICTION OF THE IMMEDIATE AND LONG-TIME DEFLECTIONS OF THE PRETENSIONED I-GIRDER

Taking the flexural deflection as δ, Fig. 14–16 shows that the midspan deflection of the girder from the plane of the casting bed, due to pretension and gravity load may be computed by moment-area principles:

Unit elastic strain = 1 psi/E_c = 1/4,080,000   = 0.245×10^{-6}
Long-time unit *creep*, *steel relaxation*, plus *shrinkage*
    strain, from Code Sec. 909(d) = 1.7(0.245 × 10⁻⁶) = $\underline{0.415 \times 10^{-6}}$
                                            Total = $\overline{0.660 \times 10^{-6}}$

Since the girder is uncracked, the long-time total strain and deflection will be about $0.66/0.245 = 2.69$ times the elastic.

Due to D.L. and P/S:

$$EI\delta_t = 2.69\{\tfrac{2}{3}(143)(29)[\tfrac{5}{8} \times 29] - 385(29)[14.5]\} = -301,000 \text{ kip-ft.}^3$$

Taking also the 101,685 elastic I of the uncracked section:

$$\delta_t = -\frac{301,000(12)^3(1000)}{4,080,000(101,685)} = -1.25 \text{ in.} \quad \text{(upward)}$$

Due to L.L., applied intermittently, the elastic deflection will be:

$$\delta_L = \frac{(\tfrac{2}{3})(573)(29)[\tfrac{5}{8} \times 29](12)^3(1000)}{4,080,000(101,685)} = +0.84 \text{ in.} \quad \text{(downward)}$$

This means that the girder would then still be cambered above the surface of the casting bed $1.25 - 0.84 = 0.41$ in.

If the L.L. becomes permanent, the long-time total deflection with

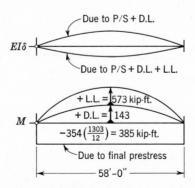

Fig. 14–16. Pretensioned girder deflections.

respect to the surface of the casting bed will be about:

2.69(0.84) − 1.25 = 1.01 in. downward, or *about* $\frac{1}{690}$ *of the span.*

Compare with Code Sec. 909(e)(2) limitation.

14–25. ANCHORAGE OF PRETENSIONED REINFORCEMENT

When the prestressing jacks of Fig. 14–7 are released, the prestressing force, F_t, is *transferred* to the concrete of the beam end locality principally via a superior type of bond stress that is basically different from the *flexural* bond stress or the *anchorage* bond stress taken up in Chapters 3 and 10, namely, *prestress transfer bond stress.*

This particular type of bond resistance results from the *expansion* of strand diameter as the stress in the beam end of Fig. 14–17 decreases from the 175-ksi initial pretension to progressively smaller *safe load range* values over the *transfer length* L_t. The zero stress at the extreme end means that the strand diameter thereat has increased to its original size, following Poisson's ratio. The gradation inward to smaller diameters results in a beneficial wedge-like action. This bond resistance is mostly frictional, resulting as it does from large normal forces developed as the steel expands.

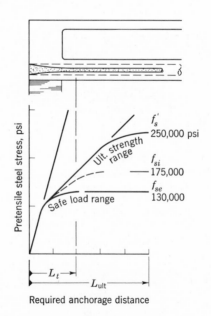

Fig. 14–17. Development of the anchorage of pretensioned girder reinforcement.

That the required anchorage distance, L_t, extends into the clear span of the beam somewhat is unimportant because the prestress prevents any cracking of the concrete at transfer.

In the ultimate strength range approaching beam failure not much additional *prestress transfer bond* can be developed on the returning from the 130-ksi final prestress value pictured in Fig. 14–17 to the initial prestress of 175 ksi, at which it theoretically becomes zero. For developing the additional anchorage, L_{ult}-L_t, that may be required to prevent disastrous strand slippage in the ultimate strength range, the conventional[16] (pull-out) bond allowable of Code Ch. 18 may be used, though its unit value is much smaller than the *prestress transfer* one, as indicated by the greatly decreased straight-line slope of the upper part of the graph of Fig. 14–17.

[16] Since the strand then is stressed to *more* than the initial 175 ksi, it is, therefore, *decreasing* in diameter like a conventional reinforcing bar.

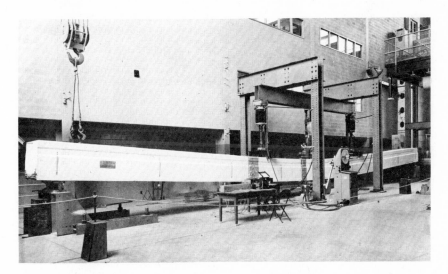

Plate 14–2. Seventy-foot box-section pretensioned-prestressed bridge beam near failure in test at Fritz Engineering Laboratory, Lehigh University. The beam was 3 ft. wide by 2 ft. 9 in. deep and contained forty-six $\frac{3}{8}$-in. seven-wire strands with an ultimate tensile strength of 250,000 psi. It was fundamentally an I-section because of a 27-by-24-in. cavity which extended over its full length, except for 2-ft. solid bulkheads at its ends and the midsection. The failure was due to excessive compression in the upper fibers of the concrete at midspan and directly under one of the load points. The steel was highly stressed, but there was no evidence of any excessive inelastic elongation, since the cracks remained quite small up to the instant of failure.

Although Janney's tests [6], and those of Hognestad and Janney [7], are well-recognized ones, and Professor Lin's [8] thorough treatment of the subject is an excellent contribution, the ACI has decided that for the next few years the following empirical formula of Sec. 2611(a) for *minimum* anchorage length L in pretensioned flexural members using seven-wire strand of nominal diameter D may be used:

$$L = (f_{su} - \tfrac{2}{3}f_{se})D$$

where f_{su} and f_{se}, as defined in Code Sec. 2600, are in ksi, and L and D are in inches. The anchorage length L is the distance from the extreme end of the beam to "those cross sections nearest the end of the member that are required to develop their ultimate (flexural) strength under the specified load."

For the 58-ft. pretensioned I-girder of Examples 14–2 and 14–3, subject only to our uniformly distributed loading: f_{su}, from Example 14–3, is 228 ksi; f_{se}, effective final prestress, from item (h) of the "W-S investigational check," is 130 ksi. Then $L = [230 - (\tfrac{2}{3})130](\tfrac{7}{16}) = 63$ in. = *5 ft. 3 in.*

C. Posttensioned Beams

14–26. POSTTENSIONING VERSUS PRETENSIONING

As mentioned in Art. 14–6, the concrete of posttensioned beams is typically placed around removable sleeves, thereby forming a channel through which the steel is later threaded, and stressed by jacking against the hardened concrete. One advantage is that since the elastic com-

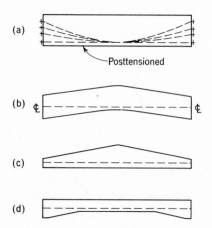

Fig. 14–18. Solutions for the problem of high end-section stresses.

pressing of the concrete is eliminated, and the shrinkage and creep losses are considerably reduced, the total loss of steel tension can be decreased by one third to one half.   Also, when the steel is left unbonded, its tension may be conveniently adjusted at some later time if desired.

The most important advantage of posttensioning has been that the steel can be *draped*, as in Fig. 14–18a, to (1) avoid tensile stress in the top concrete at end[17] sections, (2) provide diagonal tension reinforcement, and (3) avoid possible interference of the mechanical end-anchors used.   Furthermore, the reinforcement need not be of small diameter, since bond is typically not relied upon for anchoring the ends.   Posttensioning is also advantageous for girders too large to be conveniently transported through traffic to the job site.

The disadvantages include possible rusting of the reinforcement (unless it is post-grouted), relatively expensive field labor must be used to position the steel and tension it, and a considerably lower ultimate strength[18] for the member if the reinforcement is unbonded to the concrete at intermediate points (or only partially so).

It should be added that some of the original differentiations between pretensioned and posttensioned beams are now fast disappearing, as exemplified by the thorough postbonding of posttensioned reinforcement, and the draping of pretensioned strands by pushing them downward and confining them in saddles attached to the casting bed.

14–27. MECHANICAL END ANCHORAGES

There are several forms of end anchorages, which are a necessity for posttensioned beams.   The wedging principle is most employed.   The *Freyssinet cone*, which can accommodate up to eighteen wires, and the *Magnel sandwich plates* are examples.   For excellent descriptions of these and several other makes, refer to Professor Lin's Chapter 3 (Reference 8).

The *Strandvise* device of Fig. 14–6 is primarily intended for use on *pretensioned* beams, to hold the pretension until *transfer*.

14–28. SUMMARY OF PRESTRESSING PRINCIPLES

In prestressed beams the concrete tensile stress is offset by a compressive prestress initially introduced by tensioning the reinforcement. Such beams are dependably crack-free under the design service loading, and can have large span/depth ratios without deflecting excessively.

[17] Other solutions are represented at (b), (c), and (d).
[18] Compare Formulas 26–6 and 26–7 of Code Sec. 2608.

Prestressed beams are usually *designed* at the service load level by working stress methods, then always *investigated* at the failure level for adequate ultimate resisting moment.

Such members should be proportioned to have, just after transfer, a substantially triangular distribution of precompressive concrete stress, with base downward. This is accomplished by arranging the prestressed reinforcement so that its centroid is in the neighborhood of the lower kern point of the (uncracked) cross section.

The later application of gravity loads should cause a flexural stress diagram of such magnitude that, when added to the prestress stress diagram, it will produce a triangular diagram of combined compressive stress *with base upward*. This means no tension in the bottom fibers of concrete under the design service loading.

The section of the member should be taken of sufficient depth that the product of the required prestress force, F, times the distance between the upper and lower kern points (of the section) is greater than the live load bending moment. When the dead load bending moment is relatively large, the section must sometimes be made arbitrarily deeper in order to take care of it.

The tendency of the losses of steel pretension is to allow tensile cracking to develop. To prevent cracking, they must be computed and allowed for in the designing. The values of the principal ones are closely related to the strength and strain properties of the concrete and should not be stated as a percentage of the initial pre-tensile stress in the steel, to which they are not directly related.

As the failure load of a prestressed beam is approached, the inelastic (permanent) deformation of the reinforcement erases the prestress, allowing cracking. The beam thereafter performs substantially as an overloaded conventional reinforced concrete beam, not only with respect to flexure, but also as to diagonal tension and anchorage. The greatly increased strengths then demanded in these latter two respects require that the provision of web reinforcement and lengths of embedment for anchorage be calculated at the ultimate strength level. This will prevent an undesirable sudden shear-related type of failure.

QUESTIONS

1. Define *prestressed concrete, pretensioning, posttensioning, transfer stage, live load range, dead load range limit, live load double eccentricity,* and *dead load eccentricity.*
2. List five unusual characteristics of prestressed beams, as compared with conventional reinforced concrete beams.
3. Can prestressed beams always be proportioned for live load only? Explain.
4. Enumerate, in order, the steps necessary to design a pretensioned concrete slab. What two internal force relationships should be kept in mind at all times?
5. How can the ultimate strength of prestressed beams be predicted? Why?

6. List the losses of pretension. Show how to calculate each, stating typical values. Do likewise for posttensioned beams.

7. Tell in what several respects the determination of the concrete dimensions of a pretensioned I-girder differs from that for a pretensioned slab.

8. Explain why both maximum and minimum steel percentages are set for prestressed flexural members.

9. Explain why the stresses at the end sections of prestressed beams sometimes become prohibitively high. Mention at least three ways of lowering them. Why are somewhat higher stresses sometimes permitted at such points?

10. It is sometimes said that the losses of prestress have the same effect upon the concrete stresses as the dead and live loads. Confirm or disprove, giving reference.

11. Is the working stress in pretensioned reinforcement equal to the initial pretension minus the losses? Explain.

12. Tell in detail how to predict the overload required to cause flexural cracking of pretensioned beams.

13. Discuss at length the important manner in which the bonded anchorage of pretensioned reinforcement differs from that of conventional reinforced concrete beams.

14. State the advantages and disadvantages of pretensioned beams versus posttensioned ones.

REFERENCES

1. *The Structural Use of Prestressed Concrete in Buildings.* British Standard Code of Practice CP 115. London: The Council for Codes of Practice, British Standards Institution, 1959.

2. GUYON, Y. *Prestressed Concrete.* New York: John Wiley & Sons, Inc., 1960 (Vols. 1–2).

3. ROSS, A. D. "The Loss of Prestress in Concrete," *Civil Engineering and Public Works Review* (London), May 1950, Vol. 45, No. 527, p. 307.

4. ASHTON, L. A., and BATE, S. C. C. "Fire Resistance of Prestressed Beams," *Proc. ACI,* 1961, Vol. 57, pp. 1417–1440.

5. KESLER, CLYDE E. "Statistical Relation Between Cylinder, Modified Cube and Beam Strength of Plain Concrete," *Proc. ASTM,* Vol. 54; Technical Papers, p. 1178; and Fig. 4 in particular. Consult also Fig. 2–23 in Chapter 2 of this text.

6. JANNEY, J. R. "Nature of Bond in Pre-tensioned Prestressed Concrete," *Proc. ACI,* 1954, Vol. 50, pp. 717–736.

7. HOGNESTAD, E., and JANNEY, J. R. "The Ultimate Strength of Pretensioned Prestressed Concrete Failing in Bond," *Magazine of Concrete Research* (Cement and Concrete Association, London), June 1954, Vol. 6, No. 16, p. 35.

8. LIN, T. Y. *Design of Prestressed Concrete Structures* (2d ed.). New York: John Wiley & Sons, Inc., 1963.

Appendix

Appendix A:
FLEXURE CALCULATIONS BY USD CHART

Beam Formulas and Chart. After the fundamental methods of Chapter 2 are thoroughly understood, a means for doing such work speedily is needed. This may be accomplished by evolving general formulas for the several relationships, then constructing *charts* or *tables* therefrom which embrace the whole practical range of each function. Such aids are widely used by practicing designers.

Figure A–1 illustrates certain items of standard notation not previously discussed.

The stress in the compressive "stress block" is *always* taken at $0.85f'_c$. The *steel ratio*, $p = A_s/bd$, is commonly expressed as a percentage. The subscript b indicates a strain-balanced condition. The ultimate concrete strain is taken as 0.003 in. per in.

Design (ideally balanced).

$$c_b = \frac{0.003}{0.003 + f_y/E_s} (d) \qquad \text{(based on strains, from USD fundamentals)}$$

With k_1-value from ACI Sec. 1503(g):

$$a_b = k_1 c_b, \quad j_b = 1 - \tfrac{1}{2}(a_b/d), \quad M_{u_b} = C_u j_b d = T_u j_b d$$

Design with ACI $(\tfrac{3}{4})p_b$ maximum. $\qquad\qquad p = A_s/bd$

$$a_{\max} = (\tfrac{3}{4})a_b, \quad p_{\max} = (\tfrac{3}{4})p_b, \quad jd_{\max} = d - \tfrac{1}{2}a_{\max}, \quad M_{u\max} = T_u jd_{\max}$$

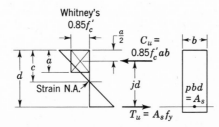

Fig. A–1. USD rectangular beam notation.

543

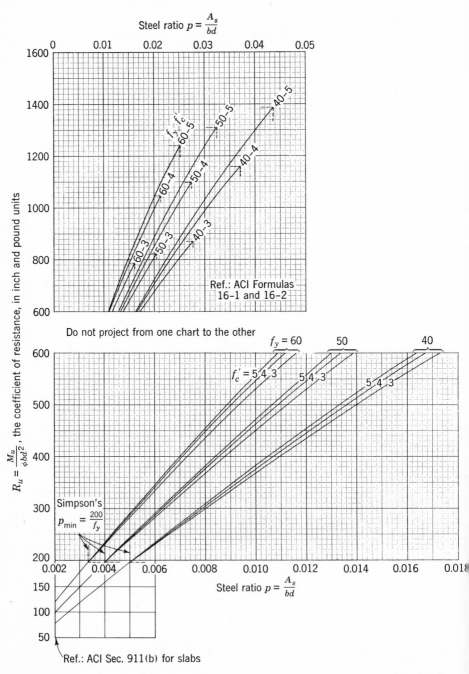

Chart A–1. Ultimate strength coefficients of resistance, $R_u = M_u/\phi bd^2$, for ACI rectangular USD sections.

Use of USD Rectangular Section Beam Chart A–1. For a review of the subscripts to M_u, refer to Table 2–1 of Chapter 2, and to the introductory statements of the Examples which follow it directly.

U-S Designing

EXAMPLE 2–3[1]

Given. A design M_u/ϕ value of 118 kip-ft. $= M_{ud}$. The specification is 50,000 and 3000 psi. If $b = 8$ in., **find** the required d and A_s from Chart A–1.

Solution. At the tip of the curve marked 50–3 find the coordinates $M_u/(\phi b d^2)$ $= 820$ psi, and a steel ratio, $p = 0.0206$. Then

$$d^2 = (118)(12,000)/(8)(820) = 215.0, \text{ and the reqd. } d = \underline{\qquad 14.66 \text{ in.}}$$
$$\text{Corresp. reqd. } A_s = pbd = 0.0206(8)(14.66) = \underline{\qquad 2.42 \text{ sq. in.}}$$
$$\text{A satisfactory check.}$$

EXAMPLE 2–4

Given. The beam, bending moment, and ACI specification of Example 2–3, but with its depth d arbitrarily increased to 15.50 in. **Calculate** the new required A_s.

Solution. The coefficient of resistance, $M_u/(\phi b d^2)$, now equals $(118)(12,000)/(8)(15.50)^2 = 737$.

From the chart, find on the 50–3 curve at the elevation 737, $p = \underline{\qquad 1.78\%}$

Then the required $A_s = pbd = 0.0178(8)(15.50) = \underline{\qquad 2.21 \text{ sq. in.}}$

U-S Investigating

EXAMPLE 2–5

Given. The 8-in.-wide beam, chart-designed in Example 2–3 for a design M_{ud} of 118 kip-ft.

Required to chart-investigate it for its ACI-rated ultimate resisting moment M_u.

Solution. Locate the point on Chart A–1 from which to read the desired ultimate resisting moment. The specification was 50–3 ksi.

The actual $p = A_s/bd = 2.42/(8)(14.66) = 0.0206 = 2.06\%$.

The highest point on the 50–3 line is at $M_u/(\phi b d^2) = 820$ psi, so the ultimate resisting moment is

$$M_u = \frac{820(0.9)(8)(14.66)^2}{12,000} = \underline{\qquad 106 \text{ kip-ft.}}$$

Comments. The lower portion of Chart A–1 uniquely includes the coefficients of resistance for the very small steel ratios permitted by ACI Sec. 911(b) for slabs, grade beams and other members much deeper than necessary for strength. Additionally, refer to Art. 2–21 and Example 2–12.

---

[1] Example 2–2 of Chap. 2 involves a large steel content not permitted by ACI practice. Consequently the results are not deducible from Chart A–1.

Table A–1. Limiting Values of ACI USD Rectangular Section Beam Properties

f_y, psi	f'_c, psi	ACI Max. Stress Block Depth a/d	Corre- sponding Minimum j	ACI Max. p, %	Maximum R_u, psi For Design- ing	For Investigat- ing
60,000	6000	0.333	0.833	2.84	1415	1274
	5000	0.355	0.822	2.54	1254	1129
	4000	0.377	0.811	2.15	1041	937
	3000	0.377	0.811	1.61	783	705
50,000	6000	0.357	0.822	3.64	1496	1346
	5000	0.381	0.809	3.24	1312	1181
	4000	0.405	0.797	2.75	1097	986
	3000	0.405	0.797	2.06	821	738
40,000	6000	0.386	0.807	4.90	1582	1424
	5000	0.411	0.794	4.36	1384	1245
	4000	0.436	0.782	3.72	1162	1046
	3000	0.436	0.782	2.78	870	783

In Table A–1 are summarized the values of the ACI USD maximum permissible steel percentages in singly reinforced rectangular beam sections for various combinations of f'_c and f_y, and the corresponding beam properties. Before using these tabulated data, the student should make sure that he knows how to derive them from fundamental principles.

Appendix B: SOLUTION OF CUBIC EQUATION WITH REAL COEFFICIENTS

The following procedure to extract a real root of a cubic algebraic equation is numerical and iterative. It is sometimes referred to as the **Birge-Vieta** procedure, and is a combination of **Newton-Raphson's method** and **synthetic division with detached coefficients.** Only the method of performing the computations by this procedure will be described below; for proofs and wherefores underlying the procedure, the reader should refer to any standard book on numerical analysis (for example, K. S. Kunz, *Numerical Analysis* [New York: McGraw-Hill Book Co., Inc., 1957]).

Given a cubic equation:

$$f(x) = x^3 + ax^2 + bx + c = 0$$

where the coefficient of the leading term containing x^3 has previously been reduced to unity.

Make a reasonable guess at the real root in question, say, x_n.

If x_n is not quite the correct value, a better value, x_{n+1}, may be obtained by means of the Newton-Raphson technique as:

$$x_{n+1} = x_n - \frac{f(x_n)}{f'(x_n)}$$

in which $f(x_n)$ = value of the function $f(x)$ upon substitution of $x = x_n$
$f'(x_n)$ = value of the function $f'(x)$ obtained by differentiating $f(x)$ with respect to x and then substituting $x = x_n$.

As many cycles of similar iteration may be repeated as needed to yield the value of the required root to any desired precision.

The evaluation of $f(x_n)$ and $f'(x_n)$ may be most efficiently performed by synthetic division as follows:

Arrange the coefficients of the terms in *descending* order, taking care to list zero coefficients if any. Carry out the computations exactly as indicated in the diagram following on the next page.

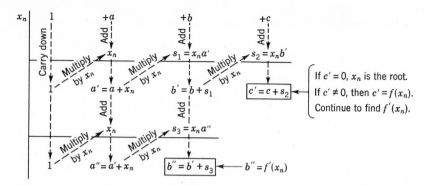

In the computations above, if x_n is found to be the desired root, then the "reduced" quadratic equation obtained by $f(x)/(x - x_n) = 0$, will have its coefficients given in descending order by 1, a', and b'.

EXAMPLE B–1

Given $f(x) = x^3 - 18x^2 + 60.84x - 1107 = 0$, **find** a root in the neighborhood of $x = 17.0$.

Solution.

Trial 1.

$x = 17.0$	1	-18.0	60.84	-1107
		17.0	-17.0	745.3
	1	-1.0	43.84	$\boxed{-361.7}$ $\leftarrow f(17.0)$
		17.0	272.0	
	1	16.0	$\boxed{315.84}$ $\leftarrow f'(17.0)$	

Improved value of $x = 17.0 - (-361.7/315.84) = 18.15$

Trial 2.

$x = 18.15$	1	-18.0	60.84	-1107
		18.15	2.72	1154
	1	0.15	63.56	$\boxed{47}$ $\leftarrow f(18.15)$
		18.15	332.2	
	1	18.30	$\boxed{395.76}$ $\leftarrow f'(18.15)$	

Improved value of $x = 18.15 - (47/395.76) = 18.03$

Trial 3.

$x = 18.03$	1	-18.0	60.84	-1107
		18.03	0.54	1107
	1	0.03	61.38	$\boxed{0}$ $\leftarrow f(18.03)$

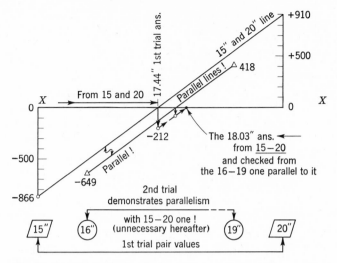

Fig. B–1. Graphical solution of preceding cubic equation.

Since $f(18.03) = 0$, the root is $x = 18.03$. The reduced quadratic equation obtained by dividing $f(x) = 0$ by $(x - 18.03)$ is then:

$$x^2 + 0.03x + 61.38 = 0$$

whose roots may be easily found if desired.

Comment. Alternately, a graphical solution may be used to determine a root of a cubic equation. Figure B–1 demonstrates how the cubic equation of Example B–1 may be handled graphically.

Note in Fig. B–1 that the 15–20-in. trial was the only one necessary. Determine the (-212) inconsistency of its coordinates, using the X-intercept (17.44), and redraw parallel to the 15–20 line, to the intersection (18.03) with the X-axis.

Appendix C: COLUMN CHARTS[1]

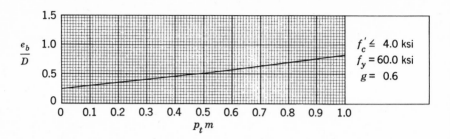

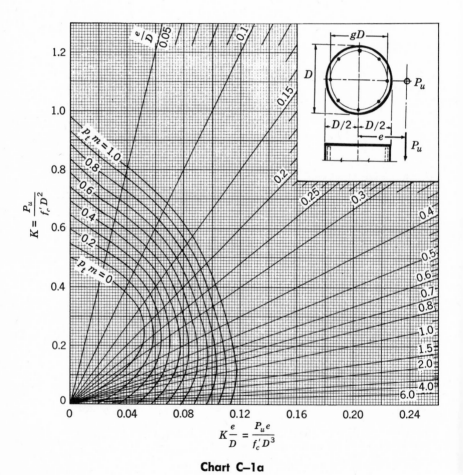

Chart C–1a

---

[1] For examples of the use of column charts, see Arts. 5–24 and 5–25.

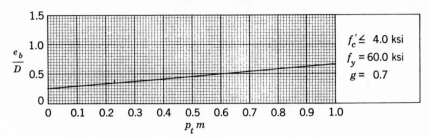

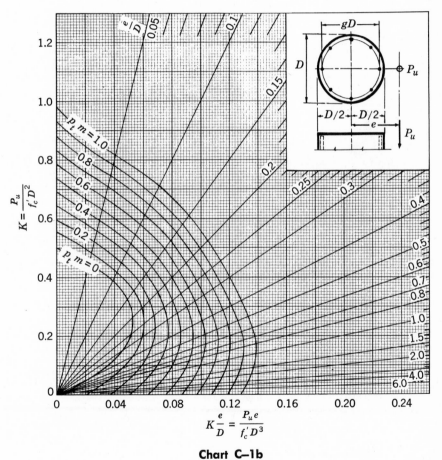

Chart C–1b

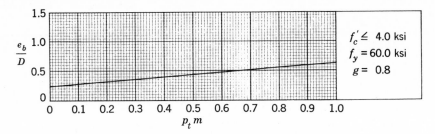

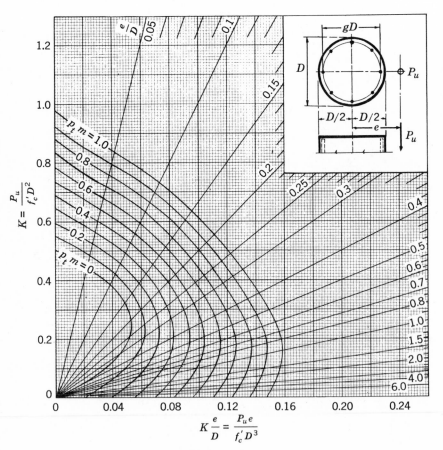

$$K \frac{e}{D} = \frac{P_u e}{f'_c D^3}$$

Chart C–1c

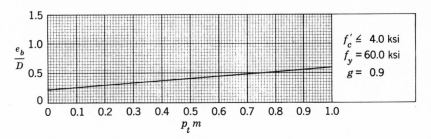

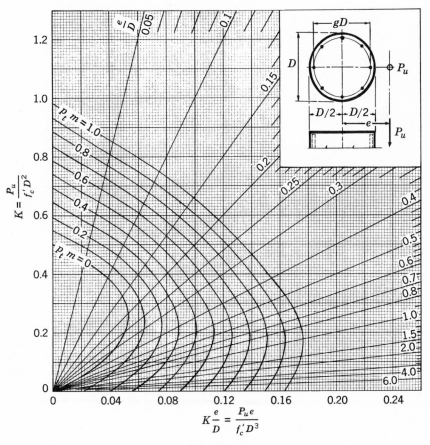

Chart C–1d

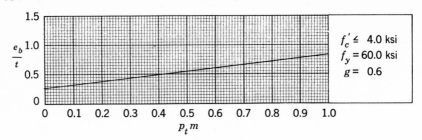

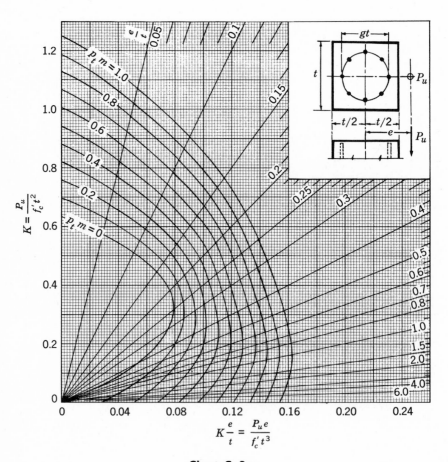

Chart C–2a

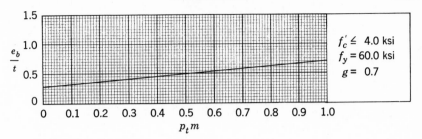

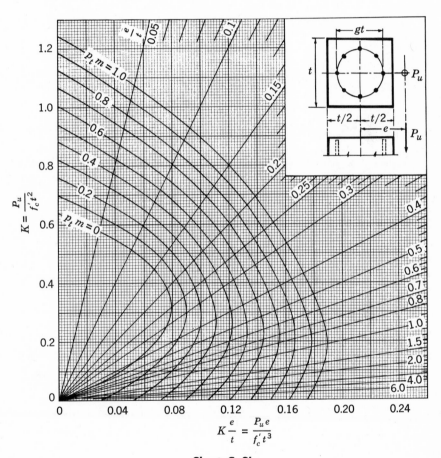

$$K = \frac{P_u}{f_c' t^2}$$

$$K \frac{e}{t} = \frac{P_u e}{f_c' t^3}$$

Chart C–2b

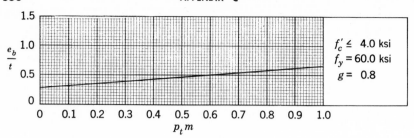

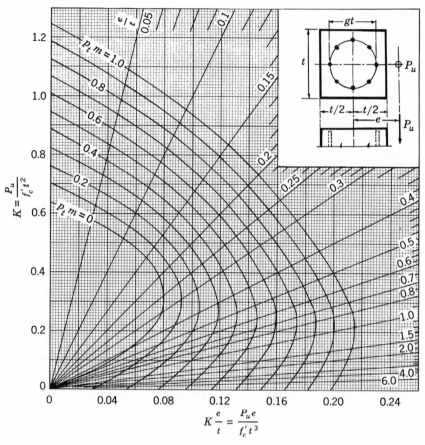

Chart C–2c

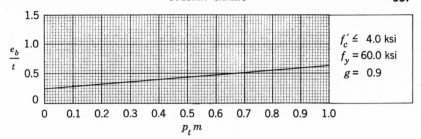

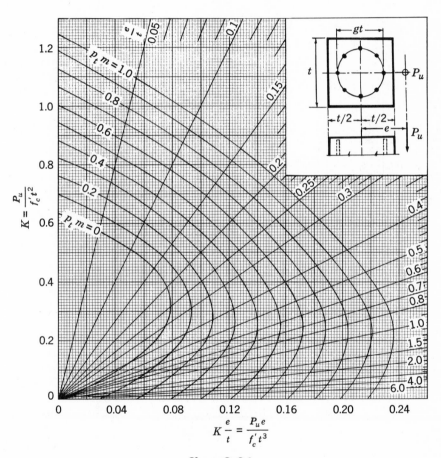

Chart C–2d

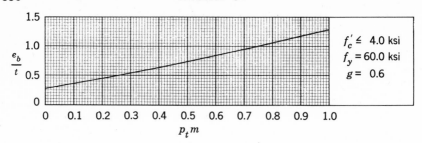

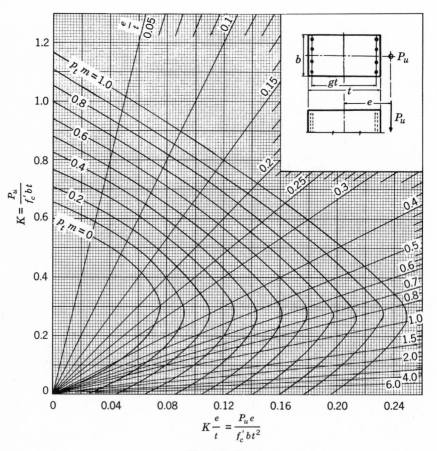

$$K \frac{e}{t} = \frac{P_u e}{f_c' b t^2}$$

Chart C–3a

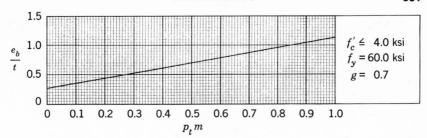

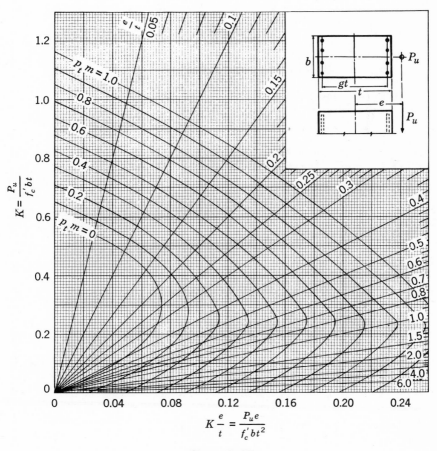

Chart C—3b

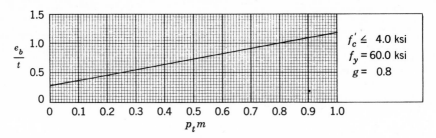

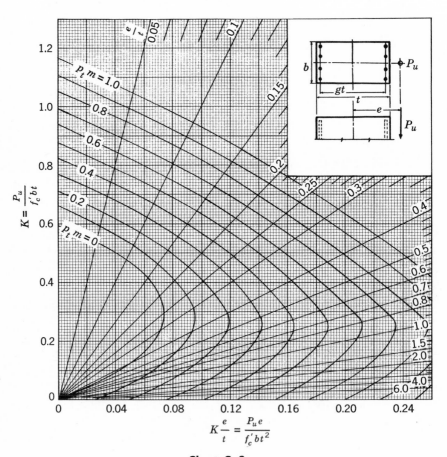

Chart C–3c

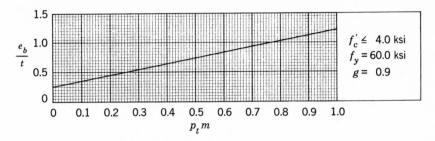

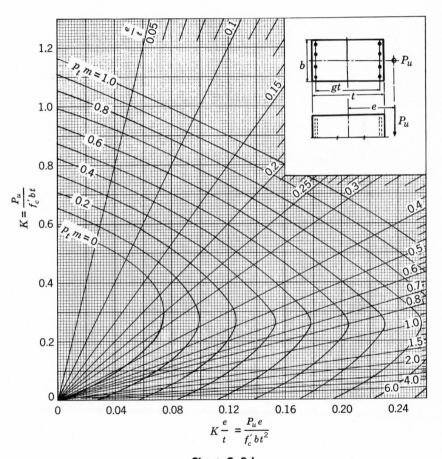

Chart C–3d

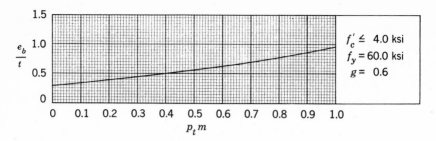

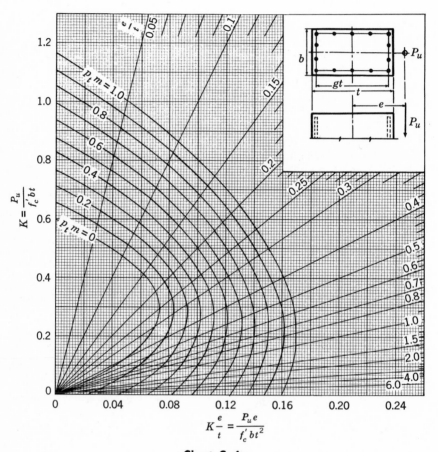

Chart C–4a

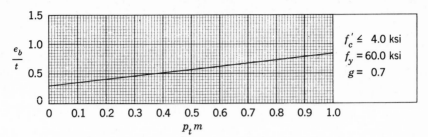

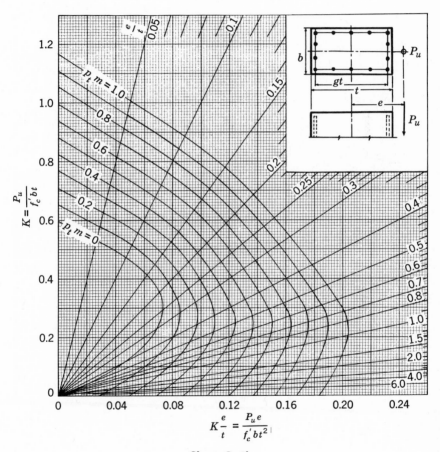

Chart C–4b

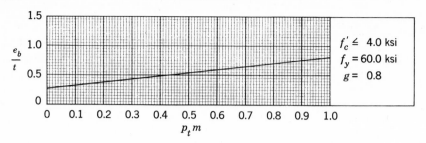

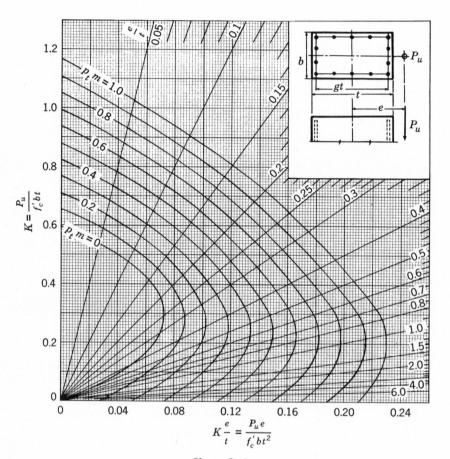

Chart C–4c

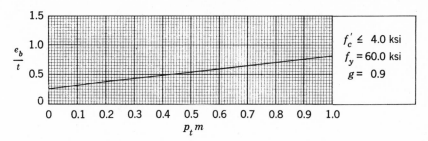

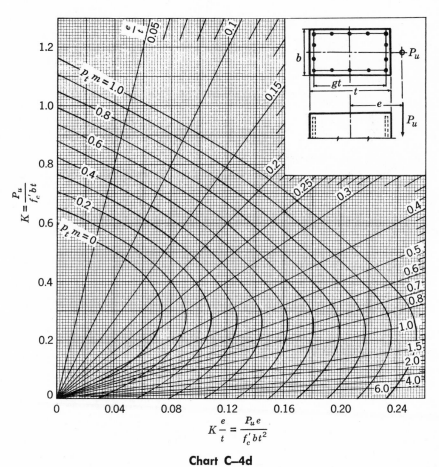

Chart C–4d

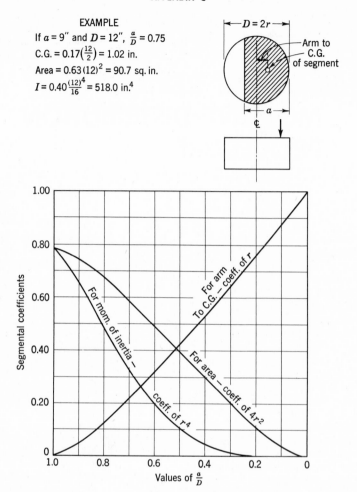

EXAMPLE

If $a = 9''$ and $D = 12''$, $\frac{a}{D} = 0.75$

C.G. $= 0.17\left(\frac{12}{2}\right) = 1.02$ in.

Area $= 0.63(12)^2 = 90.7$ sq. in.

$I = 0.40\frac{(12)^4}{16} = 518.0$ in.^{4}

Chart C–5. Properties of segments of circular sections. (Courtesy of Prof. J. R. Shank)

Appendix D: REVIEW OF MOMENT DISTRIBUTION PROCEDURE

EXAMPLE D–1

Given a four-span continuous beam on non-yielding knife-edge supports as shown in Fig. D–1a. The spans are identical in length and cross section and each is subject to uniform loads of w_D dead and w_L live. **It is required** to find the dead load moments and the maximum live load moments.

Solution. The **stiffness** at B of span AB, with A considered *hinged* at all times, is $3(EI/L)$. The stiffness at each end of BC is $4(EI/L)$ when the far end is *fixed*. Similarly for spans CD and DE.

The **distribution factors** at B are therefore:

$$3(EI/L)/[3(EI/L) + 4(EI/L)] = 3/7 = 0.4286 \text{ for } AB$$
$$4(EI/L)/[3(EI/L) + 4(EI/L)] = 4/7 = 0.5714 \text{ for } BC$$

The distribution factors at C are obviously 0.5000 for each of the two adjacent spans. The distribution factors at D are, of course, the same as at B, from symmetry of the beam.

The **fixed-end moments** in span BC or CD when subject to a uniform load of w are $(1/12)(w)(L)^2$ or $0.0833(w)(L)^2$. The rotational sign convention for bending moments in the moment distribution procedure used herein is as shown in Fig. D–1b.

The fixed-end moment at B in span AB, with A treated as *hinged*, is $[(1/12) + (1/24)](w)(L)^2$ or $0.125(w)(L)^2$. That at end A is zero at all times, and no distribution of moments is needed thereat; nor will there be any moments carried over thereto or therefrom—similarly for span DE. Span BC and CD each has a **carry-over factor** of 0.5.

Case 1—D.L. on all spans. As shown in Fig. D–2, the moment distribution procedure for this loading is carried out in tabular form. All moments are in

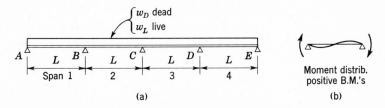

$\{ w_D$ dead
$\{ w_L$ live

A L B L C L D L E

Span 1   2   3   4

Moment distrib. positive B.M.'s

(a)   (b)

Fig. D–1. Example D–1.

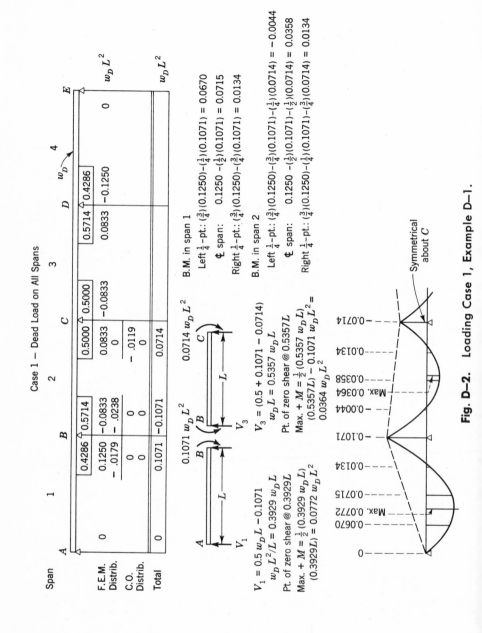

Case 1 – Dead Load on All Spans

Span	1		2		3		4	
	A	B		C		D		E
		0.4286	0.5714	0.5000	0.5000	0.5714	0.4286	
F.E.M.	0	0.1250	−0.0833	0.0833	−0.0833	0.0833	−0.1250	0
Distrib.		−.0179	−.0238	0	0			
C.O.		0	0	0	−.0119			
Distrib.		0	0	0	0			
Total	0	0.1071	−0.1071	0.0714	−0.0714	0.0833	−0.1250	0

$0.1071\,w_D L^2 \qquad 0.0714\,w_D L^2 \qquad w_D L^2$

$w_D L^2$

$V_1 = 0.5\,w_D L - 0.1071$
$w_D L^2 / L = 0.3929\,w_D L$
Pt. of zero shear @ $0.3929L$
Max. + M = $\frac{1}{2}(0.3929\,w_D L)$
$(0.3929L) = 0.0772\,w_D L^2$

$V_3 = (0.5 + 0.1071 − 0.0714)$
$w_D L = 0.5357\,w_D L$
Pt. of zero shear @ $0.5357L$
Max. + M = $\frac{1}{2}(0.5357\,w_D L)$
$(0.5357L) − 0.1071\,w_D L^2 =$
$0.0364\,w_D L^2$

B.M. in span 1
Left $\frac{1}{4}$-pt.: $(\frac{3}{4})(0.1250)−(\frac{1}{4})(0.1071) = 0.0670$
$\mathbb{C}$ span: $0.1250 −(\frac{1}{2})(0.1071) = 0.0715$
Right $\frac{1}{4}$-pt.: $(\frac{3}{4})(0.1250)−(\frac{3}{4})(0.1071) = 0.0134$

B.M. in span 2
Left $\frac{1}{4}$-pt.: $(\frac{3}{4})(0.1250)−(\frac{3}{4})(0.1071)−(\frac{1}{4})(0.0714) = −0.0044$
$\mathbb{C}$ span: $0.1250 −(\frac{1}{2})(0.1071)−(\frac{1}{2})(0.0714) = 0.0358$
Right $\frac{1}{4}$-pt.: $(\frac{3}{4})(0.1250)−(\frac{1}{4})(0.1071)−(\frac{3}{4})(0.0714) = 0.0134$

0 − 0.0670 − Max. 0.0772 − 0.0715 − 0.0134 − 0.1071 − 0.0044 − Max. 0.0364 − 0.0358 − 0.0134 − 0.0714

Symmetrical about C

Fig. D–2. Loading Case 1, Example D–1.

Case 2 — Live Load on Spans 1 and 3

Span	A	1 (w_L) B	B 2	2 C	C 3 (w_L)	D	D 4	E	
		0.4286	0.5714	0.5000	0.5000	0.5714	0.4286		
F.E.M.	0	0.1250	0	0	−0.0833	0.0833	0	0	$w_L L^2$
Distrib.		− .0536	−0.0714	0.0416	.0417	− .0476	−0.0357		
C.O.		0	.0208	− .0357	− .0238	.0208	0		
Distrib.		− .0089	− .0119	.0298	.0297	− .0119	− .0089		
C.O.		0	.0149	− .0060	− .0060	.0149	0		
Distrib.		− .0064	− .0085	.0060	.0060	− .0085	− .0064		
C.O.		0	.0030	− .0042	− .0042	.0030	0		
Distrib.		− .0013	− .0017	.0042	.0042	− .0017	− .0013		
C.O.		0	.0021	− .0008	− .0008	.0021	0		
Distrib.		− .0009	− .0012	.0008	.0008	− .0012	− .0009		
C.O.		0	.0004	− .0006	− .0006	.0004	0		
Distrib.		− .0002	− .0002	.0006	.0006	− .0002	− .0002		
C.O.		0	.0003	− .0001	− .0001	.0003	0		
Distrib.		− .0001	− .0002	.0001	.0001	− .0002	− .0001		
Total	0	0.0536	−0.0536	0.0357	−0.0357	0.0535	−0.0535	0	$w_L L^2$

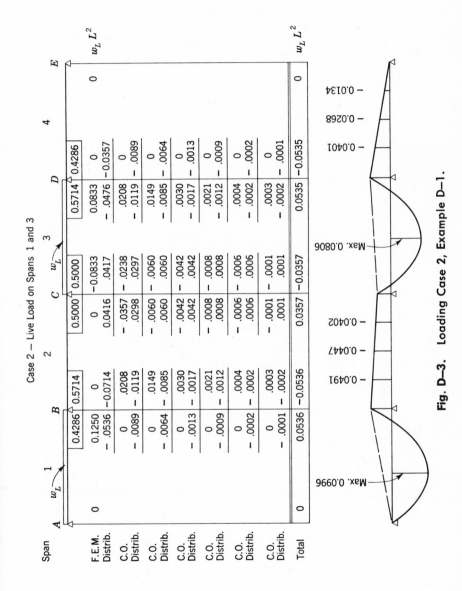

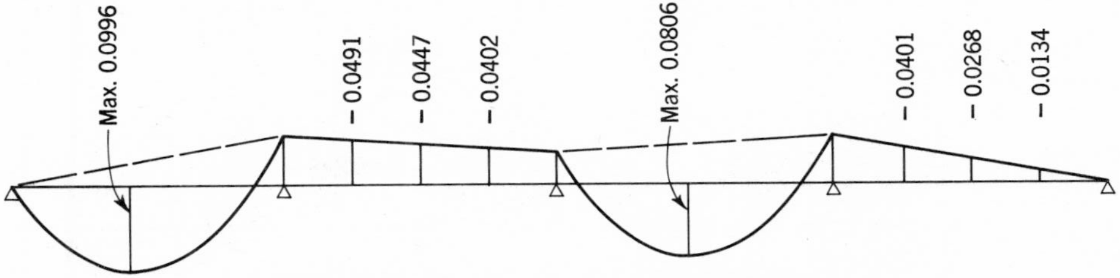
Max. 0.0996
− 0.0491
− 0.0447
− 0.0402
Max. 0.0806
− 0.0401
− 0.0268
− 0.0134

Fig. D–3. Loading Case 2, Example D–1.

Span

Case 3 — Live Load on Spans 1, 2, and 4

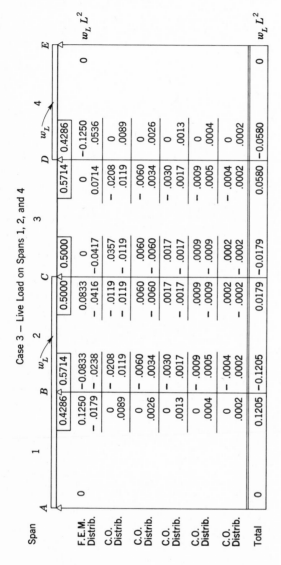

Span	A	B (0.4286)	B (0.5714)	C (0.5000)	C (0.5000)	D (0.5714)	D (0.4286)	E
F.E.M. Distrib.	0	0.1250 − .0179	−0.0833 − .0238	0.0833 − .0416	0 −0.0417	0 0.0714	−0.1250 .0536	0
C.O. Distrib.		0 .0089	− .0208 .0119	− .0119 − .0119	.0357 − .0119	− .0208 .0119	0 .0089	
C.O. Distrib.		0 .0026	− .0060 .0034	− .0060 − .0060	.0060 − .0060	− .0060 .0034	0 .0026	
C.O. Distrib.		0 .0013	− .0030 .0017	.0017 − .0017	.0017 − .0017	− .0030 .0017	0 .0013	
C.O. Distrib.		0 .0004	− .0009 .0005	− .0009 − .0009	.0009 − .0009	− .0009 .0005	0 .0004	
C.O. Distrib.		0 .0002	− .0004 .0002	− .0002 − .0002	.0002 − .0002	− .0004 .0002	0 .0002	
Total	0	0.1205	−0.1205	0.0179	−0.0179	0.0580	−0.0580	0

$w_L L^2$

$w_L L^2$

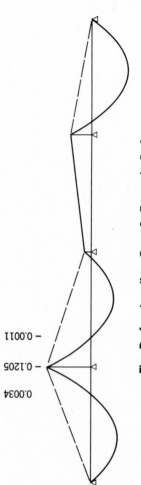

Fig. D–4. Loading Case 3, Example D–1.

−0.0011

−0.1205

0.0034

Table D-1. Summary of Bending Moment Coefficients for Four-Span Continuous Beam of Example D-1

Loading	End Span					Interior Span				
	Max. Pos. B.M.	Minimum Positive Bending Moment			Support B Max. Neg. B.M.	Max. Pos. B.M.	Minimum Positive Bending Moment			Support C Max. Neg. B.M.
		¼	℄	¼			¼	℄	¼	
D.L. Case 1	0.077	0.067	0.072	0.013	−0.107	0.036	−0.004	0.036	0.013	−0.071
⎰Case 2	0.100	−0.013	−0.027	−0.040	−0.121	0.081	−0.049	−0.045	−0.040	
L.L. ⎱Case 3				0.003			−0.001			
⎰Case 4									0.005	−0.107

Case 4 — Live Load on Spans 2 and 3

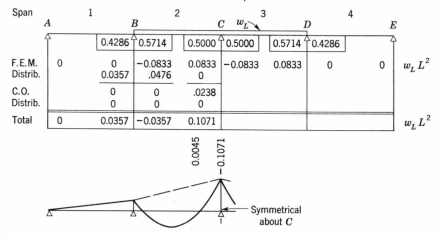

	Span 1		2		3	4			
	A	B		C w_L		D		E	
		0.4286	0.5714	0.5000	0.5000	0.5714	0.4286		
F.E.M. Distrib.	0	0 / 0.0357	−0.0833 / .0476	0.0833 / 0	−0.0833	0.0833	0	0	$w_L L^2$
C.O. Distrib.		0 / 0	0 / 0	.0238 / 0					
Total	0	0.0357	−0.0357	0.1071					$w_L L^2$

0.0045   −0.1071

Symmetrical about C

Fig. D–5.   Loading Case 4, Example D–1.

terms of $(w_D)(L)^2$. Since there is symmetry, the distribution is performed for one-half of the beam only.

After the support moments have been found, the moment diagrams may be obtained readily by superposing the support moments on the simple-beam moment diagrams of all the spans as shown in Fig. D–2. The moments at the quarter-points may also be calculated in a similar fashion as shown therein. The maximum positive moment near the center of each span, which occurs at the point of zero shear, may be calculated using simple statics, as shown in Fig. D–2.

Case 2—L.L. on spans 1 and 3. The calculations and the moment diagram for this loading are shown in Fig. D–3. This loading produces the maximum live load positive moments near the center of spans 1 and 3. It also produces the *minimum* live load positive moments in the interior of spans 2 and 4.

Case 3—L.L. on spans 1, 2, and 4. This loading produces the maximum live load negative moment at support B adjacent to spans 1 and 2. The calculations and the moment diagram are shown in Fig. D–4.

Case 4—L.L. on spans 2 and 3. This loading produces the maximum live load negative moment over support C. Again, by symmetry, only one-half of the beam is used in the moment distribution procedure. Figure D–5 shows all the calculations and the moment diagram.

A summary of the bending moment coefficients for the four loading cases is presented in Table D–1.

REFERENCES

1. CROSS, HARDY. "Analysis of Continuous Frames by Distributing Fixed End Moments," *Trans. ASCE*, 1932, Vol. 96, p. 1. Note that Cross used a sign convention different from that used here.
2. LARGE, GEORGE E., and MORRIS, CLYDE T. "The Moment Distribution Method of Structural Analysis Extended to Lateral Loads and Members of Variable Sections," *Ohio State University Engineering Experiment Station Bulletin No. 66*, 1931.

Appendix E: LOADING CRITERIA FOR COLUMNS OF RIGID FRAMES

These loading patterns (Fig. E–1), worked out by G. E. Sutila[1] for frames of an infinite number of equal spans and story heights, may be applied without appreciable error to regular frames of finite extent.   The bending moments may then be found by the moment distribution method, or short-cut adaptations thereof, taking only a few adjacent members.

Loading criteria for maximum live load bending moments in the <u>columns</u> of a rigid frame building

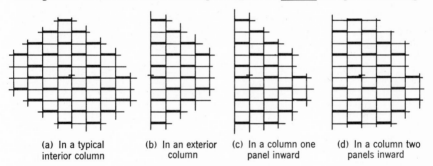

| (a) In a typical | (b) In an exterior | (c) In a column one | (d) In a column two |
| interior column | column | panel inward | panels inward |

Fig. E–1

In each case the cross mark indicates the point at which the loading shown produces the maximum bending moment.

These loading patterns are accurate for column/girder stiffness ratios, I/L, up to 3 or 4.

---

[1] "Accuracy of Live Load Bending Moments Obtained from Cut-Out Portions of Extensive Rigid Frames as Revealed by the Superposition of Moment Patterns" (Master's thesis, Ohio State University, 1949).

Appendix F: COLUMN LIVE LOAD REDUCTIONS

Each floor of a building must be designed for the full dead plus live loading. However, due to the improbability of having full live load on all floors at any instant, members which support several floors, such as columns and footings, are customarily designed for a decreased live loading depending upon the number of floors carried, as shown in the accompanying table:

U. S. Department of Commerce
Report of Building Code Committee

Number of Floors Carried by the Member	Permissible Reduction in Total Live Load Carried
1	0%
2	10
3	20
4	30
5	40
6	45
7 or more	50%

Appendix G: THE "LADDER" OF BEAM CURVES

G–1. INTRODUCTION

Before considering the continuity of the members in reinforced concrete construction, and the methods for evaluating the bending moments therein, one needs to have the mechanics and curve geometry of beams clearly in mind. **Elasticity,** as revealed in the deflection curve, is the basis for all studies of continuity. The common lack of comprehension of the relationship of the deflection curve to the other four beam curves is understandable, since one or two of the latter curves are usually omitted from textbook illustrations, and the remaining ones are frequently shown in an illogical order.

The following paragraphs present an orderly procedure for drawing beam curves which leads easily from the known *load curve* to the deflection curve.

EXAMPLE G–1

Given the simple beam of Fig. G–1, of 20-ft. span, carrying a uniformly distributed downward load of 3 kips per lin. ft. **Required** to draw all five beam curves, to write their equations, and to evaluate the maximum ordinates thereof. The **solution** will be found in the following articles.

G–2. THE RELATIONSHIP OF BEAM CURVES

Figure G–1 illustrates Professor More's "five-rung ladder" of beam curves, taking a uniformly loaded simple span. The three lower curves, *load,* *shear,* and *moment,* are the familiar statics curves. They lead upward to the **theta** and **deflection** curves needed to express elastic relationships.[1]

When the five curves of any beam are arranged in the ascending natural order shown, each curve is the summation, or integral, of the one immediately below it. The equation of the load curve is written first, and successive

---

[1] The modulus of elasticity, E, and moment of inertia, I, are usually constants and are so considered here.

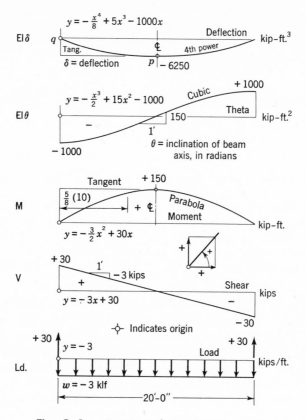

Fig. G–1. The five related beam curves.

integrations thereof yield the equations of all the higher curves.   The constant terms are found by inspection.

To write the beam curve equation, establish an origin at the left end and consider upward ordinates and rightward abscissae positive.   This also makes counterclockwise angles and slopes inclined upward to the right positive, as in mathematics.   When concentrated loads are encountered, establish a new origin at that point for the portion of the beam to the right thereof.

G–3. SIGNS CONVENTION FOR BEAM CURVES

In drawing beam curves the following situations are always considered *positive,* and pictured *above* the beam (X) axis:

Upward deflections.

Counterclockwise angles, in radians, as in mathematics.

Bending moments compressive upon the top fiber.

Upward shears, to the left of a section.

Upward acting loads[2] and reactions.

G–4. THE LAWS OF RELATED BEAM CURVES

The following laws follow from the beam curves relationships and make it possible to determine completely the curves for the simpler forms of loading without writing equations or performing integrations:

I. The **ordinate** at any point on any curve equals the **slope** at the corresponding point on the **next higher** curve.

II. The **area**[3] between any two ordinates of any curve equals the **change in ordinate** between the corresponding two points on the **next higher** curve.

III. The **ordinate distance** of any point *q* on any curve, measured **from a** tangent drawn to the curve at any other point *p*, is equal to the **moment of the area of the second lower curve** between the two points, **about the** point *q*.

In Fig. G–1, by Law I, the load curve *uniform negative ordinate* of three (−3 kips) establishes the shear curve *uniform negative slope* of three (−3). The known 30-kip reaction locates the shear curve vertically. Since the beam is simply supported, the moment curve will pass through the end origin. By Law I, since the *ordinates* of the shear curve decrease uniformly to zero at midspan, the *slope* of the moment curve must also decrease uniformly to zero at midspan. From Law II, the 150 kip-ft. (positive) area of the left half of the shear curve equals the rise of the moment curve from the left end to midspan.

Since the *ordinates* of the moment curve increase from zero at the left end to 150 at midspan, the *slopes* of the $EI\theta$ curve correspond. The *position* of the $EI\theta$ curve vertically may be fixed by anticipating the shape of the $EI\delta$ curve (the sag of the beam) and noting that, by Law I, the $EI\theta$ ordinate must be zero at midspan. The value of $EI\theta$ at the left end may be computed by Law II from the area of the moment curve, which is $(\frac{2}{3})(150)(10)$; or, by Law III, from the moment of the area of the corresponding shear curve about the midspan point, which is $(\frac{30}{2})(10)[6.67]$.

The value of $EI\delta$ at midspan is, by Law III, the moment of the area of the moment curve between *p* and *q*, *about q*, equals $(\frac{2}{3})(150)(10)[6.25]$

---

[2] Note carefully that the downward loading in Fig. G–1 is negative, so it must be shown *below* the *X*-axis.

[3] Laws II and III were first presented as applicable only to the moment, theta, and deflection curves by Prof. C. E. Greene at the University of Michigan, and called the *moment-area* principles. For their derivation see any standard text on strength of materials. As phrased here they constitute the three *generalized moment-area laws*.

or $+6250$ kip-ft. The positive sign indicates an upward measurement *from* the tangent *toward* the curve. Also consult Art. G–5.

*Learn to draw the curves in their correct relation by inspection. Do not plot laboriously to scale. Always show all loads and reactions acting **away** from the beam axis. Ordinates on one curve equal slopes above. Areas equal ordinate changes above. Calculate deflections by the law of the tangent (Law III).*

For nonuniform loading distributions, write the equations of the curves along the X-axis and integrate them to get areas and centroids. Highly irregular loadings require finite integration.[4]

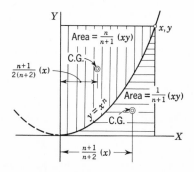

Fig. G–2.   Properties of power curves.

G–5. PROPERTIES OF POWER CURVES

The accompanying expressions in Fig. G–2 are useful in finding the areas and moments of areas of beam curves. They are strictly applicable only to single term equations, such as $y = 4x^3$, but they may be used without error on polynomials, such as $y = 4x^3 + 3x^2 + 2x$, *provided they are applied to each term thereof separately,* and the results later added.

[4] The curves are quite useful for computing the unequal fixed end moments for cases of irregular loading distributions. Simply represent them *below* the moment axis as two overlapping span-length triangles, and apply the *curves laws* to evaluate them.

Appendix H: TRANSLATIONAL MOMENT DISTRIBUTION

H-1. TRANSLATIONAL MOMENT DISTRIBUTION

The basic procedure for moment distribution outlined in Appendix D is strictly applicable only when the joints of a structure *merely rotate* about a fixed axis. Such a condition exists in a symmetrical rigid[1] frame carrying a symmetrical loading, since the shortening of the column members is always disregarded as being relatively insignificant.

If a rigidly constructed frame is unsymmetrically loaded, as in Fig. H-1a and b, or is unsymmetrical in form as in c, its upper portion will shift sidewise when loaded, and the axes of rotation of the two upper corner joints will be displaced horizontally, or **translated**. The same condition will exist at (d), where both form and loading are unsymmetrical. These movements affect the bending moments in the members. For all such cases, the following *extended* moment distributional procedure, developed by Prof. Clyde T. Morris for the analysis of wind stresses in building frames, works well.

EXAMPLE H-1

Given the unsymmetrical rigid frame of Fig. H-2a subject to a 16-kip lateral load.

Required to find the bending moments at the ends of the members by translational moment distribution.

[1] When the connections, or *joints*, between members are so rigid that no relative angular movement occurs between the axes of the ends of the members when load is applied, the structure is said to be *continuous* if a beam, or *rigid* if a frame.

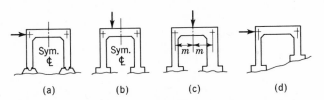

Fig. H-1. Rigid frames subject to joint translation.

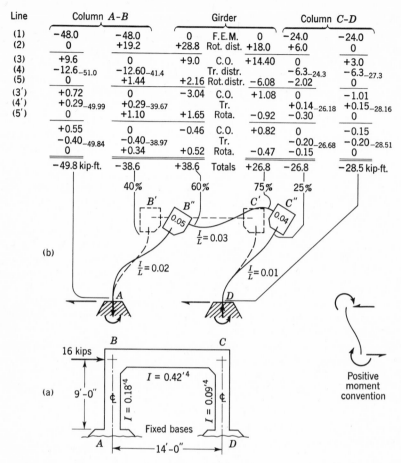

Line	Column A-B		Girder			Column C-D	
(1)	−48.0	−48.0	0	F.E.M.	0	−24.0	−24.0
(2)	0	+19.2	+28.8	Rot. dist.	+18.0	+6.0	0
(3)	+9.6	0	+9.0	C.O.	+14.40	0	+3.0
(4)	−12.6$_{-51.0}$	−12.60$_{-41.4}$		Tr. distr.		−6.3$_{-24.3}$	−6.3$_{-27.3}$
(5)	0	+1.44	+2.16	Rot. distr.	−6.08	−2.02	0
(3′)	+0.72	0	−3.04	C.O.	+1.08	0	−1.01
(4′)	+0.29$_{-49.99}$	+0.29$_{-39.67}$		Tr.		+0.14$_{-26.18}$	+0.15$_{-28.16}$
(5′)	0	+1.10	+1.65	Rota.	−0.92	−0.30	0
	+0.55	0	−0.46	C.O.	+0.82	0	−0.15
	−0.40$_{-49.84}$	−0.40$_{-38.97}$		Tr.		−0.20$_{-26.68}$	−0.20$_{-28.51}$
	0	+0.34	+0.52	Rota.	−0.47	−0.15	0
	−49.8 kip-ft.	−38.6	+38.6	Totals	+26.8	−26.8	−28.5 kip-ft.

Fig. H–2. Analysis of a laterally loaded rigid frame by translational moment distribution.

Procedure

1. Make a working sketch of the structure as at (b), showing the *sidesway* greatly exaggerated in order to portray clearly the rotation of the joints and the bending of the members. Compute the stiffness factors, I/L.

2. To find the translational fixed end moments, conceive the joints to be held vertical by some external means while being displaced laterally to $B'C'$ in the direction of the load. This movement does not deform the girder member, lying in the direction of the displacement, or induce any moment into it. It may be proved that such lateral displacement of the column tops induces end bending moments proportional to I/L^2 (law of the tangent). Equal-length columns will assume fixed end bending moments proportional to their moments of inertia, I.

For equilibrium, the sum of the moments at the top and base of all columns of a frame story must equal "the shear in the story times the story height," or 144 kip-ft. in this case. This accounts for the two −48 and −24 kip-ft. items at the top and bottom of the left and right hand columns respectively, line (1) of the tabulation.

3. Allow the joints to rotate, while remaining in the same location. Distribute the fixed end moments as usual, in line (2), and relock each joint in its rotated position.

4. Carry over one-half of the distribution items, line (3), as formerly.

5. The sum of the moments now at the ends of the columns is different from the story moment, so a corrective story column moment must be introduced and **translationally distributed** thereto. In this case the situation is 106.2 versus 144 kip-ft. This means that additional translation must occur to build up 37.8 kip-ft. more moment at the tops and bases of the columns, line (4), distributed as in step (2) above. See column items −12.6 and −6.3 and the new position of the joints at B'' and C''.

6. Again make a *rotational distribution*, line (5), of all the moments accumulated at each joint since it was last allowed to rotate, and then relock.

7. Repeat the carry over–translational distribution–rotational distribution cycle until the change in moment totals per cycle comes within the percentage of error to be tolerated.

8. Make a partial check by computing the horizontal reactions at the base of the frame from the final column moments and comparing with the applied lateral load. $(\Sigma H \equiv 0.)$

The translational moment distribution method is unexcelled for the analysis of most quadrilateral frames subject to sidesway, such as multistory (building) wind bents, rigid frame bridges, and Vierendeel trusses. Frames with a large number of members, which defy analysis by algebraic methods within a reasonable time, can be investigated rapidly.

Appendix I: DESIGN OF FLAT SLABS BY THE ACI CODE

The following articles of the 1963 "Building Code Requirements for Reinforced Concrete" are reproduced (pp. 583–595) by kind permission of the American Concrete Institute. This Code is subject to revision whenever the studies of the committees responsible indicate that developments in concrete design and construction warrant a change.

The original numbering of the sections has been preserved.

CHAPTER 21 — FLAT SLABS WITH SQUARE OR RECTANGULAR PANELS

2100—Notation

A = distance in the direction of span from center of support to the intersection of the center line of the slab thickness with the extreme 45-deg diagonal line lying wholly within the concrete section of slab and column or other support, including drop panel, capital and bracket

b_o = periphery of critical section for shear

c = effective support size [see Section 2104(c)]

d = distance from extreme compression fiber to centroid of tension reinforcement

f_c' = compressive strength of concrete (see Section 301)

h = distance from top of slab to bottom of capital

H = story height in feet of the column or support of a flat slab center to center of slabs

K = ratio of moment of inertia of column provided to I_c required by Eq. (21-1)

L = span length of a flat slab panel center to center of supports

M_o = numerical sum of assumed positive and average negative moments at the critical design sections of a flat slab panel [see Section 2104(f)1]

R_n = factor for increasing negative moment [Section 2104, Eq. (21-2)]

R_p = factor for increasing positive moment [Section 2104, Eq. (21-3)]

t = thickness in inches of slab at center of panel

t_1 = thickness in inches of slab without drop panels, or through drop panel, if any

t_2 = thickness in inches of slab with drop panels at points beyond the drop panel

w' = uniformly distributed unit dead and live load

W = total dead and live load on panel

W_D = total dead load on panel

W_L = total live load on panel, uniformly distributed

2101—Definitions and scope

(a) *Flat slab* — A concrete slab reinforced in two or more directions, generally without beams or girders to transfer the loads to supporting members. Slabs with recesses or pockets made by permanent or removable fillers between reinforcing bars may be considered flat slabs. Slabs with paneled ceilings may be considered as flat slabs provided the panel of reduced thickness lies entirely within the area of intersecting middle strips, and is at least two-thirds the thickness of the remainder of the slab, exclusive of the drop panel, and is not less than 4 in. thick.

(b) *Column capital* — An enlargement of the end of a column designed and built to act as an integral unit with the column and flat slab. No portion of the column capital shall be considered for structural purposes which lies outside of the largest right circular cone with 90-deg vertex angle that can be included within the outlines of the column capital. Where no capital is used, the face of the column shall be considered as the edge of the capital.

(c) *Drop panel* — The structural portion of a flat slab which is thickened throughout an area surrounding the column, column capital, or bracket.

(d) *Panel strips* — A flat slab shall be considered as consisting of strips in each direction as follows:

A middle strip one-half panel in width, symmetrical about panel center line.

A column strip consisting of the two adjacent quarter-panels, one each side of the column center line.

(e) *Ultimate strength design* — Flat slabs shall be proportioned by Part IV-A only, except that Part IV-B may be used if the following modifications are made in the design:

1. For either empirical or elastic analysis the numerical sum of the positive and negative bending moments in the direction of either side of a rectangular panel shall be assumed as not less than

$$M_o = 0.10 \; WLF \left(1 - \frac{2c}{3L}\right)^2$$

in which $F = 1.15 - c/L$ but not less than 1.

2. The thickness of slab shall not be less than shown in Table 2101(e).

TABLE 2101(e)—MINIMUM SLAB THICKNESS

f_y	With drop panels*	Without drop panels
40,000	L/40 or 4 in.	L/36 or 5 in.
50,000	L/36 or 4 in.	L/33 or 5 in.
60,000	L/33 or 4 in.	L/30 or 5 in.

*To be considered effective, the drop panel shall have a length of at least one-third the parallel span length and a projection below the slab of at least one-fourth the slab thickness.

2102—Design procedures

(a) *Methods of analysis* — All flat slab structures shall be designed in accordance with a recognized elastic analysis subject to the limitations of Sections 2102 and 2103, except that the empirical method of design given in Section 2104 may be used for the design of flat slabs conforming with the limitations given therein. Flat slabs within the limitations of Section 2104, when designed by elastic analysis, may have resulting analytical moments reduced in such proportion that the numerical sum of the positive and average negative bending moments used in design procedure need not exceed the sum of the corresponding values as determined from Table 2104(f).

(b) *Critical sections* — The slab shall be proportioned for the bending moments prevailing at every section except that the slab need not be proportioned for a greater negative moment than that prevailing at a distance A from the support center line.

(c) *Size and thickness of slabs and drop panels*

1. Subject to limitations of Section 2102(c)4, the thickness of a flat slab and the size and thickness of the drop panel, where used, shall be such that the compression due to bending at any section, and the shear about the column, column capital, and drop panel shall not exceed those permitted in Part IV-A or Part IV-B. When designed under Section 2104, three-fourths of the width of the strip shall be used as the width of the section in computing compression due to bending, except that on a section through a drop panel, three-fourths of the width of the drop panel shall be used. Account shall be taken of any recesses which reduce the compressive area.

2. The shear on vertical sections which follow a periphery, b_o, at distance, $d/2$, beyond the edges of the column, column capital, or drop panel, and concentric with them, shall be computed as required and limited in Chapters 12 or 17.

3. If shear reinforcement is used, the first line shall be not further than $d/2$ from the face of the support.

4. Slabs with drop panels whose length is at least one-third the parallel span length and whose projection below the slab is at least one-fourth the slab thickness shall be not less than $L/40$ nor 4 in. in thickness.

Slabs without drop panels as described above shall be not less than $L/36$ nor 5 in. in thickness.

5. For determining reinforcement, the thickness of the drop panel below the slab shall not be assumed to be more than one-fourth of the distance from the edge of the drop panel to the edge of the column capital.

(d) *Arrangement of slab reinforcement*

1. The spacing of the bars at critical sections shall not exceed two times the slab thickness, except for those portions of the slab

area which may be of cellular or ribbed construction. In the slab over the cellular spaces, reinforcement shall be provided as required by Section 807.

2. In exterior panels, except for bottom bars adequately anchored in the drop panel, all positive reinforcement perpendicular to the discontinuous edge shall extend to the edge of the slab and have embedment, straight or hooked, of at least 6 in. in spandrel beams, walls, or columns where provided. All negative reinforcement perpendicular to the discontinuous edge shall be bent, hooked, or otherwise anchored in spandrel beams, walls, or columns.

3. The area of reinforcement shall be determined from the bending moments at the critical sections but shall be not less than required by Section 807.

4. Required splices in bars may be made wherever convenient, but preferably away from points of maximum stress. The length of any such splice shall conform to Section 805.

5. Bars shall be spaced approximately uniformly across each panel strip, except:

a. At least 25 percent of required negative reinforcement in the column strip shall cross the periphery located at a distance of d from the column or column capital.

b. At least 50 percent of the required negative reinforcement in the column strip shall cross the drop panel, if any.

c. The spacing for the remainder of the column strip may vary uniformly from that required for a or b to that required for the middle strip.

(e) *Openings in flat slabs*

1. Openings of any size may be provided in flat slabs if provision is made for the total positive and negative moments and for shear without exceeding the allowable stresses except that when design is based on Section 2104, the limitations given therein shall not be exceeded.

2. When openings are provided within the area common to two column strips, that part of the critical section shall be considered ineffective which either passes through an opening, or is covered by a radial projection of any opening to the centroid of the support.

(f) *Design of columns*

1. All columns supporting flat slabs shall be designed as provided in Chapter 14 or 19 with the additional requirements of this chapter.

(g) *Transfer of bending moment between column and slab* — When unbalanced gravity load, wind or earthquake cause transfer of bending moment between column and slab, the stresses on the critical section shall be investigated by a rational analysis, and the section proportioned accordingly by the requirements of Part IV-A or IV-B. Concentration of reinforcement over the column head by additional reinforcement or closer spacing may be used to resist the moment of the section. A slab width between lines that are 1.5t each side of the column may be considered effective.

2103—Design by elastic analysis

(a) *Assumptions* — In design by elastic analysis the following assumptions may be used and all sections shall be proportioned for the moments and shears thus obtained.

1. The structure may be considered divided into a number of bents, each consisting of a row of columns or supports and strips of supported slabs, each strip bounded laterally by the center line of the panel on either side of the center line of columns or supports. The bents shall be taken longitudinally and transversely of the building.

2. Each such bent may be analyzed in its entirety or each floor thereof and the roof may be analyzed separately with its adjacent columns as they occur above and below, the columns being assumed fixed at their remote ends. Where slabs are thus analyzed separately, it may be assumed in determining the bending at a given support that the slab is fixed at any support two panels distant therefrom provided the slab continues beyond that point.

3. The joints between columns and slabs may be considered rigid, and this rigidity (infinite moment of inertia) may be assumed to extend in the slabs from the center of the column to the edge of the capital, and in the column from the top of slab to the bottom of the capital. The change in length of columns and slabs due to direct stress, and deflections due to shear, may be neglected.

4. Where metal column capitals are used, account may be taken of their contributions to stiffness and resistance to bending and shear.

5. The moment of inertia of the slab or column at any cross section may be assumed to be that of the cross section of the concrete. Variation in the moments of inertia of the slabs and columns along their axes shall be taken into account.

6. Where the load to be supported is definitely known, the structure shall be analyzed for that load. Where the live load is variable but does not exceed three-quarters of the dead load, or the nature of the live load is such that all panels will be loaded simultaneously, the maximum bending may be assumed to occur at all sections under full live load. For other conditions, maximum positive bending near midspan of a panel may be assumed to occur under three-quarters of the full live load in the panel and in alter-

nate panels; and maximum negative bending in the slab at a support may be assumed to occur under three-quarters of the full live load in the adjacent panels only. In no case, shall the design moments be taken as less than those occurring with full live load on all panels.

(b) *Critical sections* — The critical section for negative bending, in both the column strip and middle strip, may be assumed as not more than the distance *A* from the center of the column or support and the critical negative moment shall be considered as extending over this distance.

(c) *Distribution of panel moments* — Bending at critical sections across the slabs of each bent may be apportioned between the column strip and middle strip, as given in Table 2103 (c). For design purposes, any of these percentages may be varied by not more than 10 percent of its value, but their sum for the full panel width shall not be reduced.

2104—Empirical method

(a) *General limitations* — Flat slab construction may be designed by the empirical provisions of this section when they conform to all of the limitations on continuity and dimensions given herein.

1. The construction shall consist of at least three continuous panels in each direction.

2. The ratio of length to width of panels shall not exceed 1.33.

3. The grid pattern shall consist of approximately rectangular panels. The successive span lengths in each direction shall differ by not more than 20 percent of the longer span. Within these limitations, columns may be offset a maximum of 10 percent of the span, in direction of the offset, from either axis between center lines of successive columns.

4. The calculated lateral force moments from wind or earthquake may be combined with the critical moments as determined by the empirical method, and the lateral force moments shall be distributed between the column and middle strips in the same proportions as specified for the negative moments in the strips for structures not exceeding 125 ft high with maximum story height not exceeding 12 ft 6 in.

(b) *Columns*

1. The minimum dimension of any column shall be as determined by a and b below, but in no case less than 10 in.

   a. For columns or other supports of a flat slab, the required minimum average moment of inertia, I_c, of the gross concrete section of the columns above and below the slab shall be determined from Eq. (21-1) and shall be not less than 1000 in.[4] If there is no column above the slab, the I_c of the column below shall be $(2 - 2.3h/H)$ times that given by the formula with a minimum of 1000 in.[4]

$$I_c = \frac{t^3 H}{0.5 + \dfrac{W_D}{W_L}} \dots\dots\dots\dots\dots\dots (21\text{-}1)$$

where t need not be taken greater than t_1 or t_2 as determined in (d), H is the average story height of the columns above and below the slab, and W_L is the greater value of any two adjacent spans under consideration.

TABLE 2103 (c)—DISTRIBUTION BETWEEN COLUMN STRIPS AND MIDDLE STRIPS IN PERCENT OF TOTAL MOMENTS AT CRITICAL SECTIONS OF A PANEL

Strip		Moment section			
		Negative moment at interior support	Positive moment	Negative moment at exterior support	
				Slab supported on columns and on beams of total depth equal to the slab thickness*	Slab supported on reinforced concrete bearing wall or columns with beams of total depth equal or greater than 3 times the slab thickness*
Column strip		76	60	80	60
Middle strip		24	40	20	40
Half column strip adjacent and parallel to marginal beam or wall	Total depth of beam equal to slab thickness*	38	30	40	30
	Total depth of beam or wall equal to or greater than 3 times slab thickness*	19	15	20	15

*Interpolate for intermediate ratios of beam depth to slab thickness.

Note: The total dead and live reaction of a panel adjacent to a marginal beam or wall may be divided between the beam or wall and the parallel half column strip in proportion to their stiffness, but the moment provided in the slab shall not be less than that given in Table 2103(c).

b. Columns smaller than required by Eq. (21-1) may be used provided the bending moment coefficients given in Table 2104(f) are increased in the following ratios:

For negative moments

$$R_n = 1 + \frac{(1-K)^2}{2.2\,(1 + 1.4 W_D/W_L)} \cdots\cdots\cdots (21\text{-}2)$$

For positive moments

$$R_p = 1 + \frac{(1-K)^2}{1.2\,(1 + 0.10 W_D/W_L)} \cdots\cdots\cdots (21\text{-}3)$$

The required slab thickness shall be modified by multiplying w' by R_n in Eq. (21-4) and (21-5).

2. Columns supporting flat slabs designed by the empirical method shall be proportioned for the bending moments developed by unequally loaded panels, or uneven spacing of columns. Such bending moment shall be the maximum value derived from

$$\frac{W L_1 - W_D L_2}{f}$$

L_1 and L_2 being lengths of the adjacent spans ($L_2 = 0$ when considering an exterior column) and f is 30 for exterior and 40 for interior columns.

This moment shall be divided between the columns immediately above and below the floor or roof line under consideration in direct proportion to their stiffness and shall be applied without further reduction to the critical sections of the columns.

(c) *Determination of "c" (effective support size)*

1. Where column capitals are used, the value of c shall be taken as the diameter of the cone described in Section 2101(b) measured at the bottom of the slab or drop panel.

2. Where a column is without a concrete capital, the dimension c shall be taken as that of the column in the direction considered.

3. Brackets capable of transmitting the negative bending and the shear in the column strips to the columns without excessive unit stress may be substituted for column capitals at exterior columns. The value of c for the span where a bracket is used shall be taken as twice the distance from the center of the column to a point where the bracket is 1½ in. thick, but not more than the thickness of the column plus twice the depth of the bracket.

4. Where a reinforced concrete beam frames into a column without capital or bracket on the same side with the beam, for computing bending for strips parallel to the beam, the value of c for the span considered may be taken as the width of the column plus twice the projection of the beam above or below the slab or drop panel.

5. The average of the values of c at the two supports at the ends of a column strip shall be used to evaluate the slab thickness t_1 or t_2 as prescribed in (d).

(d) *Slab thickness*

1. The slab thickness, span L being the longest side of the panel, shall be at least:

$L/36$ for slab without drop panels conforming with (e), or where a drop panel is omitted at any corner of the panel, but not less than 5 in. nor t_1 as given in Eq. (21-4).

$L/40$ for slabs with drop panels conforming to (e) at all supports, but not less than 4 in. nor t_2 as given in Eq. (21-5).

2. The total thickness, t_1, in inches, of slabs without drop panels, or through the drop panel if any, shall be at least

$$t_1 = 0.028L\left(1 - \frac{2c}{3L}\right)\sqrt{\frac{w'}{f_c'/2000}} + 1\tfrac{1}{2} \ \ \dots \dots \ (21\text{-}4)\,*$$

3. The total thickness, t_2, in inches, of slabs with drop panels, at points beyond the drop panel shall be at least

$$t_2 = 0.024L\left(1 - \frac{2c}{3L}\right)\sqrt{\frac{w'}{f_c'/2000}} + 1 \ \dots \dots \ (21\text{-}5)\,*$$

4. Where the exterior supports provide only negligible restraint to the slab, the values of t_1 and t_2 for the exterior panel shall be increased by at least 15 percent.

(e) *Drop panels*

1. The maximum total thickness at the drop panel used in computing the negative steel area for the column strip shall be $1.5t_2$.

2. The side or diameter of the drop panel shall be at least 0.33 times the span in the parallel direction.

3. The minimum thickness of slabs where drop panels at wall columns are omitted shall equal $(t_1 + t_2)/2$ provided the value of c used in the computations complies with (c).

(f) *Bending moment coefficients*

1. The numerical sum of the positive and negative bending moments in the direction of either side of a rectangular panel shall be assumed as not less than

$$M_o = 0.09\ WLF\left(1 - \frac{2c}{3L}\right)^2 \dots \dots \dots \ (21\text{-}6)$$

in which $F = 1.15 - c/L$ but not less than 1.

2. Unless otherwise provided, the bending moments at the critical sections of the column and middle strips shall be at least those given in Table 2104 (f).

3. The average of the values of c at the two supports at the ends

---

*In these formulas t_1 and t_2 are in inches, L and c are in feet, and w' is in pounds per square foot.

TABLE 2104(f)—MOMENTS IN FLAT SLAB PANELS IN PERCENTAGES OF M_0

Strip	Column head	Side support type	End support type	Exterior panel — Exterior negative moment	Exterior panel — Positive moment	Exterior panel — Interior negative moment	Interior panel — Positive moment	Interior panel — Negative moment
Column strip	With drop		A	44				
			B	36	24	56	20	50
			C	6	36	72		
	Without drop		A	40				
			B	32	28	50	22	46
			C	6	40	66		
Middle strip	With drop		A	10				
			B	20	20	17*	15	15*
			C	6	26	22*		
	Without drop		A	10				
			B	20	20	18*	16	16*
			C	6	28	24*		
Half column strip adjacent to marginal beam or wall	With drop	1	A	22				
			B	18	12	28	10	25
			C	3	18	36		
		2	A	17				
			B	14	9	21	8	19
			C	3	14	27		
		3	A	11				
			B	9	6	14	5	13
			C	3	9	18		
	Without drop	1	A	20				
			B	16	14	25	11	23
			C	3	20	33		
		2	A	15				
			B	12	11	19	9	18
			C	3	15	25		
		3	A	10				
			B	8	7	13	6	12
			C	3	10	17		

Percentage of panel load to be carried by marginal beam or wall in addition to loads directly superimposed thereon	Type of support listed in Table 2104(f) — Side support parallel to strip	Type of support listed in Table 2104(f) — Side or end edge condition of slabs of depth t	Type of support listed in Table 2104(f) — End support at right angles to strip
0	1	Columns with no beams	
20	2	Columns with beams of total depth $1\frac{1}{4}t$	A
40	3	Columns with beams of total depth $3t$ or more	B
		Reinforced concrete bearing walls integral with slab	
		Masonry or other walls providing negligible restraint	C

*Increase negative moments 30 percent of tabulated values when middle strip is continuous across support of Type B or C. No other values need be increased.

Note: For intermediate proportions of total beam depth to slab thicknesses, values for loads and moments may be obtained by interpolation.

of a column strip shall be used to evaluate M_o in determining bending in the strip. The average of the values of M_o, as determined for the two parallel half column strips in a panel, shall be used in determining bending in the middle strip.

4. Bending in the middle strips parallel to a discontinuous edge shall be assumed the same as in an interior panel.

5. For design purposes, any of the moments determined from Table 2104(f) may be varied by not more than 10 percent, but the numerical sum of the positive and negative moments in a panel shall be not less than the amount specified.

(g) *Length of reinforcement* — In addition to the requirements of Section 2102(d), reinforcement shall have the minimum lengths given in Tables 2104(g)1 and 2104(g)2.* Where adjacent spans are unequal, the extension of negative reinforcement on each side of the column center line as prescribed in Table 2104(g)1 shall be based on the requirements of the longer span.

(h) *Openings in flat slabs*

1. Openings of any size may be provided in a flat slab in the area common to two intersecting middle strips provided the total positive and negative steel areas required in (f) are maintained.

2. In the area common to two column strips, not more than one-eighth of the width of strip in any span shall be interrupted by openings. The equivalent of all bars interrupted shall be provided by extra steel on all sides of the openings. The shear stresses given in Section 2102(c)2 shall not be exceeded following the procedure of Section 920(b).

3. In any area common to one column strip and one middle strip, openings may interrupt one-quarter of the bars in either strip. The equivalent of the bars so interrupted shall be provided by extra steel on all sides of the opening.

4. Any opening larger than described above shall be analyzed by accepted engineering principles and shall be completely framed as required to carry the loads to the columns.

*Figures I–1 and I–2 contain substantially the same information as Tables 2104(g)1 and 2104(g)2.

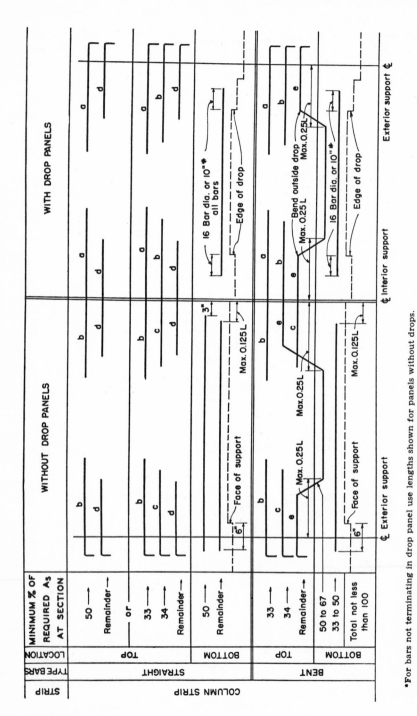

Fig. I–1. See Fig. I–2 for ACI's caption.

*For bars not terminating in drop panel use lengths shown for panels without drops.

594

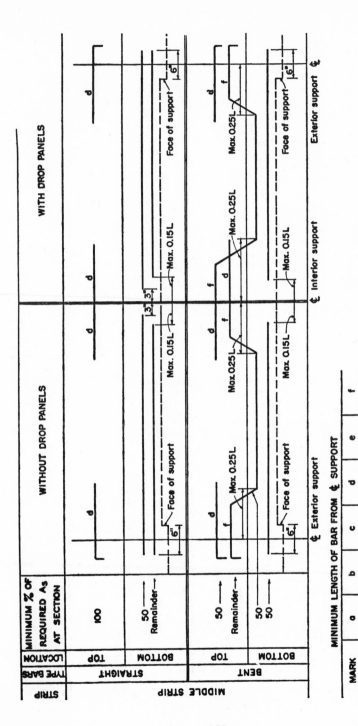

Fig. I–2. Minimum bar lengths.

595

Appendix J: THE COULOMB FORMULAS FOR EARTH PRESSURE[1]

To keep the expressions simple, so that comparisons of pressures for the several conditions can be drawn easily, these cases are limited to an assumed frictionless vertical wall supporting a level granular backfill. For orientation, consult Chapter 11, Arts. 11–2 and 11–3, for an earlier treatment, by components of forces, of the case described in Art. J–1.

For an excellent extended treatment involving sloping backfills and walls with friction, refer to *Substructure Analysis and Design*, by Paul Andersen (New York: The Ronald Press Company, 1956).

J–1. THE ACTIVE BACKFILL CASE

Referring to Figure J–1a:

$$W = \tfrac{1}{2}\gamma h^2 \tan f$$

wherein γ is the unit weight of the backfill material. Furthermore, by trigonometry:

$$W = N \sin f + N \cos f \tan \phi$$
$$P_A = N \cos f - N \sin f \tan \phi$$

[1] With variations applicable to several cases involving greatly increased pressure.

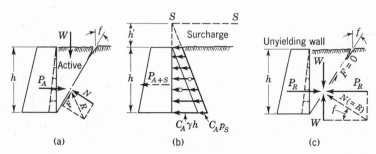

Fig. J–1.   Earth pressure variations.

and

$$P_A = \tfrac{1}{2}\gamma h^2 \frac{\tan f - \tan^2 f \tan \phi}{\tan f + \tan \phi}$$

from which by differentiating P_A with respect to f and simplifying:

$$\text{Max. } P_A = \tfrac{1}{2}\gamma h^2 \tan^2 (45° - \phi/2) \qquad (\text{J--1})$$

NOTE: Equation J–1 is the same as Rankine's (1860). He always disregarded wall friction.

Refer to Art. 11–3 of Chapter 11 for fundamental discussion of the Coulomb theory.

PROBLEM

J–1. A gravity retaining wall is 12 ft. high by 6 ft. thick. The internal friction angle, ϕ, is 35°, and the unit weight of the backfill, γ, is 100 pcf.

Compute the maximum intensities of both the horizontal and vertical pressures in ksf.   Ans.   0.323 and 1.20 ksf, respectively.

Definition. *The hydrostatic pressure ratio, C,* is the ratio, at any chosen point, of the unit lateral earth pressure to the unit vertical pressure. In Problem J–1 it was $323/1200 = 0.27$, or only 27% of the hydrostatic pressure. Retaining walls have often been designed for an arbitrarily specified so-called *equivalent fluid pressure* of from 25 to 30 pcf.

Re-examination of Eq. J–1 above will show that $C_A = \tan^2 (45° - \phi/2)$, so

$$P_A = C_A \frac{\gamma h^2}{2} \qquad (\text{J--2})$$

QUESTION

Does a C-value of 1.00 mean the same pressure as an equal head of water?   Explain.

J–2. THE SURCHARGE CASE

When the surface of a backfill is *uniformly loaded*, as by being used as a storage yard, the vertical pressures within the backfill are increased by the amount of such live loading, p_s, which is called *surcharge*.

As indicated in Fig. J–1b the surcharge load may be conceived to be replaced by an equal weight of additional earth of depth $h' = p_s/\gamma$, and the stress distribution diagram drawn from the higher level *S-S*.

Referring to Coulomb Eq. J–1, the lateral pressure upon a surcharged wall will be

$$P_{A+S} = \left(\frac{\gamma h}{2} + p_s\right) h \tan^2 (45° - \phi/2) \qquad (\text{J--3})$$

or

$$P_{A+S} = C_A \left(\frac{\gamma h}{2} + p_s\right) h \qquad (\text{J--4})$$

The elevation of P_{A+S} may be deduced from Fig. J–1b.

Concentrated surcharge loads may be taken care of by using the Culmann method, or by converting them to equivalent uniformly distributed ones.

Refer to Example 11–3 of Chapter 11 for designing involving surcharge.

PROBLEM

J–2. Take the same wall as in Problem J–1 above except that the backfill will be loaded with 700 psf of surcharge.   Compute the magnitude and elevation of the resultant force P_{A+S}.   Ans.   4212 lb. at 5.06 ft. up.

J–3. THE AT-REST CASE

If a wall cannot yield, as by being securely connected to some much larger structure, the supporting frictional force, F in Fig. J–1c, cannot develop along the failure plane because of lack of movement of the sand grains.   As before, $W = \frac{1}{2}\gamma h^2 \tan f$, but P_R, the *at-rest* value of the earth pressure, will be, from the parallelogram of forces:

$$P_R = W \cot f = \frac{1}{2}\gamma h^2, \quad \text{the full hydrostatic pressure} \quad \text{(J–4a)}$$

The corresponding C value = 1.00.

Note that a tremendous price would have to be paid for theoretically complete rigidity.   Terzaghi found C values as high as 0.50 experimentally.

J–4. THE PASSIVE BACKFILL CASE

When for any reason a wall moves horizontally *toward* an earth mass, as in Fig. J–2a, rather than away from it, a large *passive resistance* is built up, which may be of the order of ten to fifteen times the corresponding active pressure value.   What happens is that the earth frictional force, F, "that always acts to oppose movement," which had an upward

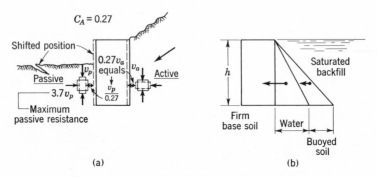

Fig. J–2. Passive and saturated conditions.

value in Fig. J–1a, and a zero value in Fig. J–1c, develops a downward value. Referring to the algebraic expressions of Art. J–1, and changing only the direction of F to work for the *minimum* value of the passive resistance:

$$P_P = \tfrac{1}{2}\gamma h^2 \tan^2 (45° + \phi/2) \tag{J–5}$$

or, since C passive $= 1/C_A$:

$$P_P = \frac{\gamma h^2}{2C_A} \tag{J–6}$$

In Fig. J–2a the deformations of unit cubes of soil and the corresponding typical unit pressures may be traced from the active toward the passive side of the wall.

Refer to the latter part of Example 11–3 for application to the design of a base shear key.

PROBLEM

J–3. Given a 12-ft. wall height of the 100 pcf sandy soil previously taken. It is required to compute the total passive pressure if the wall should be forced against the backfill, and the unit pressure at the base. Take $\phi = 35°$.

Ans. $P_P = 26.6$ kips and 4.44 ksf.

(Compare 4.44 ksf with the 0.323 ksf *active* value of Problem J–1.)

J–5. THE SATURATED BACKFILL CASE

If a granular backfill becomes fully saturated, as by clogging of the drainage system, the pressure upon a wall may increase to about three times the *active case* value for which it was designed.

The total lateral pressure will be the sum of the full hydrostatic pressure of the water of saturation, plus the earth pressure of the *buoyed* weight of the granular backfill, with ϕ unchanged. Consider the sand immersed in the all-pervading mass of water.

EXAMPLE J–1

Refer to Fig. J–2b. **Given** the 12-ft. vertical wall and level backfill of the previous discussions, consisting of 100-pcf sand filled with water of saturation. Effective angle of internal friction still 35°. Specific gravity of sand rock = 2.65. **It is required** to find the pressure upon the wall, assuming no wall friction, as formerly.

Solution.

	Total pressure, kips	Equivalent fluid pressure, pcf

Water pressure (hydrostatic) $= \dfrac{0.0624(12)^2}{2} =$ 4.50   62.4

Sand pressure

Principle: A solid immersed in a liquid is buoyed up to the extent of the weight of the liquid displaced.
Solid volume of 1 cu. ft. of the sand
$= 100/2.65(62.4) = 0.605$ cu. ft.
Buoyed weight of 1 cu. ft. of the sand
$= 100 - 0.605(62.4) = 62.2$ pcf
Referring to Eq. J–1:
$P_A = \frac{1}{2}\gamma h^2 \tan^2 [45° - \phi/2]$
$\quad = \frac{1}{2}(0.0622)(12)^2(0.5206)^2 \qquad =$ 1.21   16.8

Total lateral pressure $=$ 5.71   79.2

The above results correspond to a C_A of $79.2/100.0 = 0.792$, or $0.792/0.27 = 2.93$ times the lateral pressure computed earlier for dry sandy soil.

For good granular soils, engineers often use 80 to 85 pcf to calculate the lateral pressure at possible saturation.

J–6. THE CASE OF A CLAY BACKFILL

This is still a hazardous situation which should not be tolerated.

Appendix K: AREA SPECIFICATIONS FOR RETAINING WALLS[1]

B. Information Required

3. Loads

Loads to be superimposed either on the wall or abutment, or on the backfill, shall be indicated.

4. Character of Backfill

Backfill is defined as all material behind the wall, whether undisturbed ground or fill, that contributes to the pressure against the wall.

The backfill shall be investigated and classified with reference to the following soil types:

TYPES OF BACKFILL FOR RETAINING WALLS

Type

1. Coarse-grained soil without admixture of fine soil particles, very free-draining (clean sand, gravel or broken stone).
2. Coarse-grained soil of low permeability due to admixture of particles of silt size.
3. Fine silty sand; granular materials with conspicous clay content; or residual soil with stones.
4. Soft or very soft clay; organic silt; or soft silty clay.
5. Medium or stiff clay that may be placed in such a way that a negligible amount of water will enter the spaces between the chunks during floods or heavy rains.

---

[1] Reprinted by permission of the American Railway Engineering Association from the 1953 AREA Specification. The original numbering of the sections has been maintained in these excerpts.

5. Character of Foundation

The character of the foundation shall be determined by means of test pits, auger borings, or core borings, of a type and to an extent consistent with the magnitude of the project.

If the subsoil is essentially sandy or gravelly in character, the ground-water level shall be ascertained.   In addition, the relative density of the material shall be investigated, preferably by means of penetration tests or static load tests.   The penetration test shall consist of driving a sampling spoon (2-in. O.D.; $1\frac{3}{8}$-in. I.D.) into the material by means of a weight of 140 lb. falling through a distance of 30 in.   The relative density is measured by the number of blows, N, required to obtain a penetration of 1 ft.

If the subsoil consists of clay, it is advisable to obtain intact specimens suitable for determination of the unconfined compressive strength.   In the absence of such samples, the consistency of the clay shall be described in the following terms:

CONSISTENCY OF CLAY

Consistency	Field Identification	Ultimate Unconfined Compressive Strength Tons per Sq. Ft.
Very Soft...	Easily penetrated several inches by fist............	Less than 0.25
Soft........	Easily penetrated by thumb......................	0.25 to 0.50
Medium....	Can be penetrated by thumb with moderate effort...	0.50 to 1.0
Stiff........	Readily indented by thumb but penetrated only with great effort................................	1.0 to 2.0
Very Stiff..	Readily indented by thumbnail...................	2.0 to 4.0
Hard.......	Indented with difficulty by thumbnail.............	Over 4.0

Where seasonal changes in the consistency of clay subsoils are likely to occur, their influence shall be taken into consideration.

Other procedures for investigating the relative density of sands or the consistency of clays may be used in place of those recommended in the preceding paragraphs, provided such procedures lead to numerical results.

C. Computation of Applied Forces

1. Loads Exclusive of Earth Pressure

In the analysis of retaining walls and abutments, due account shall be taken of all superimposed loads carried directly on them, such as building walls, columns, or bridge structures; and of all loads from surcharges caused by railroad tracks, highways or building foundations supported on the fill back of the walls.

In calculating the surcharge due to track loading, the entire load shall be taken as distributed uniformly over a width of 14 ft. for a single track or tracks spaced more than 14 ft. centers, and as distributed over 14 ft., plus the distance center to center of tracks, where tracks are spaced 14 ft. or less.

Impact shall not be considered unless the bridge bearings are supported by a structural beam, as in a spill-through abutment.

2. Computation of Backfill Pressure

Values for the unit weight, cohesion, and angle of internal friction of the backfill material shall be determined directly by means of soil tests or, if the expense of such tests is not justifiable, by means of the following table referring to the soil types defined in Sec. B, Art. 4. Unless the minimum cohesive strength of backfill material can be evaluated reliably the cohesion shall be neglected and only the internal friction considered.

Soil Type	Unit Weight Lb. per Cu. Ft.	Cohesion c Lb. per Sq. Ft.	Angle of Internal Friction Degrees
1	105	0	33°42' (38° for broken stone)
2	110	0	30°
3	125	0	28°
4	100	0	0
5	120	240	0

The magnitude, direction and point of application of the backfill pressure shall be computed on the basis of appropriate values of the unit weight, cohesion and internal friction, by means of one of the following procedures.

When the backfill is assumed to be cohesionless; when the surface of the backfill is or can be assumed to be plane; when there is no surcharge load on the surface of the backfill; or when the surcharge can be converted into an equivalent uniform earth surcharge, Rankine's or Coulomb's formulas may be used under the conditions to which each applies . . .

When the backfill cannot be considered cohesionless, when the surcharge of the backfill is irregular, or when the surcharge cannot be converted to an equivalent uniform earth surcharge, the trial wedge methods . . . may be used.

If the wall or abutment is not more than 20 ft. high and if the backfill has been classified according to Sec. B, Art. 4, the [Peck, Hanson and Thornburn] charts given in [AREA] Appendix C may be used.

If the wall or abutment is prevented from deflecting freely at its crest, as in a rigid-frame bridge or some types of U-abutments, the computed backfill pressure shall be increased 25 per cent.

In spill-through abutments, the increase of pressure against the columns due to the shearing strength of the backfill shall not be overlooked. If the space between columns is not greater than twice the width across the back of the columns, no reduction in backfill pressure shall be made on account of the openings. No more than the active earth pressure shall be considered as the resistance offered by the fill in front of the abutment. In computing the active earth pressure of this fill, the negative or descending slope of the surface shall be taken into consideration.

If local conditions do not permit the construction of drains and, consequently, water may accumulate behind the wall, the resulting additional pressure shall be taken into account.

D. Stability Computation

1. Point of Intersection of Resultant Force and Base

The resultant force on the base of a wall or abutment shall fall within the middle third if the structure is founded on soil, and within the middle half if founded on rock, masonry or piles. The resultant force on any horizontal section above the base of a solid gravity wall should intersect this section within its middle half. If these requirements are satisfied, safety against overturning need not be investigated.

2. Resistance Against Sliding

The factor of safety against sliding at the base of the structure is defined as the sum of the forces at or above base level available to resist horizontal movement of the structure divided by the sum of the forces at or above the same level tending to produce horizontal movement. The numerical value of this factor of safety shall be at least 1.5. If the factor of safety is inadequate, it shall be increased by increasing the width of the base, by the use of a key, by sloping the base upward from heel to toe, or by the use of batter piles.

In computing the resistance against sliding, the passive earth pressure of the soil in contact with the face of the wall shall be neglected. The frictional resistance between the wall and a non-cohesive subsoil may be taken as the normal pressure on the base times the coefficient of friction f of masonry on soil. For coarse-grained soil without silt, f may be taken as 0.55; for coarse-grained soil with silt, 0.45; for silt 0.35.

If the wall rests upon clay, the resistance against sliding shall be based upon the cohesion of the clay, which may be taken as one-half the unconfined compressive strength.   If the clay is very stiff or hard the surface of the ground shall be roughened before the concrete is placed.

If the wall rests upon rock, consideration shall be given to such features of the rock structure as may constitute surfaces of weakness.   For concrete on sound rock the coefficient of friction f may be taken as 0.60.

The factor of safety against sliding on other horizontal surfaces below the base shall be investigated and shall not be less than 1.5.

3. Soil Pressure

The factor of safety against a bearing capacity failure at the toe of the structure is defined as the ultimate bearing capacity of the material beneath the toe divided by the maximum pressure beneath the toe.   The value of this factor of safety shall be not less than 2 if the structure rests on sand and gravel, or 3 if it rests on clay.

*   *   *

The ultimate bearing capacity of sand and gravel shall be estimated on the basis of the relative density or angle of internal friction ϕ of the material.   If the relative density has been investigated by means of the penetration test described in Sec. B, Art. 5, the ultimate bearing capacity corresponding to the appropriate N value can be determined by means of the chart, Fig. 2 [reproduced here in Fig. K–1].   The same chart can be used if the value of ϕ is known.   The value of N or ϕ shall be the

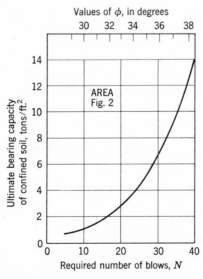

Fig. K–1.   AREA bearing capacity chart.

average within the significant depth below the base of the footing. This depth may be taken as equal to the width of the base, unless the upper part of the subsoil is appreciably looser than the lower. In this event, the average value for the looser part shall be used. If groundwater level is closer to the base of the footing than a depth equal to one-half the width of the base, the ultimate bearing capacity shall be taken as one-half the values determined from the chart. For positions of the water table intermediate between the base and a depth equal to one-half the width of the base, the appropriate values may be determined by interpolation.

The ultimate bearing capacity of a clay subsoil may be considered equal to three times the average unconfined compressive strength of the clay within the significant depth below the base of the footing. This depth may be taken as equal to the width of the base unless the upper part of the subsoil is appreciably softer than the lower. In this event, the average value for the softer part shall be used. The position of the groundwater table is immaterial.

4. Settlement and Tilting

The soil pressures determined in accordance with Sec. D, Art. 3, provide for adequate safety against failure of the soil beneath the structure. If the subsoil consists of soft clay or silt it is necessary to determine the compressibility of the soil and to estimate the amount of settlement.

If the compressibility of the subsoil would lead to excessive settlement or tilting, the movement can be reduced by designing the wall so that the resultant of the forces acting at the base of the wall intersects the base near its midpoint.

If the pressure on a subsoil containing fairly thick layers of soft clay or peat is increased by the weight of the backfill, the wall may tilt backward because of the compression of the clay or peat. The tilt may be estimated on the basis of a knowledge of the compressibility of the subsoil. If the tilt is likely to be excessive, it is advisable to use backfill of lightweight material, to replace the backfill by a structure, or otherwise to change the type of construction so as to avoid overloading the subsoil.

5. Progressive Creep or Movement

If the weight of the backfill is greater than one-half the ultimate bearing capacity of a clay subsoil, progressive movement of the wall or abutment is likely to occur, irrespective of the use of a key, a tilted base, or batter piles. In such cases, it is advisable to use backfill of lightweight material, to replace the backfill by a structure, or otherwise to change the type of construction so as to avoid overloading the subsoil.

E. Design of Backfill

1. Drainage

The material immediately adjacent to the wall should be noncohesive and free draining. Cinders shall not be used.   If a special back drain is installed, the grain size of the drain shall be coarse enough to permit free flow of water, but not so coarse that the fill material may ultimately move into it and clog it.   Where economical, it is preferable that free-draining material be used within a wedge behind the wall bounded by a plane rising at 60 deg. to the horizontal.   Water from the free-draining material shall be removed, preferably by horizontal drain pipes or by weep holes.   Horizontal drain pipes, if used, shall not be less than 8-in. diameter and shall be installed in such a position that they will function properly.   Such drains shall be accessible for cleaning.   Weep holes are considered less satisfactory than horizontal drains.   If used, they shall have diameters not less than 6 in. and shall be spaced not over 10 ft.

2. Compaction

The backfill shall preferably be placed in layers not to exceed 12 in. in thickness.   Each layer shall be compacted before placing the next, but overcompaction shall be avoided.

No dumping of backfill material shall be permitted in such a way that the successive layers slope downward toward the wall.   The layers shall be horizontal or shall slope downward away from the wall.

F. Details of Design and Construction

1. General

The principles of design and permissible unit stresses for walls and abutments shall conform to the (AREA) Specifications for Design of Plain and Reinforced Concrete Members, with the modifications or additions in the following paragraphs.

Retaining walls and abutments shall preferably be of the gravity or semi-gravity type.   The width of the stem of a semi-gravity wall, at the level of the top of the footing, shall be at least one-fourth of its height.

The base of a retaining wall or abutment supported on soil shall be located below frost line, and in no case at a depth less than 3 ft. below the surface of the ground in front of the toe.   The base shall be located below the anticipated maximum depth of scour.   Where this is not practicable the base shall be supported by piles or piers.

To prevent temperature and shrinkage cracks in exposed surfaces, not less than 0.25 sq. in. of horizontal metal reinforcement per foot of height shall be provided, irrespective of the type of wall. Consideration shall be given to providing additional reinforcement above horizontal joints.

The backs of retaining walls and abutments shall be damp-proofed by an approved material.

At horizontal joints between the bases and stems of retaining walls, raised keys are considered preferable to depressed keys. The unit shearing stress at the base of such a key shall not exceed[2] $0.08f'_c$.

Vertical grooved lock joints shall be placed not over 60 ft. apart to care for temperature changes. They shall be protected by membrane waterproofing or noncorrosive metal water stops.

The walls above the footings shall be cast as units between expansion joints, unless construction joints are formed in accordance with the provisions of these specifications.

The heels of cantilever, counterfort and buttress retaining walls shall be proportioned for maximum resultant vertical loads, but when the foundation reaction is neglected the permissible unit stresses shall not be more than 50 per cent greater than the normal permissible stresses.

2. Cantilever Walls

The unsupported toe and heel of the base slabs shall each be considered as a cantilever beam fixed at the edge of the support.

The vertical section shall be considered as a cantilever beam fixed at the top of the base.

3. Counterfort and Buttress Walls

The face walls of counterfort and buttress walls and parts of base slabs supported by the counterforts or buttresses shall be designed in accordance with the requirements for a continuous slab, AREA Specifications for Design of Plain and Reinforced Concrete Members. Due allowance shall be made for the effect of the toe moment on shears and bending moments in the heel slabs of counterfort walls.

Counterforts shall be designed in accordance with the requirements for T-beams. Stirrups shall be provided to anchor the face slabs and the heel slabs to the counterforts. These shall be proportioned to carry the end shears of the slabs. Stirrups shall be U-shaped with their legs in the counterforts, and shall extend as close to the exposed face of face walls and the bottom of base slabs as the requirements for protective covering permit. It is desirable to run reinforcing bars through the loops of the U.

[2] Per October 1954 advice.

Buttresses shall be designed in accordance with the requirements for rectangular beams.

* * *

(AREA's) Appendix C

Earth Pressure Charts for Walls Less than 20 ft. High

AREA's Figs. 4 and 5 may be used for estimating the backfill pressure if the backfill material has been classified in accordance with Sec. B, Art. 4.

AREA's Fig. 4 is for backfills sloping upward from the top of the wall, or for horizontal backfills.   It is the same as Fig. 11–4 of Chapter 11 of this textbook.

AREA's Fig. 5 is for backfills sloping upward from the top of the wall, then changing to the horizontal.   For it, refer to page 8–5–18 of the complete AREA Specification.

Appendix L: USE OF THE WSD BEAM FLEXURE CHARTS[1]

Beam Formulas and Charts. After the fundamental methods of Chapter 9 are thoroughly understood, one needs a means for doing such work speedily. This may be accomplished by evolving general formulas for the several relationships, then constructing *charts* or *tables* therefrom which embrace the whole practical range of each function. Such aids are universally used by practicing designers.

Rectangular Beams

Figure L–1 illustrates certain items of standard notation not previously discussed.

The *steel ratio, $p = A_s/bd$*, is commonly expressed as a percentage. The following expressions have been derived from fundamental concepts, and used to construct the time-saving Charts L–1 through L–4.

INVESTIGATIONS

$$k = \sqrt{2pn + (pn)^2} - pn \qquad \text{(See Chart L–5)} \qquad \text{(L–1)}$$
$$j = 1 - (k/3) \qquad \text{(L–2)}$$

[1] The rectangular beam charts, L–1, L–2, L–3, and L–4, and the T-beam charts L–6, L–7, L–8, and L–9 have been reproduced by permission after F. E. Turneaure and E. R. Mauer, *Principles of Reinforced Concrete Construction* (New York: John Wiley & Sons, Inc., 1907).

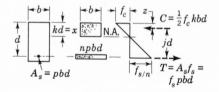

Fig. L–1. Rectangular beam notation.

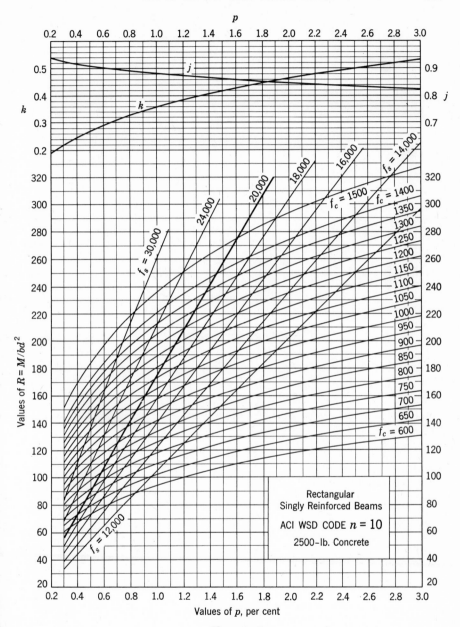

Chart L–1

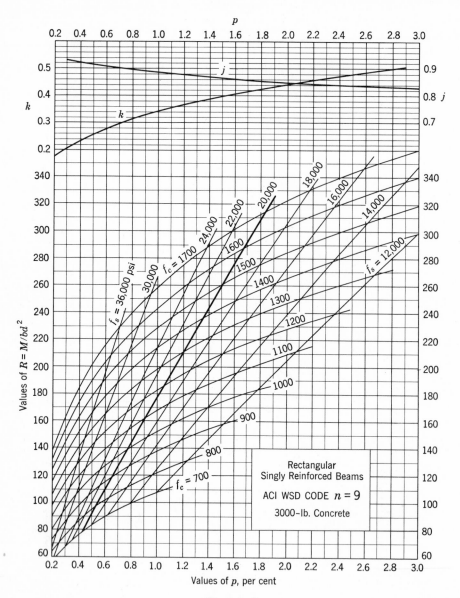

Chart L–2

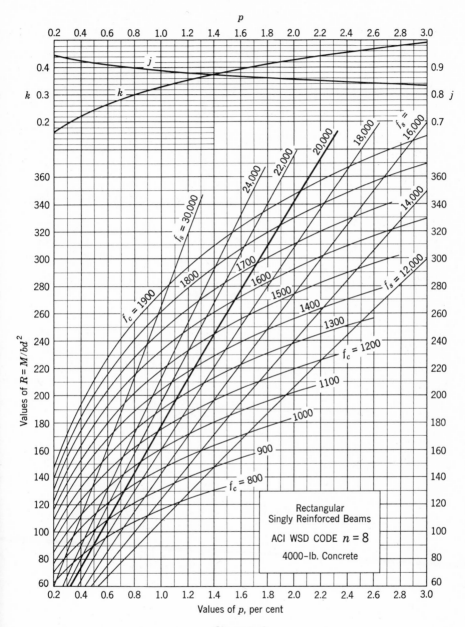

Chart L–3

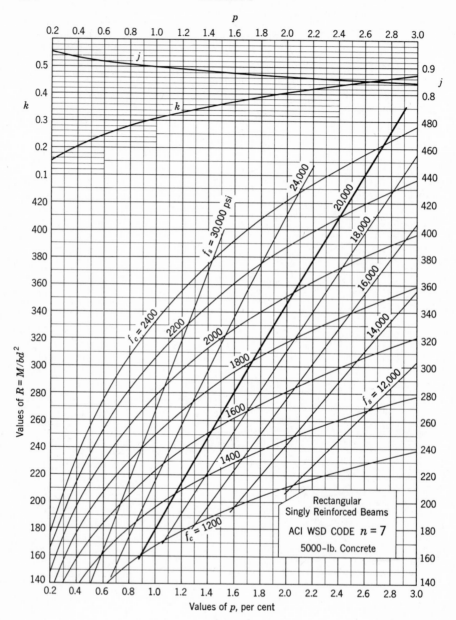

Chart L–4

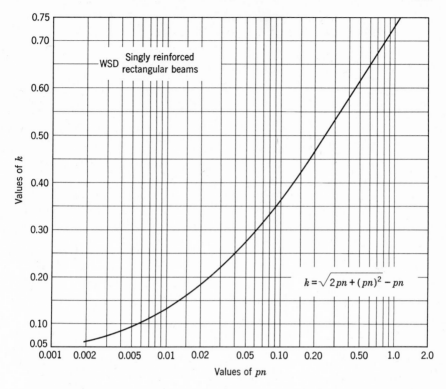

Chart L–5. Values of k versus pn for finding the investigational neutral axis in WSD singly reinforced rectangular beam calculations. It is convenient when n has an odd value not contemplated by the rectangular beam Charts L–1 through L–4. Also, it is useful in creep type of beam investigations in which magnified values of n, such as $4 \times 10 = 40$, are used.

The maximum safe bending moment is given by:

Concrete side:

$$M_c = Cjd = \tfrac{1}{2}f_c kj(bd^2) = R_c(bd^2) \tag{L–3}$$

Steel side:

$$M_s = Tjd = f_s pj(bd^2) = R_s(bd^2) \tag{L–4}$$

wherein the allowable values of the unit stresses are used, and R is known as the *coefficient of resistance.*

When the applied bending moment is given, the expressions above yield the unit stresses.

DESIGN (BALANCED)

$$k = \frac{1}{1 + \dfrac{f_s}{n f_c}} \tag{L-5}$$

$$j = 1 - (k/3) \tag{L-6}$$

Equating T and C from Fig. L–1, and later eliminating k from Eq. L–5, the ideal (balanced) steel content is:

$$p = \frac{f_c}{2 f_s} k = \frac{1}{2} \frac{1}{\dfrac{f_s}{f_c} \left(\dfrac{f_s}{n f_c} + 1 \right)} \tag{L-7}$$

And, as in Eqs. L–3 and L–4,

$$bd^2 = \frac{M}{f_s p j} = \frac{M}{(\frac{1}{2}) f_c k j} = \frac{M}{R} \tag{L-8}$$

USE OF RECTANGULAR BEAM CHARTS

Refer to the singly reinforced rectangular beam examples of Chapter 9. Specification: 20,000–1350–9.

Learn to use the charts without referring to the curves of j and k.

W-S Investigation

EXAMPLE 9–1

Given. B.M. = 50.4 kip-ft., b = 8 in., d = 17 in., A_s = 2.0 sq. in.
Find the stresses from the n = 9 Chart L–2.
Solution. The coordinates of the required point are given by:

$$p = \frac{A_s}{bd} = \frac{2}{8(17)} = 1.47\%$$

$$R = \frac{M}{bd^2} = \frac{50.4(12,000)}{8(17)^2} = 262$$

Find f_s = 20,500 and f_c = 1510.

EXAMPLE 9–2

Given. The beam cross section of Example 9–1 and the allowable stresses 20,000 and 1350.
Find the maximum safe bending moment.
Solution.

$$p = 2/(8)(17) = 1.47\%, \text{ as before}$$

Find the greatest value of R such that neither allowable stress is exceeded:

$$R_{safe} = 233.5$$

Then $\qquad\qquad M = Rbd^2 = \dfrac{233.5(8)(17)^2}{12,000} = \qquad$ 45.0 kip-ft.

W-S Designing

EXAMPLE 9–3

Given. B.M. = 50.4 kip-ft., Specification: 20,000–1350–9.
Design a balanced beam.
Solution. At the intersection of the two allowable stress curves find $R = 223.5$ and $p = 1.28\%$.
From $R = M/bd^2$,

$$bd^2 = \frac{50.4(12,000)}{223.5} = 2708$$

If $b = 8$ in. is chosen, then $d = 18.40$ in.
Corresponding $\qquad\qquad A_s = pbd = 0.0128(8)(18.40) = 1.88$ sq. in.

EXAMPLES 9–4 AND 9–5

Given. B.M. = 50.4 kip-ft., allowables of 20,000 and 1350, and any arbitrary values of b and d.
Find the steel area required.
Solution. Say $b = 8$ in. and $d = 20$ in:

$$R = \frac{M}{bd^2} = \frac{50.4(12,000)}{8(20)^2} = 189$$

For safe stresses, find $p = 1.08\%$

$$A_s = pbd = 0.0108(8)(20) = 1.73 \text{ sq. in.}$$

If $b = 8$ in., and $d = 16$ in:
$$R = 295, \; p = 3.35\% \text{ (by extrapolation)}, \; A_s = 4.30 \text{ sq. in.}$$

Note that when the chart is used it is not necessary to know whether the given space is too large or too small.

RECTANGULAR BEAM PROBLEMS

L–1. Perform step by step derivations of Eqs. L–1 to L–8 inclusive, from fundamental concepts.

L–2. Solve the rectangular beam problems of Chapter 9 which are marked with a star ($\star$), using the charts.

T-Beams

Figure L–2 illustrates the additional notation needed to express the T-beam formulas. Note carefully how the steel ratio p is always computed.

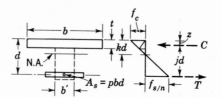

Fig. L–2. T-beam notation.

The compression in the stem has been ignored. When a preliminary study indicates that the neutral axis is within the slab the rectangular beam formulas apply.

The following basic expressions were utilized to constitute the accompanying time-saving singly reinforced T-beam Charts L–6, L–7, L–8, and L–9.

By moments of transformed section areas:

$$kd = \frac{2ndA_s + bt^2}{2nA_s + 2bt} \tag{L–9}$$

or

$$k = \frac{2pn + \dfrac{t^2}{d^2}}{2pn + 2\dfrac{t}{d}} \tag{L–10}$$

By moments of compressive stress volumes:

$$z = \frac{3kd - 2t}{2kd - t}\left(\frac{t}{3}\right) \tag{L–11}$$

$$jd = d - z \tag{L–12}$$

Substituting in Eq. L–12 the values of k and z from Eqs. L–10 and L–11:

$$j = \frac{6 - 6(t/d) + 2(t/d)^2 + \dfrac{(t/d)^3}{2pn}}{6 - 3(t/d)} \tag{L–13}$$

Also

$$\frac{f_s}{f_c} = \frac{n(1 - k)}{k} \tag{L–14}$$

USE OF T-BEAM CHARTS

Refer to the T-beam Examples of WSD Chapter 9, beginning with Art. 9–7. Specification: 20,000–1350–9 throughout.

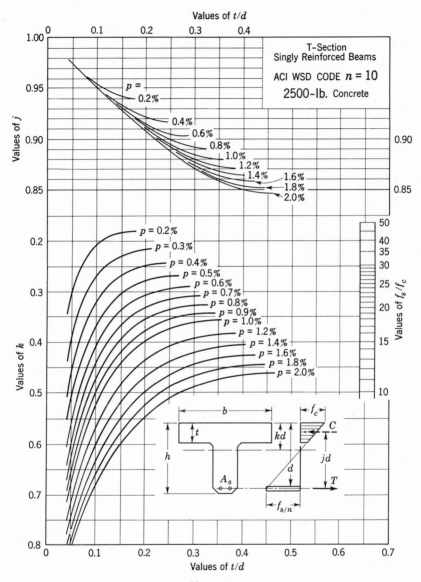

Chart L–6

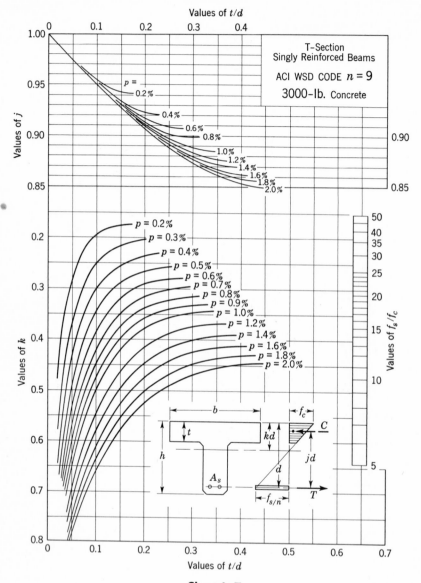

Chart L–7

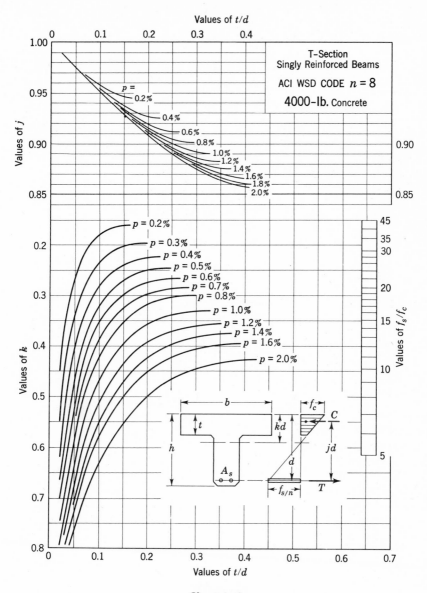

Chart L–8

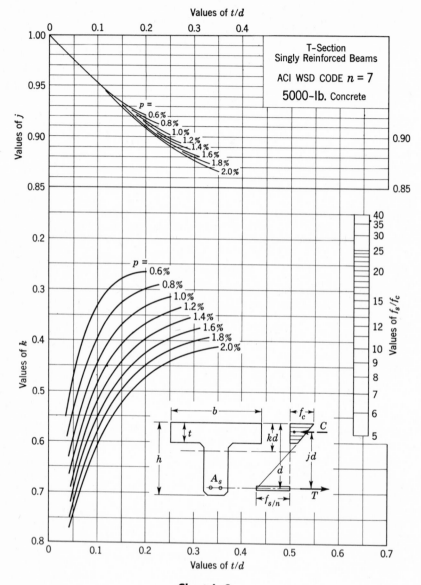

Values of t/d

T-Section
Singly Reinforced Beams
ACI WSD CODE $n = 7$
5000-lb. Concrete

$p =$
0.6%
0.8%
1.0%
1.2%
1.4%
1.6%
1.8%
2.0%

Values of j

Values of k

Values of f_s/f_c

Values of t/d

Chart L–9

W-S Investigation

EXAMPLE 9–8a

Given. B.M. = 70 kip-ft. A T-shaped section with $b = 40$ in., $d = 18$ in., and $A_s = 3.00$ sq. in., has a slab thickness $t = 6$ in.

Find the stresses. Use the $n = 9$ T-beam Chart L–7.

Solution. The coordinates of the required point on the chart are given by:

$$\frac{t}{d} = \frac{6}{18} = 0.33$$

$$p = \frac{A_s}{bd} = \frac{3}{40(18)} = 0.42\%$$

Since this point falls beyond the limits of the curves, *the neutral axis is within the slab.* Solve for the stresses using the *rectangular* beam chart, as in Example 9–1, taking the $n = 9$ Chart L–2.

EXAMPLE 9–8b

Same as (a) above except that t has been decreased to 4 in.

Solution. Re-try Chart L–7:

$$t/d = 4/18 = 0.222$$
$$p = 3/(40)(18) = 0.416\%$$

Find $j = 0.92, f_s/f_c = 28.7$:

$$f_s = \frac{M}{A_s jd} = \frac{70(12,000)}{3(0.92)(18)} = \qquad \underline{16,900 \text{ psi}}$$

$$f_c = \frac{16,900}{28.7} = \qquad \underline{590 \text{ psi}}$$

EXAMPLE 9–8c

Same section as in Example 9–8b, **to find** the maximum safe bending moment if the allowables are 20,000 and 1350.

Solution. Find $j = 0.92$ and $f_s/f_c = 28.7$, as above.

Since $28.7 > (20,000/1350)$, the steel will work at 20,000, and the concrete at < 1350.

$$M_{\text{safe}} = A_s f_s jd = \frac{3(20,000)(0.92)(18)}{12,000} = \qquad \underline{82.8 \text{ kip-ft.}}$$

W-S Designing

EXAMPLE 9–9

Given. B.M. = 30.2 kip-ft., Specification: 20,000–1350–9.

Required to design a balanced T-beam having a t/d of 0.21. Refer to Fig. 9–11 and T-beam Chart L–7.

Solution. The coordinates of the desired point on the chart are given by:

$$f_s/f_c = (20{,}000/1350) = 14.8$$
$$t/d \text{ chosen} = 0.21$$

Find $p = 1.04\%$, $j = 0.908$:

$$A_s d = \frac{M}{f_s j} = \frac{30.2(12{,}000)}{20{,}000(0.908)} = 19.94$$

If two #8 bars are taken:

$$\text{Reqd. } d = \frac{19.94}{1.58} = 12.64 \text{ in.}$$

From $A_s = pbd$:

$$\text{Reqd. } b = \frac{1.58}{0.0104(12.64)} = 12.0 \text{ in.}$$

Note that other solutions are possible.

EXAMPLE 9–10

Given. Total B.M. $= 26.3$ kip-ft., and a 10-in. pan from Fig. 9–12. F'p'f'g = 1 in., $b = 25$ in., slab thickness, $t = 2\frac{1}{2}$ in.

Required to design the steel using Chart L–7.

Solution. Assuming that the bars will be of 1-in. dimension:

$$d = 11 \text{ in.}, \quad t/d = (2.5/11) = 0.227$$

Since balance is uncertain, the ratio f_s/f_c is unknown; but we can select a trial value of j from the curves, based upon the known t/d value:

$$\text{Trial } j = 0.905$$
$$\text{Trial } A_s = \frac{M}{f_s j d} = \frac{26.3(12{,}000)}{20{,}000(0.905)(11)} = 1.58 \text{ sq. in.}$$

assuming also that the steel can work at its allowable.

The steel percentage can now be calculated from the trial steel content:

$$p = (1.58)/(25)(11) = 0.574 \%$$

The corresponding improved value of $j = 0.91$, and

Reqd. $A_s = (0.905/0.910)(1.58) = 1.57$ sq. in.   Tentatively use two #8 bars.

Checking on stresses, find that the corresponding chart value of $f_s/f_c = 24$:

$$f_c = \frac{20{,}000}{24} = 830, \; < 1350 \qquad\qquad \text{Satisfactory.}$$

T-BEAM PROBLEMS

L–3. Perform step-by-step derivations of Eqs. L–9 to L–14 inclusive, from fundamental concepts.

L–4. Solve Problems 9–13 through 9–18 of Chapter 9, which are marked with a star (★), using the proper T-beam chart.

INDEX

References in brackets are to the 1963 ACI Code.